ELECTRONICS SOURCE BOOK

for Teachers

ELECTRONICS SOURCE BOOK

for Teachers

HAROLD S. SPIELMAN, B.S., M.S., Ed. D.

Associate Professor of Education
The City College,
City University of New York

VOLUME II

HAYDEN BOOK COMPANY, INC., NEW YORK
a division of HAYDEN PUBLISHING COMPANY, INC.

621.38
S 755
v. 2

Copyright © 1965

HAYDEN BOOK COMPANY, INC.

Library of Congress Catalog Card Number 65–14296

Printed in the United States of America

CONTENTS
VOLUME II

Note for VOLUME II

The foreword and table of contents for all three volumes, a long introductory chapter on the New Science of Electronics, and a full discussion of electronic principles, vacuum tubes of all kinds, cathode-ray tubes, oscillators, detectors, photometers, and related devices are to be found in Volume I. The appendix and index for all three volumes are to be found in Volume III, along with discussions of microwaves, ultrasonics, electronic heating, thermo-electric principles, nuclear electronics, computers, automation, and the like.

17 - TRANSISTORS AND RELATED SEMICONDUCTOR DEVICES

17.1 *History of the transistor*

A remote ancestor of the transistor was developed as far back as 1923. During that year, C. G. Smith of the Raytheon Manufacturing Company announced the development of a germanium current amplifier.[1] The development of the point-contact transistor was first announced by the Bell Telephone Laboratories in 1948.[2] In 1956, William Shockley and W. H. Brattain, the two co-inventors of this device, and John Bardeen, who performed the basic physical research leading to the development of the transistor, were awarded the Nobel Prize in physics for their achievements (Fig. 17-1).[3] The fundamental principles of operation of this extremely useful device were discovered as a result of a basic research study in solid-state physics that dealt with the behavior of electrons in solids and with the surface properties of crystalline semiconductors such as germanium.

Courtesy, Bell Telephone Laboratories

FIG. 17-1. INVENTORS OF THE TRANSISTOR: DRS. WILLIAM SHOCKLEY, WALTER H. BRATTAIN AND JOHN BARDEEN (LEFT TO RIGHT)

Courtesy, American Telephone & Telegraph Co.
FIG. 17-2. A GROUP OF TRANSISTORS

The transistor, a crystal-type amplifying device consisting mainly of germanium or silicon, soon demonstrated that it was capable of duplicating many of the functions that were being performed by electronic tubes, such as amplification, detection, and oscillation (Fig. 17-2). Moreover, it soon became apparent that it could perform these functions with an even greater degree of efficiency and dependability.[4] Here at last was a device to challenge the imaginations and energies of those who had stated: "There's nothing wrong with electronics that the elimination of a few vacuum tubes would not fix!"[5]

The name transistor is derived from the fact that the device is essentially a resistor that is capable of amplifying electrical signals. The early research workers in this field, who were really searching for new methods of producing non-linear resistors, called this device a transit resistor. This name was soon shortened to transistor. However, other writers claim that this name is derived from the words transfer and resistor.

Continued research by personnel at Bell Telephone Laboratories resulted in the development of new and improved types of transistors. In 1950, announcement was made of the invention of the phototransistor by Shive of Bell Telephone Laboratories. This was followed a year later by the announcement of the invention of the junction transistor by Shockley. In 1952, Wallace added a fourth electrode to the transistor and produced the first tetrode transistor.

17.2 *Semiconductor principles*

All transistors contain semiconductive materials, and a transistor may be described as a semiconductive device containing two junctions. Semiconductors are substances such as germanium, silicon, silicon carbide, selenium, copper oxide, and galena, whose conductivities are lower than those of metals but higher than those of insulators (Fig. 17-3). The conductivities of these semiconductive materials lie in this intermediate range because the conductivity of any semiconductor is determined by

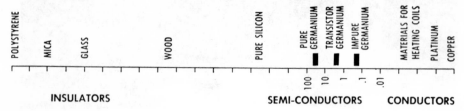

Courtesy, Radio Corporation of America
FIG. 17-3. RESISTANCE OFFERED BY VARIOUS MATERIALS (OHMS PER CUBIC CENTIMETER)
Pure germanium offers about 60 ohms resistance; a good conductor, copper, gives much less resistance.

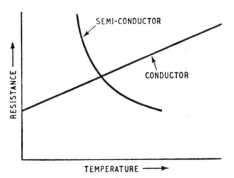

FIG. 17-4. VARIATION OF RESISTANCE WITH
TEMPERATURE FOR A CONDUCTOR AND A
SEMICONDUCTOR

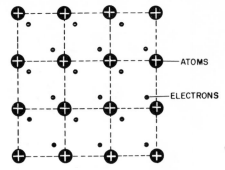

Courtesy, Westinghouse Electric Corp.

FIG. 17-5. CONDUCTION IN A METALLIC CON-
DUCTOR

the number of charge carriers present; and the mechanism by which the current carriers are generated in a semiconductor is different from the situation that prevails inside metallic solids. The number of carriers and the resultant conductivities will vary with certain conditions, such as the direction of current flow, the presence of other electric fields, or the amount of light falling upon the substance.

Semiconductor research has had a relatively long history. As far back as 1833, Faraday observed that while the resistances of most conductors increased with an increase in temperature, silver sulphide was characterized by possessing a negative temperature-coefficient of resistance (Fig. 17-4). By 1855, scientists had noted four of the fundamental properties of semiconductors: negative temperature-coefficient of resistance, rectification, photoconductivity, and the photovoltaic effect.[6]

An important and fundamental difference between semiconductors and ordinary metallic conductors is that while conduction in metals is wholly dependent upon the movement of negative current carriers or valence electrons (Fig. 17-5), conductivity in a semiconductor can also be produced by the movement of positive current carriers called *holes*.

Semiconductor electronics is based largely upon the presence of imperfections. A crystal becomes a semiconductor when its order is disturbed by a distribution of imperfections in its structure (Fig. 17-6). One type of imperfection produces excess electrons which, unlike normal or valence electrons, cannot find a place to settle down. Excess electrons are unstable and mobile and move readily under the pressure of electric fields (Fig. 17-7). Since the movements of these excess electrons produces small currents, the crystal has been transformed from an insulator into a semiconductor.

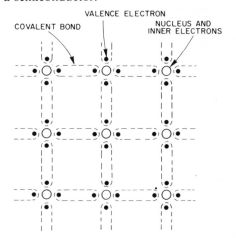

FIG. 17-6. A TWO-DIMENSIONAL VIEW OF A
CRYSTAL

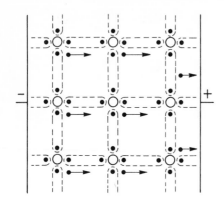

FIG. 17-7. MOTION OF FREE ELECTRONS TO-WARDS POSITIVE TERMINALS

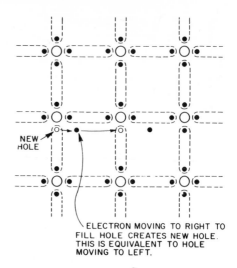

ELECTRON MOVING TO RIGHT TO FILL HOLE CREATES NEW HOLE. THIS IS EQUIVALENT TO HOLE MOVING TO LEFT.

FIG. 17-9. MOVEMENT OF ELECTRONS AND HOLES IN AN INTRINSIC SEMICONDUCTOR

The hole is a second type of imperfection, which is the result of removing an electron from a crystal (Fig. 17-8). The hole functions as a positive mobile particle, moving by a replacement process in which a normal electron adjacent to the hole moves into it, thereby creating a new hole behind it. Thus, the holes move and carry current like excess electrons, but in the opposite direction (Figs. 17-9 and 17-10).[7]

Another important point is that the current in a semiconductor flows be-tween various regions that are separated by internal barriers (Fig. 17-11). The carriers can be induced to flow across these barriers without the expenditure of the relatively large amount of energy that is required to liberate electrons from the surface of a hot cathode. In addition, the flow of carriers through these barriers may be either accentuated or inhibited by the application of the proper electrode potentials, making this device analogous to an electron tube (Fig. 17-12). Since low accelerating potentials may be employed, and there is no high-temperature cathode, these devices operate with great efficiency.[8]

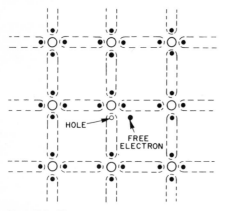

FIG. 17.8. HOLES AND ELECTRONS IN AN INTRINSIC (PURE) SEMICONDUCTOR

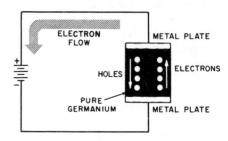

FIG. 17-10. FLOW OF ELECTRONS AND HOLES

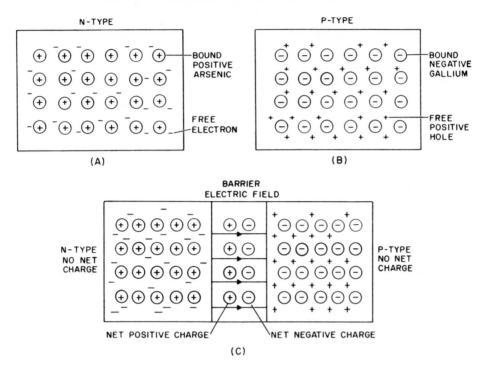

Courtesy, Bell Telephone Laboratories

FIG. 17-11. POTENTIAL BARRIER PRODUCED BY A P-N JUNCTION

(A) N-type, or electron-rich, silicon, is made by adding minute traces of an element like arsenic to silicon. From each arsenic atom that is added, one electron (unit negative charge) detaches itself, thus becoming free to move, and leaves behind the arsenic atom with unit positive charge bound into the crystal structure. Thus, n-type silicon consists of silicon to which is added equal numbers of free electrons and bound positive charge, so that there is no net charge. (B) P-type, or hole-rich silicon is made by adding minute traces of an element like gallium to silicon. For each gallium atom that is added, one hole (unit positive charge) detaches itself, thus becoming free to move, and leaves behind the gallium atom with unit negative charge bound into the crystal structure. Thus, p-type silicon consists of silicon to which is added equal numbers of free positive holes and bound negative charge, so that there is no net charge. (C) When p-type and n-type silicon meet at a junction, the free holes and free electrons try to intermix like gases. However, the holes which enter the n-type material disappear and leave behind negatively charged gallium atoms, and the electrons which enter the p-type material disappear and leave behind positively charged arsenic atoms. These fixed charges constitute an electrical barrier, or field, which prevents the rest of the holes in the p-side and electrons in the n-side from intermixing.

Nearly all commercial transistors utilize germanium as the semi-conducting solid. Silicon is the second most commonly employed transistor semiconductor.

Silicon carbide is another semiconductor that has recently received considerable study. It has displayed some very desirable high-temperature operating characteristics. While germanium transistors are generally limited to a maximum operating temperature of 190°F, and silicon transistors are limited to 450°F, single crystals of silicon carbide can operate at temperatures as high as 1,800°F. However, progress has been hampered by the difficulties involved in preparing single, pure crystals

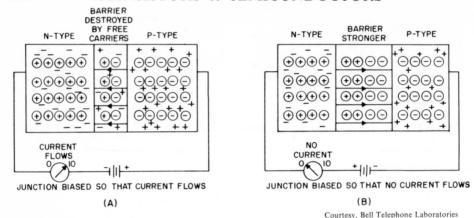

Courtesy, Bell Telephone Laboratories

FIG. 17-12. RECTIFYING ACTION OF A P-N JUNCTION

(A) The electrical barrier is responsible for the rectifying properties of p-n junctions. If a voltage is applied across the junction in a way such that the natural barrier-field is overcome by the applied voltage, then holes are encouraged to flow from the p-side into the n-side, and electrons are encouraged to flow into the p-side. This flow of free charge is an electric current. (B) If a voltage is applied across the junction in a way such that the natural barrier-field is reinforced, the barrier becomes wider and stronger and the holes are more firmly captured in the p-side and the electrons in the n-side. No free charge can cross the barrier and therefore no current flows.

of this material that are large enough to permit reliable measurements of its properties.[9]

In 1959, it was announced that Frank A. Halden of the Stanford Research Institute had developed a promising process for producing crystals of silicon carbide. This involves melting pure silicon in a carbon receptacle. Some of the carbon then diffuses into the molten silicon, forming a localized area of supersaturated solution from which silicon carbide crystals can be grown.[10] It is believed that this material will eventually rank behind only germanium and silicon in importance as a semiconductor for applications in the fields of transistors, thermoelectricity, and electroluminescence.

Mention may be made of the recent development by Welker, a German scientist, of a new group of materials called intermetallic semiconductors. These are the so-called "three-five" compounds, which are compounds of elements that contain three valence electrons, such as aluminum, gallium,

and indium, with elements that contain five valence electrons such as phosphorus, arsenic, and antimony. The average number of valence electrons in one of these compounds is four. The compounds display semiconductor characteristics similar to those of germanium and silicon, which also have four valence electrons. Among the intermetallic semiconductors that have been developed are indium phosphide, indium arsenide, indium antimonide, gallium phosphide, and gallium arsenide.[11]

Certain of these three-five compounds are distinguished by electron mobilities that are much greater than those of germanium and silicon, making possible the reduction of the series resistances of devices that employ these semiconductors. Other intermetallic compounds, such as gallium arsenide, are capable of operating at higher temperatures than ordinary semiconductors such as silicon. It is anticipated that these new intermetallic materials will provide a wider range of electronic properties, particularly those associated with frequency and temperature characteristics, than are obtainable with germanium or silicon. Some of these semiconductors have also been employed in Hall-effect devices, similar to those that were described in an earlier chapter dealing with crystal-diode rectifiers.

Harvey L. Goering, head of the rare-earth group at Battelle Memorial Institute, has reported the possibility of developing rare-earth compounds for semiconductive applications. His group has been studying the characteristics of the selenides and tellurides of rare-earth elements such as lanthanum, gadolinium, and yttrium. According to preliminary reports, these compounds display semiconductive behavior.

Investigations are also currently under way that are concerned with the semiconductive properties of a form of carbon known as graphite, and of many organic carbon compounds such as anthracene, naphthalene derivatives, conjugated unsaturated polyolefins, and many of the halogen and sulphur compounds of certain aromatic hydrocarbons. In this connection, it may be mentioned that two Russian scientists, A. V. Topchiev and M. A. Geiderikh, have recently reported that certain organic plastics, such as specially prepared polyacrylonitrile, possess semiconductive characteristics and can operate at much higher temperatures than germanium can. However, it should also be pointed out that this claim has been largely discounted by many scientists in this country although Bell Telephone Laboratories has reported that the heat treatment of polystyrene has produced a similar type of organic semiconductor.

During the brief period of time since 1948, there has been an unprecedented expansion of semiconductor

Courtesy, Westinghouse Electric Corporation
FIG. 17-13. TYPICAL SEMICONDUCTOR COMPONENTS

technology (Fig. 17-13). By 1958, almost half of the electronic development effort in the United States was devoted to semiconductor research. In recent years, the semiconductor section of the electronic industry has been expanding about four times as rapidly as the remainder of this fast-growing industry.

This has led many authorities to the conclusion that the nature of the electronics industry will change radically during the next few years. Thus D. E. Noble, executive vice-president of Motorola, Inc., has stated his belief that the industry is now entering a thirty to forty-year period in which solid-state semiconductor physics will be the dominating influence. According to Dr. Noble, the future will rest with thin films, special ceramics, and intermetallic semiconductor compounds.

17.3 *P-type and N-type germanium*

In its purest state, germanium displays the characteristics of an insulator (Figs. 17-14, 17-15, 17-16, and 17-17). However, the addition of almost infinitesimal amounts of certain impurities—quantities as small as one atom of impurity to each 100 million atoms of semiconductor material—can increase

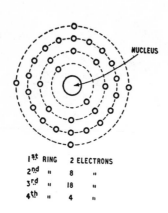

FIG. 17-14. STRUCTURE OF THE GERMANIUM ATOM

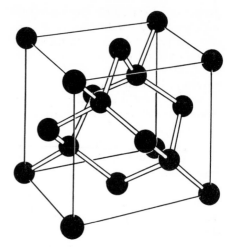

FIG. 17-16. CRYSTAL OF GERMANIUM SHOWING THE LATTICE PATTERN

its conductivity by a factor of 16 times. This process is often referred to as *doping*.

One type of impurity, of which antimony, arsenic, and phosphorus are good examples, is called a donor. These impurities contain five valence electrons per atom, while the germanium atom contains four valence electrons. A donor impurity atom is comparable in size to a germanium atom. It can therefore take the position in the crystal

lattice that is normally occupied by a germanium atom.

When one of these donor atoms replaces a germanium atom in a crystal, the fifth valence electron of the donor atom can be removed by the expenditure of very little energy (Fig. 17-18). It is then free to wander in a random manner through the crystal. This electron contributes to the conductivity of the crystal in a manner resembling that of a free electron in a metallic

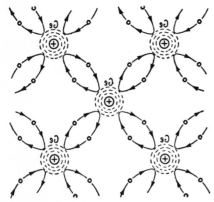

FIG. 17-15. COVALENT BONDS IN A CRYSTAL OF PURE GERMANIUM
For simplicity, only electrons in the valence rings are shown.

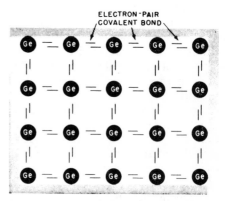

FIG. 17-17. TWO-DIMENSIONAL REPRESENTATION OF THE COVALENT BONDS IN A CRYSTAL OF GERMANIUM

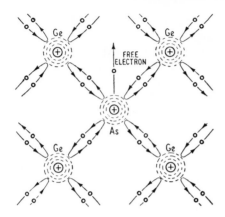

FIG. 17-18. COVALENT BONDS PRODUCED WHEN AN ATOM OF A PENTAVALENT ELEMENT IS INTRODUCED INTO A CRYSTAL OF PURE GERMANIUM

conductor. Germanium that has an excess of electrons due to donor-atom impurities is known as N-type germanium (Fig. 17-19). The symbol N represents a semiconductor that has an excess of negative charges. When a source of direct voltage is applied across this N-type crystal, the free electrons are attracted to the positive terminal, while additional electrons enter the crystal at the negative terminal. This constitutes a flow of current. As long as this difference of potential exists, a stream of electrons will flow through the germanium crystal. Due to crystal imperfections, the rate of flow of electrons through the

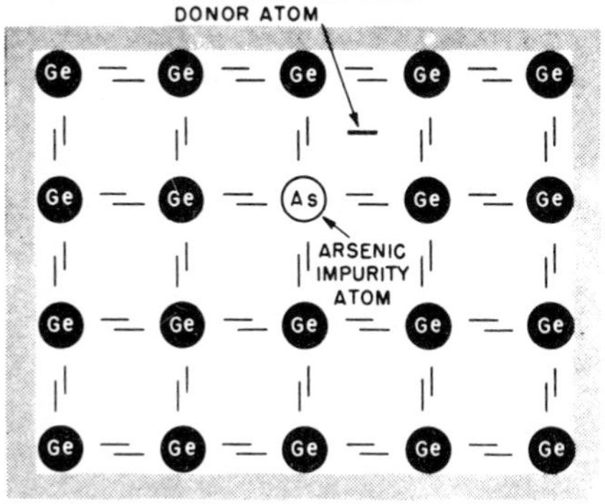

semiconductor is slower than the rate of flow through a metallic conductor.

A second useful type of impurity consists of substances such as aluminum, boron, gallium, and indium, which contain three valence electrons per atom. These atoms are called acceptors, and the germanium that contains these impurities is called P-type or positive germanium.

When a trivalent acceptor atom replaces a quadrivalent germanium atom in the crystal, there is a deficiency of the one electron that is required to enable the acceptor atom to complete its covalent bond with its neighboring atom (Figs. 17-20 and 17-21). This area, which contains an incomplete group of covalent electrons resulting from a deficiency of electrons, is called a hole. The hole behaves as if it were a positively charged particle similar to a positron. If the acceptor atom borrows an electron from a neighboring atom in order to complete its covalent-bond structure, the positive hole moves to that atom. This concept of a hole as a mobile positive charge with a definite mass and velocity dates back to 1931.[12]

When a source of direct voltage is applied across a crystal of P-type ger-

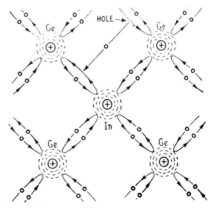

FIG. 17-20. COVALENT BONDS PRODUCED BY AN ATOM OF A TRIVALENT ELEMENT INTRODUCED INTO A CRYSTAL OF PURE GERMANIUM

FIG. 17-19. CRYSTALLINE STRUCTURE OF N-TYPE GERMANIUM

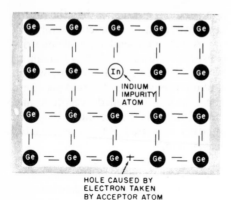

HOLE CAUSED BY
ELECTRON TAKEN
BY ACCEPTOR ATOM

FIG. 17-21. CRYSTALLINE STRUCTURE OF P-TYPE GERMANIUM

manium, electrons jump into the holes and the holes appear to migrate toward the negative terminal (Fig. 17-22). The rate of travel of these holes through the material is somewhat slower than that of electrons through N-type germanium. With an electric field of 1 volt per centimeter, an electron will move through germanium at the rate of 3,600 centimeters per second, while a hole will only move at the rate of 1,700 centimeters per second.[13]

When a hole reaches the negative terminal, it accepts an electron from that terminal and is cancelled out. At

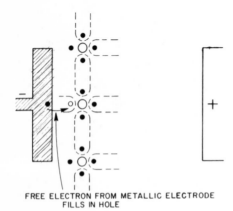

FREE ELECTRON FROM METALLIC ELECTRODE
FILLS IN HOLE

FIG. 17-22. MOVEMENT OF HOLES IN AN INTRINSIC SEMICONDUCTOR

the same time, the positive terminal removes an electron from one of the covalent bonds, forming a new hole which begins to migrate toward the negative terminal. As long as this difference of potential is applied, a continuous stream of holes will flow through the crystal from the positive to the negative terminal. This flow of holes produces the same effect as the flow of electrons in the opposite direction, from the negative to the positive terminal.

17.4 *Manufacture of transistors*

Since the heart of the transistor is a crystal of germanium or silicon, the first step in manufacturing the transistor involves the obtaining and purification of the semiconductor. The electrical characteristics of the transistor are affected by the conductivity of the transistor, which in turn is affected by the presence of impurities. If these impurities are present to the extent of one atom of impurity to 10 million atoms of germanium, the material becomes too conductive and the transistor operates poorly.

While germanium has been obtained in Great Britain from coal ash and flue-dust residue, the principal source of germanium in the United States is the dust collected in the stacks of zinc smelters. Hundreds of tons of zinc ore must be processed in order to obtain enough by-product dust to produce one pound of germanium. Consequently, the cost of a pound of germanium is somewhere between that of gold and that of platinum, the current market value varying between 200 and 350 dollars a pound. However, since only a small amount of germanium is required for a transistor, there is only about two cents worth of germanium in each transistor. Similarly, although the price of pure silicon varies between 270 and

1,500 dollars a pound, the amount of silicon used in a transistor is worth about seven cents.

The germanium is usually sold to the transistor manufacturer as powdered germanium dioxide. This powder is then reduced at a high temperature by means of hydrogen gas (Fig. 17-23). An ingot of germanium with a purity of 99.9 per cent is produced. Since this degree of purity is too low for transistor manufacture, the germanium is further refined by a process called zone melting or zone refining that was developed in 1952 by W. G. Pfann of Bell Telephone Laboratories.[14] It was this process that provided the step which made the transistor a commercially practical device.[15]

In this process, a long, thin strip of germanium is surrounded by several concentric induction-heating coils which gradually move down the length of the strip, producing molten zones that travel from one end of the strip to the other (Fig. 17-24). The principle upon which this process is based is that impurities are usually more soluble in the liquid phase of a substance than in the solid phase. As the molten zone moves along the length of the strip, most of the impurities are carried along to the end of the strip, where they are concentrated. The impure section is then cut off and discarded. This process is repeated several times, and in this manner germanium with a purity of 99.99999999 per cent has been obtained. This is equivalent to one atom of impurity for every 10 billion atoms of germanium.[16] Recently, this process has been improved to the extent that purity levels of one atom of impurity in 1,000 billion atoms of germanium or silicon can be realized.

The germanium thus produced is too pure to be used. In addition, it is composed of hundreds of individual crystals instead of one large crystal. The germanium is therefore melted and

FIG. 17-23. FIRST STEP IN TRANSISTOR MAKING
Powdered germanium dioxide is placed in furnace where it is "cooked" in hydrogen gas and reduced to solid germanium in ingot form.

doped, that is, the desired impurity is added until it is present in a ratio of one part per 100 million. A small single crystal is dipped in the molten germanium and then removed (Fig. 17-25). The molten germanium freezes to this seed crystal, with the same crystal orientation as that of the seed. This process is repeated many times until a long, single crystal is obtained (Fig. 17-26). This

Courtesy, Bell Telephone Laboratories
FIG. 17-24. ZONE REFINING APPARATUS (W. G. PFANN, THE INVENTOR, AT LEFT)

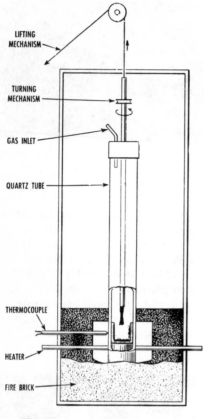

LIFTING MECHANISM

TURNING MECHANISM

GAS INLET

QUARTZ TUBE

THERMOCOUPLE

HEATER

FIRE BRICK

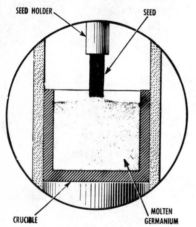

SEED HOLDER   SEED

CRUCIBLE   MOLTEN GERMANIUM

Courtesy, Radio Corporation of America

FIG. 17-25. APPARATUS FOR GROWING SINGLE CRYSTALS

Rotated seed is slowly withdrawn. Inset shows early stage as the crystal starts to form.

Courtesy, Radio Corporation of America

FIG. 17-26. GROWTH OF A LONG SINGLE GERMANIUM CRYSTAL

Dr. S. M. Christian holds a single crystal of germanium from which thousands of transistors can be made. In front of him is a laboratory furnace for growing experimental germanium crystals. The shaft above the furnace rotates and slowly draws a crystal from a container of molten germanium in the shielded base section.

method of growing crystals is sometimes named the Czochralski technique, after the man who contributed greatly to its development. A diamond saw is then used to cut the large crystal into tiny pellets and wafers suitable for use in transistors. The germanium thus prepared has a value of 10,000 dollars a pound.[17]

In 1959, Westinghouse scientists reported that they had developed a new method of growing germanium crystals

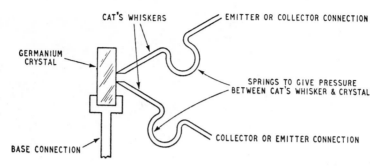

FIG. 17-27. ESSENTIAL CONSTRUCTION FEATURES OF A POINT-CONTACT TRANSISTOR

as thin, continous, uniform, flat ribbons known as dendrites, instead of in the conventional form of round ingots. This new technique enables the semiconductor to be grown directly in the correct form required for use in transistors, and semiconductor devices can be made from a dendrite by constructing them directly and automatically on its surface.[18] [19]

Point-contact transistors are produced by soldering a tiny wafer of N-type germanium to a support. Two fine pointed wires are then caused to make pressure contact with the crystal, as shown in Fig. 17-27. A plastic coating is then applied to protect the transistor from air and light. A momentary surge of high current is then passed through the junction of wire and wafer. The heat that is produced converts some of the germanium in the region of the point contact into P-type germanium (Fig. 17-28).

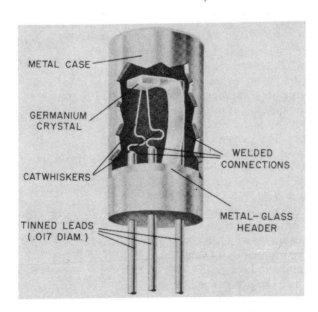

Courtesy, CBS-Hytron

FIG. 17-28. CUTAWAY VIEW OF A POINT-CONTACT TRANSISTOR

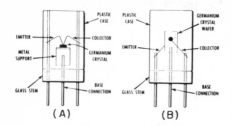

Courtesy, Radio Corporation of America
FIG. 17-29. ELEMENTS OF POINT-CONTACT TYPE (A) AND JUNCTION TYPE (B) TRANSISTORS

Junction transistors (Fig. 17-29) are often produced by placing two dots of indium on opposite sides of a thin wafer of N-type germanium. When the indium is heated, P-type germanium is produced in the vicinity of the dots (Fig. 17-30). The result is a junction transistor in which N-type germanium is sandwiched between two layers of P-type germanium. The transistor is then classified as a P-N-P type (Fig. 17-31). An analogous process can be used to produce N-P-N junction transistors (Fig. 17-32).

In 1954, Bell Telephone Laboratories announced the development of the diffusion technique—a major breakthrough in transistor technology. By means of this technique, minute amounts of impurities may be introduced in a controlled manner. This permits reducing the thickness of the center layer to as little as 0.00003 in. and enables the resulting transistor to operate at frequencies above 1,000 mc.[20]

Among the other advantages associated with this diffused-junction technique are the readiness with which it lends itself to the production of large-area junctions, and the high degree of accuracy with which the process can be controlled. This latter characteristic makes possible the manufacture of highly-reproducible characteristics.[21]

Courtesy, Radio Corporation of America
FIG. 17-30. MODEL OF RCA DEVELOPMENTAL JUNCTION TRANSISTOR

An actual transistor is mounted in the white block on the base of the stand. On the model, the rectangular plate represents the tiny sliver of germanium crystal at the heart of a junction transistor. The round dot (being pointed at) represents a speck of indium heated into the germanium to form one of its two junctions.

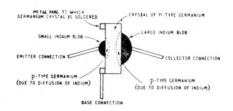

FIG. 17-31. CONSTRUCTION OF AN ALLOY-JUNCTION P-N-P GERMANIUM TRANSISTOR

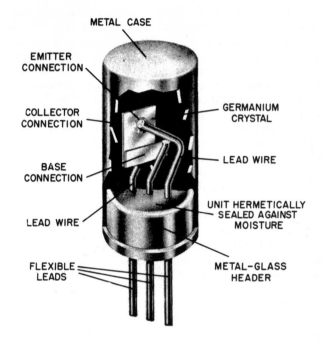

METAL CASE

EMITTER
CONNECTION

COLLECTOR
CONNECTION

GERMANIUM
CRYSTAL

BASE
CONNECTION

LEAD WIRE

LEAD WIRE

UNIT HERMETICALLY
SEALED AGAINST
MOISTURE

FLEXIBLE
LEADS

METAL-GLASS
HEADER

Fig. 17-32. Cutaway view of an N-P-N junction transistor

In manufacturing an N-P-N transistor, it is necessary to explore the surface of the crystal with the aid of a meter in order to locate the center of the P-layer to which the base connection must be attached. This work is extremely fatiguing, and a high percentage of transistors produced in this manner must be rejected. In 1955, Wallace and Riescz of Bell Telephone Laboratories developed a machine to carry out automatically the series of fifteen steps required to produce a transistor. This machine detects the proper places to which leads should be connected, welds wires to the correct places, and checks the completed transistor, all within the period of less than one minute.[22]

Another major problem that has been solved is that of attaching leads to the semiconductor materials. In 1957, Bell Telephone Laboratories announced the development of a thermocompression bonding technique in which the leads are attached by a combination of temperature, pressure, and time. In one method, the lead is forced against the semiconductor surface by means of a heated wedge-shaped tool. In a second method, the balled end of the wire is butted against the heated semiconductor by means of a capillary tube. Neither the temperature nor the pressure is permitted to become great enough to damage the semiconductor, and the time is short enough to permit rapid assembly. This technique possesses the following advantages over soldering techniques: there is less danger of contamination, leads can be attached to very small areas, and the bond is stronger than the wire lead itself.[23]

In 1959, Philco's Lansdale Tube Company announced that a highly automated production line capable of producing 450 transistors an hour was in operation. In this manufacturing technique, small germanium blanks are soldered to tabs that are held on a carrier block. These carriers convey the blanks from one automatic operation to the next. The blank is automatically etched and plated, and electrodes are attached by means of an automatic mechanism involving phototubes and servomechanisms. The transistor is then cleaned, dried, and tested. The final operation of branding, final-testing, and packing are the only three operations of the total of 27 operations that are performed under human supervision.[24][25]

Even this relatively high rate of speed of transistor manufacture is too slow to meet the demands of the International Business Machines Corporation, which, in 1958, adopted a policy of complete transistorization of its computers. Since a computer may contain more than 50,000 transistors, it soon became necessary to develop an automatic production line that was capable of turning out a large number of uniform, high-quality, and inexpensive transistors in a short period of time.

In 1960, IBM spokesmen announced that they had developed such a self-checking automatic assembly line that was capable of fabricating transistors from pre-formed parts at the rate of 1,800 transistors per hour. In this process, each transistor is assembled and inspected individually, and units with defective, missing, or poorly positioned parts are automatically rejected.[26]

17.5 Transistor symbols

Since most transistors operate as triodes, they contain three wire leads which enable the user to make electrical connections with the three transistor electrodes (Fig. 17-33). One electrode, called the emitter, corresponds to the cathode of an electron tube. The emitter injects current carriers. These may be either electrons in an N-P-N unit or holes in a P-N-P unit. These carriers are injected into the base, which corresponds to the grid of a tube. The third electrode is called the collector. It corresponds to the plate of a tube, since it attracts and collects the current carriers.

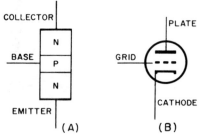

FIG. 17-33. COMPARISON BETWEEN TRANSISTOR (A) AND VACUUM-TUBE (B) ELEMENTS

The most commonly employed symbols for N-P-N and P-N-P transistors are shown in Fig. 17-34. The base is indicated by a straight line which may be placed either vertically or horizontally. The emitter and the collector are indicated by lines placed at an angle to the base. A useful convention is to draw the arrowhead of the emitter so that it is pointing away from the base in an N-P-N transistor and toward the base in an P-N-P transistor. However, this convention has not been universally accepted, and the same symbol is sometimes used to represent both types of transistors. When this convention is employed, the emitter arrow indicates whether the

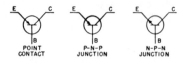

Courtesy, CBS-Hytron

FIG. 17-34. SYMBOLIC REPRESENTATIONS OF TRANSISTORS

transistor is P-N-P or N-P-N by pointing from the P-region to the N-region.

The N-P-N transistor employs electrons as carriers and corresponds to the conventional triode (Fig. 17-35). In biasing this device, the base is considered the reference point. Note that the emitter is biased negatively, while the collector is biased positively. The P-N-P transistor employs positive charges or holes as carriers. The emitter is biased positively and the collector is biased negatively (Fig. 17-36).

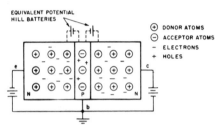

FIG. 17-35. BASIC N-P-N TRANSISTOR CIRCUIT

It may be observed that the emitter or input circuit is always biased in the forward or conducting direction, giving the input circuit a low impedance of between 10 and 100 ohms. The collector circuit is always biased in the reverse direction, giving this circuit a high impedance ranging between 5,000 and 50,000 ohms.

A convenient method of remembering the correct collector-voltage polarity required by each type of transistor is to refer to the middle letter of

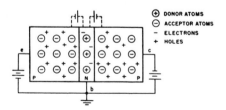

FIG. 17-36. BASIC P-N-P TRANSISTOR CIRCUIT

its notation. Thus, in the N-P-N type, the middle letter is P, and the collector requires a positive voltage. Similarly, the P-N-P type has N as a middle letter, and the collector requires a negative voltage.

17.6 Complementary symmetry

Although the N-P-N and the P-N-P forms have opposite current-flow and voltage-polarity characteristics, their functions are symmetrical. This similar, but opposite, action is known as complementary symmetry. It permits the design of a complementary, transistor, push-pull amplifier circuit employing a P-N-P and an N-P-N transistor, and which requires no center-tapped input or output transformers or other types of phase inverters (Fig. 17-37). The elimination of the costly and sometimes distortion-producing output transformer has long been a goal of many audio enthusiasts.[27] As a result, many transistor manufacturers have developed a series of N-P-N transistors to complement their P-N-P line.

The choice of either type of transistor for a particular application is affected by the polarity of the voltages required and the availability of

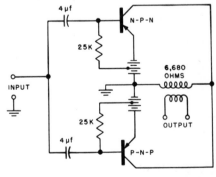

FIG. 17-37. A SYMMETRICAL PUSH-PULL TRANSISTOR AMPLIFIER STAGE

transistors that possess characteristics suitable for the desired application.[28] Since either type of transistor may be used in most circuits, it is often necessary for the experimenter or repairman to refer to a schematic diagram or to the manufacturer's specifications in order to determine whether a given transistor is of the N-P-N or the P-N-P type. If biasing voltages of incorrect polarities are applied, even momentarily, the transistor may be ruined. As a general rule, because of their greater availability and lower price, P-N-P transistors are employed with greater frequency than the N-P-N types.

17.7 *Principles of transistor amplification*

During the process of considering how a transistor amplifies, it should be noted that while an electron tube is a voltage-operated device, a transistor is a current-operated device. While the electron tube works best with a constant-voltage power source, a transistor requires a constant-current power supply. In a transistor, the important operating characteristic is alpha (α), which is the current-amplification factor under grounded-base operating conditions.

Alpha may be defined as the ratio of a small change in collector current to a small change in emitter current when the potential of the emitter is maintained constant. Thus, if a signal change of 1 ma in the emitter circuit produces a change of 0.95 ma in the collector circuit, the value of alpha is 0.95.

When the transistor is operating, a signal causes carriers, which may be either electrons or holes, to be ejected by the emitter toward the base (Fig. 17-38 and 17-39). Since the polarity of the collector is opposite to that of the base,

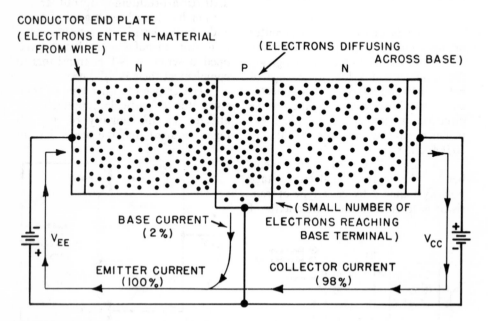

CONDUCTOR END PLATE
(ELECTRONS ENTER N-MATERIAL FROM WIRE)

(ELECTRONS DIFFUSING ACROSS BASE)

N   P   N

BASE CURRENT (2%)

(SMALL NUMBER OF ELECTRONS REACHING BASE TERMINAL)

V_{EE} V_{CC}

EMITTER CURRENT (100%)

COLLECTOR CURRENT (98%)

(NOTE: CURRENT IN WIRE IS ELECTRON CURRENT)

FIG. 17-38. OPERATION OF AN N-P-N JUNCTION TRANSISTOR AMPLIFIER IN WHICH THE CHIEF CURRENT CARRIERS ARE ELECTRONS

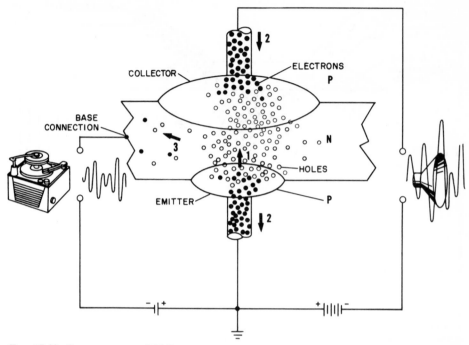

FIG. 17-39. OPERATION OF A P-N-P JUNCTION TRANSISTOR AMPLIFIER IN WHICH THE CHIEF CURRENT
CARRIERS ARE HOLES
*Small signal from phonograph is amplified to activate loudspeaker. If the signal changes by 1 million
electrons, for example, there will be a voltage difference between emitter and base which starts 50
million holes flowing out of emitter (1). All but 1 million holes get to collector, inducing 49 million
electrons to flow and carry current in collector circuit (2). The remaining holes flow to the base completing
base-emitter circuit (3).*

the collector pulls the carriers through
the base. A few of the carriers are lost
or neutralized within the base, but most
of them reach the collector where they
add to the normal flow of collector current. In a typical junction transistor,
approximately 5 per cent of the carriers
are thus neutralized, resulting in the
production of an alpha whose value is
0.95. Thus it can be seen that when an
alternating signal is introduced into the
emitter circuit, the number of carriers
that are collected at the collector will
be a function of this signal.

In a typical point-contact transistor,
a complex secondary reaction occurs at
the collector that involves the formation
of a space charge. This produces values

of current amplification as high as 2.5
(Fig. 17-40). However, even this current-amplification value is low when it is
compared with the voltage amplification of a typical electron tube.

The solution to this paradoxical
situation lies in the fact that high voltage gains can be obtained in a transistor even with low values of alpha, because of the fact that the output collect-
or circuit has a much higher impedance
than the input emitter circuit. The ratio
between these two impedances is called
the resistance gain, and it may be of the
order of 1,000. Since the input voltage
is equal to the product of input current
and input resistance, while the output
voltage equals the product of output

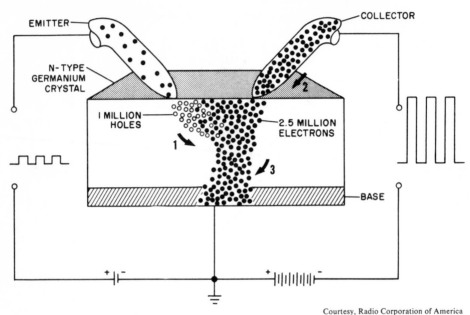

FIG. 17-40. OPERATION OF A POINT-CONTACT AMPLIFIER

If a signal injects 1 million holes at emitter, they will be attracted towards collector (1). Near collector, holes reduce barrier to electron flow (2) allowing some 2.5 million electrons to pass into crystal. Of these, 1 million neutralize the holes; the others flow to base (3). Pulses at left and right are of type employed in computers.

current and output resistance, the voltage gain equals the product of alpha and the resistance gain. In a similar manner, the power gain equals the square of alpha multiplied by the resistance gain. Thus, in some transistors, the value of this gain may be over 100,000.

The resulting high voltage and power amplifications are dependent upon the fact that a signal is applied to a low-impedance circuit and is removed from a high-impedance circuit. It is interesting to note that although the alpha of a junction transistor is always smaller than that of a point-contact transistor, the much greater resistance gain of the junction transistor causes its voltage gain to be considerably higher than that of the point-contact type.

In some junction-transistor amplifier circuits, the emitter, rather than the base, serves as the electrode that is common to both the input and the output circuits. The resultant value of current amplification is called beta (β). Beta is equal to the ratio of a small collector-current change to a small base-current change, and it may have a value that is many times greater than the value of alpha for the same transistor. The value of beta may be obtained as follows:

$$\beta = \frac{\alpha}{1 - \alpha}$$

Thus, if a signal change of 0.05 ma in the base circuit produces a change of 0.95 ma in the collector circuit, beta equals 19. Since beta, unlike alpha is a number that is always greater than 1, and the common-emitter type of circuit is the predominant circuit employed in transistor radio receivers, the beta measurement is a more convenient one for comparing similar transistors. Today, beta is regarded as the most pertinent parameter for measuring how good or how efficient the action of a transistor really is.

An even higher value of beta may be obtained when the collector serves as the common electrode. In this type of transistor circuit, the value of beta may be determined as follows:

$$\beta = \frac{1}{1 - \alpha}$$

17.8 *Point-contact transistors*

This type of transistor, historically the oldest type, consists of a pellet of N-type germanium, approximately the size of the head of a pin, to which the base electrode is connected. The collector and emitter electrodes consist of two fine wires, called cat-whiskers, which are spaced a few thousandths of an inch apart and which maintain contact with the germanium surface (Fig. 17-41).

During the process of manufacture, an electroforming process involving the application of heavy pulses of current causes areas of P-type germanium to be formed around the contact points, thus producing what may be regarded as a special type P-N-P junction transistor. The advantage of using the cat-whiskers is that they enable a relatively low battery voltage to produce an electric field of high intensity at the points without the danger of burning out the transistor or causing a breakdown. However, point-contact transistors will not operate at voltages as low as the junction type will.

Unlike junction transistors, point-contact transistors have current-amplification factors that are always greater than unity. Alpha may have a value as high as 50, although typical values range between 1 and 5. When operating as a power amplifier, a point-contact transistor can boost the power of a signal by 20 db, or approximately 100 times.

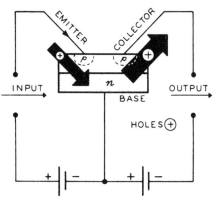

Courtesy, American Telephone and Telegraph Co.
FIG. 17-41. POINT-CONTACT TRANSISTORS
(Top) Size compared to a dime; (bottom) use as an amplifier.

The power-handling capabilities of these transistors are relatively low, being limited by the considerable amount of heat that is usually generated at the collector points. Consequently, point-contact transistors should not be employed in applications where power output is of primary concern.

Because of their high value of alpha, point-contact-transistor amplifier circuits are relatively unstable and are very likely to break into oscillation. Unless care is taken, the transistor may easily be damaged or destroyed. When point-contact transistors are used in the grounded-emitter and grounded-collector circuits which will be described later, the input and output impedances may acquire negative values, indicating potential instability. Consequently, point-contact, grounded-base circuits are generally employed for amplifier applications, while grounded-emitter and grounded-collector circuits are generally employed for oscillator and trigger-circuit applications.

An outstanding feature of the point-contact transistor is its high-frequency capabilities. Because of this, they can be employed in amplifier circuits that operate at frequencies as high as 100 mc, and in efficient oscillator circuits that operate at frequencies above 300 mc. This is far beyond the range of the ordinary junction-triode transistor. In addition, when point-contact transistors are used as amplifiers, they have a relatively flat frequency response over the entire broadcast band. These characteristics make the point-contact transistor applicable for uses in i-f amplifier, r-f amplifier, and oscillator circuits; and in other circuits not associated with the high-power stages of r-f systems.

Another important advantage of the point-contact transistor is associated with its negative-resistance characteristics under certain operating conditions. Over a certain range of operating conditions, the current decreases as the voltage increases. This enables the transistor to be used in circuits designed to perform electronic switching operations, to generate and trigger pulses of various waveforms, and to store information in computers.

The transistor is the most effective electronic switch presently known. The best gas tube can function as a switch that is capable of providing a resistance of several megohms in its non-conducting condition, and a few hundred ohms in its conducting condition. In contrast, the transistor provides a resistance that varies from several meg-ohms to a fraction of an ohm. In addition, it operates in a fraction of a microsecond and is stable in either the open or the closed condition.

Of the approximately 400 different types of EIA transistors, approximately 20 are of the point-contact type. In general, the applications of point-contact transistors have tended to dwindle and today these transistors are employed mainly in military applications and in the communication equipment of the Bell Telephone System. Their continued use in these applications is probably due to the vast amount of proven point-contact circuitry available.[29]

17.9 *Junction transistors*

The junction transistor, which was invented by Shockley in 1951, differs considerably from the point-contact type in physical appearance and operating characteristics. It is a physical combination of 2 germanium diodes—consisting of a sandwich of one type of germanium placed between two layers of the opposite type of germanium, to form either a P-N-P or N-P-N combination. The middle layer is the base, while the outer layers comprise the emitter and collector respectively. In contrast with the high-resistance point contacts employed in the emitter and collector electrodes of point-contact transistors, junction-transistor electrodes are soldered so as to make low-resistance contacts (Fig. 17-42).

There are two major types of junction transistors in common use. One is the rate-grown type in which the impurities that are required to produce the alternate layers are introduced as the crystal is grown (Fig. 17-43). The second and most common type is the diffused-junction type, in which small pieces or dots of P-type material are fused to opposite sides of a wafer of N-

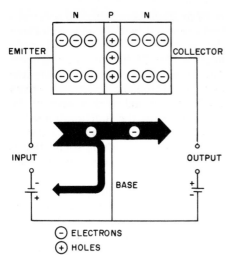

FIG. 17-42. ACTION OF AN N-P-N JUNCTION
TRANSISTOR

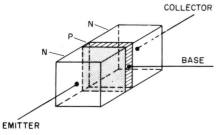

Courtesy, Sylvania Electric Products, Inc.
FIG. 17-43. RATE-GROWN JUNCTION TRANSISTOR

type germanium, or vice versa (Fig. 17-44). A great deal of confusion has resulted from the fact that this latter type of junction transistor is also known under several other names, such as alloy, alloyed, alloy-junction, fused-junction, fusion-alloy, diffused-alloy, fused-alloy, diffused-junction, and alloy-diffusion.

The two types of junction transistors possess somewhat different characteristics. The diffused type has good gain at audio frequencies and is suitable for medium power audio amplifiers, since it can pass currents up to 500 ma. It is not suitable for high-frequency amplifiers, since the large indium dots produce a high capacitance between the collector and the base, making the unit inherently unstable at high frequencies. On the other hand, the grown type has low collector capacitance and produces excellent gain up to frequencies of several megacycles. It is stable at high frequencies and is suitable for use in the r-f sections of broadcast receivers. It also makes an excellent unit for high-speed gating and counting circuits.[30]

The junction transistor has proved to be extremely effective as a low and

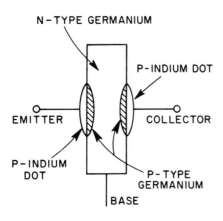

FIG. 17-44. DIFFUSED-TYPE JUNCTION TRANSISTOR

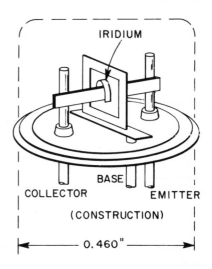

medium-frequency amplifier. Its stability is greater than that of the point-contact type, because its current-amplification factor approaches unity. It can produce power gains as high as 50 db or 100,000 times, in contrast with the gain of 20 db or 100 times obtainable from the point-contact type. In addition, the absence of the wire cat-whiskers makes the junction transistor much more rugged than the point-contact type.

Among the most remarkable features of the junction transistor are its low power consumption and low voltage requirements, which are considerably less than those of the point-contact transistor. For example, a junction-transistor audio-frequency oscillator circuit can be constructed which requires only 0.1 volts and 0.6 microwatts of power. Over 20,000 such junction-transistor circuits could be operated by means of the power required to operate one subminiature type of electron tube. Another a-f oscillator has been developed by Wallace of Bell Telephone Laboratories which requires only 0.08 microwatts at 0.05 volts. It can be powered by the output of a photovoltaic cell or by a simple cell consisting of a coin and a paper clip separated by a piece of moist paper.[31]

Other important features of the junction transistor are its relatively high power-handling capacity and efficiency. This type of transistor can be designed to dissipate up to 2 watts of power. When operating as a Class A amplifier, efficiencies as high as 49 per cent are obtainable, in contrast with the efficiency of 30 per cent obtained with the point-contact transistor and with vacuum-tube amplifiers. When it is operating as a Class C amplifier, efficiencies as high as 98 per cent may be realized.

Another interesting characteristic is its relatively low noise figure, which is 10 to 20 db above thermal noise at a frequency of 1,000 cps, in contrast with the point-contact type whose noise figure is 45 to 55 db above thermal noise. This noise, which is caused by undesired and uncontrollable electron activity within the crystal, is thus over 10,000 times lower in the junction-transistor. This reduces considerably the loudness of the annoying rushing sound that is produced in the headphones or loudspeaker.

The physical arrangement of the closely spaced germanium wafer resembles that of a capacitor. The resultant capacitance effect sets an upper-frequency limit for effective junction-transistor operation. The principal frequency limitation is due to the slow transit speed of the carriers through the base layer. These movements are much slower than the movements of electrons through a vacuum tube. Consequently, the maximum gain of the junction transistor is obtained at a frequency of a few kilocycles, and the amount of gain falls off rapidly as the frequency increases beyond this point. However, it is possible to obtain useful gains at frequencies as high as 1 mc.

Reducing the thickness of the intervening base layer should produce the effect of reducing the transit time. When impurities are introduced in a controlled manner by the diffusion process, this layer can be made as thin as 0.00003 in. Unfortunately, when the base thickness is reduced, the capacitance between the emitter and the collector electrodes is increased, nullifying some of the advantages that had been obtained by increasing the other factor that was limiting the frequency response. Another undesirable consequence of the reduction of the thickness of the base layer is that it produces an increase in its cross-sectional resistance. The wire that is connected to the base lead no longer grounds the entire layer effectively, and considerable degeneration is produced.[32]

The majority of the transistors that are now commercially available are of the junction type. They are the workhorse amplifiers in radio and television-receiver circuits, in phonograph amplifiers, in low-repetition-rate multivibrator circuits, and in many other applications where small size, low power drain, high reliability, and long life are required.

17.10 *Basic transistor-amplifier circuits*

There are three different types of basic transistor amplifier circuits: the grounded-base, the grounded-emitter, and the grounded-collector. These designations do not refer to circuit ground or to the actual connecting to ground of a specific electrode but indicate which of the three electrodes is common to both the input and output circuits. Some authorities prefer to call these circuits by the names common-base, common-emitter, and common-collector. A connection to the system ground can be made at any convenient point in any of these three circuits.

The junction-transistor grounded-base amplifier shown at the left in Fig. 17-45 is approximately equivalent to the grounded-grid vacuum-tube amplifier that is shown at the right. It is characterized by low input impedance, ranging from 20 to 1,000 ohms; and high output impedance, ranging from 10,000 ohms to 13.5 megohms. The voltage gain may be in the order of 1,500, and when the impedances are properly matched, power gains of 50 db can readily be achieved. The current amplification or alpha is less than unity, usually in the order of 0.98 to 0.99, and no signal inversion or phase reversal of the signal occurs between the input and output circuits.

This type of circuit is suitable for d-c coupling and for use in a preamplifier circuit that requires the matching of a low-input impedance to a high output impedance. This circuit possesses the best frequency-response characteristics of the three and is extremely stable. It is therefore employed quite frequently with point-contact transistors.

The junction-transistor grounded-emitter amplifier circuit that is shown in Fig. 17-46 corresponds to the vacuum-tube grounded-cathode amplifier also shown in the same diagram. This type of circuit is the only one of the three that produces a phase reversal between the input and output signals. This circuit also provides the highest voltage and power gains. The current amplification or beta is quite high. It is characterized

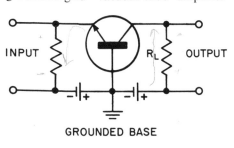

GROUNDED BASE

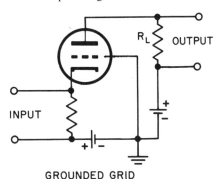

GROUNDED GRID

FIG. 17-45. COMPARISON BETWEEN A TRANSISTOR GROUNDED-BASE AND A VACUUM-TUBE GROUNDED-GRID CIRCUIT

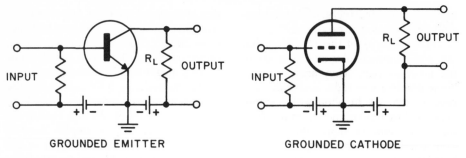

GROUNDED EMITTER   **GROUNDED CATHODE**

FIG. 17-46. COMPARISON BETWEEN A TRANSISTOR GROUNDED-EMITTER AND A VACUUM-TUBE GROUNDED-CATHODE CIRCUIT

by a medium value of input impedance, ranging between 300 and 1,000 ohms, and a medium value of output impedance, ranging between 5,000 and 50,000 ohms. The grounded-emitter circuit is the one that is in most common use today.

The junction-transistor grounded-collector transistor circuit is shown in Fig. 17-47. It is similar to the vacuum-tube grounded-plate or cathode-follower circuit shown at the right in that illustration. Like the grounded-base circuit, its output signal is in phase with its input. The power gain obtainable from this type of circuit is relatively low, being only 15 to 20 db. This circuit is characterized by a relatively high input impedance in the neighborhood of 100,000 ohms and a rather low output impedance of less

than 1,000 ohms. Its beta current-amplification factor is high, being of the same order as that of the grounded-emitter circuit; but the voltage amplification, like that of an electronic cathode-follower circuit, is less than unity. This circuit is also characterized by the highest frequency-response capabilities of the three types of circuits. Another interesting characteristic is that its high input impedance is not a constant but is directly dependent upon the impedance of the output load circuit.

A unique characteristic of this type of amplifier is that it is capable of bilateral or two-way amplification. By interchanging the connections to the input and output circuits, a signal may be amplified in either the forward or the reverse direction.

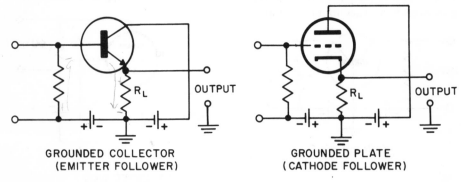

GROUNDED COLLECTOR (EMITTER FOLLOWER)   **GROUNDED PLATE (CATHODE FOLLOWER)**

FIG. 17-47. COMPARISON BETWEEN A TRANSISTOR GROUNDED-COLLECTOR AND A VACUUM-TUBE GROUNDED-PLATE OR CATHODE-FOLLOWER CIRCUIT

Because of the high input imped-ance of the grounded-collector circuit, which approaches that of an electron tube, it can be used for the input circuit of transistorized instruments such as electronic voltmeters, Geiger counters, and signal tracers. Like the electronic cathode-follower circuit, it can also be used as an interstage impedance-matching device and as a buffer ampli-fier. Combinations of either grounded-base or grounded-emitter stages fol-lowed by a grounded-collector stage are occasionally encountered. These com-binations are effective in producing low noise output, high power output, and great gain without the use of inter-stage transformers.

17.11 *Comparison of transis-tor and vacuum-tube circuits*

The transistor, like the vacuum tube, is readily adaptable to all types of circuits. Today, transistor manufacture has advanced to such a point that tran-sistors are capable of performing the functions of approximately 70 per cent of present-day electron tubes.[33] In many instances, transistor circuitry is even simpler than vacuum-tube circuitry, since there is no problem produced by a common filament supply. By making use of the complementary symmetry of P-N-P and N-P-N junction transistors, it is possible to design simple push-pull amplifier circuits which require neither center-tapped coupling transformers nor phase-inverting circuits. Problems of shielding are minimized by the low impedance of transistor-input circuits.

However, transistors are not inter-changeable with vacuum tubes in the sense that a tube can be removed from a circuit and a transistor substituted for it. The transistor requires specially de-signed circuits and components in order that it may be employed with the great-est effectiveness and efficiency. Al-though transistor circuits can be under-stood on the basis of analogy to vacuum-tube circuits, transistors must often be connected and operated in a manner quite different from that of vacuum tubes. Consequently, experience ob-tained with vacuum-tube circuits can-not always be applied to transistor cir-cuitry.

While the collector, base, and emitter of the transistor may be consi-dered analogous to the plate, grid, and cathode, respectively, of the vacuum tube, the corresponding elements are not equivalent to each other. Unlike those of the vacuum tube, the input and output circuits of the transistor are not isolated from each other. Consequently, the output impedance of the transistor is affected by the input impedance and by the impedance of the signal source. The various transistor parameters are interdependent and affect each other. It should also be noted that while the grid of a tube is generally biased nega-tively with respect to the cathode, and the plate is generally positive with res-pect to the cathode, the emitter of a transistor may be either positive or neg-ative with respect to the base, and the collector may be either negative or pos-itive with respect to the base.

Another important difference is based on the fact that the transistor always requires some input or drawing power. The grid circuits of most elec-tronic amplifiers are usually considered to be equivalent to open circuits, and the power input is negligible. This is not true of a transistor circuit, in which a power input must always be provided in order to obtain a power output. In addition, since transistors are current amplifiers rather than voltage amplifiers, it is desirable to have low input imped-ances rather than high input impedances in order to obtain maximum amplifica-tion.

Still another important difference to be considered is related to operating conditions. While vacuum tubes operate with constant plate and grid-bias voltages, transistors operate with constant collector voltages and constant base-bias currents. While bias in a vacuum tube is a voltage that is applied between the grid and the cathode, bias in a transistor is a current that flows in the emitter-base circuit. In a vacuum tube, increasing the bias voltage decreases the amount of plate current, while in a transistor, increasing the bias current increases the amount of collector current. When a vacuum tube is biased to cutoff, the plate current drops to zero. When a transistor is cut off by removing its bias, there will still be a small amount of current flowing. This current is known as the cutoff current.[34]

When converting vacuum-tube circuits into equivalent transistor circuits, attention must be paid to the principle of duality. A component or circuit is the dual of another when current in one circuit behaves like voltage in the other. Thus, in converting a tube circuit into a transistor circuit, a series capacitor would be replaced by a shunt inductor, a series-resonant circuit by a parallel-resonant circuit, a resistance by a conductance, a T-circuit by a pi-circuit, a voltage step-up transformer by a current step-down transformer, a circuit loop by a node or junction, a voltage supply by a current supply, plate voltage by collector current, plate current by collector voltage, and grid-bias voltage by base-bias current. While there are limitations to this principle of duality, it has become a useful tool in designing transistor circuits.[35]

Thus it may be seen that while the transistor is in some respects a formidable competitor of the electron tube, the most important contribution of the transistor is not the fact that it may replace the electron tube in certain applications but that it has opened up entirely new domains in technology and in the field of solid-state physics.

17.12 *Advantages of transistors*

Transistors are small in size, the average unit being between $\frac{1}{2}$ and 1 in. high. Some transistors are only one-fifth of the size of the smallest electron tubes (Fig. 17-48). Their power requirements are very low, ranging between 1 and 100 microwatts, in comparison with the power levels of 0.05 to 5 watts required by most vacuum tubes. Transistors can therefore be employed in portable equipment that is powered by small, lightweight batteries.

Courtesy, Radio-Electronics and General Electric Co.
FIG. 17-48. COMPARISON OF THE SIZE OF A RATE-GROWN TRANSISTOR (RIGHT) WITH THAT OF A CONVENTIONAL VACUUM TUBE (LEFT) AND A MINIATURE VACUUM TUBE (CENTER)

The absence of a filament not only eliminates the need for a warm-up period and solves the problem of filament burn out, but it simplifies the circuitry by enabling many circuit components to be reduced in size or omitted. It also means negligible heat output, permitting components to be located close to each other without the danger of damage caused by excessive heating.

Another advantage is the low anode-voltage requirement. Anode potentials of 10 volts are frequently employed, while anode potentials as high as 50 volts are rather rare. Corresponding hot-cathode electron tubes frequently require anode potentials of 100 volts, while potentials as low as 50 volts are rare.[36]

Transistors are extremely rugged, being able to withstand vibration up to 100 G, and shock up to 30,000 G. In contrast, the shock limitation of the average tube is 750 G. Transistors can also be subjected to severe vibration without producing the unpleasant ringing or microphonic sound effects characteristic of vacuum tubes. However, the flexible leads of transistors are easily damaged, and every effort should be made to avoid twisting or bending them.

One of the few causes of transistor failure is the presence of water vapor. However, sudden transistor failures are usually unknown. When a transistor does occasionally fail, the failure generally occurs slowly and gradually over a long period of time. It is believed that the life expectancy of the average transistor is extremely high, ranging from 70,000 to 100,000 hours, or approximately 10 years, in contrast with that of a tube which is approximately 5,000 hours.

Life tests that have been conducted by General Electric scientists since 1954 have shown practically no transistor failures after 18,000 working hours at full output. In addition, these transistors still look and act like new transistors.[37] Some transistors have been on life tests for more than 26,000 hours with no change of characteristics. It has been concluded that transistors have a demonstrated survival rate of 98 per cent at 10,000 hours. This may be contrasted with the 80 per cent survival rate of

commercial vacuum tubes at 1,000 hours of operation.

Another test that was conducted by Raytheon scientists, in which 200 germanium switching transistors were life-tested for 1,000 hours, revealed no failures after 1,000 hours, and negligible changes in current gain.[38] Experts have concluded that if a transistor is carefully manufactured and hermetically sealed, there is, at present, no known reason why it should ever deteriorate.[39]

The high degree of reliability that is attainable with these semiconductor devices has created new concepts concerning the feasibility of making complex and intricate electronic systems capable of operating for long periods of time without equipment failure. As a consequence, there are now available transistorized clocks, dictating machines, paging devices, speed-measuring systems, and high-frequency fluorescent-lighting systems.

As a result of the advantageous properties of the transistor, the end of the employment of the vacuum tube in several fields has been predicted. One such application is that of the home radio receiver. Today, nearly 90 per cent of the radio receivers that are being manufactured are transistorized. Another field is that of computers. Nearly all of the leading computer manufacturers are already marketing completely transistorized, general-purpose digital computers (Figs. 17-49 and 17-50) and electronic data-processing systems. Another area in which the transistor has tended to replace the electron tube is that of hearing aids.[40] [41]

17.13. *Limitations of transistors*

Although transistors possess excellent, inherent reliability characteristics, their fullest potential can be realized

Courtesy, International Business Machines Corp.
FIG. 17-49. PRINTED WIRING AND PANEL FOR IBM 608 COMPUTER

only when careful attention is also paid to their limitations. This involves paying attention to factors such as line-voltage transients, adverse thermal conditions, instability produced by changes in temperature or voltage, and short-duration overloads—factors which are relatively minor ones when working with electron tubes.[42]

One important limitation of present-day transistors is that the temperature dependence of the electrical properties of germanium is such that the performance of the transistor is impaired at temperatures above 100°C. In contrast, tubes can operate at temperatures as high as 500°C. A promising solution to this problem lies in the development of transistors containing silicon, which appears to be potentially capable of operating at high temperatures.

Silicon transistors have stood up well at temperatures as high as 300°C. Another promising solution seems to be offered by the development by Middleton of the Batelle Memorial Institute of

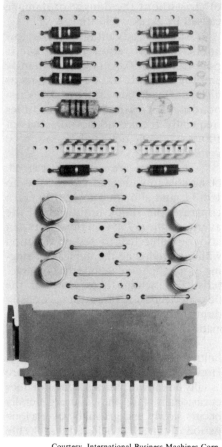

Courtesy, International Business Machines Corp.
FIG.17-50. TRANSISTORIZED PRINTED WIRING CARD EMPLOYED IN CERTAIN ALL-TRANSISTOR COMPUTERS

high-temperature transistors that employ a semiconductor consisting of a combination of aluminum and antimony. Still in the process of development are special semiconductor devices that are capable of operating at temperatures between −271°C and 1,500°C.

While it is true that transistors are temperature sensitive, the vacuum tube is actually even more temperature sensitive. However, the vacuum tube is equipped with a set of built-in ovens which keep its temperature fairly constant, while transistor circuits must be designed so as to compensate for possible temperature variations.[43]

Because of the temperature sensitivity of the ordinary transistor, special precautions must be observed when one is soldering the leads of a germanium transistor. A heat sink, such as a pair of long-nose pliers, should be clamped between the transistor and the soldering iron. In this manner, much of the heat is conducted away and is prevented from passing into the transistor. It is good practice to keep the transistor pigtail leads as long as possible and to complete the soldering job as quickly as possible. The soldering operation should be performed with a light iron or with a soldering pencil that has a fine tip.

The correct polarities and magnitudes of the applied voltages are very important factors in transistor circuits. Many transistors may be burned out or hopelessly damaged by the application of excessive voltages or by reversing the polarity of the voltage that is applied to the collector electrode.[44] It is for this reason that transistors should be removed from their sockets before an ohmmeter is used to obtain resistance measurements of a transistor circuit.

It should, however, be pointed out that the damage to a transistor is produced only when the polarities are reversed in a transistor common-base circuit. Today, the common-emitter type of circuit is far more popular, and the common-base type circuit is seldom employed in practical equipment. When the battery polarities are reversed in a common-emitter circuit, no damage will be done to the transistor, and, under certain circumstances, the circuit may even perform better than it did previously.[45]

A transistor may also be damaged by excessive transient surges of voltage and current produced by switching, by turning the equipment on or off, by discharging of capacitors, by inductive kickback effects, and by signal pulses possessing steep leading or trailing edges. In order to reduce the possibility of damage, power should be turned off when a transistor is being inserted into a circuit or is being removed from the circuit. If this is not possible, the base lead should be connected first and disconnected last, so that bias is applied when the other elements make contact. Limiting devices, such as series resistors in the emitter and collector circuits, can reduce the magnitudes of these transients.

Many investigations have been conducted into the nature and causes of the voltage breakdown of transistors. It has been discovered that the voltage at which a transistor breaks down is a function of both the transistor characteristics and its associated circuitry. It has also been discovered that there are three basic modes of breakdown. These have been labelled as avalanche, alpha multiplication, and punch through. These modes and mechanisms are too complex to be described in this book. However, it has been discovered that it is not the voltage breakdown itself that is responsible for the damage done to the transistor, but it is the heat developed by the unusually high current flow under breakdown conditions that causes permanent degradation of the transistor's characteristics.[46]

Transistor limitations related to noise, power dissipation, and frequency range will be discussed in the sections which follow.

17.14 *Transistor noise*

While the mechanisms that are responsible for transistor noise are not too well understood, it is believed that most of the noise is the result of molecular agitation produced by the movement of carriers through the semiconductor. Additional noise is produced by the random division of the emitter current between the collector and the base and by random variations in the currents crossing the emitter and collector junctions. The noise figure is usually specified in terms of decibels above thermal noise at a frequency of 1,000 cps. The level of the noise generated by the transistor sets a limit to the minimum strength of the signal that can be applied to the transistor circuit.

The large amount of noise generated by early point-contact transistors was a very serious obstacle to their application. Today, the noise figure of the point-contact transistor has been reduced from a level of 60 db to one of 45 db, while commercial junction transistors have been developed with a noise figure of 20 db. Experimental junction transistors have been built whose noise figures are as low as 3 db, which compares very favorably with the noise figures of most vacuum tubes. Since the transistor contains no cathode, and cathode heating is one of the major sources of electron-tube noise, the transistor is potentially capable of operating at lower noise levels than the electron tube.

While the noise level of a vacuum tube increases when the electrodes are subjected to shock or vibration, the noise of a given junction transistor is relatively fixed and does not increase appreciably with vibration, since the noise produced by a junction transistor is related to the ratio of the sizes of the collector and emitter junctions.

The noise level of a transistor tends to decrease as the operating frequency is increased. Thus, a point-contact transistor with a noise figure of 48 db at a frequency of 1 kc will have a noise figure of 18 db at a frequency of 1 mc. Low noise factors can also be achieved by operating the transistor at low emitter currents and collector voltages and by proper adjustment of the resistance of the source that feeds the transistor circuit.

17.15 *Power transistors and power dissipation*

One of the greatest disadvantages of early types of transistors was the low power output that was obtainable. These outputs of a few tenths of a watt were suitable only for specialized applications such as test instruments, hearing aids, and small radio receivers. In 1955, the power transistor emerged from the laboratory stage and became commercially available. By 1958, the total production of power transistors was almost 30 million units.

Typical of these transistors was the type 2N57 P-N-P power transistor that was developed in 1955 under the direction of Larsen of the Minneapolis-Honeywell Regulator Company. Its 20-watt collector-power-dissipation rating was more than 100 times greater than that of other transistors available at the time. This enabled the device to do things that were previously impossible with transistors, such as operating servomechanisms, motors, valves, relays, modulators, intercommunication and public-address systems, and switching circuits.

It may help to illustrate the rapid rate of development of power transistors if it is noted that by late 1956 the Minneapolis-Honeywell P-11 transistor had a power-dissipation rating of 60 watts. By early 1957, experimental transistors were available with power dissipation ratings up to 100 watts.[47] By 1959, there were transistors available that were capable of handling kilowatt loads, and multi-kilowatt transistors were in the developmental stage. It may also be of some interest to note that one of the first important large-scale commercial applications of these new transistors was in the power-amplifier stage of the hybrid automobile radio receiver that was developed during the late 1950's.[48]

The key to the development of these powerful units lies in the discovery of effective means of removing heat from the germanium-alloy junction. If the temperature rise is too great, several undesirable effects are likely to occur. Should the transistor contain indium, the indium may melt. Second, excessive heat may also cause the atoms of the impurity to diffuse throughout the transistor.[49] Finally, if the temperature of the transistor increases beyond a certain value, there is a tendency for the germanium to behave like an ordinary conductor. Many more current carriers are produced. This causes the emitter current to lose control of the collector current, thus decreasing the ability of the transistor to amplify. Furthermore, this increase in collector current causes more heat to be generated which, in turn, causes the collector current to increase to a still higher value. This cumulative action may eventually cause destruction of the transistor.

The collector junction dissipates the most power and is therefore the one most likely to be damaged. In order to reduce heat damage, it is usually necessary to mount the transistor in a metal case and place it in close contact with a metallic heat sink or dissipator—such as a set of radiating metal fins—that is capable of removing the heat generated during normal operation (Fig. 17-51). A unit of this type generally has a very large collector-junction area. In order to dissipate the heat liberated in this area, the collector junction is often mounted on a copper stud, which is attached to a metal chassis.[50]

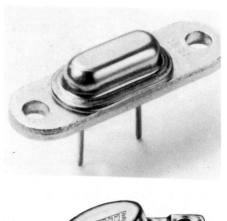

Courtesy, Transistor Div., Clevite Corp.
FIG. 17-51. GERMANIUM POWER TRANSISTORS

Until fairly recently, because of their high junction capacitance plus other factors, power-transistor applications were limited to audio-frequency circuits. However, in 1958, Bell Telephone Laboratories announced the development of a high-frequency power transistor. It was rated at 5 watts and could be used as an oscillator or amplifier for frequencies as high as 10 mc.

Another approach to the problem of power transistors is to use silicon (Fig. 17-52). Silicon transistors can

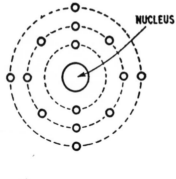

1st RING   2 ELECTRONS
2nd "   8   "
3rd "   4   "

FIG. 17-52. STRUCTURE OF THE SILICON ATOM

operate at temperatures considerably higher than germanium transistors can withstand. However, the silicon transistor possesses the disadvantage that its properties change at high temperatures. Experimenters are currently working on germanium-silicon alloy transistors in an attempt to combine the best features of each material.[51] Another disadvantage of the silicon transistor is that it costs considerably more than the germanium type. This factor has thus far limited its use to military and industrial applications, where operation over a wide range of temperatures is necessary.

There is little doubt that the development of silicon transistors characterized by relatively high power-handling capabilities can be expected to increase the trend toward transistorization of equipment and the development of many new applications for transistors. It might also be noted that considerable research is currently under way to explore the possibilities of employing silicon carbide and similar compound semiconductors, the crystals of which, like those of silicon and germanium, possess the form of a diamond lattice and which are

characterized by improved high-temperature properties.[52] It may also be noted that the sales of silicon transistors have increased at a more rapid rate than the over-all sales of transistors.

17.16 *Frequency limitations of transistors*

Mention has previously been made of the fact that the frequency-limiting factors of a transistor depend upon its internal geometry, which in turn effects the capacitance between the various elements, transit-time effects, and base resistance. One interesting consequence is the fact that an N-P-N transistor possesses a better frequency response than a similar P-N-P type, because the electron current carriers of the former are more mobile than the hole current carriers of the latter.

The poor response characteristics at higher frequencies impose serious limitations to certain applications of transistors. While the frequency limit of an electron tube that is serving as an amplifier is approximately 60,000 mc, the frequency limit for an ordinary junction transistor is approximately 5 mc, and that of a point-contact transistor, 70 mc.

One common transistor specification is known as the alpha cutoff frequency. This is the frequency at which the grounded-base current gain has decreased to 70.7 per cent of its value at low audio frequencies. It may also be defined as the frequency at which the response is 3 db below that of the mid-frequency value. For audio-frequency transistors, the alpha cutoff frequency should be in the region of 1 mc; for intermediate-frequency transistors, this frequency should be between 2.0 and 2.5 mc; while for radio-frequency transistors, this frequency should be between 3 and 15 mc.[53]

There are also several other methods of expressing the high-frequency response of a transistor. One is the beta cutoff frequency, which is the frequency at which the grounded-emitter current gain is 70.7 per cent of its gain at low audio frequencies. Another specification is the figure of merit, which is the frequency at which the gain of the transistor is unity. For practical purposes this may be regarded as the highest frequency at which the transistor can be employed as an oscillator.

17.17 High-frequency P-N-I-P transistors

A great deal of research has been conducted in the direction of improving the frequency-response characteristics of transistors. At Bell Telephone Laboratories, an intrinsic-barrier transistor was developed in 1954 that is capable of producing oscillations at a frequency of 3,000 mc and which can provide uniform amplification over a band of frequencies hundreds of megacycles in width (Fig. 17-53). An intrinsic region may be defined as one that contains neither donor nor acceptor impurities, and which therefore has very high resistance.

This type of transistor, which is also known as the P-N-I-P transistor, consists of layers of P-type, N-type, intrinsic-type, and P-type silicon (Fig. 17-54). The base region is very thin and is heavily doped in order to produce high conductivity. The emitter efficiency is kept high by doping the emitter even more heavily than the base. The intrinsic region separates the collector and base regions, thereby lowering considerably the amount of capacitance between the collector and the base. This layer permits better control of the stream of carriers, isolates the input and output sections, and permits operation

Courtesy, Bell Telephone Laboratories
FIG. 17-53. INTRINSIC-BARRIER TRANSISTOR
This ultra-high-frequency transistor, much smaller than a man's fingernail, can increase an original electrical impulse a thousand-fold when used as an amplifier.

at higher voltages. In certain respects the intrinsic layer resembles the screen grid of a tetrode vacuum tube. The intrinsic layer allows the base to be built larger and thinner, thus reducing the base resistance. The lowering of this base resistance and the reduction of the capacitance between the collector and the base improves the transistor's high-frequency response, while the employ-

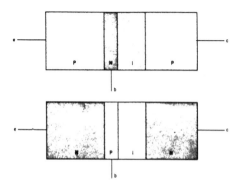

FIG. 17-54. P-N-I-P AND N-P-I-N TRANSISTORS

ment of silicon permits it to operate at higher temperatures and increases its power-handling capabilities by a factor of 10.[54][55] Thus, a recently developed P-N-I-P power transistor can provide an output of more than 5 watts at 10 mc as an amplifier or oscillator and has an alpha cutoff frequency of 100 mc.[56] Before leaving this type of transistor, it may be mentioned that there is also a similar complementary type of intrinsic-barrier transistor that is called the N-P-I-N transistor.

17.18 *Tetrode transistors*

The tetrode transistor was developed in 1952 by Wallace of Bell Telephone Laboratories in an attempt to improve the relatively poor frequency characteristics of junction transistors.[57] It contains a fourth electrode that is connected to the P-type base layer of a N-P-N junction transistor in the same manner as the original base electrode is connected but on the opposite side of the base (Fig. 17-55). A negative bias of approximately 6 volts is applied to this second base electrode (Fig. 17-56). This electrode then repels the electrons coming from the emitter, so that they pass through the base layer in the vicinity of the first base lead. This makes the transistor equivalent to a transistor possessing a much smaller equivalent cross-section, reduces the collector capacitance, and improves the useful frequency range by a factor of 10. It also reduces the base resistance from 1,000 ohms to 40 ohms and reduces the current gain from 0.95 to 0.75. The tetrode transistor can amplify signals at frequencies up to 10 mc and can produce oscillations as high as 250 mc.

A recently developed tetrode transistor is capable of amplifying signals whose frequencies are as high as 50 mc and can produce oscillations at a fre-

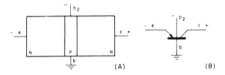

FIG. 17-55. TETRODE JUNCTION TRANSISTOR *(A) Structural representation; (B) symbolic representation.*

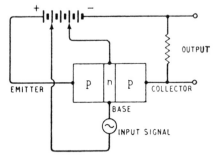

FIG. 17-56. A P-N-P TETRODE TRANSISTOR AMPLIFIER CIRCUIT

quency of 1,000 mc. In this transistor, the junction area in the vicinity of the second base electrode is reduced by removing some of the active material by an etching process. A powerful magnet makes use of the fundamental principle of the motor to deflect moving electrons and to reduce transit time by causing the electrons to travel directly from the emitter to the collector.[58] It appears quite likely that this type of tetrode transistor will be employed within the near future as an i-f amplifier in television receivers.

The tetrode can also be employed for other purposes. Since biasing the second base electrode negatively reduces the current gain, the tetrode can be employed in low-level, automatic-gain-control circuits. In a typical grounded-emitter amplifier circuit, the output signal can be attenuated or weakened as much as 20 db by introducing a current of less than 100 microamperes into the second base lead.

Another application of this tetrode is as a modulator. In this application, the first base electrode is grounded and the carrier-signal source is connected to the emitter electrode and ground. The modulating audio-signal source is connected between the second base electrode and ground.[59] It might also be noted that the tetrode shows promise of being a rather versatile device for the field of switching.

Another type of tetrode, which was developed by Blakely of IBM, has two emitter electrodes. Each emitter can be fed from a separate input-signal source, and the tetrode can be used to mix or heterodyne the two signals.[60]

It is not always possible to identify a tetrode transistor by counting the number of leads, since some triode transistors, like the drift transistor which will be described in the following section, may be provided with an internal interelectrode shield that is brought out to a fourth terminal lead. It is easier to distinguish between tetrodes and triodes by their type numbers. If the prefix begins with a 3, as in the Texas Instrument 3N25, it is a tetrode. If the prefix begins with a 2, such as the RCA 2N544, it is a triode, even though it may possess four terminal leads.

17.19 *Drift transistors*

RCA scientists have developed a technique for manufacturing transistors that do not depend upon the random diffusion of carriers to transmit the signal across the base region. These transistors, called drift transistors, diffused-base transistors, or graded-base transistors, are characterized by a relatively-short transit time. Instead of diffusing, the carriers are propelled across the base region by a built-in electric field (Fig. 17-57).

This field is produced by utilizing an impurity density which varies from one side of the base to the other, being high next to the emitter and low next to the collector. The resulting field tends to accelerate the motion of holes from the emitter to the collector, permitting the drift transistor to be used at much higher frequencies than transistors of conventional design.[61] [62] These devices can oscillate at frequencies as high as 300 mc and are usable as amplifiers at very high frequencies.

The Philco 2N502 a microalloy diffused-base transistor, is capable of producing oscillations at a frequency

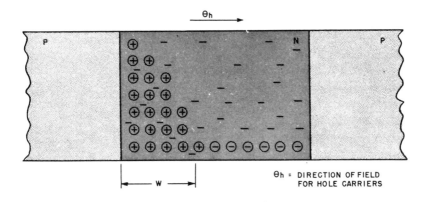

FIG. 17-57. DRIFT TRANSISTOR

of 500 mc. Another transistor, which was developed at Bell Telephone Laboratories, employs a diffusion technique to produce a base layer with a thickness of 0.00005 in. This transistor operates at frequencies as high as 600 mc. A diffused-base transistor developed by Motorola is reported to be capable of operating at a frequency of 1,000 mc, while oscillator frequencies in excess of 1,100 mc have been obtained with developmental graded-base transistors.[63] In 1959, IBM scientists reported that they had developed an experimental drift transistor that could oscillate at frequencies as high as 1.550 mc.[64]

17.20 *Surface-barrier transistors*

The surface-barrier transistor, which was developed in 1953 by the Philco Corporation, is a modified P-N-P junction transistor (Fig. 17-58). It is produced by directing two fine jets of indium sulphate solution upon opposite sides of a wafer of N-type germanium.

A direct current is then passed through the solution. This removes or etches away some of the germanium by electrolytic action. When a sufficient amount of germanium has been etched

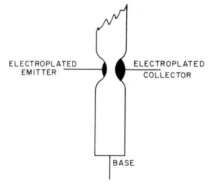

FIG. 17-58. SURFACE-BARRIER JUNCTION TRANSISTOR

away, the direction of current flow is reversed, and two dots of indium are electroplated on opposite sides of the wafer. These dots are connected to the emitter and collector electrodes, while the wafer is connected to the base lead. This manufacturing process is capable of producing transistors with a high degree of uniformity.

These transistors have a very-low noise figure that is between 4 and 8 db. The thinning of the base by the etching process reduces the hole transit time across the base, thereby improving the high-frequency response. As a result, these transistors are capable of reliable operation, even above 70 mc. When a special type of surface-barrier transistor is constructed by means of a diffusion process, it is possible to obtain a significant amount of amplification at frequencies as high as several hundred megacycles.[65]

An additional advantage lies in the fact that this type of transistor requires low collector voltage and produces linear response even when the collector voltage is lower than that of the base. This enables the transistor to be directly coupled, the collector of one being tied directly to the base of the next transistor.[66] They can also produce power gains in the order of 1,000 and require only 5 milliwatts of battery power. Consequently, they are ideally suited for battery-operated and airborne military-electronic equipment.[67]

These transistors are also well adapted to applications in switching circuits and have been employed for that purpose in Philco's Transac Transistorized Automatic Computer, a fast airborne computer that occupies less than 3 cu ft of space, weighs only 150 lb, and requires only 60 watts of power. This computer can handle all of the computations required to control a military jet aircraft from take off, through weapon delivery or enemy interception, to the final landing.

17.21 *Microalloy bonded-barrier transistors*

The physical appearance of the microalloy bonded-barrier transistor resembles that of a point-contact type, but it is really a junction transistor. The process by which it is manufactured resembles that of the surface-barrier transistor. A slab of germanium is etched by means of a jet spray. As in the manufacture of the surface-barrier transistor, the emitter and the collector are plated on the surface. In contrast, the device is then heated. Alloying then takes place, creating a shallow alloyed region. Because of its thin base, this type of transistor also possesses good, high-frequency characteristics. However, due to the thinness of the base, the maximum collector voltage must be kept to a very low value, limiting the power output of this device.[68] This type of transistor, which is also known as the MADT or microalloy-diffused type, can also be employed in oscillators at frequencies as high as 1,000 mc.

17.22 *The mesa transistor*

Unfortunately, tetrodes, surface-barrier transistors, and MADT transistors possess a common weakness. They are capable of handling only small amounts of power. When they are used in r-f oscillator circuits, the amount of power that is generated is measured in milliwatts. The mesa transistor is an ultra-high-frequency transistor whose power-handling capabilities are comparable to those of small vacuum tubes (Fig. 17-59). Thus, Texas Instrument's 2N1141 diffused-base mesa transistor has an alpha cutoff frequency of 750 mc and

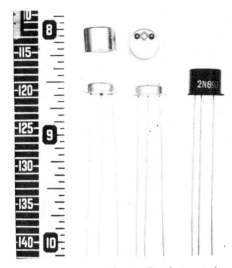

Courtesy, Texas Instruments, Inc.
FIG. 17-59. VIEWS OF MESA TRANSISTORS

a collector-dissipation rating of 0.75 watts.[69]

This device obtains its name from the fact that the base region is etched away to form a mesa or plateau (Fig. 17-60). The reduction of the total base area provides a higher frequency response characteristic.

17.23 *The P-N-P-N transistor*

The P-N-P-N or hook transistor, which was developed by Ebers of Bell Telephone Laboratories, is a special type of junction transistor that contains

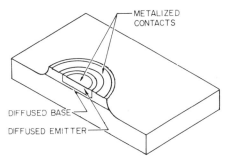

METALIZED CONTACTS

DIFFUSED BASE

DIFFUSED EMITTER

Courtesy, Texas Instruments, Inc.
FIG. 17-60. STRUCTURE OF A MESA TRANSISTOR

four zones (P, N, P, and N) and three junctions (Fig. 17-61). The central N and P regions are very narrow. This type of transistor, unlike other junction transistors, is capable of producing a current gain that may be as high as 50.[70]

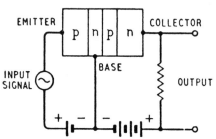

FIG. 17-61. BASIC P-N-P-N TRANSISTOR AMPLIFIER CIRCUIT

One explanation for this extremely high value of alpha is based upon the space-charge effect produced by holes that are trapped at the third junction, which is located between the central P-layer and the end N-layer that is attached to the collector electrode. Another explanation views this transistor as consisting of two stages of transistor amplification that are electronically coupled with each other (Fig. 17-62).

Among the disadvantages of the hook transistor is the fact that it cannot be used at high frequencies. It also has a tendency to become unstable. Application may be made of this instability by employing it in oscillator circuits.[71]

Unfortunately, this type of transistor has found little application as an amplifier.[72]

17.24 The P-N-P-N transistor diode

The P-N-P-N diode or four-layer diode which was mentioned in an earlier chapter dealing with solid-state diodes, is a two-terminal, four-region transistor switch that was invented by Shockley (Fig. 17-63). It is also known as the four-layer bistable transistor diode and was designed to replace electromechanical switches in computers and dial-switching systems.

It consists of four layers of semiconductor material that form three P-N junctions. The center P-N junction is reverse-biased while the outer P-N junctions are forward-biased. This device may be regarded as consisting of two separate junction transistors that are connected to each other.

In the off condition, the device has a resistance of 100 megohms. When it is switched to the on position by means of a pulse of voltage that is applied across the terminals, a breakdown point is approached, and this resistance drops to a value of 2 ohms. The diode will remain in this condition until the current drops below a critical threshold value, at which time it returns to

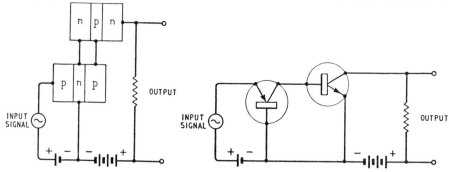

FIG. 17-62. EQUIVALENT CIRCUITS OF THE P-N-P-N TRANSISTOR AMPLIFIER

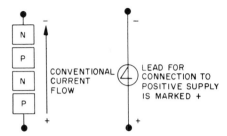

FIG. 17-63. P-N-P-N DIODE
The symbol for the Shockley 4-layer diode is a modified "4"; the slant line of the "4" indicates the forward direction of current passing through the device when in the "on" state.

its former high-impedance condition. The device can be used to switch currents as great as 100 ma in less than 0.5 microseconds.[73][74][75] This device may also be regarded as the equivalent of a thyratron tube, and it may be employed in a similar type of saw-tooth oscillator circuit.

17.25 *The silicon controlled rectifier*

A device that very closely resembles a P-N-P-N diode is the silicon controlled rectifier or thyrode, which was developed by General Electric scientists. This is a three-terminal semiconductor device which combines the features of a rectifier and a transistor, providing characteristics similar to those of a thyratron (Fig. 17-64). It is a P-N-P-N semiconductor, consisting of three rectifying junctions. A lead called the gate is attached to the center P-region. The device does not conduct until an appropriate signal is applied to this gate. As soon as the signal is applied, an avalanche breakdown occurs and a large amount of current flows. By this method, a large amount of current can be controlled by a small amount of gate-electrode power. The device is also capable of functioning as a switch, switching up to 1,000 watts in microseconds.

FIG. 17-64. SILICON CONTROLLED RECTIFIER
This three-terminal silicon device can be used to control large blocks of power up to 300 volts and currents up to 50 amperes.

As in the thyratron, the gate loses control once the device has been fired, and removal or reversal of anode voltage is necessary in order to turn off the current. However, unlike the thyratron, gate current rather than voltage determines the firing point of the controlled rectifier. It is anticipated that this device will first be employed in the power-supply circuits of missile-control systems and for switching applications in automatic machinery that is controlled by computers, punched cards, or magnetic tapes.[76][77][78][79] Thus, silicon controlled rectifiers have been successfully employed as power amplifiers in the drive-regulating system of a paper machine of the Consolidated Water Power and Paper Company of Wisconsin.

17.26 *The unijunction or double-base diode*

The unijunction transistor or double-base diode, which was invented by Lesk of General Electric consists of a bar of an N-type semiconductor, generally silicon, with two base-lead connections, one at each end of the bar (Fig. 17-65). An aluminum emitter electrode is connected to a P-N junction that is formed by placing an indium dot at a point on one edge of the bar.[80] This is the closest solid-state equivalent of the controlled-grid thyratron.

When this device is in operation, the resistance between the two base leads is very high. Very little current flows until sufficient voltage is applied to the emitter. The application of this voltage reduces the resistance, and a much greater amount of current flows between the two electrodes. This is analogous to the condition in a thyratron in which a very-high resistance exists between the cathode and the anode until the application of the proper voltage to the control grid causes the resistance to decrease and the tube to fire. The unijunction transistor may be used in switching, pulse-forming, and multivibrator relaxation-oscillator circuits.[81]

17.27 *The thyristor and similar switching transistors*

The thyristor is a type of transistor that approaches the ideal electron switch for high-speed switching applications in computers and automatic-control systems. It was developed in 1957 by Mueller, Hilibrand, and Barton of RCA.

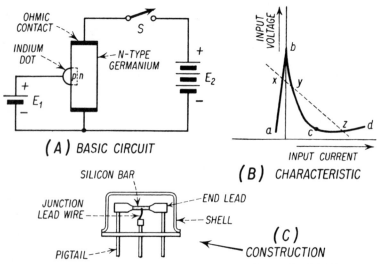

(A) BASIC CIRCUIT

(B) CHARACTERISTIC

(C) CONSTRUCTION

Courtesy, Cornell-Dubilier Electronics Div.

FIG. 17-65. UNIJUNCTION TRANSISTOR

While it possesses many of the properties of gas-switching tubes, it is markedly superior in many respects. For example, the thyristor may be switched from on to off and then back to on by merely changing the polarity of low-energy pulses that are applied to the base. A gas-switching tube cannot be switched off in the same manner that it is switched on. The device can switch substantial amounts of current from one circuit to another in periods as short as 50 microseconds. It can also function as a conventional high-frequency amplifying transistor.[82]

A somewhat similar unit is the previously described Philco field-accelerated MADT or microalloy diffused-base transistor. It can operate at frequencies as high as 1,000 mc and also function as a super-high-speed switch. As a matter of fact, its switching action is so rapid that it is described in units of light-feet instead of microseconds. A typical MADT will switch a circuit on or off within a period of 10 light-feet, which represents the length of time required for light to travel a distance of 10 ft.

17.28 *Tandem transistors*

A tandem transistor consists of two direct-coupled transistors that have been placed in the same case, thus providing a single space-saving unit (Fig. 17-66). It is connected so as to function as a two-stage cascade circuit. The first stage operates as a common-collector amplifier, providing bias and signal current for the second stage, which is usually operated as a common-emitter amplifier. Thus the first stage acts as the input circuit for the second stage and also serves as a d-c matching transformer. With this type of transistor, current gains as high as 75 db may be obtained without the necessity of using matching transformers.

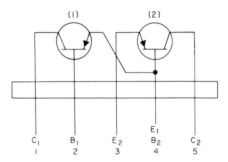

Courtesy, Mar Velco Electronics Div., National Aircraft Corp.

FIG. 17-66. DIAGRAM OF TANDEM TRANSISTOR

17.29 *Field-effect triode transistors*

The field-effect triode transistor is based upon a principle that was described by Shockley in 1952. This principle makes practical application of the field effect, discovered by Lilienfeld in 1928, in which charge carriers in semiconductors were deflected from their paths under the action of an electric field.

The device consists of two coaxial cylinders, a central cylinder of N-type material, and an outer cylinder of P-type material (Fig. 17-67).[83] Attached to the ends of the central cylinder are two electrodes, one called the source and the other the drain. A gate electrode, which is attached to the outer cylinder, produces a transverse electric field that controls the flow of current between the source and the drain. The input and output-impedance levels are high and

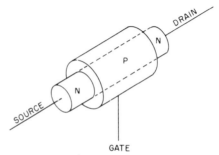

FIG. 17-67. FIELD-EFFECT TRANSISTOR

resemble those of vacuum-tube triodes. As a result, the field-effect transistor can be employed in many vacuum-tube circuits with only minor changes (Fig. 17-68).[84]

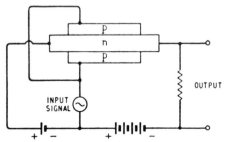

17.30 *Field-effect tetrode*

In 1959, Bell Telephone Laboratories announced the development by H. A. Stone and R. M. Warner of a field-effect tetrode that was capable of performing functions that were previously considered impossible or that required extensive circuitry (Fig. 17-69). This device can function as a transformer, an electrically controlled resistor, a negative resistance, a modulator, or an isolator. It can also convert the reactance of a capacitor into that of an inductor of high Q. It is believed that the areas of usefulness of this device have barely been explored, since it displays potential characteristics within a single

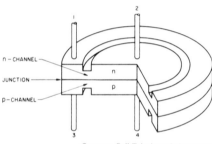

FIG. 17-69. FIELD EFFECT TETRODE

device which previously either could not be obtained at all, or only through extensive circuitry.[85]

17.31 *The tecnetron*

This semiconductor amplifying device was developed in 1958 by Teszner, a French scientist. Its most remarkable feature is that its transconductance increases with frequency, unlike most semiconductor amplifiers whose performances fall off as the frequency increases. The device has operated at frequencies of 500 mc, and there seems to be nothing to prevent it from functioning at 1,000 mc or higher.

It consists of a short rod of N-type germanium that is provided with two contact electrodes at each end. One end functions as the cathode, while the other end serves as the anode. The electrodes act solely as electrical conductors and not as transistor junctions. A load resistance and a potential difference of 50 volts are connected across these two electrodes.

The center of the germanium rod is reduced in diameter to form a bottleneck. Around this neck is placed a cylinder of indium, which forms a metal-to-semiconductor barrier-layer contact. The neck is biased negatively with respect to the cathode, and the indium cylinder functions as a control grid. The device resembles Shockley's field-effect transistor in that it makes use of the Lilienfeld field effect. As a negative signal voltage is applied to the indium cylinder, the electrons that are travelling between the cathode and the anode are deflected toward the center, and they travel through a reduced section of the germanium rod. This increases the apparent resistance of the rod and reduces the cathode-to-anode current. Thus, variations in cylinder voltage produced by the signal generate corresponding variations in the cathode-to-anode current, which in turn creates amplified voltage variations across the load resistor.

An important advantage of the tecnetron is its high input impedance of several megohms and its output impedance of over 1 megohm. A research program is currently under way which may lead to the development of a power tecnetron and an ultra-high-frequency type of tecnetron.[86]

17.32 *Photosensitive transistors*

There are three major groups of photosensitive transistors: (1) the phototransistor, (2) the point-contact photosensitive transistor, and (3) the P-N junction photosensitive transistor. They resemble conventional transistors in being rugged and small and are employed to control photoelectric devices such as automobile-headlight dimmers, burglar alarms, counting mechanisms, automatic door openers, and flame detectors.

One of the most interesting applications of photoelectric transistors is in connection with the routing of long-distance telephone calls. Punched holes on metal cards are used to provide information telling how a call should be handled. When a call arrives, the appropriate instruction card is displaced in such a manner that its pattern of holes is projected by means of light beams upon a bank of phototransistors (Fig. 17-70). These phototransistors then produce signals which enable switches to set up the necessary circuit connections.

Other phototransistor applications include punched-card accounting machines, punched-tape readout equipment, optical sound-on-film pickups, kinescope automatic-brilliance controls, liquid-level controls, industrial

Courtesy, Bell Telephone Laboratories
FIG. 17-70. PHOTOTRANSISTOR CARD TRANSLATOR IN A TOLL OFFICE
A switchman is about to insert a new routing card. Transistor voltage amplifiers can be seen in cabinet below.

safety devices, and smoke-density controls (Fig. 17-71).

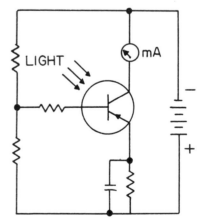

FIG. 17-71. LIGHT-METER CIRCUIT EMPLOYING A PHOTOTRANSISTOR

17.33 *The phototransistor*

The phototransistor or transistor photocell was developed in 1950 by Shive of Bell Telephone Laboratories (Fig. 17-72). It can be described as a miniature, light-sensitive, P-N-P or N-P-N junction transistor, whose current carriers are released by light energy rather than by an electrical-signal input. It is designed to perform the same functions as a phototube, with the added advantages of smaller size and weight, reduced power requirements, and higher directional sensitivity. It can also be described as a solid-state photodiode with a built-in, hook-type amplifier.

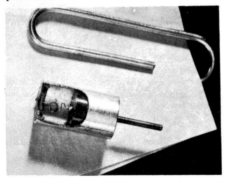

Courtesy, Bell Telephone Laboratories
FIG. 17-72. BELL LABORATORIES PHOTOTRANSISTOR

Because of its current-amplifying characteristics, it is one of the most sensitive photoelectric devices produced.[87] The electronic phototube usually delivers current that is measured in microamperes, and one or more stages of amplification are required to build up the strength of the signal variations to a value that is high enough to operate automatic equipment. On the other hand, a phototransistor delivers milliamperes of current, which is generally sufficient to activate a relay without additional amplification. Consequently, phototransistor circuits require less as-sociated equipment than phototube circuits do and are much more efficient.

Another advantageous characteristic of the phototransistor is the fact that its spectral-response curve covers not only the visible region of the spectrum but extends far into the infrared. This makes it especially useful for black-light applications.

One example of a phototransistor is the Radio Receptor Type RR 66. It is a P-N-P transistor hermetically sealed within a glass envelope, through which three leads emerge. The photosensitive surface consists of an annulus or ring that surrounds the emitter junction. This region has an area of 1 square millimeter. When it is used with unmodulated light, the base connection floats or is left open (Fig. 17-73). With chopped or modulated light, a grounded-emitter circuit is most frequently employed (Fig. 17-74).[88]

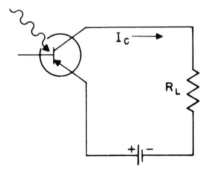

Courtesy, General Instrument Corp.
FIG. 17-73. BASIC PHOTOTRANSISTOR CIRCUIT FOR UNMODULATED LIGHT

A second phototransistor is the Transistor Products Type X-25. This is an N-P-N junction type transistor suspended and sealed in a transparent plastic. The photosensitive region has an area of 0.5 square millimeters; it is located in the base layer in the immediate vicinity of the junction with the emitter layer. The bias battery is adjusted so that very little current flows through the transistor. When light is focused on the base section, holes are formed in sufficient quantities to produce enough current to operate a relay directly.

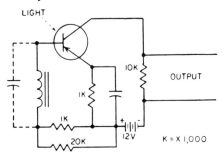

Courtesy, General Instrument Corp.

FIG. 17-74. RECOMMENDED PHOTOTRANSISTOR CIRCUIT FOR MODULATED LIGHT

17.34 *The point-contact phototransistor*

The point-contact phototransistor contains a photosensitive pellet of N-type germanium. It also contains a pointed collector electrode which is mounted, together with the pellet, in a small coaxial cylindrical housing. During the process of manufacture, power is applied to the emitter and base leads in order to make the emitter surface photosensitive. After this has been accomplished, the emitter lead is usually removed so that maximum use can be made of the photosensitive surface. Consequently, many phototransistors have only two leads, in comparison with ordinary transistors which have three.

When the device is operating, the collector is biased negatively with respect to the base. If a light beam strikes the photosensitive emitter, the absorbed energy causes some of the valence bonds to be disrupted. This produces free electrons and holes. As a result, the resistance between the collector and the base is reduced, and there is an increase in the collector current.

17.35 *The P-N junction phototransistor*

A third type of P-N junction phototransistor is called the wide-area junction photocell or the gold-on-germanium photocell (Fig. 17-75). It contains a P-N junction that is produced by the evaporation and diffusion of a thin film of gold onto a circular piece of germanium.

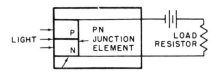

FIG. 17-75. CONSTRUCTION OF A P-N JUNCTION PHOTOCELL

When light is directed at the junction, this device displays photovoltaic properties. It requires neither biasing voltage nor power supply for its operation, although a biasing voltage may be used, if desired.[89]

Although photoelectric transistors are still relatively high-priced, they reduce the cost of photoelectric equipment because they do not require sensitive and expensive amplifiers, power supplies, and other components. The simplicity of phototransistor circuits also reduces maintenance costs (Fig. 17-76).

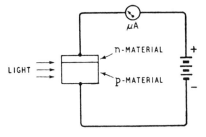

FIG. 17-76. SIMPLE LIGHT-METER CIRCUIT EMPLOYING A JUNCTION PHOTODIODE

17.36 *The spacistor*

In 1957, Hermann Statz, Robert Pucel, and Conrad Lanza of the Raytheon Company announced the development of a semiconductor amplifying device called the spacistor (Fig. 17-77). It is claimed that this device combines many of the best features of the vacuum tube and the transistor.

It can be constructed of high-temperature semiconductor materials and is capable of operating at temperatures as high as 500°C, making it useful for rocket and guided missile applications. The device contains four independent external electrodes and resembles a tetrode transistor in size and appearance. Its compactness and ruggedness give it a high degree of reliability. Like the transistor, it requires no heater, but its power consumption is slightly greater than that of a transistor.[90]

The spacistor utilizes the forces of high electric fields that are applied between the base and the collector to accelerate the motion of charge carriers

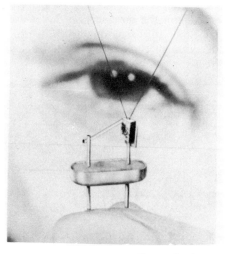

Courtesy, Raytheon Co.

FIG. 17-77. THE SPACISTOR

through the base region. The device consists of a P-N junction that is separated by a space-charge region containing two biased, pressure-contact electrodes called the injector and the modulator (Fig. 17-78).

The spacistor bears a close physical and electrical similarity to a tetrode

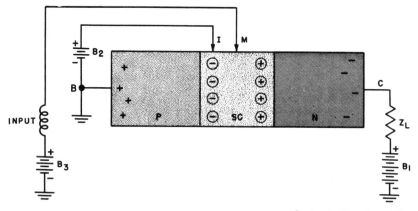

Courtesy, Raytheon Co. and *Electronic Design*

FIG. 17-78. TYPICAL SPACISTOR AND EXTERNAL CIRCUITS
The space-charge region of a P-N junction biased in reverse is indicated by the area SC. A suitable electron emitting contact I is placed into the space-charge region. The contact I is connected to terminal B through a battery which biases the contact negatively with respect to the potential of the underlying space-charge region. Note the potential of point I is still positive with respect to B. Electrons are emitted from this contact into the space-charge region where they are modulated by a field set up by M. The electrons flow to the N-side, through the load, and back to the point I.

vacuum tube. The injector acts as the cathode, the N-region acts as the anode, and the modulator serves as both the control grid and the screen grid. The screening action of the modulator isolates the output circuit from the input circuit.

The P-N junction is reverse-biased, a negative voltage being applied to the P-section, while a positive voltage is applied to the N-section. The voltage that is applied to the injector causes electrons to enter the region of the electric field, where they flow rapidly to the collector instead of diffusing slowly. This current is modulated by the application of a signal to the modulator. The accelerated motion of the carriers, which reduces transit-time effects, combined with the low output capacitance of the spacistor, makes operation possible at frequencies as high as 10,000 mc.

Unlike the transistor, the spacistor possesses both high input and high output impedances, both being in the vicinity of 30 megohms (Fig. 17-79). Another desirable characteristic is its high gain. It is capable of achieving low-frequency power gains of 70 db and voltage gains of 3,000 times.

17.37 *Liquid-filled transistors*

An experimental liquid-filled transistor was developed in 1958 by Dewald of Bell Telephone Laboratories. This device employs a crystal of zinc oxide immersed in a highly conductive electrolyte which replaces the semiconductor junctions (Fig. 17-80). The electrolyte consists of 5 per cent sodium tetraborate and boric acid solutions.

One end of the crystal is biased negatively with respect to the electrolyte, while the other end is biased posi-

	VACUUM TUBE	SPACISTOR	TRANSISTOR
FREQUENCY LIMIT	HIGH (1.000 Mc)	HIGH (10,000Mc)	MEDIUM (250 Mc)
HEATER POWER	REQUIRED	NONE	NONE
HIGH TEMPERATURE MATERIALS	AVAILABLE	AVAILABLE	NOT AVAILABLE
THEORETICAL LIFE	LIMITED	UNLIMITED	UNLIMITED
VACUUM ENVELOPE	REQUIRED	NONE	NONE
CIRCUIT WEIGHT AND SPACE	HIGH	LOW	LOW
STRATEGIC MATERIALS	REQUIRED	NONE	NONE
COMPLEXITY OF MULTIPLE-STAGE CIRCUITRY	LOW	LOW	HIGH
INPUT AND OUTPUT IMPEDANCES	HIGH	VERY HIGH	LOW

Courtesy, Raytheon Co.

FIG. 17-79. COMPARATIVE CHARACTERISTICS OF THE VACUUM TUBE, THE SPACISTOR, AND THE TRANSISTOR

tively and is placed in series with a load (Fig. 17-81). A platinum electrode, which serves as the signal grid, is mounted to one side of, and near the center of, the zinc oxide crystal. The electric field produced by these signals causes changes in the resistance of the crystal. This causes a variation in the amount of current flowing through the load, which results in the production of an amplified version of the signal voltage.[91]

17.38 *Miscellaneous types of transistors*

In addition to the transistors that have just been described, there are a great many additional types of transistors that have been designed for special applications. Space limitations permit making only brief mention of some of these special transistors. Among them are the following:

1. The point-junction transistor, which is a hybrid type with a junction emitter and a point-contact collector.

2. The symmetrical transistor, which is a junction transistor whose collector and emitter junctions are identical. Either end may be used as the emitter or collector.

3. The fieldistor, which consists of a metal electrode that is placed near a reverse-biased junction. The field produced by this electrode controls the flow of reverse current.

17.39 *Transistor testing*

Transistors, like other circuit components, may be tested by the simple method of substitution. A transistor known to be good is placed in the circuit in place of the suspected one. This

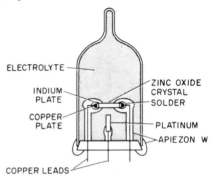

Courtesy, Industrial Laboratories and Bell Telephone Labs.
FIG. 17-80. LABORATORY MODEL LIQUID-FILLED TRANSISTOR

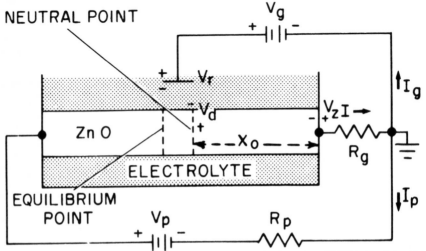

Courtesy, Industrial Laboratories and Bell Telephone Laboratories
FIG. 17-81. LABORATORY MODEL LIQUID-FILLED TRANSISTOR CIRCUIT

procedure is sometimes hazardous and expensive, since the circuit conditions which caused the first transistor to fail may damage the replacement. Transistors may also be damaged during the process of employing the sometimes suggested method of checking their condition by using an ohmmeter to measure the forward and reverse resistances between the base and the emitter and between the base and the collector. This is due to the fact that some instruments that are used for measuring resistance may employ higher voltages than the transistors can tolerate.

Consequently, experimenters have been busy designing circuits that can safely measure those characteristics that indicate the quality and performance of a transistor.[92] [93] The characteristics that are generally considered most significant are collector leakage, current gain, and output impedance.

The collector leakage or cutoff current is a good indicator of the aging of a transistor. It is measured by connecting the base directly to the emitter while a small d-c voltage is applied between the emitter and the collector (Fig. 17-82). A microammeter is inserted in the collector circuit to measure the amount of reverse collector current that flows under conditions of zero base current. Good transistors generally show a collector leakage of less than 10 microamperes. Excessive leakage means reduced output, lowered efficiency, and probable distortion.

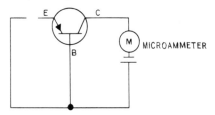

FIG. 17-82. CIRCUIT FOR MEASURING COLLECTOR LEAKAGE CURRENT

The most useful single transistor measurement probably is that of current gain, which is the dual of the amplification factor of an electron tube. It may be recalled that the alpha current gain of a junction transistor is always less than unity. These decimal fractions are difficult to compare with each other. On the other hand, the beta current factor for grounded-emitter operation is expressed in numbers that are greater than unity. It is easier to compare the beta values of 24 and 49 than it is to compare the corresponding alpha values of 0.96 and 0.98. Consequently, many transistor testers employ the grounded-emitter circuit and a signal of 1,000 cps to determine the beta current factor of the transistor being tested. Once this has been found, alpha can be computed, if desired, from the following relationship:

$$\alpha = \frac{\beta}{\beta + 1}$$

The measurement of gain can be used to predict the performance of a transistor as an amplifier or oscillator, and as has been previously mentioned, is probably the best single indication of transistor quality.[94]

Cheap transistor testers often use a d-c method of measuring beta that is not altogether satisfactory (Fig. 17-83). A better method of measuring beta is to use an oscillator circuit whose feedback is controlled by a dial calibrated in units of current gain. This dial is turned until a tone is heard, which indicates that oscillations are being sustained. The fact that high-gain transistors require little feedback while low-gain transistors require a great deal of feedback makes it possible to read the value of beta directly from the dial.[95]

In 1959, the Philco Corporation announced that its engineers had developed an "in-circuit" transistor tester.

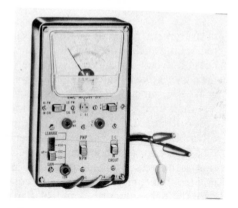

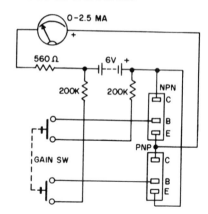

Courtesy, Electronics Measurements Corp.

FIG. 17-83. TRANSISTOR ANALYZER AND AN ANALYZER CIRCUIT

It is claimed that this instrument can check the beta of a transistor with an accuracy of 5 per cent without removing the transistor from its circuit.[96]

The third useful transistor characteristic is the output impedance, rho. This may be determined from the grounded-emitter static-characteristic curve in which collector current is plotted against collector voltage for a constant value of base current (Fig. 17-84). The output impedance is then equal to the reciprocal of the slope of the curve at the point where the collector current is 1 ma and the collector voltage is 10 volts. The common range of output impedances is between 25,000 and 65,000 ohms.

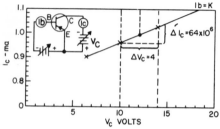

Courtesy, Measurements Corp.

FIG. 17-84. METHOD OF DETERMINING OUTPUT IMPEDANCE. RHO. OF A GROUNDED-EMITTER JUNCTION TRANSISTOR

$$Rho = \frac{\Delta V_c}{\Delta I_c} = \frac{4\ volts}{64 \times 10^{-6} amps} = 62,500\ ohms$$

17.40 *Transistor power supplies*

The type of power supply that is employed in connection with electron tubes is generally of the low-impedance, constant-voltage type. In contrast, the transistor requires a constant-current type of power supply, and the point-contact transistor requires in addition a high-impedance power supply (Fig. 17-85).

This constant-current source is usually provided by placing a high resistance in series with a constant-potential source. As a result, 80 per cent of the power used by the transistor circuit is wasted as heat that is dissipated by this series resistor.[97] This creates a challenge to the battery manufacturers to produce a constant-current source rather than a constant-potential source.

Other characteristics that are considered desirable in a transistor power supply are long life and small size

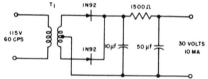

FIG. 17-85. TRANSISTOR POWER SUPPLY

to match the corresponding characteristics of the transistor.

While there will undoubtedly be some transistor applications in which it may be desirable to obtain power by rectifying a source of alternating voltage, batteries will most likely be used to power most transistorized devices. This is due to the greater portability batteries afford, and the fact that the minute power requirements of transistor circuits are so small that the life expectancies of the batteries, even when they are subject to frequent use, are also the same as their normal shelf lives.

Consequently, a need has arisen for small batteries that are capable of maintaining uniform voltage for long periods of operation under low-current drains and of retaining their energy over long periods of non-usage. The Burgess Company has attempted to satisfy this demand by producing a series of redesigned zinc-carbon batteries that are hermetically sealed in plastic and are interconnected by a silver conductor (Fig. 17-86).

Other manufacturers. such as P. R.

Courtesy, Burgess Battery Co.

FIG. 17-86. TYPICAL ZINC-CARBON ACTIVATOR CELLS AND BATTERIES FOR TRANSISTOR CIRCUITS

Mallory and RCA, have concentrated on developing mercury cells that produce energy as a result of the reaction between zinc and mercuric oxide in an electrolyte of potassium hydroxide (Fig. 17-87 and Fig. 17-88). This cell is more

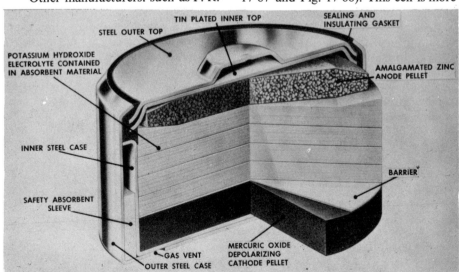

Courtesy, P.R. Mallory and Co.

FIG. 17-87. SECTION THROUGH A MERCURY CELL

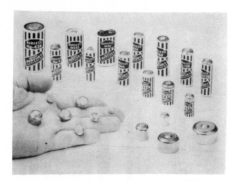

Courtesy, Burgess Battery Co.
FIG. 17-88. TYPICAL MERCURY ACTIVATORS FOR TRANSISTOR CIRCUITS

expensive than the zinc-carbon type but is more stable and rugged and produces about four times the energy of a zinc-carbon cell of the same physical size. The chemicals employed are very stable, and there is almost no reaction within the cell until electric energy is drawn from it. Consequently, the shelf life of this type of cell is relatively long, being greater than two years. The mercury cell is also capable of maintaining its dependable characteristics over a very wide range of temperatures. Mercury cells of this type are used to drive the motor of the automatic electric-eye system of the Bell and Howell 16-mm motion-picture camera. This motor receives information from a photoelectric cell concerning the amount of light coming from the area toward which the camera is pointed. It then operates a train of gears so as to open or close the lens opening.[98]

Another battery that offers great promise is one which was patented in 1954. It employs the principle of the printed circuit. This lightweight battery is printed by applying layers of metallic inks to a sheet of plastic or paper.

In 1957, Goldberg and Reed of the Naval Ordnance Laboratory announced the invention of a miniature rechargeable dry cell delivering 0.9 volts and with a capacity of 1.5 ampere-hours.

Adaptable for use in transistorized circuits, it is almost indestructible, has an estimated operating life of 10 years, and can be produced at a cost that is only 50 per cent greater than that of the mercury batteries presently in use.[99]

In this discussion of the power requirements of transistor circuits, it is worth noting that it is possible to design loudspeaker-type, free-power, transistorized receivers that require no local power source for use in the vicinity of a powerful radio station. These receivers utilize the radio-frequency energy of the carrier wave of the local station to detect and amplify weak signals reaching them from distant transmitters. This secondary energy may also be employed to power a local oscillator and thus to radiate a signal on a different frequency band. It is believed that this principle may eventually prove useful in the operation of unattended repeater stations, automatic-control systems, meteorological radiosonde equipment, and other types of systems of telemetry.[100]

Before leaving the subject of transistor power supplies, it should be noted that since the power requirements of many transistor circuits are measured in milliwatts or even in microwatts, it is possible to operate many of these circuits by means of the electrical energy generated by a photocell (Fig. 17-89). This type of power supply has been employed by the armed forces to power the radio equipment that is mounted in the helmets of soldiers.

17.41 *Additional transistor applications*

While commercial battery-operated transistor radio receivers had appeared on the market before 1956, it was not until that year that these receivers

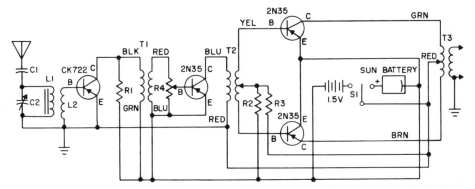

Courtesy, International Rectifier Corp.

FIG. 17-89. SCHEMATIC FOR SUN BATTERY RADIO USING FOUR A-10 INTERNATIONAL RECTIFIER PHOTO-ELECTRIC CELLS

began to receive really wide-spread consumer attention and acceptance (Fig. 17-90). Several large manufacturers began turning out large quantities of these receivers, and transistor portables began to make frequent appearances at beaches, picnic grounds, and ball parks. By 1960, approximately 90 per cent of the radio receivers sold for home use were of the transistor type.

In the fall of 1956, some automobile manufacturers introduced transistor receivers in their new model cars. These receivers, which operated from the 12-volt car battery, were hybrid types. Transistors were employed for the final a-f stages, while tubes operating on 12 volts were employed for the preceding stages. This type of receiver eliminated the noisy vibrator type of power supply, which is a frequent cause of trouble, and it also reduced the drain on the car battery.

In 1959, an Italian manufacturer introduced a 5-transistor, 2-diode car radio that operated from the 12-volt car battery. This radio was small enough to be mounted on the rear-view mirror of an automobile.

During 1957 many manufacturers were also at work on the development of a transistorized portable television

receiver that would use transistors in place of all of the electron tubes except for the picture tube. Scientists at RCA constructed an experimental receiver of this type that employed a 5-in. picture tube. It contained 37 transistors, its dimensions were 12 by 13 by 7 in., and it weighed 27 lb with its batteries. Its total power consumption of 14 watts was less than one-tenth that of an average table-model television receiver. This receiver was capable of producing a satisfactory picture at a distance of 15 miles from the transmitter.

In 1958, Raytheon announced the development of a 30-lb, portable, bat-

Courtesy, Regency Div., Industrial Development Engineering Associates, Inc.

FIG. 17-90. FIRST COMMERCIAL TRANSISTORIZED RADIO RECEIVER

tery-operated, transistorized television receiver. The set, which had a 14-inch screen, employed 2 nickel-cadmium batteries and 31 transistors, and consumed 12 watts of power.[101] [102] [103] [104]

Toward the end of 1958, General Electric announced the development of a completely transistorized television receiver that weighed approximately 10 lb and was the approximate size of an automatic toaster. It contained 22 transistors, could be operated from either the house current or from a rechargeable silver-cadmium battery, and its sensitivity and performance characteristics compared favorably with those of a conventional television receiver.[105]

In the summer of 1959, the Philco Corporation introduced the Safari, a truly portable, 21-transistor television receiver. It weighs 15 lb, contains a lens system that produces an image equivalent to that produced by a 14-in. tube, and is powered by an alkaline secondary battery that is capable of operating the set for 4 hours.[106] [107] This was followed a year later by the production by Sony of a direct-view transistorized portable television-receiver (Fig. 17-91).

Another interesting transistor application was announced late in 1956 by Fallgren, Hankinson, and Wright, three amateur radio operators who were in the employ of the Raytheon Co. They constructed a two-transistor transmitter that was powered by a penlight cell and two 6-volt batteries that delivered a power output of 0.08 watts. With this transmitter, they were able to reach Puerto Rico, Costa Rica, England, and finally Denmark, 3,600 miles away. This marked the first recorded trans-Atlantic radio contact made with a transistorized transmitter.[108]

It was not very long before even this fine performance was excelled. Late in 1958, D. L. Stoner of Ontario, Calif., another amateur radio operator,

Courtesy, Sony Corporation of America

FIG. 17-91. SONY ALL-TRANSISTORIZED PORTABLE TELEVISION RECEIVER

used a 2-transistor, 0.09-watt transistorized transmitter to establish contact with another amateur in Johannesburg South Africa, over a transmission path of more than 16,000 miles. At about the same time, M. Gilbert of Los Angeles, Calif., conversed with other amateurs in Illinois, 2,000 miles away. He employed a transistorized receiver and a transistorized 0.06 watt transmitter that were powered entirely by silicon solar cells.[109]

The applications of the transistor which have been described represent but a small fraction of the transistorized devices that are in the process of development (Fig. 17-92). For example, RCA is developing an all-transistor tape recorder for use in broadcasting and home sound-recording systems. Other manufacturers are applying transistors to d-c power converters, high-speed counters, frequency and interval meters, and computer systems.

In recent years, as has been prev-

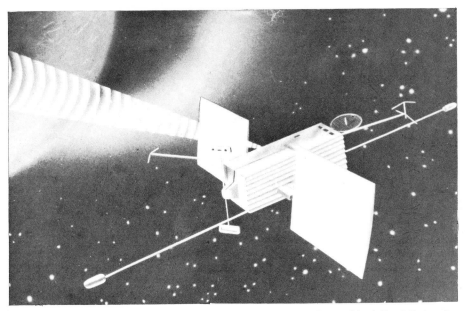

Courtesy, Sylvania Electric Products, Inc.

FIG. 17-92. USE OF SOLID-STATE TRANSMITTER AND RECEIVER FOR SPACE COMMUNICATIONS
The transmitter-receiver package can be utilized within devices such as that shown here, The ultra reliable receiver is the size of a transistor portable radio. Engineers are completing development of circuitry to make it one-tenth its present size through the use of micro-miniaturized electronic elements.

iously mentioned, most of the leading computer manufacturers have brought out new solid-state versions of their electronic computers employing transistors and magnetic amplifiers. In general, these solid-state computers are more compact, require far less power, and provide fewer maintenance problems than their vacuum-tube counterparts.[110]

The Electric Auto-Lite Company has developed a transistorized automobile ignition system in which a transistor switches the heavy current that is required in the primary ignition circuit. This arrangement reduces contact current and contact erosion, improves ignition-system reliability, and makes it possible to eliminate the ignition coil and the distributor capacitor.[111 112 113]

Undoubtedly, during the next few years, many more transistorized devices will make their appearance and will re-

place the bulky and less-efficient vacuum tubes in present-day electronic equipment. The initial cost of these transistorized devices will probably be greater than that of present-day devices, and whether or not they will gain acceptance will depend upon whether this higher cost can be offset by other advantages.

17.42 *Possible future competitors of the transistor*

During the past few years, noteworthy advances have been made in the direction of developing additional devices that are also potentially capable of replacing the electron tube. Among the leading devices that promise to give the transistor stiff competition in certain applications are the tunnel diode, the cryotron, the solion, the field-effect electrolytic amplifier, the nuvistor, and hybrid solid-state semiconductor junction-emission tubes.

The tunnel diode. The tunnel diode is a revolutionary semiconductor device that is a first cousin of the transistor. According to Guy Suits, director of research at General Electric, it is "the most important advance in the field of electronics since the transistor." First reported in 1958 by Leo Esaki, a physicist who was employed by Sony Corporation of Japan, it consists of a wire leading to an alloy, which is soldered to a germanium or silicon semiconductor crystal (Fig. 17-93). It is also possible to employ other semiconductors such as gallium arsenide, gallium antimonide, and indium antimonide. A rectangular metal plate that is attached to the crystal serves as the other electrode. The entire unit is smaller than a paper clip.

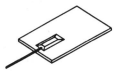

Fig. 17-93. Tunnel diode
Connecting wire (left) leads to an alloy that is soldered to germanium crystal. Crystal in turn is soldered to rectangular metal plate.

It is basically a heavily doped P-N junction diode, which, under certain conditions, displays negative-resistance characteristics that enable it to be used as an oscillator or as an amplifier. If a low value of forward bias is placed across the diode, and the bias value is gradually increased, the current will increase more rapidly than is predicted by conventional diode theory. It is believed that electrons which ordinarily would not possess sufficient energy to pass over the thin barrier between the P and N sections are able to "tunnel" under it in a quantum-mechanical manner at the speed of light. As the bias is further increased, the tunneling effect drops off and the current actually decreases. This produces the negative-resistance portion of the voltage-current curve of the diode. As the voltage is again increased the current will now increase in a normal and conventional manner.

The device possesses many advantageous characteristics. It is very stable and extremely insensitive to temperature variations, and it can operate at very low cryogenic temperatures, such as that of liquid helium, and at temperatures as high as 600°F. It can also operate at high frequencies (Fig. 17-94). Oscillator frequencies of 2,000 mc have been reported, and it is believed that this device can operate at frequencies as high as 100,000 mc. Its power requirements are less than 1 per cent of those of transistors and are measured in microwatts; its noise level is low compared with those of transistors and vacuum tubes; and it can control and switch circuits 100 times faster than a transistor can. It is also extremely resistant to the damaging effects of nuclear radiation, because it is less dependent than the transistor is upon the structural properties of its crystal.

Courtesy, General Electric Co.
Fig. 17-94. Miniature tunnel-diode transmitter with a range of one-half mile
Unit consists of three capacitors, a coil that tunes to the operating frequency (which may be over one kilomegacycle/second), and the diode, located inside the "can" in the center of the device.

Among its disadvantages is its high price. As of 1959, experimental units were selling for 75 dollars each. However, General Electric spokesmen claim that once they are set up for mass production of tunnel diodes, the price will drop to a lower value than those of transistors that perform comparable functions.

Another disadvantage is the design problem resulting from the fact that since the tunnel diode is a two-terminal device, it cannot be cascaded or connected in series with other tunnel diodes. Engineers are currently working on the problem of designing multi-stage tunnel-diode circuits.

It is believed that the tunnel diode will have important applications in earth satellites, portable receivers, UHF communications, control and switching circuits, high-speed digital computers, and wherever light weight, independence from environment, low noise at high frequencies, and rapid action are important characteristics.[114][115][116][117][118]

The cryotron. The operation of the cryotron is based upon the phenomenon of superconductivity first discovered by Heike Kamerlingh Onnes in 1911. At extremely low temperatures, the resistance of certain metals decreases practically to zero. Onnes also discovered that the transition temperature at which superconductivity occurs is related to the strength of the magnetic field, this temperature approaching absolute zero as the strength of the magnetic field is increased. This makes it possible to restore electrical resistance merely by the application of a magnetic field.

The cryotron was developed in 1953 by Dudley A. Buck of MIT. In this device, the superconductor is a piece of tantalum wire 1 in. long and 0.009 in. in diameter; it is kept at a temperature of 4.2°K, which is the boiling point of liquid helium at atmospheric pressure. Around this wire is a coil consisting of 250 turns of insulated niobium wire with a diameter of 0.003 in. This coil functions as a control winding. A change in the flow of current through the winding

changes the strength of the magnetic field. This controls the resistance of the tantalum wire, causing the wire to shift back and forth between its superconducting and normally conducting states. Thus, when the current through the coil exceeds 100 ma, the magnetic field changes the resistance of the tantalum wire from zero ohms to 0.008 ohms. This behavior enables the cryotron to function either as an amplifier or as a switch or gate (Fig. 17-95).[119]

FIG. 17-95. EXPERIMENTAL, THREE-STAGE CRYOTRON RING OSCILLATOR FOR TESTING CRYOTRON CHARACTERISTICS

Newer types of cryotrons employ printed circuits in place of wires. The material for the superconductor is formed as a flat strip of film that is deposited on a piece of glass (Fig. 17-96). In place of the control coil, a second material is deposited upon the first, and a layer of insulation is used to separate the two layers.[120]

The cryotron is so small that a hundred of them will fit into an ordinary thimble. It is planned at present to employ this device in computer circuits in place of transistors and tubes (Fig. 17-97). On the basis of results obtained with experimental circuits, a large-scale digital computer can be made to occupy a volume of 1 cu ft, not including refri-

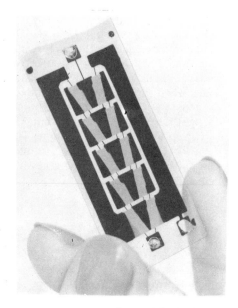

Courtesy, Arthur D. Little, Inc.
FIG. 17-96. SIX-CRYOTRON CIRCUIT OF TIN AND LEAD VAPORIZED AND DEPOSITED AS THIN FILMS ON GLASS

geration and terminal equipment. In contrast, one of today's digital computers completely fills several rooms. It is believed that by 1964, superconductive cryotron computers, greatly reduced both in size and cost, will be commercially available.[121]

Two of the cryotron's major disadvantages are its requirements for low-temperature refrigerators known as cryostats and its relatively slow operating speed (Fig. 17-98). The refrigeration problem is being solved by the development of commercial helium liquifier units and thermos-type containers for the bath of liquid helium. These containers hold liquid nitrogen in their jackets.

The first cryotron had switching speeds that were only slightly faster than those of relays. However, recent laboratory reports on experiments with new metals and alloys such as tin and lead reveal that switching speeds up to

100,000 per second have been obtained and that switching times measurable in thousandths of a microsecond are within the realm of possibility.[122]

The average amount of power dissipation of a cryotron is approximately 0.1 milliwatts. Most cryotron devices require a power source that is capable of delivering large currents at low voltages. Eventually, it will probably be necessary to design special battery power supplies for cryotron work.

Among the advantages associated with the use of the cryotron are simplicity, reliability, economy of electric power, and compactness. The basic simplicity of the cryotron also permits easy manufacture of this device. However, the need for refrigeration units

Courtesy, International Business Machines Corp.
FIG. 17-97. EXPERIMENTAL CRYOGENIC THIN-FILM MEMORY PLANE
The memory plane consists of 135-cryotron devices built up in a 19-layer "sandwich." About the size of a large postage stamp, it stores 40 separate "bits" of information in 120 of its cryotrons. Of the remaining 15 cryotrons, 10 permit access to the stored bits of information; the other 5 are "in-line" cryotrons which switch bits of information from one memory plane to another.

Courtesy, Arthur D. Little, Inc.
FIG. 17-98. LABORATORY DEWAR FLASK BEING FILLED WITH LIQUID HELIUM PRODUCED BY A CRYOSTAT

limits the amount of space that can be saved by using this device.

The solion. The solion, an electrochemical diode device that was developed in 1957 as a result of investigations conducted under the direction of Muzzey and Estes at the U.S. Naval Ordnance Laboratory, may eventually give both the vacuum tube and the transistor serious competition as a basic electronic component. For certain applications, this device requires less power than a transistor does and offers greater selectivity, sensitivity, ruggedness, reliability, and efficiency than can be obtained from either the vacuum tube or the transistor.

The name solion is derived from the fact that the operation of this device depends upon the movements of ions in solution. The term solion does not actually describe a specific device but is really the generic name for a group of devices that employ ions in solution as a means of carrying current. There are some rather complicated types of solion units, but this discussion will deal only with the simplest and most com-mon of them, the solion diode (Fig. 17-99).[123]

In this diode, the previously mentioned movement of ions takes place between two platinum electrodes that are immersed in a solution of potassium iodide and iodine. The ends of the unit are sealed by diaphragms. The flow of ions is started by connecting a dry cell in series with the unit and is stimulated and made to vary by changes in temperature, pressure, light, sound, or acceleration.

During operation, the potassium iodide breaks up into positive potassium ions and negative iodide ions. The iodine molecules drift toward the cathode at a rate that is nearly independent of the applied voltage. At the cathode, the iodine molecules acquire electrons and are reduced to negative iodide ions. These ions then move toward the anode where they are oxidized, giving up electrons to the anode and reforming iodine molecules. This action produces a small current through the external circuit that is called a diffusion current. This diffusion current can be varied by the application of mechanical energy such as stirring the solution or varying the amount of pressure applied to the diaphragms.[124] Very little power is consumed by the device during this process.

Since the current carriers are ions which have a mass approximately 233,000 times greater than that of an electron, at present the maximum freq-

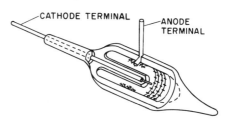

CATHODE TERMINAL   ANODE TERMINAL

Courtesy, Texas Research and Electronic Corp.
FIG. 17-99. CONSTRUCTION OF TYPICAL SOLION DIODE

uency response is limited to about 400 cps. However, this limitation is actually an advantage in systems whose basic frequency is only a fraction of a cycle per second, since vacuum tube and transistor amplifiers will not usually operate at these low frequencies without the addition of such complications as chopping, modulating, or direct coupling. An additional advantage is the fact that in many applications the solution cannot only replace vacuum tubes and transistors but can also replace the circuitry that usually accompanies them. This makes the solion well-suited for airborne applications and for portable equipment.[125]

One proposed application of the solion is in electronic control systems. Changes in the flow of ions produced by changes in pressure, temperature, or acceleration can be used to actuate larger control devices. Thus, the solion could be used as an accelerometer in the inertial-guidance system of a missile to detect any change in speed or direction from a predetermined course and to produce a signal that would activate the necessary devices needed to bring the missile back to its correct course. This electronic control function could be accomplished by a small device weighing only a few ounces rather than the complex electronic circuit now required that weighs several hundred pounds.

A second application of the solion now being tested by the Air Force is as a sound-exposure meter or noise dosimeter designed to protect personnel from the danger of deafness; it provides such protection by measuring the total amount of exposure of each individual to the harmful low-frequency sounds of jet engines. The sound vibrations are converted into electric currents by means of a microphone (Fig. 17-100). This signal is then amplified by a two-

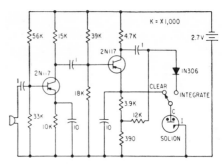

Courtesy, Texas Research and Electronic Corp.
FIG. 17-100. SCHEMATIC DIAGRAM OF TRANSISTORIZED NOISE DOSIMETER USING A SOLION FOR VISUAL READOUT INTEGRATION

transistor amplifier and afterwards rectified by a diode. When these currents pass between the electrodes of a solion, iodine is reduced to iodide at the cathode and iodide is oxidized to iodine at the anode. The change in iodine concentration can be measured by employing a color chart. This provides an estimate of the integrated value of the current, which in turn provides an estimate of total exposure to sound energy. This estimate is accurate to within 10 per cent—a degree of accuracy that is sufficient for this type of application.[126]

Other proposed applications of the solion include pressure indicators, transducers, flow meters, burglar and fire alarms, heat controls, furnace regulators, and analog elements such as differentiators and integrators for computer circuits (Figs. 17-101, 17-102, and 17-103).

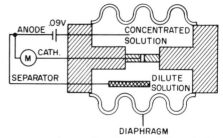

Courtesy, Texas Research and Electronic Corp.
FIG. 17-101. SOLION LINEAR DETECTOR USED FOR PRESSURE OR FLOW TRANSDUCER

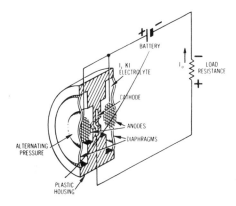

Courtesy, Texas Research and Electronic Corp.
FIG. 17-102. CROSS-SECTION OF SOLION ENERGY
TRANSDUCER

Courtesy, Texas Research and Electronic Corp.
FIG. 17-104. SOLION TETRODE

Other types of solions are still under development (Figs. 17-104 and 17-105). By hydraulically coupling a device to a solion flow detector, for example, it is possible to construct a solion amplifier which will perform certain mathematical functions. This type of unit, called an electroosmotic driver or micro pump, can produce current amplifications of 300 or more, and in its more complex variations can carry out mathematical operations upon an input signal, such as obtaining derivatives, products, and ratios.[127]

It is expected that when production problems such as keeping contaminants out of these devices and holding dimensions of plastic parts to within 0.0001 in. are solved, the price of the solion

will be less than that of equivalent tubes or transistors.[128]

The electrochemical cell. An electrochemical cell has been developed by S. R. Ovshinsky for switching or modulating high-wattage alternating currents by means of small direct currents. It consists of two electrodes of tantalum and a platinum grid-control element

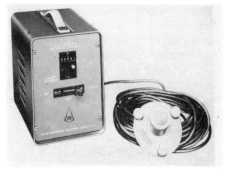

Courtesy, Texas Research and Electronic Corporation.
FIG. 17-105. SOLION SUNLIGHT INTEGRATOR
The sunlight integrator is an instrument designed to measure accurately the solar energy at the sensor over a period ranging from several minutes to several days. A cadmium sulfide light-dependent resistor is used as the sensor and a solion tetrode as the integrator, driving a four-place direct reading counter

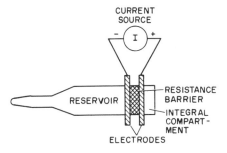

Courtesy, Texas Research and Electronic Corp.
FIG. 17-103. SOLION DESIGNED AS VISUAL READ-OUT INTEGRATOR

which are immersed in an electrolyte and sealed in a small container.

The electrodes are normally coated with a nonconducting oxide film. The application of voltage to the control element polarizes the electrodes and makes the oxide film conductive, permitting currents to flow between the two electrodes. Thus, a direct current of 32 ma can control a second alternating current of up to 770 ma, and other units have been constructed that are capable of handling up to 15 amperes of alternating current.[129]

Hybrid semiconductor-junction emission tubes. Westinghouse engineers are hopefully investigating the possibility of employing a hybrid tube that uses a semiconductor silicon-carbide junction as an electron emitter for a standard vacuum tube (Fig. 17-106).

In 1957, J. A. Burton of Bell Telephone Laboratories reported observing considerable electron emission from a cesium-coated silicon junction. Shortly afterwards, W. J. Choyke and Lyle Patrick of Westinghouse discovered that when a sufficiently high voltage was applied across a silicon-carbide junction, electroluminescence was produced. At the same time, small blue spots of light appeared near the junction and electrons escaped from these spots.

Westinghouse scientists are now trying to apply this principle by using the semiconductor to replace the hot

FIG. 17-106. HYBRID SOLID-STATE ELECTRON TUBE
This experimental tube gets its supply of electrons from tiny crystals of silicon carbide inside the cartridge at right.

cathode of a vacuum tube. The most obvious advantage of a cold-emission tube is the fact that it would require only a negligible amount of power, since no power would be needed to heat the cathode. In addition, it would emit electrons instantly as soon as the required potential was applied.

However, it is believed that considerable time and effort must be expended before a practical tube of this type is developed. One of the most difficult problems to be solved is that which is associated with many high-field emission devices, namely the problem of how to obtain reliable emission.[130][131]

The nuvistor. It is quite possible that in the future the transistor may encounter unexpected competition from the very device that it is attempting to supplant, namely the vacuum tube. Spurred by the threat of the transistor, tube manufacturers have been engaged in an active program of research leading toward the development of tubes with reduced size and power requirements, improved performance, and increased reliability. The RCA nuvistor is one type of tube that has been developed as an outgrowth of a research program of this nature.

Nuvistor, which means the new look in electron tubes, is a name that has been given to a group of tiny electron tubes that include a triode, a small-signal tetrode, and a beam-power tube (Fig. 17-107). Each of these tubes occupies only one-fifth the volume of the next largest general type of tube currently being manufactured. These nuvistors employ a new type of tube design in which concentric cylindrical electrodes are supported only at the bottom in an open-ended cantilever construction (Figs. 17-108, 17-109, and 17-110). This technique eliminates the need for mica support discs or spacers. The resulting

Courtesy, Electron Tube Div., Radio Corporation of America

FIG. 17-107. RCA NUVISTOR TUBES

configuration and low mass enable the
assembled units to withstand 850 G of
shock and vibrations as high as 2 G at 5
kc. This type of construction also eliminates the need for employing spot-weld-
ing techniques. Spot welding usually
produces residual strains capable of
twisting tube elements. Consequently,
the elimination of spot welding also eliminates a possible source of shorts and
tube failures, and also eliminates the
need of a human operator possessing a

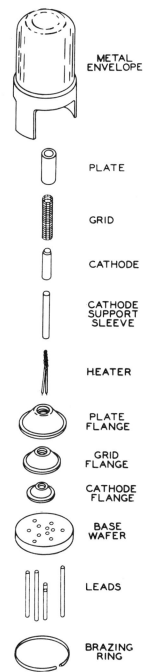

METAL ENVELOPE

PLATE

GRID

CATHODE

CATHODE SUPPORT SLEEVE

HEATER

PLATE FLANGE

GRID FLANGE

CATHODE FLANGE

BASE WAFER

LEADS

BRAZING RING

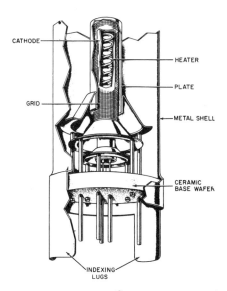

Courtesy, Electron Tube Div., Radio Corporation of America

FIG. 17-108. CUTAWAY VIEW OF A NUVISTOR
TRIODE

Courtesy, *Radio-Electronics* and Radio Corporation of America

FIG. 17-109. EXPLODED VIEW OF A NUVISTOR
TRIODE

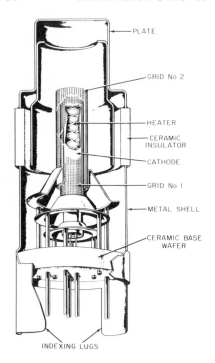

PLATE

GRID No 2

HEATER

CERAMIC INSULATOR

CATHODE

GRID No 1

METAL SHELL

CERAMIC BASE WAFER

INDEXING LUGS

Courtesy, Electron Tube Div., Radio Corporation of America

FIG. 17-110. CUTAWAY VIEW OF A NUVISTOR TETRODE

very high degree of skill.[132] This type of construction is therefore well-suited to mass production.

The nuvistor tubes are obviously far more rugged, reliable, and efficient than ordinary tubes. The operation of these tubes is not affected when they are dropped repeatedly on a metal block from a height of several feet. Although life-testing investigations have not yet been completed, it is believed that these tubes may have a useful life expectancy of hundreds of thousands of hours of normal operation.[133]

In many amplifier circuits, the power required to operate a nuvistor is only 5 per cent of that required by conventional miniature tubes. This may possibly be reduced even further in the future by incorporating some of the recent developments in cold-cathode design. This tube also requires plate voltages that are much lower than those of conventional tubes. Thus, one nuvistor triode will oscillate with a plate voltage of only 2.5 volts.[134] Because these tubes can operate at moderate voltages, asociated components such as capacitors are less expensive than those used in conventional tube circuits.

The nuvistor compares favorably in size and efficiency with the transistor. It also possesses several significant advantages over the transistor. Nuvistors are superior to transistors for high-frequency operation. At these frequencies, the noise factors and gains of nuvistors are superior to those of transistors. The nuvistor can operate over a much wider ambient temperature range. In tests, the nuvistor has operated successfully in liquid nitrogen at a temperature of −320°F and in the heating coils of a special furnace at a temperature of 660°F. While a transistor will break down completely with irreparable damage when its maximum voltage ratings are exceeded, the nuvistor, like other vacuum tubes, is capable of handling momentary overloads and overvoltages without permanent damage. Furthermore, the tube is inherently less susceptible than the transistor to damage by high-intensity radiation.

Although the nuvistor is only in its early advanced development stage, it is expected to lead to new electronic developments and to more compact equipment in television and communications receivers and in electronic computers.[135] At the end of 1959, samples were made available to equipment manufacturers, and limited commercial production was in progress by the middle of 1960.[136][137]

REFERENCES

1. "The Fabulous Crystal," *Tomorrow's Scientists,* 1:7, Dec. 1956.
2. "The Transistor," *Bell Laboratories Record,* 26:321, Aug. 1948.
3. "Nobel Prize in Physics," *Radio-Electronics,* 28:14, Jan. 1957.
4. Frank H. Rockett, "The Transistor," *Scientific American,* 179:52, Sept. 1948.
5. John A. Doremus, "Point-Contact and Junction Transistor," *Radio and Television News* (Engineering Edition), 47:14A, Apr. 1952.
6. R. M. Ryder, "Ten Years of Transistors," *Radio-Electronics,* 29:34, May 1958.
7. William Shockley, "Transistor Electronics Has Good Future," *Industrial Laboratories,* 9:52, May 1958.
8. Donald R. Mason, *The Relationship of Silicon and Its Properties to the Electronics Industry,* Aries Laboratories, Inc., N.Y., 1957, p. 3.
9. Walter F. Leverton and David Rubenfien, "Semiconductors: A Dynamic New Industry," *Industrial Research,* 1:75, Jan. 1959.
10. "Crystals for Hot Transistors," *Stanford Research Institute for Industry,* 11:2-3, Sept. 1957.
11. R. M. Ryder, *Op. cit.,* pp. 34-37.
12. *RCA Transistors and Semiconductor Diodes,* RCA Semiconductor Div., Somerville, N. J., 1957, p. 2.
13. *Transistor Manual,* EGC-187, General Electric Semiconductor Products Dept., Syracuse, N.Y., p. 4.
14. Donald C. Bennett, "Induction Heating in Zone Refining, Zone Levelling, and Crystal Growing," *Lepel High Frequency Heating Review,* 1:1-7, No. 6.
15. Eric Leslie, "99.99999999% Pure," *Radio-Electronics,* 30:38, Sept. 1959.
16. Joseph B. Kushner, "Super-Pure Metals," *Science Digest,* 37:18-22, Sept. 1955.
17. Clyde Hostetter, "Tiny Giant of Electronics," *Science Digest,* 45:35, Mar. 1959.
18. "New Way to Grow Germanium," *Electronics World,* 62:47, Aug. 1959.
19. "New Technique May Permit Automatic Manufacture of Transistors," *Design News,* 14:4, Aug. 17, 1959.
20. R. M. Ryder, *Op. cit.,* pp. 36-37.
21. Franklin A. Carlson, "Emphasis Shifts Toward the Diffused Diode Transistor," *Industrial Laboratories,* 10:82, Aug. 1959.
22. "Transistor Manufacture," *Radio-Electronics,* 6:6 Apr. 1955.
23. R. M. Ryder, *Op. cit.,* p. 37.
24. "Transistor TV's", *Radio-Electronics,* 30:6, Mar. 1959.
25. "Transistors Produced by Automatic Line," *Radio and TV News,* 61:140, Mar. 1959.
26. "Miniature Line Produces 1800 Transistors Hour," *Industrial Science and Engineering,* 7:20, Mar. 1960.
27. Richard S. Burwen, "Direct-Coupled Transistor Amplifier," *Electronics World,* 62:42, Sept. 1959.
28. H. Debbi, "Transistor Fundamentals," *Sylvania News,* 24:5-6, Apr. 1957.
29. H. E. Marrows, "Marketing and Production Trends in the Semiconductor Industry," *Semiconductor Products,* 1:43, Jan. 1958.
30. *Transistor Manual, Op. cit.,* p. 6.
31. H. S. Renne, "The Junction Transistor," *Radio and Television News,* 47:39, Apr. 1952.
32. John R. Pierce, "Transistors," *Radio-Electronics,* 24:44, June 1953.
33. "Transistors - The First Ten Years," *Industrial Laboratories,* 9:28, Aug. 1958.
34. Ed. Bukstein, "Transistors Are Different," *Radio and TV News,* 60:62, Dec. 1958.
35. I. Queen, "New Transistor Circuit Design Method," *Radio-Electronics,* 23:64, Oct. 1951.
36. M. J. Kelly, *Op. cit.,* p. 25.
37. "Transistor Life Tests," *Radio and Television News,* 57:104, Jan. 1957.
38. George R. Spencer, "Transistors—Past, Present, Future," *Radio-Electronics,* 29:40, May, 1958.
39. J. S. Schaffner, "Transistor Applications," *General Electric Review,* 57:53, Mar. 1954.
40. "Transistorized Computer Monitors Power Plant," *Design News,* 13:10, June 23, 1958.
41. *Philco Transac,* Philco Corp., Phila., Pa., p. 3.
42. Arthur H. Wulfsberg, "The Price of Reliability," *Collins Signal,* 7:10 No. 4, 1959.
43. Louis E. Garner, Jr., "Transistors ... Fact and Fiction—Part I", *Radio-Electronics,* 30:49, July 1959.
44. Rufus P. Turner, "Care of Transistors," *Radio and Television News,* 49:40, Feb. 1953.
45. L. E. Garner, Jr., *Op. cit.,* p. 49.
46. Donald C. Mogen, *Fundamental Voltage Limitations of a Transistor,* Minneapolis-Honeywell Regulator Co., Semiconductor Products Div., Minneapolis, Minn., 1959, p. 1.
47. H. L. Aronson, "Applying Power Transistors to Control," *Control Engineering,* 3:79, Oct. 1956.
48. L. E. Garner, Jr., *Op. cit.,* p. 49.
49. Paul Penfield, Jr., "Power Transistors," *Radio and Television News;* 55:37, Feb. 1956.
50. Rufus P. Turner, "Power Transistors Are Here," *Radio-Electronics,* 26:90-92, Aug. 1955.
51. P. Penfield, Jr., *Op. cit.,* p. 37.
52. J. J. Brophy, *Op. cit.,* p. 141.
53. *Transistor Manual, Op. cit.,* p. 9.
54. Paul Penfield, Jr., "Confused ... About Transistor Types?," *Radio-Electronics,* 27:106, Oct. 1956.
55. J. M. Early, "P-N-I-P- and N-P-I-N Junction Transistor Triodes," *Bell System Technical Journal,* 33:517, May 1954.
56. R. M. Ryder, *Op. cit.,* p. 37.
57. R. L. Wallace, Jr., L. G. Schimp, and E. Deckten, "A Junction Transistor Tetrode for High-Frequency Use," *Proc. IRE,* 40:1395, Nov. 1952.
58. "High Frequency Transistors," *Radio-Electronics,* 26:113, June 1955.
59. Nathaniel Rhita, "4-Terminal Transistors," *Radio-Electronics,* 25:108, Sept. 1954.

60. I. Queen, "What's New in Transistors," *Radio-Electronics*, 25:76, June 1954.
61. *RCA Transistors and Semiconductor Diodes, Op. cit.*, p. 4.
62. Paul Penfield, Jr., "More About Transistor Types—Part I," *Radio-Electronics*, 28:35-36, Nov. 1957.
63. "Transistor Testing with Type 874 Coaxial Elements," *General Radio Experimenter*, 32:4, Oct. 1957.
64. "Experimental 1000-MC Transistor," *Electronics World*, 62:62, Sept. 1959.
65. Milton S. Kiver, *Understanding Transistors*, Allied Radio Corp., Chicago, Ill., 1959, p. 28.
66. Nathaniel Rhita, "Direct-Coupled Transistor Circuits," *Radio-Electronics*, 30:3.', Sept. 1959.
67. "Philco's Surface-Barrier Transistor," *Radio and Television News*, 51:78, Feb. 1954.
68. Paul Penfield, Jr., "More About Transistor Types—Part 2," *Radio-Electronics*, 28:108, Dec. 1957.
69. Lou Garner, "Transistor Topics," *Popular Electronics*, 10:96, June 1959.
70. N. Rhita, "4-Terminal Transistors," *Op. cit.*, p. 108.
71. P. Penfield, Jr., "Confused . . . About Transistor Types?," *Op. cit.*, p. 78.
72. Royce G. Kloeffler, *Industrial Electronics and Control*, John Wiley and Sons, N.Y., 2nd Edition, 1960, p. 68.
73. Harold B. McKay, "Gating with Diodes," *Radio-Electronics*, 29:30, Aug. 1958.
74. "Transistor Switch," *Radio-Electronics*, 30:112, July 1959.
75. R. M. Ryder, *Op. cit.*, p. 37.
76. "Solid State Rectifier Can Replace Thyratron," *Electronic Design*, 6:7, Jan. 8, 1958.
77. "Semiconductor Progress: The Controlled Rectifier Nears Production," *Control Engineering*, 5:32-35, Feb. 1958.
78. "Semiconductor Thyratron," *Military Automation*, 2:59, Mar. 1958.
79. Lowell S. Pelfrey, "An Introduction to the Thyrode," *IRC Rectifier News*, June, 1959, pp. 3-6.
80. Louis E. Garner, Jr., "Using the Unijunction," *Radio-Electronics*, 28:91, July 1957.
81. H. B. McKay, *Op. cit.*, p. 29.
82. "RCA Develops New High-Speed Switching Transistor," *Datamation*, 3:35, Nov. 1957.
83. W. Shockley, "A Unipolar Field-Effect Transistor," *Proc. IRE*, 40:1377, Nov. 1952.
84. P. Penfield, Jr., *Op. cit.*, pp. 78, 80.
85. "Bell Labs Semiconductor Device," *Radio-Electronics*, 30:16 June 1959.
86. E. Aisberg, "The Tecnetron," *Radio-Electronics*, 29:60-61, May 1958.
87. Harry Mileaf, "The Phototransistor," *Radio-Electronics*, 25:96, Nov. 1954.
88. "Modern Photocells," *Cornell-Dubilier Capacitor*, 20:9, June 1955.
89. Edward D. Padgett, "Phototransistors and Photoelectrets," *Radio-Electronics*, 26:61-62, Feb. 1955.
90. Robert Pucel, Conrad Lanza, and Hermann Statz, "The Spacistor—A New High-Frequency Semiconductor Amplifier," *Semiconductor Products*, 1:34, Jan 1958.
91. Lou Garner, "Transistor Topics," *Popular Electronics*, 9:81-82, Sept. 1958.
92. Edwin Bohr, "Junction Transistor Tester," *Radio Electronics*, 25:30, Aug. 1954.
93. Edward D. Padgett, "Practical Transistor Tests," *Radio-Electronics*, 26:32, July 1955.
94. R. Zarr, "Transistor Tester," *Radio and Television News*, 56:140, Sept. 1956.
95. Edwin Bohr, "Improved Transistor Tester," *Radio Electronics*, 28:82, March 1957.
96. Lou Garner, "Transistor Topics," *Popular Electronics*, 11:134, Aug. 1959.
97. J. A. Doremus, *Op. cit.*, p. 20.
98. Lloyd Stouffer, "Look What They're Doing to Batteries," *Popular Science*, 170:232, June 1957.
99. "Wrist-watch Size Storage Battery Invented," *Aminco Lab. News*, 14:4, Sept. 1957.
100. H. E. Holman, "Free-Power Receivers," *Radio-Electronics*, 28:86-91, April 1957.
101. "Battery Operated Portable TV Uses 31 Transistors," *Design News*, 13:7, Feb. 3, 1958.
102. "Transistorized TV," *Electronic Design*, 6:5, Feb. 5, 1958.
103. "An All-Transistor TV Set," *Radio and TV News*, 59:136, Apr. 1958.
104. Douglas W. Taylor, "All Transistor Portable Television," *Semiconductor Products*, 1:21-22, Mar. 1958.
105. "Transistorized Midget TV," *Radio and TV News*, 61:105, Jan. 1959.
106. "You 'Can Buy This Transistorized TV," *Electronics World*, 62:56, July 1959.
107. Allan R. Curll and Paul V. Simpson, "Transistor TV Portable," *Radio-Electronics*, 30:46, Aug. 1959.
108. Gus Fallgren and Al Hankinson, "Transistorized Amateur Transmitter," *Radio and Television News*, 57:37, Feb. 1957.
109. "Two Ham Records," *Radio-Electronics*, 30:10, Jan. 1959.
110. Jay W. Schnackel, "Solid-State Developments," *Sperryscope*, 15:7-8, Third Quarter, 1959.
111. *The World's First Transistorized Ignition System*, Form G-270A, Electric Auto-Lite Co., Toledo, Ohio, 1959, pp. 8-12.
112. "Transistors Make Cars Run Better," *Radio-Electronics*, 30:43, May 1959.
113. Hubert Luckett, "Big Changes Coming in Auto Electric Systems," *Popular Science*, 174:96. 262, May 1959.
114. "G-E Reports Tunnel Diode Has Come of Design Age," *Industrial Laboratories*, 10:4-5, Aug. 1959.
115. "Tunnel Diode," *Radio-Electronics*, 30:6, Sept. 1959.
116. "Tunnel Diodes—Experimental Semiconductors," *Electronics World*, 62:41, Oct. 1959.
117. "The Tunnel Diode," *General Electric Research Laboratory Bulletin*, Winter 1959, pp. 5-7.
118. "Marvelous Midget of Electronics," *Electronic Age*, 19:18-19, Winter 1959.
119. S. R. Parker, "The Cryotron—A New Computer Device," *Electronic Design*, 5:28-29, May 15, 1957.
120. Ray Vicker, "Supercold: Versatile Science Tool," *Science Digest*, 44:38, Aug. 1958.

121. "Cryotron Switch," *Instruments and Control Systems,* 32:1290, Sept. 1959.

122. S. R. Parker, *Op. cit.,* p. 31.

123. R. N. Lane and D. B. Cameron, *Characteristics and Applications of Four Solion Types,* National Carbon Co., N. Y., 1959, p. 1.

124. Eric Leslie, "Two New Approaches to Amplification," *Radio-Electronics,* 28:33-34, Nov. 1957.

125. *Solions for Industry,* Eveready Electronic Products Engineering Bull. 1, National Carbon Co., New York, Nov. 1957, pp. 1-2.

126. R. N. Lane and D. B. Cameron, *Current Integration with Solion Liquid Diodes,* National Carbon Co., New York, 1959, p. 2.

127. R. N. Lane and D. B. Cameron, *Characteristics and Applications of Four Solion Types, Op. cit.,* pp. 26-32

128. "Solion Shows Promise," *Control Engineering,* 4:32, Aug. 1957.

129. "New Device," *Radio-Electronics,* 30:6, Sept. 1959.

130. "Transistorized Electron Tube," *Electronics World,* 62:48, Nov. 1959.

131. E. J. Gross, "Solid-State Electron Tubes," *DeVry Tech. News,* 20:6, Dec. 1959.

132. Larry Steckler, "Nuvistor, New Kind of Electronic Tube," *Radio-Electronics,* 30:40, June 1959.

133. "Tiny Vacuum Tube Rivals Transistor," *Electronics World,* 61:100, May 1959.

134. *Threshold Plus 1 - Nuvistor The New Look in Electron Tubes,* Form 4F984, RCA Electron Tube Div., Harrison, N.J., 1959, p. 18.

135. "Nuvistors and Micro-Modules," *Think,* 25:31, June 1959.

136. "Introducing the Nuvistor," *Electronics Illustrated,* 2:62-63, June 1959.

137. "Nuvistors and Micro-Modules," *Popular Electronics,* 10:56, June 1959.

18 - MINIATURIZATION, PRINTED CIRCUITS AND MODULES

18.1 *History and principles of miniaturization*

A serious problem associated with electronic equipment is the one of size. Complex equipment tends to become bulky and cumbersome. Miniaturization has become almost mandatory in most military electronic equipment and highly desirable in many consumer products. One writer states that miniaturization is a matter of imperative necessity for survival. He estimates that at least 80 per cent of the miniaturization effort is directly or indirectly concerned with national defense and points out that the primary force behind the growth of miniaturization has been the increasing complexity and multiplicity of modern weapons. As new weapons of defense and offense are developed, they must somehow or other be fitted into the small amount of room available in aircraft, surface vessels, submarines, and guided missiles; and the only way by which some space can be made available is by miniaturizing existing devices.[1] Thus, the reduction of 1 lb of excess weight enables a missile to travel 18,000 ft higher and reduces the cost of a jet fighter plane by 7,000 dollars.

It is believed that the term miniaturization was first coined during World War II by Harry Diamond, a scientist who headed the team that developed the first important miniaturized device, the proximity fuze. This device consis-

ted of a miniature radar set that was placed in the warheads of artillery shells to insure hits by causing the shell to explode when it approached its target.[2]

Miniaturization may be defined as the design process which reduces equipment size or provides additional functions without increasing size, and which saves weight and space. It may also be described as the process of reducing unused space by "engineering out the air." It has been whimsically defined as the design process in which the size and weight of a given piece of equipment are reduced, while the functions are increased, until the device weighs nothing, takes up no space, and does everything.[3]

David McLean of Bell Telephone Laboratories states that in order for an object to deserve the use of the term miniature, it should be between 50 and 75 per cent smaller than the previous standard version of that object. Consequently, a sub-miniature device should be at least half the size of the preceding miniature version. When this process of miniaturization is continued further, the terms micro-miniature and ultra-miniature may be employed (Fig. 18-1).[4]

The significance of even a slight degree of miniaturization becomes evident when it is pointed out that a dimensional reduction of 10 per cent reduces volume and weight by 27 per cent; and a dimensional reduction of 25 per

Courtesy, *Radio-Electronics* and General Ceramics Corp.

FIG. 18-1. MINIATURIZED COMPUTER MEMORY STACK

Stack is 1/50th the size of the adjacent conventional stack.

cent shrinks volume and weight by 58 per cent (Fig. 18-2).[5] Miniaturization tends to produce products that are more efficient and that can be manufactured and distributed at lower cost. Miniaturization also reduces the cost of manufacturing the products, since it utilizes components that are small enough to be handled conveniently by automated machinery. The ultimate goal of miniaturization is the production of insect-sized electronic circuits that are so small that further size reduction is of no practical interest.

However, it is necessary to point out some of the dangers of overstressing the miniaturization of equipment without giving sufficient thought to the problems of reliability, maintenance, and operation. In this connection, one writer has stated: "In recent years, miniaturization has been one of the big goals in electronic design, but it would seem that too often the difficulty of providing compatibility between small size and reliability has not been recognized.. both the customer and the design engineer should be most conservative in the matter of space and weight allocations, since virtually every factor concerning reliability and maintainability is adversely affected by reduction in size and weight."[6]

Admiral Bennett, Chief of Naval Research, has applied the term "perverted miniaturization" to some equipment that is "beautifully miniaturized—a tremendous variety of functions compressed in a small package that takes hours to warm up completely and reach operating stability."[7] He also points out that only when small size is combined with high performance is miniaturization truly effective.

It should also be pointed out that while the process of miniaturization may eventually reduce the cost of many products, at present many of these miniaturization techniques are relatively new and untried, and these products are not being turned out by means of low-cost mass-production techniques. Few truly miniaturized devices have been made available to the public, since, with the exception of the transistor, miniature components are usually quite expensive. Thus, a miniaturized version of a 29-cent potentiometer may cost over 6 dollars. Outside of military and industrial applications, the only truly miniaturized devices that have made their appearance have been in cost-does-not-matter types of applications, such as hearing aids and medical devices.[8]

The process of miniaturization of electronic equipment proceeded rapidly even before the invention of the transistor. Compact electronic hearing aids and portable radio receivers containing

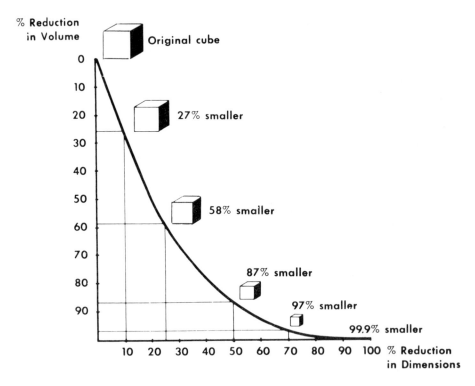

FIG. 18-2. RELATIONSHIP BETWEEN REDUCTION IN DIMENSIONS AND REDUCTION IN VOLUME

miniature and sub-miniature tubes are a far cry from the clumsy and inefficient devices produced only 25 years ago. In order to reduce the size of these devices, it was also necessary to reduce the size of the accompanying components, such as sockets, transformers, resistors, and capacitors.

18.2 *Miniaturization and the transistor*

Miniaturization intensifies one of the deficiencies of the electronic tube, namely the large amount of heat dissipated by this device. As the equipment is made more compact, it becomes increasingly more difficult to remove the heat by circulation of air. The temperature tends to rise, reducing the opera-

ting life of most of the circuit components. The development of the transistor accelerated the process of miniaturization. This was due not so much to the small size of the transistor, but to the fact that the power requirements of the transistor are so small that heating is almost infinitesimal, thus eliminating the principal cause of the high-temperature problem.

It is therefore fairly obvious that semiconductor devices lend themselves admirably to the miniaturization of equipment. However, it is not enough that the semiconductor itself be miniature in form. The components associated with the semiconductor must be miniature as well. The development of transistors has shifted the responsibility for miniaturization back to the manufacturers of resistors, capacitors, transformers, and other components.

These manufacturers have responded by developing new components, such as miniature potentiometers, suitable for use as volume and tone controls in transistorized circuits. Today there is a wide variety of miniature components available as stock items that may be readily purchased across the counter. However, there are still a great many manufacturing problems to be solved relating to the design and construction of special machines, tools, gauges, jigs, and fixtures needed to produce some of these almost microscopically small parts. The problem is aggravated by the lack of personnel equipped to handle these small parts and to make the necessary machines.[9]

18.3 *Miniaturized transformers and inductors*

The trend towards miniaturization of electronic equipment has created a demand for large numbers of extremely small components wound with multi-turn wire coils, for use as transformers, reactances, computer-memory units, and other electronic parts.

The design of miniature inductors involves much more than a mere scaling down of dimensions. The reduction in size of a transformer reduces the amount of surface area available to dissipate heat, forcing the transformer to operate at higher temperatures. The solution to this problem required the development of new heat-resistant substances, such as silicone-impregnated fiber glass and adhesive teflon tapes to provide better heat insulation and Formvar for use as a wire coating. Some miniature transformers employ certain fluorocarbon compounds that possess excellent heat-transfer and dielectric properties. These compounds remove heat from the transformer windings by vaporizing and then condensing on the inner surface of the transformer case.

If a transformer is to handle large amounts of direct current, the core material must be large in order to prevent magnetic saturation and consequent distortion of the signal. Fortunately, the amounts of direct current flowing in transistor circuits are generally so small that the core materials can be made very small. These cores are generally fabricated from materials such as molybdenum-permalloy powder, grain-oriented Silectron steel, or grain-oriented Hipersil steel. Another group of substances that have been successfully employed as the core materials of miniaturized inductors is the group known as the ferrites. These substances not only possess unique magnetic properties but also lend themselves readily to the fabrication of desired core structures by means of molding techniques. Today, manufacturers offer several hundred different types of miniature transformers and inductors to meet all manners of impedance-matching configurations and other circuit requirements.[10]

Until recently, a bottleneck existed in the manufacture of many of these coils, which were too small to be wound by available commercial machinery. The manufacturing processes required the costly, laborious, and time-consuming winding of the hair-thin wires through and around the tiny cores. In 1958, a device was developed by Matovich of Stanford Research Institute, which provided a method of eliminating this bottleneck. It consisted of a coil-winding machine capable of producing coils in sizes that cannot be obtained with ordinary coil-winding machinery. It can wind multi-turn coils on small cores through holes no larger than the eye of a small needle.[11]

18.4 *Miniaturized capacitors*

A similar story of improvement can be told concerning the development of the low-voltage, high-capacity capacitors required for coupling and by-passing applications in low-impedance transistor circuits. These low impedances necessitate the use of much-higher coupling and by-passing capacitances than are employed in comparable vacuum-tube circuits. In order to obtain high capacitance in a small amount of space, electrolytic capacitors are frequently employed in miniaturized transistor circuits in places where they seldom are found in conventional tube circuits.[12]

Some manufacturers have designed small conventional electrolytic capacitors with high capacities per unit volume. Others are producing miniature tantalum electrolytic capacitors consisting of a tantalum anode, a silver or copper cathode, and an electrolyte that may consist of solid manganese dioxide or tantalum oxide (Figs. 18-3 and 18-4).

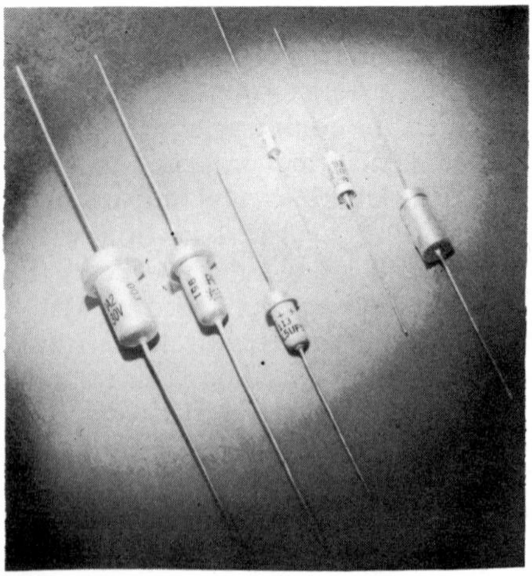

It may be of some interest to note that the peculiar fitness of tantalum for use in electrolytic capacitors was first demonstrated as far back as 1926 by Guntherschulze (Fig. 18-5).[13]

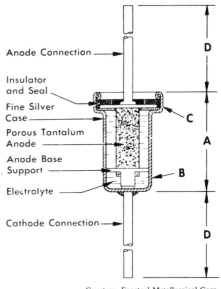

Anode Connection

Insulator and Seal

Fine Silver Case

Porous Tantalum Anode

Anode Base Support

Electrolyte

Cathode Connection

D
C
A
B
D

Courtesy, Fansteel Metallurgical Corp.

FIG. 18-4. CROSS SECTION OF A TANTALUM CAPACITOR

Courtesy, Fansteel Metallurgical Corp.

FIG. 18-3. TANTALUM CAPACITORS

One of the most recent developments is the production of capacitors employing dielectrics formed from metallized cast plastic films, from silicone, epoxy, or styrene-polyester resins, from methyl polysiloxane, and from ceramic materials containing barium titanate.[14]

As a result of developments such as these, capacitors as large as 30 μfd are now available with d-c working voltages ranging from 6 to 125 volts; they occupy a space less than 0.1 cubic inches. Bell Telephone Laboratories has produced an experimental tantalum unit with a capacity of 25 μfd, suitable for 5-volt operation, that has a volume of only 0.005 cu in.[15]

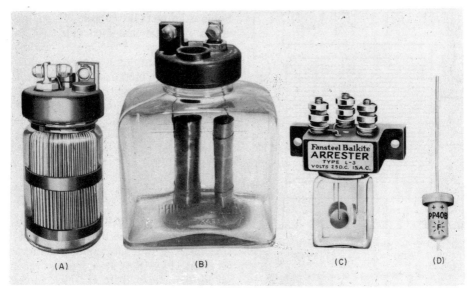

Courtesy, Fansteel Metallurgical Corp.

FIG. 18-5. EVOLUTION OF TANTALUM CAPACITORS

(A) One of the first commercial tantalum capacitors, made in 1930, used crimped tantalum sheet in a cell about the size of a pint jar. Capacity 800 mfd. at 24 volts; (B) 1932 model used coiled tantalum sheet welded to support wires, providing 675 mfd. at 24 volts for telephone service; (C) first porous tantalum anodes were used in the surge arrester for railway signal equipment in 1936; (D) in 1949 the porous tantalum capacitor took the form which, with modifications and improvements, is the present design.

18.5 *Miniature resistors*

Resistors are also holding their own in the field of component miniaturization. Precision resistors have been developed whose working bodies have a diameter of 8 mils or 0.008 in. A resistor of this type consists of a chromium-metallized glass fiber protected by a glass tube. The resistor material consists of very thin layers (ranging between 200 and 2000 angstroms) of nickel-chromium, chromium, tantalum, tungsten, or other conductive alloys deposited on the glass substrate. Thin films of metal oxide can be deposited in a similar manner to serve as a dielectric for capacitors. Glass is employed for the substrate, rather than ceramics or plastics, because of its lower cost and reproducibly smooth surface.[16]

In addition, there are many investigations now in progress aimed at improving the characteristics of printed resistors and metal films that can be deposited directly on a circuit board or a module.[17] Thus, in 1959, Daystrom, Inc. announced the development of solid-state microminiature resistors in the form of a ceramic wafer 10 mils thick and 0.35 in. square (Fig 18-6). The wafers are inscribed with a series of isolation lines which produce the resistor characteristics desired. Each wafer contains four resistors, ranging in value from 10 ohms to 1 megohm and a pound of these wafers would contain 40,000 resistors.[18] These wafers may combine to form modules of standard size and shape comprising circuit subassemblies.

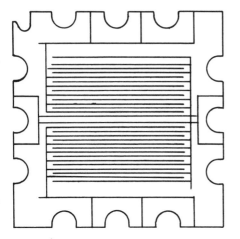

Courtesy, Weston Instruments Div., Daystron, Inc.

FIG. 18-6. WESTON   MOLECULAR-STRUCTURAL
RESISTOR

During the same year, D. A. McLean of the Bell Telephone Laboratories announced the development of a sputtering technique by means of which tantalum capacitors and interconnectors, as well as tantalum resistors as thin as 1 mil, could be deposited on a small glass or ceramic plate (Fig. 18-7). In the sputtering technique, ionized gas molecules bombard a metallic cathode, dislodging atoms of metal that then redeposit on nearby surfaces.[19] [20] [21] This is accomplished by creating a low-pressure glow discharge in an inert gas. The cathode is made of the material to be deposited. The ionized gas atoms then bombard this cathode, dislodging small particles from it. The particles then reform on the material that is used as the substrate.

18.6 *Miniature loudspeakers*

Scientists at RCA have developed what is claimed to be the smallest loudspeaker ever built for commercial radio receivers (Fig. 18-8). It is slightly over 2 in. in diameter and 0.5 in. thick and is

Courtesy, Radio Corporation of America

FIG. 18-8. MINIATURE LOUDSPEAKER

The speaker held next to the match book is only $2\frac{1}{8}$ in. in diameter and little over $\frac{1}{2}$ in. thick. Unlike speakers such as the type in the foreground, it contains its magnetic structure within the shell surrounding its vibrating cone. In the older type, the magnet is housed in a relatively bulky structure projecting from rear of the cone.

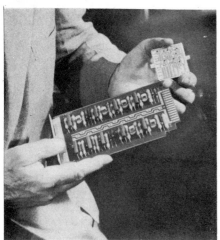

Courtesy, *Radio-Electronics* and Bell Telephone Laboratories

FIG. 18-7. MINIATURE PRINTED CIRCUIT WITH SPUTTERED RESISTORS COMPARED TO CONVENTIONAL PRINTED CIRCUIT BOARD

intended for use in pocket-size transistor radios. The reduction in size and weight is achieved by placing the magnetic structure within the steel surrounding the vibrating cone. The performance of this speaker is comparable to that of earlier types of loudspeakers of considerably greater dimensions.[22]

18.7 *Miniature batteries*

Battery manufacturers have also been busy miniaturizing their products. One outstanding example is a miniature version of the mercury battery that is used in space satellites. This battery, which won the 1960 award of the Miniaturization Awards Committee as an outstanding example of size reduction, is manufactured by Mallory Battery Company. It is the size of an aspirin tablet, and is used in hearing aids and in similar electronic devices where space is at a premium (Fig. 18-9).

18.8 *Other miniaturized devices*

One of the major electronic industries involved in the miniaturization of equipment is the hearing-aid industry. For many years, engineers in this industry have made remarkable advances leading toward the development of an almost invisible and weightless, low-cost hearing aid. To illustrate the progress that has been made along these lines, in 1945, a Sonotone hearing aid weighed 20 oz. The comparable three-transistor 1963 model may be worn entirely in the ear, amplifies 400 times, is approximately the size of a peanut, and weighs only a quarter of an ounce with its battery (Figs. 18-10 and 18-11).[23] [24]

Centralab has announced the development of a one-transistor, packaged, high-gain audio amplifier that is capable of producing 21 db of voltage gain at 1 kc. This device is about the size of the

Courtesy, P. R. Mallory and Company, Inc.
FIG. 18-9. MALLORY RM-312 MERCURY BATTERY (ASPIRIN TABLET AT RIGHT)

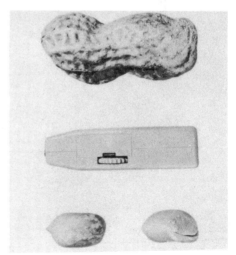

Courtesy, Sonotone Corp.
FIG. 18-10. SONOTONE WISP HEARING AID

Courtesy, The Dahlberg Co.

FIG. 18-11. DAHLBERG MIRACLE-EAR III HEARING AID

eraser located on the end of a pencil and has a volume of less than 0.013 cu in. It is intended for use in hearing aids and pocket-size recorders and radio re-

ceivers. The same company is also manufacturing miniature three- and four-transistor amplifier packages that are capable of producing voltage gains of 75 db at 1 kc (Figs. 18-12, 18-13, and 18-14). These amplifier stages offer an economy feature in addition to the space-saving feature. They accomplish this by reducing wiring costs through the elimination of two-thirds of the required soldering connections.[25]

Among some of the other interesting examples of miniaturized equipment are the following:

1. A transistorized image orthicon television camera which weighs 31 lb and uses 50 watts of power. This may be compared with previous standard types that weighed 600 lb and required 2,000 watts of power.

2. An all-transistor vidicon television camera of modular construction that contains printed circuits and weighs 4 lb. It can operate for 30 minutes on a 6-volt hearing-aid battery (Figs. 18-15 and 18-16).

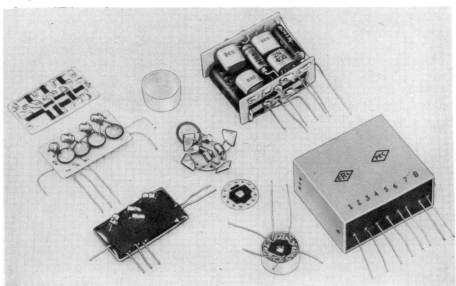

Courtesy, Centralab, Electronics Div., Globe-Union, Inc.

FIG. 18-12. PACKAGED MINIATURE TRANSISTOR AMPLIFIERS

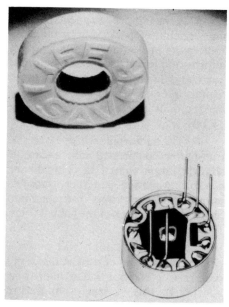

Courtesy, Centralab, Electronics Div., Globe-Union. Inc.
FIG. 18-13. CENTRALAB TA-12-B ULTRA-MINIATURE FOUR-STAGE AUDIO AMPLIFIER

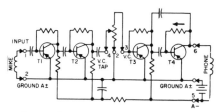

Courtesy, Centralab, Electronics Div., Globe-Union Inc.
FIG. 18-14. CIRCUIT DIAGRAM OF CENTRALAB TA-12-B ULTRA-MINIATURE AUDIO AMPLIFIER

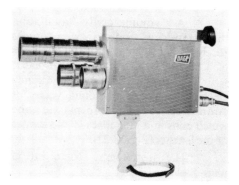

Courtesy, Dage Div., Thompson Ramo Wooldridge Inc.
FIG. 18-15. DAGE MODEL 333 ALL-TRANSISTOR VIDICON CAMERA

Courtesy, Dage Div., Thompson Ramo Wooldridge Inc.
FIG. 18-16. PRINTED-CIRCUIT BOARDS AND PLUG-IN MODULAR CONSTRUCTION OF THE DAGE MODEL 333 TELEVISION CAMERA

Courtesy, Dage Div., Thompson Ramo Wooldridge Inc.
FIG. 18-17. TRANSISTORIZED TELEVISION CAMERA AND TRANSMITTER FOR USE IN ROCKET NOSE CONE

3. A completely transistorized television station that includes a 4-lb camera and 15-lb battery-powered transmitter that can be carried by one man. It transmits television signals as far as one mile for rebroadcast purposes.[26] A more powerful version of this device has been developed for use in the nose-cone of a rocket (Fig. 18-17).

Courtesy, Burroughs Corp.

FIG. 18-18. MOCK-UP OF A MINIATURE COMPUTER

By using miniaturized components presently under development, this computer will nestle 290,000 parts in a cubic foot of space. The concept, named "Macro-Module," embodies triangular chips as a base for components that fit snugly between the fins of a heat exchanger.

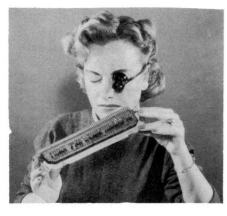

Courtesy, Hughes Aircraft Co.

FIG. 18-19. DIGITAIR AIRBORNE DIGITAL COMPUTER

4. A 15-oz transistorized interphone system for Air Force ground crewman.

5. A computer magnetic-memory unit capable of packing 100,000 electronic parts and storing 1 million bits of information in a space the size of a shoe box (Fig. 18-18). Also a miniaturized digital airborne computer capable of making 6,250 decisions per minute (Fig. 18-19).

6. The radio pill, which is an FM transmitter compressed into a capsule slightly larger than 1 in. This device can be swallowed and then transmits information concerning the condition of the digestive tract of the patient (Figs. 18-20 and 18-21).

7. A system which will make it possible for victims of cardiac disease to maintain a 24-hour watch over their hearts. In this system, a miniature microphone, the size of a grain of wheat, is implanted in the heart. By this means, a steady record of the heartbeat is transmitted to a central receiving station. Any deviation from the normal will cause an automatic warning signal to be broadcast to the individual and to any other persons concerned. This system could well employ the Megacoder, a radio receiver with a volume of 1 cu in., that may be preset to respond selectively to a certain coded signal broadcast by a transmitter at a given frequency.[27]

8. A commercially available, three-transistor, battery-powered radio receiver that is built into the earpieces of a pair of sunglasses. The transducer, which converts the audio-frequency electrical impulses to sound waves, is connected to a flexible plastic tube which ends in a plug that fits into the ear of the listener (Fig. 18-22).[28]

9. The instruments contained in man-made satellites (Figs. 18-23 and 18-24). In a typical satellite, these instruments may have a total weight of only 10.5 lb, but they are capable of

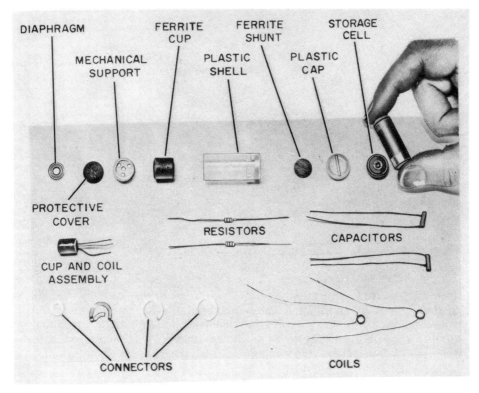

Courtesy, *Radio-Electronics* and Radio Corporation of America

FIG. 18-20. RADIO PILL

The new pill is a plastic capsule $1\frac{1}{8}$ in. long and $\frac{4}{10}$ in. in diameter. It is the world's smallest FM radio broadcast station. Heart of the capsule is a transistor oscillator whose frequency is modulated by fluctuations of fluid or gaseous pressures in the intestinal tract. The small storage battery has a life of fifteen hours and can be recharged.

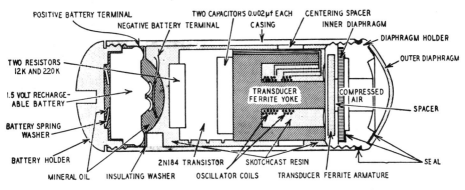

Courtesy, *Radio-Electronics*

FIG. 18-21. CROSS-SECTION OF RADIO PILL

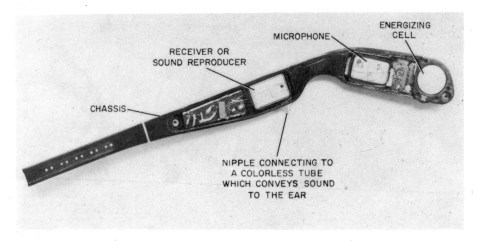

Courtesy. Acousticon International Div., Dictograph Products, Inc.

FIG. 18-22. INTERIOR VIEW OF THE MODEL A900 HEARING AID

telemetering and transmitting 200 different pieces of information simultaneously. These instruments include the satellite's radio transmitter, which weighs less than 15 oz. In 1958, announcement was made by the DuKane Corporation of the development of a new satellite transmitter which weighed less than 3 oz and occupied less than 6 cu in., which is less than the volume of

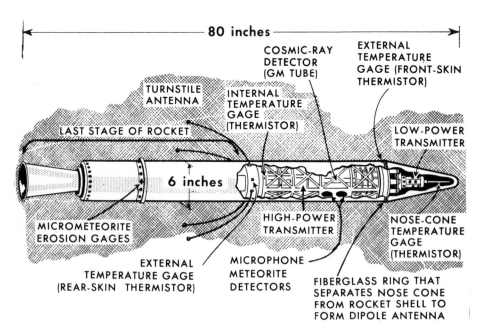

FIG. 18-23. INSTRUMENTATION OF THE EXPLORER I SATELLITE

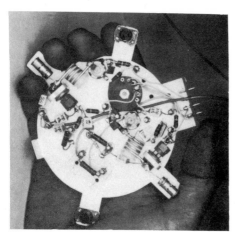

FIG. 18-24. TRANSISTORIZED 80-MILLIWATT TRANSMITTER FOR SATELLITE TELEMETRY SYSTEM

a package of cigarettes (Fig. 18-25). It is highly efficient, requiring only 930 milliwatts of input power to produce 500 milliwatts of output, and is capable of operating indefinitely in space, since it can be powered by a solar battery.[29][30] In 1959, the Philco Corporation also announced the development of an all-transistor, 20-megacycle telemetering transmitter for U.S. Army space satellites. This transmitter weighed less than

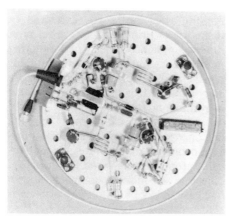

Courtesy, DuKane Corp.

FIG. 18-25. DuKANE 3 oz. HALF-WATT VANGUARD SATELLITE TRANSMITTER

10 oz and delivered considerably more output power than the transistorized transmitters that were currently being used in U.S. Army satellites.[31]

18.9 *Printed circuits*

A factor which is second only to the production of the transistor in stimulating the growth of miniaturization is the development of printed electronic circuits. The term printed circuit has usually been applied to any electrical or electronic conductive pattern reproduced on an insulating support. Thus, the term printed circuit has come to be a catch phrase used to describe anything from a piece of tin foil cemented on a plastic plate to a carbon-backed piece of adhesive tape.

Some authorities criticize this loose terminology, claiming that these devices should be referred to as printed wiring and the term printed circuit should be applied to printed wiring plus components such as resistors, inductors, and capacitors made by similar techniques. Thus, Arthur Ansley states: "The true printed circuit, in its original meaning, consisted of printed components as well as printed wiring. The proximity fuze of World War II was of this type . . . ."[32]

An additional complication is the fact that the term printed is not always accurate, since some processes do not employ printing techniques. However, they are referred to as printed because the final product resembles that obtained by the printing process.[33]

18.10 *History and development of printed circuits*

The basic concept of the printed circuit is not a very new one. The idea of using a metallic film as an electrical conductor goes back to 1883 when

Breckenridge invented a switchboard-wiring panel employing a criss-cross system of wires imbedded in a non-conductor. In 1927, Seymour patented a plated circuit, while in 1929, a patent on a system of stamped wiring was issued to Wermine. In 1937, a patent on a sprayed circuit was taken out by Arlt.[34]

A British experimenter named Sargrove developed the fundamental principle of depositing conductors and other materials to form wires and other components. However, the modern type of printed circuit was first developed in 1945 by C. Brunetti of the National Bureau of Standards in answer to a demand for a compact electronic circuit that could be used to operate a tiny radio-controlled proximity fuze in a mortar or anti-aircraft shell. These circuits were mass-produced by the Centralab Division of Globe-Union, Inc.

Applications. Since the end of World War II, the applications of various types of printed circuits have increased at an accelerating rate. While the value of 1951 production was only 100,000 dollars, by 1959 the value had reached 40 million dollars. A wide assortment of electronic devices is now making use of printed circuits. Among these devices are hearing aids, television receivers, electronic computers, test instruments, switches, and microwave antenna arrays.

In fact, even motors have been developed that employ printed-circuit rotating armatures to replace the conventional heavy iron armatures (Fig. 18-26). Several of these printed-circuit d-c motors were exhibited at the 1959 convention of the I.R.E. The armature of each motor consists of a heavy plastic disc with a thickness of less than $\frac{1}{4}$ in. The circuits are engraved on each side and connected through the disc at the

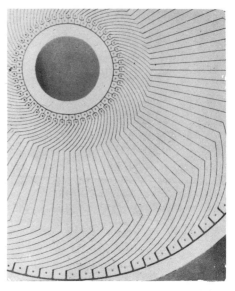

Courtesy, Photocircuits Corp.
FIG. 18-26. DISC ARMATURE OF A PRINTED-CIRCUIT MOTOR

edges. The motors operating at this exhibition had ratings up to 1 hp.[35] It was indicated that a-c motors and motors with ratings as high as 30 hp. were being developed.

It has been suggested that within the near future, the air-conditioning and appliance industries will account for much of the printed-circuit market. Among the appliances expected to make use of printed circuits are electric ranges, appliance timers, and dictating machines. Automobile instrument panels and telephone equipment are also expected to make extensive use of printed circuits.[36]

Characteristics. Printed circuits not only facilitate equipment miniaturization but also contribute to economical, automatic mass production of circuits that are uniform, compact, rugged, and easy to troubleshoot. The number of soldered leads can be reduced by 25 to 80 per cent, with a resulting cost reduction of as much as 50 per cent. In addition, since only the external leads need be soldered, assembly errors and faulty connections are minimized, and accuracy and reliability are improved.

The printed circuit not only provides a means of making electrical interconnections without wires, but also facilitates automatic production by providing a supporting medium for components in a form that is readily adaptable to machine handling and assembly. In UHF work, the printed circuit provides special advantages associated with the reduction of lead lengths and the simplification of circuit alignment resulting from the unvarying physical relationships between the printed elements. Consequently, microwave components are often made in the form of etched patterns on circuit boards, and these usually provide tremendous savings over conventional microwave plumbing.[37]

However, it must be admitted that not every electronic manufacturer has become convinced of the superiority of printed circuits over conventional handwiring. Quite a few believe that circuits wired by hand result in better performance and fewer servicing troubles. They also cite design limitations. Heavy components cannot be mounted on printed boards, and high temperatures and voltages considerably reduce their usefulness.

18.11 *Reliability and servicing of printed circuits*

A survey made by the National Alliance of Television and Electronic Service Associations (NATESA), indicated that only approximately 0.5 per cent of 90,660 service calls were caused by failures of printed-wiring boards. A similar survey conducted by RCA indicated that a television technician would have to replace only one printed circuit in every 5,000 calls. RCA concluded that printed circuits were less costly to repair and service because they developed less trouble than hand-wired circuits.

Contrary to this survey, slightly over half of the service men interviewed in the NATESA survey stated that printed-board sets required more servicing than sets without boards.

Furthermore, 90 per cent of those interviewed claimed that it was more difficult to trace a circuit through printed boards, and they requested the set manufacturers to provide more complete servicing instructions on printed-board sets. They also stated that they would like to see all components mounted on just one side of the board. Another frequent complaint was the poor accessibility of most of the boards, and the difficulty of pinpointing just which component had failed, since it is rather difficult to substitute components on a printed board.[38] This survey revealed that most of the complaints involved the following factors: board breakage; lifting of conductors; mounting of controls, tube sockets, and other components; component placement on both sides of a board; accessibility; circuit tracing; and component identification.[39]

As a result of these complaints by service men, many of the leading manufacturers, such as RCA, Westinghouse, Philco, General Electric, Motorola, and Sylvania, have produced new models of sets containing improvements, such as printing schematics on one side of the board, providing more flexible boards, mounting all components on one side only, making the boards more accessible, and using color coding to identify B plus, AGC (automatic gain control), and other key voltage and test points (Fig. 18-27).[40 41]

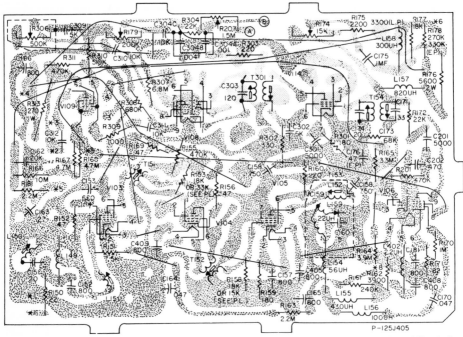

Courtesy, General Electric Co.

FIG. 18-27. TYPICAL PRINTED CIRCUIT BOARD SHOWING LOCATION OF VARIOUS COMPONENTS

18.12 *Types of base materials*

One of the major problems that faced the earlier manufacturers of printed circuits was the lack of satisfactory base materials. Most of the recent progress in printed circuitry has been made possible by the development of improved base materials upon which the circuits are fabricated.

A good base material should be resistant to the actions of chemicals and fungi and should possess high mechanical strength and low moisture-absorbing characteristics. In addition, it should have high leakage resistance, and its surface resistivity should remain essentially constant over wide ranges of temperatures and humidities. It must be capable of withstanding soldering temperatures without blistering or deteriorating. Finally, it is essential that particles of solder should not adhere to this material; otherwise the equipment may be short circuited.

The earliest printed circuits, those employed in connection with the proximity fuze, used ceramic bases. The principal advantage possessed by ceramics is that of being able to withstand high temperatures. One of the most important of these ceramics is steatite, a material composed of a mixture of clay, talc, and barium carbonate (Fig. 18-28). It possesses great strength and hardness and has excellent electrical properties that are not affected by high temperature or humidity. Electronic circuits printed with silver paint on ceramic bases are meeting increased acceptance by equipment manufacturers, especially for devices intended for high-temperature applications.[42]

Paper and cloth-base phenolic laminates are the materials most frequently employed for ordinary circuit

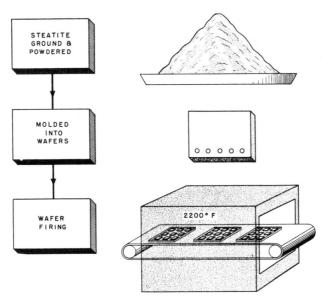

Fig. 18-28. Steps employed in molding steatite

applications. This type of material is generally composed of several layers of a good grade of rag paper impregnated with a phenolic resin or varnish (Fig. 18-29). Its cost is low; its electric characteristics, with the exception of arc-resistance, are good; and it is easily drilled, punched, or machined. In most applications, where the environmental conditions are not severe, the mechanical stresses on the board are not excessive, and high surface resistivity is not required, paper-base phenolic is the best choice.[43]

Epoxy glass, which has the greatest mechanical strength of all base materials, is used where mechanical and electrical requirements are somewhat more stringent. It is three to four times more expensive than paper-base phenolic, but its use is recommended under conditions of high humidity, high altitude, crowded circuitry, and high shock, vibration, and mechanical loading.[44]

These two materials, paper-base phenolic and epoxy glass, are used in the vast majority of printed circuits. Recently, a paper-epoxy laminate has been developed that is intermediate in cost and characteristics to both of these materials. It is coming into wide use as a compromise where cost is a major consideration, but paper-base phenolic is not adequate.

Among the other materials occasionally employed are melamine glass, silicone glass, teflon glass, and polystyrene. Melamine glass is hard and strong mechanically. However, it is very difficult to machine and possesses inferior moisture-absorbing properties. Silicone glass has low moisture-absorbing properties and withstands high temperatures. However, it is expensive, difficult to machine, and the strength of its bond to copper foil is low. Teflon glass withstands high temperatures and is used where operating temperatures may run as high as 250°C. It is the best material for microwave equipment but has low mechanical strength and is very expensive.[45] Polystyrene is an excellent base material where extremely low los-

Courtesy, National Vulcanized Fiber Corp.

FIG. 18-29. PRODUCTION METHOD OF COATING AND IMPREGNATING PAPER
The paper is fed from rolls to a dip tank of resin, then dried in a long conveyor oven.

ses at microwave frequencies is an important factor. However, it cannot be employed under conditions where the operating temperature exceeds 94°C.

18.13 *Manufacturing printed circuits*

Today, many different processes are employed to manufacture printed circuits. Among them are (1) painting, (2) spraying, (3) chemical deposition, (4) vacuum deposition, (5) die stamping, (6) dusting, (7) embossing, (8) etching, (9) plating, and (10) casting. Some of these processes will be described briefly in the following paragraphs.[46]

The painting process. The process known as painting, developed by Brunetti, is used by the Centralab Division of Globe-Union, Inc. In this process, an ink consisting of powdered silver or copper in suspension is forced through a silk-screen stencil of the desired circuit upon the surface of a steatite plate (Fig. 18-30). The circuit is then fired or

baked in to fuse the metal particles and to bond the circuit to the base (Fig. 18-31).

Resistors are added by using an ink containing a mixture of carbon and filler material. This idea is not a new one, since India ink was used as a resistance element in early types of radio receivers. The major disadvantage of this type of resistor is its low power rating, which is approximately 0.2 watts. While this rating is generally satisfactory for

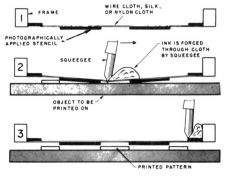

FIG. 18-30. PRINCIPLES OF SCREEN PRINTING

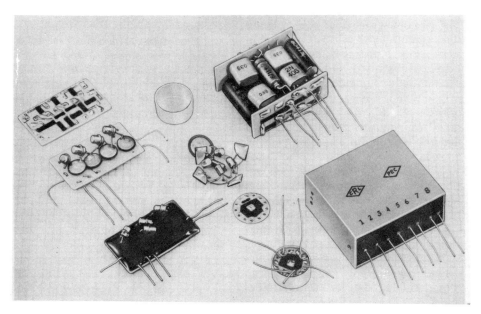

FIG. 18-31. CERAMIC PRINTED CIRCUIT AMPLIFIER

Courtesy, Centralab Div., Globe-Union, Inc.

voltage amplifiers, it is unsatisfactory for use in power-amplifier circuits.

Capacitors may be added by attaching paper-thin ceramic discs that are silvered on both sides, or by forcing ceramic capacitors containing tapered edges into connector slots that have been cut into the base (Fig. 18-32). Another method of adding capacitance is to employ a base material of high dielectric constant and to paint two silver discs of the correct size on opposite sides of the base. It is also possible to paint switches and spiral inductors such as coils and transformers.[47]

Although the silk-screen stenciling process is the most frequently used method of applying paint, paint may also be applied by hand with the aid of a brush, by the use of decalcomanias, or even by means of conventional printing presses.

Experimenters and designers prefer to use this method since it requires very little auxiliary equipment. It is also the method that has been found to work best in the repair of damaged printed circuits.

The spraying process. The spraying process employs a spray of molten metal or of conductive paint to form the

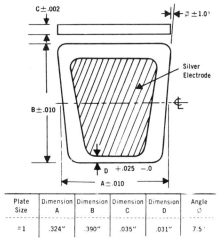

Plate Size	Dimension A	Dimension B	Dimension C	Dimension D	Angle ∅
≑1	.324″	.390″	.035″	.031″	7.5°

Courtesy, Electronic Components Div., General Electric Co.
FIG. 18-32. MECHANICAL FEATURES OF WEJCAPS FOR PRINTED WIRE BOARDS

surface conductors (Fig. 18-33). Resistance paints may also be sprayed. In some spraying processes, masking tapes or stencils are used. In others, grooves are molded or machined in the base. The metal is then sprayed over the entire base, and the surface is milled off. This removes excess metal, leaving only the metal remaining in the grooves.

The chemical-deposition process. The chemical-deposition method resembles the process of silvering mirrors. A solution of silver nitrate in ammonia is poured on a surface that is covered with a stencil. The silver is deposited as a thin uniform film in the form of the desired circuit. This film may then be plated to increase its conductance. Similarly, copper may be deposited by using formaldehyde as a reducing agent for a modified type of Fehling solution. Gold may be deposited by displacing it by means of another metal. It is also possible to deposit several metals simultaneously, such as copper, nickel, and gold, and thus produce color-coded printed wiring. It is also possible to deposit certain other metallic salts, resulting in the production of resistors.[48]

The vacuum-deposition process. In vacuum process, vaporized metallic conductors and resistors are distilled onto a cool surface through a stencil or mask. The least complicated method of accomplishing this is by means of simple evaporation produced by induction heating. A second method is known as cathode sputtering. Within an evacuated container, a high positive potential is applied between the cathode or source of metal vapor and an anode. Metal is emitted from the cathode and is attracted to the anode, where it is deposited through a stencil.

The die-stamping process. In the die-stamping process, conductors are punched out of metal foil by means of dies and are attached to an insulated base (Figs. 18-34 and 18-35). This method was first developed by A. W. Franklin, who employed it to produce spiral loop antennas that were die-stamped from thin copper or aluminum foil. Resistors may be stamped out of a specially coated plastic film as well.[49]

The dusting process. The dusting

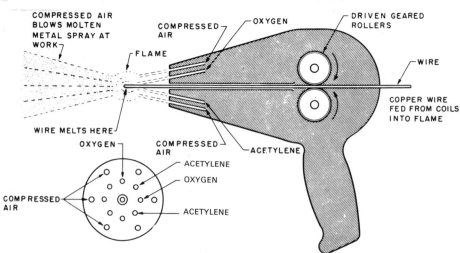

FIG. 18-33. OPERATING PRINCIPLES OF A METAL SPRAY GUN

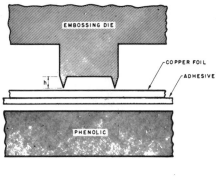

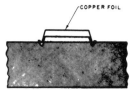

FIG. 18-34. REPRESENTATION OF A STAMPED CIRCUIT SYSTEM

process employs conducting metallic powders which are dusted onto a surface. The powders are held on either by use of a binding material such as shellac dissolved in alcohol or by an electrostatic method. After the powder is applied, the circuit is fired to fuse the metallic powder.[50] In a modified version of this process,

Courtesy, Sylvania Electric Products, Inc.

FIG. 18-35. STAMPED CIRCUITS COMING OFF THE PRESS

sometimes called the pressed-powder process, after the metallic powder is placed on the insulator, a hot die with raised sections corresponding to the desired pattern is pressed onto the surface of the powder. This squeezes the powder into a virtually-solid metal conductor which adheres to the insulating base (Fig. 18-36).

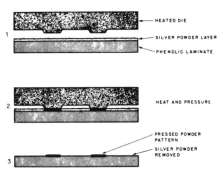

FIG. 18-36. PREPARATION OF PRESSED POWDER CIRCUITS

Embossed wiring. Embossed wiring was introduced in 1954 by the Erie Resistor Corp. In this relatively simple process, a plate is pressed into a piece of copper foil that is mounted on laminated plastic. The foil is embossed in such a manner that the desired conducting pattern is below the surface. The elevated, undesired portions of metal are then removed by means of an abrasive, leaving the conductive pattern remaining on the board (Fig. 18-37).

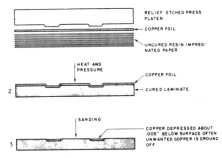

FIG. 18-37. STEPS IN EMBOSSED WIRING CIRCUIT SYSTEM

Etched circuits. Within the past few years, a new form of printed circuity known as etched or printed wiring has been developed for the manufacture of electronic equipment. Today, approximately 75 per cent of the printed circuits manufactured employ etched wiring. The principle of the etched circuit was developed and patented in 1941 by Eisler, a scientist employed by a British printing firm.

The etched circuit is made from a laminated plastic or a glass-ceramic sheet which is covered on one or both sides by a thin layer of copper. This copper is bonded to the base by means of a strong adhesive. The desired circuit pattern is then placed on the copper by using a resist, a substance that resists the action of etching chemicals. The resist circuit pattern may be applied to the copper sheet by means of silk screening, metal lithographing, offset printing, plating, or photoengraving processes (Fig. 18-38). The unwanted copper, that portion not covered by the resist, is then etched away by the action of chemicals such as ferric chloride, chromic acid, or ammonium persulphate.[51] The remaining metal, which forms the desired electrical circuit, may then be plated, if desired. When printed conductors are used on both sides of the board, through connections from one side of the board to the other may be established by means of rivets, eyelets, wire leads, or a newly developed process of plating-through holes.

It has been observed that the current-carrying capacity of an etched conductor is surprisingly high. This is probably due to the fact that the board absorbs and dissipates a great deal of the heat developed by the conductor.

RCA and Photocircuits Corporation have recently applied this etching process to the manufacture of television-receiver circuit components such as i-f transformers, coils, and filter traps (Fig. 18-39). Other manufacturers are employing this technique to produce rotary switch plates, microwave resonators and wave guides, computer code discs, and many varieties of commutators (Figs. 18-40 and 18-41). By employing this method it has been found possible to produce complex configurations at a very low cost. Unlike the process of manufacturing devices by machining, the cost of the etched printing process is affected hardly at all by the complexity of the pattern of the device being produced.

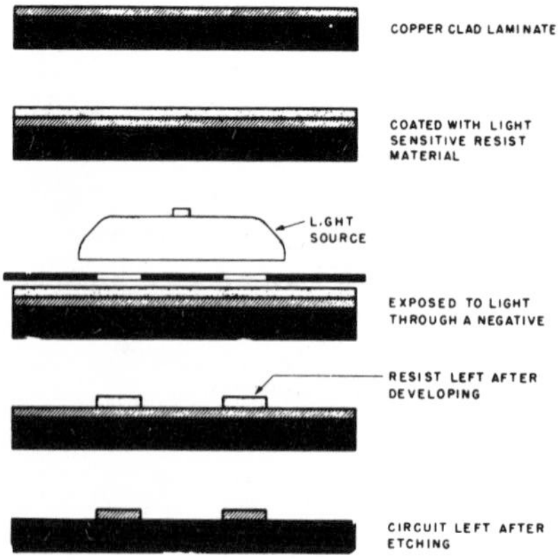

COPPER CLAD LAMINATE

COATED WITH LIGHT SENSITIVE RESIST MATERIAL

LIGHT SOURCE

EXPOSED TO LIGHT THROUGH A NEGATIVE

RESIST LEFT AFTER DEVELOPING

CIRCUIT LEFT AFTER ETCHING

FIG. 18-38. BASIC PRINCIPLES OF PHOTO PRINTING AND ETCHING

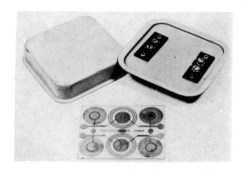

Courtesy, Photocircuits Corp.

FIG. 18-39. TELEVISION-INTERFERENCE FILTER CONTAINING EIGHT PRINTED CAPACITORS AND SIX PRINTED COILS

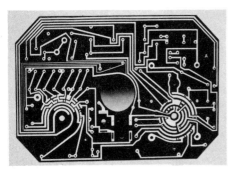

Courtesy, Photocircuits Corp.

FIG. 18-40. TYPICAL ETCHED CIRCUIT EMPLOYED IN TEST INSTRUMENTS. NOTE PRINTED SWITCH ELEMENTS

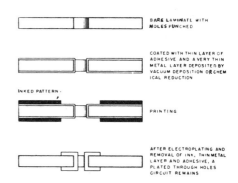

FIG. 18-42. STEPS EMPLOYED IN PLATED CIRCUIT PROCESS

Plated circuits. The plated-circuit technique, developed in 1953 by the Motorola Corp. was given the name of the Placir method. As its name indicates, it is a process in which the conducting pattern is produced by means of electroplating (Fig. 18-42). A thin silver film is applied to a sheet or panel of phenolic laminated plastic. This silver film is produced by adding formaldehyde to a solution of a silver salt. The desired pattern is then printed in reverse on the panel in the form of a resist-ink pattern. The panel is then placed at the cathode of a copper-plating bath, and copper deposits on all portions of the panel except those covered by the resist-ink. The ink is then removed. Although only a small percentage of today's printed wiring employs the electroplating technique, it seems very likely that it is destined for widespread use in the not-too-distant future (Fig. 18-43).

Cast printing. Cast printing, a recently developed, low-cost method of producing printed circuits, is the outgrowth of work conducted by Reed Research and its affiliate, Space Components, Inc. It employs injection-molding techniques involving the simultaneous casting together of conductive metals, insulating plastics, and ceramics,

Courtesy, Photocircuits Corp.

FIG. 18-41. ETCHED DIGITAL CODE DISC USED TO CONVERT SHAFT ROTATION INTO DIGITAL OUTPUT

Courtesy, Motorola, Inc.

FIG. 18-43. PLATED CIRCUITS MADE FOR A PORTABLE AND A HOME RADIO RECEIVER

to produce printed circuits and desired circuit components.

18.14 *Printed modules*

A module may be defined as an assembly of basic components which forms a new and larger component that is designed to meet functional specifications. A completed module is a physically standarized, interchangeable subassembly that combines all of the requirements of an electrical circuit with ruggedness, reliability, and compactness (Fig. 18-44).[52] [53]

The modular concept probably dates back to the 1930's, when Flewelling of RCA was issued a patent for a combination system in which flat conductors also acted as capacitor plates.

In 1947, Sargrove, a British radio engineer, developed a process for the automatic production of radio receivers, in which capacitors, resistors, and conductors were printed by a fully automatic method.[54] The output of each stage was automatically checked and inspected, and in many instances errors were automatically corrected. Sargrove called his machine ECME, for Electronic Circuit Making Equipment. Unfortunately, the machine was so complex and closely organized that a malfunction in one stage due to variations in the properties of the component parts caused the whole machine to shut down. Because of frequent electrical breakdowns, combined with material shortages, the development of ECME came to a standstill.[55]

Courtesy, ACF Industries

FIG. 18-44. COMPARISON BETWEEN A MODULE AND THE INDIVIDUAL COMPONENT PARTS REQUIRED FOR THE SAME CIRCUIT

During the same year, 1947, the Compo radio appeared. This combined components and wiring into cylinders which were plugged into chassis sockets.[56] However, the modular system developed by Project Tinkertoy was the first practical and efficient process capable of being readily adapted to the techniques of automatic assembly and manufacture.

Project Tinkertoy. Project Tinkertoy is the name given to a research project begun in 1950 and headed by Reid and Henry of the National Bureau of Standards. Its purpose was to devise a mechanized production system for military electronic equipment (Fig. 18-45). The project succeeded in developing a printed-circuit module unit. This unit contained the resistors, capacitors, inductors, and their linkages, which make up between 60 and 80 per cent of most electronic equipment and are costly to assemble.

Starting from raw materials, the machines automatically manufacture ceramic materials, adhesive carbon resistors, and disc capacitors or printed capacitors that employ a wafer-like base as the dielectric. They then paint

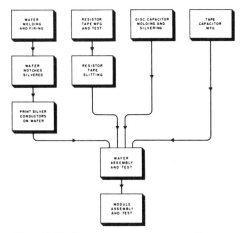

Fig. 18-45. Block diagram of the Tinkertoy process

conducting circuits and mount the resistors, capacitors, and other miniaturized component parts on standard, uniform, steatite wafers. The wafers are assembled and stacked very much like building blocks (Fig. 18-46).

Appropriate sections of each wafer are connected with each other by stiff riser wires. The assembly may also include tube or transistor sockets. The final product is a module that performs all of the functions of one or more electronic stages (Fig. 18-47).[57] Automatic inspection machines are used to check the physical and electrical characteristics of these wafers and modules at numerous stations along the production line.

The year 1957 also saw the development of a flat tape cable designed to ease the task of interconnecting modules with printed circuits. In order to facilitate making these connections, plugs and sockets matched to this cable have been developed.[58]

The window-frame module. A recent modular development, known as the window-frame module, involves a new packaging technique used for aircraft equipment. It consists of two sets of eight transistor-circuit elements mounted back-to-back in a hinged "window-frame" of aluminum. The connections for all 16 circuits are made through a single 20-pin, plug-in terminal, thus reducing the number of required connectors from 16 to one. The entire window frame and its circuits can be quickly disconnected for servicing or replacement. It provides the advantages of less weight and space, increased reliability, greater density of transistors and other components, and easy adaptation to automatic production.[59]

Employment of modules. While Project Tinkertoy and other modular-construction techniques were originally developed under the sponsorship of the

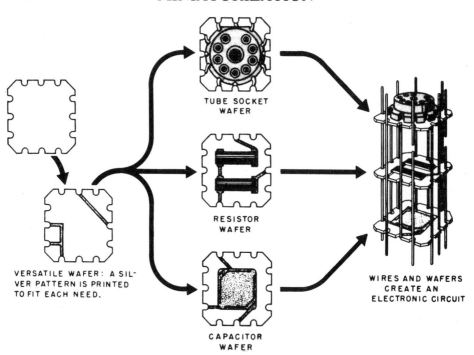

FIG. 18-46. STEPS IN PREPARING A MODULE

U.S. Navy Bureau of Aeronautics in or-. der to facilitate the production of milit-

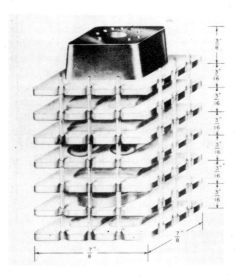

Courtesy, ACF Industries

FIG. 18-47. TYPICAL N.B.S. MODULE

ary-electronic equipment, by 1956, companies such as Motorola, Emerson, and DuMont were employing modular construction in some of their television receivers, broadcast receivers, and test instruments designed for civilian consumption (Figs. 18-48 and 18-49). Since modules permit a very high degree of standardization, it may eventually become possible to combine a few basic standard modules in various manners so as to make any radio or television

FIG. 18-48. FIVE-TUBE SUPERHETERODYNE RADIO RECEIVER EMPLOYING N.B.S. MODULES

Courtesy, ACF Industries

FIG. 18-49. TELEVISION RECEIVER CHASSIS EMPLOYING MODULES

receiver. This would simplify the stocking of parts and would reduce inventories. The modular concept can also be used to simplify the work of the designer of computer and control systems (Fig. 18-50). As an illustration, the Comptron Corp. has developed a group of transistorized, plug-in, modular, printed-circuit cards (Fig. 18-51). These cards are compatible with one another and can be combined to form any desired logical system. This permits the engineer to make up a complete system without the necessity of designing individual electronic circuits.

Repair and servicing of modules. Whether or not modular equipment requires less servicing has not yet been fully determined. The Emerson Radio Corporation is presently conducting a study in which the cost, operation, and serviceability of modularized television receivers are being compared with those of similar receivers containing conventional components. When necessary, modules can be repaired. However, repairs are usually resorted to only when replacements are not readily available, since the cost of a replacement module is generally less than 3

Courtesy, Hughes Aircraft Co.

FIG. 18-50. PLUG-IN MODULE FOR USE IN DIGITAIR AIRBORNE DIGITAL COMPUTER

dollars. Modular replacement is not only speedier but usually costs less than the labor charges involved in tracking down troubles to the individual components that have produced them.[60] It may perhaps come as a shock to taxpayers to learn that the Department of Defense considers it cheaper to throw away all modular plug-in units worth less than 300 dollars than to repair them and that there are those in the Pentagon who would raise this figure to 1,000 dollars.[61]

18.15 *Micro-miniaturization*

Additional progress in miniaturization was achieved when component manufacturers developed methods of printing resistors, capacitors, and other circuit elements on surfaces of extremely small area (Fig. 18-52). These develop-

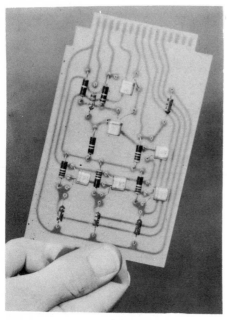

FIG. 18-51. COMPTRON PLUG-IN TRANSISTORIZED PRINTED-CIRCUIT CARDS

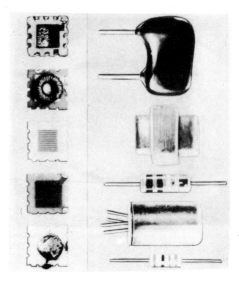

FIG. 18-52. CONVENTIONAL COMPONENTS (LEFT) AND EQUIVALENT MICRO-ELEMENTS (RIGHT)
Top to bottom: diode; capacitor; resistor; inductor; capacitor.

ments made it possible to manufacture even smaller modules than had previously been produced.

As a result of this trend toward reduction in size and weight of miniaturized equipment, C. Brunetti, one of the pioneers in the field of miniaturization and printed circuits, suggested at the 1957 I.R.E. Convention the use of a new term, micro-miniaturization, to describe these more advanced techniques.[62] By 1958, this term, as well as the terms micro-electronics and micro-module, had gained wide acceptance.

Micro-modules. The first micro-module was produced in 1958 as the result of a co-operative effort involving RCA and the U.S. Army Signal Corps. These micro-modules are units in which several micro-elements are combined to perform specific circuit functions such as amplifying, oscillating, or filtering (Figs. 18-53 and 18-54). The micro-

elements are tiny ceramic wafers, approximately 0.3 in. square and 0.01 in. thick. Conducting, semiconducting, and insulating materials are fused in each micro-element to provide the electrical characteristics of basis electronic components such as resistors, capacitors, and transistors. These materials may be deposited by evaporation, printing, electro-deposition, chemical deposition, or silk-screening. The various elements are then interconnected and evaporated to form micro-modules (Fig. 18-55).

A typical micro-modularized audio amplifier weighs less than 0.1 oz and provides 20 db gain and 1 milliwatt of power output (Fig. 18-56).[63] Over 27 micro-modules fit into a volume of 1 cu in., and experimental electronic equipment constructed with micro-modules have attained part densities of approximately 700,000 parts per cubic foot. This represents a reduction of ten times

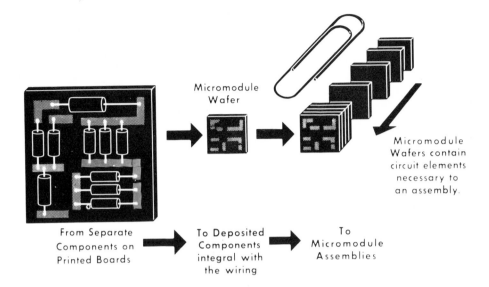

From Separate
Components on
Printed Boards

To Deposited
Components
integral with
the wiring

To
Micromodule
Assemblies

Micromodule
Wafer

Micromodule
Wafers contain
circuit elements
necessary to
an assembly.

FIG. 18-53. MICRO-MINIATURIZATION OF COMPONENTS

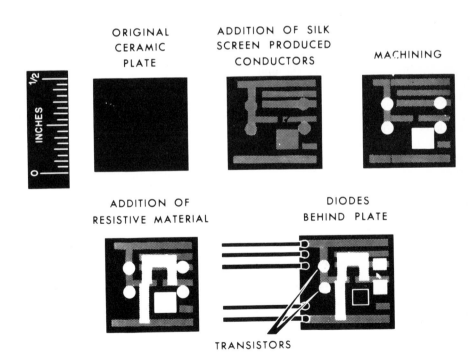

ORIGINAL
CERAMIC
PLATE

ADDITION OF SILK
SCREEN PRODUCED
CONDUCTORS

MACHINING

ADDITION OF
RESISTIVE MATERIAL

DIODES
BEHIND PLATE

TRANSISTORS

FIG. 18-54. FABRICATION SEQUENCE OF MICRO-CIRCUITRY

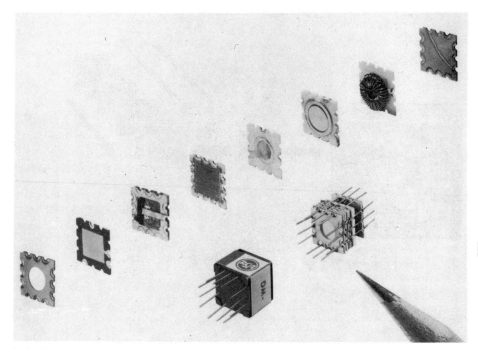

Courtesy, Radio Corporation of America

FIG. 18-55. EXPLODED VIEW OF THE ELEMENTS OF AN RCA MICRO-MODULE

over the best previously existing minia-turized equipment (Figs. 18-57 to 18-60).[64][65]

It is claimed that these micro-modules will make it possible to produce a five-stage radio receiver that is smaller than a lump of sugar; to reduce the weight of a 30-lb airborne radio

Frequency range: 300 to 3000 cps

Gain: 20 db

Power output: 1 mw

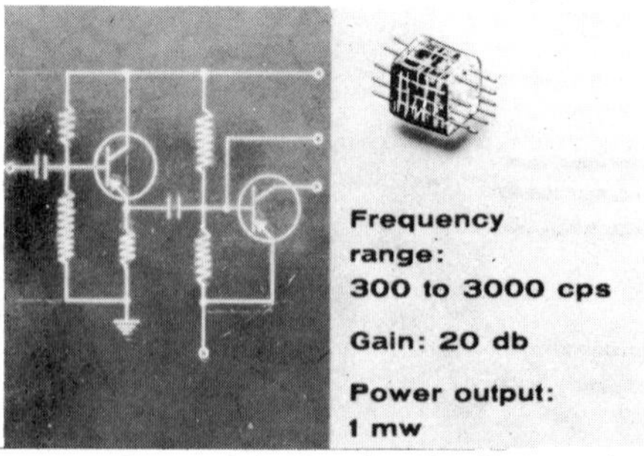

Courtesy, *Radio-Electronics* and Radio Corporation of America

FIG. 18-56. AUDIO AMPLIFIER CIRCUIT AND EQUIVALENT MICRO-MODULE

system to 4 lb; to reduce by 90 per cent the size and weight of a typical missile-guidance unit by providing it with a digital computer containing 8,000 components sealed in a can that is only 2 by 4 by 5 in.; to construct wrist-watch radios; and to build pocket size record player and recording machines.[66][67][68][69][70]

TIMM devices. General Electric has also developed a type of ceramic micro-module called TIMM, for ther-mionic integrated micro-modules (Figs. 18-61, 18-62, and 18-63). Each module has heaterless tubes and micro-miniature resistors and capacitors that are stable over a temperature change of several hundred degrees. These components can be stacked and intercon-nected by short jumpers to form tiny circuits. A circuit 0.3 by 2.6 in. may contain 10 diodes, 14 triodes, 14 resistors, and 6 capacitors, and it can operate in

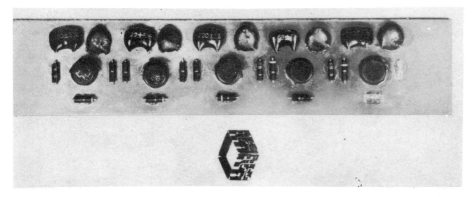

FIG. 18-57. SYLVANIA MICRO-MINIATURE MODULE
The wafer element of this module maintains a complete circuit functioning stage on a surface less than ½-in. square and $\frac{1}{100}$ in. thick. The function of a conventional printed circuit board 6 in. long and 1¼ in. wide (top) can be carried out by a six-wafer module ⅜ in. high and less than ½-in. square (bottom).

an extremely high temperature environment. Unlike conventional electronic

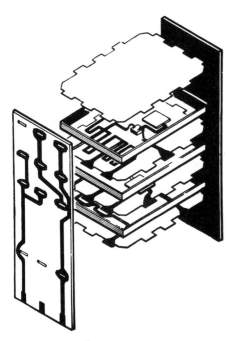

FIG. 18-58. EXPLODED VIEW OF SYLVANIA MICROMINIATURE MODULE SHOWING WAFER AND FUSED SPACER ELEMENTS AND VERTICAL INTERWIRING BOARD

units, TIMM devices do not try to get rid of heat. Instead, the environmental heat is used to produce emission from the cathode.[71][72][73][74] The sub-miniature electron tubes employed in this system can operate at temperatures up to 700°C and do not require individual heating of the cathodes. As indicated, thermionic emission is produced as a result of the high ambient temperature.

18.16 *Integrated or molecular electronics*

The terms molectronics, molecular electronics, solid-circuit electronics, and integrated electronics refer to a new technique that is designed to produce complete circuits and equipment from a single, solid piece of semiconductor material (Fig. 18-64). This is accomplished by manufacturing into the semiconductor the functions of resistance, capacitance, and amplification.[75]

Because of the fact that Westinghouse scientists had developed a previously mentioned revolutionary method of growing germanium crystals in uniform flat ribbons, in 1959 the Air Force

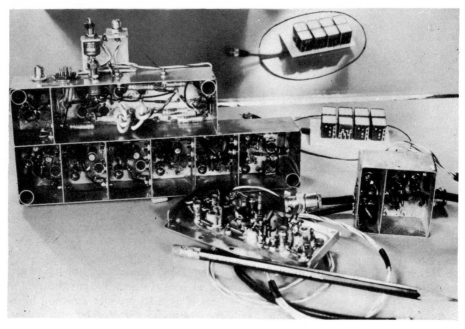

Courtesy, Sylvania Electric Products, Inc.

FIG. 18-59. SYLVANIA MICROMINIATURE AIRBORNE RADIO RECEIVER (RIGHT REAR) COMPARED WITH A CONVENTIONAL AIRBORNE RADIO RECEIVER

The microminiature receiver will operate more than 10,000 hours (nearly 14 months) without failure. The current average time between failures for a typical airborne radio receiver is 450 hours.

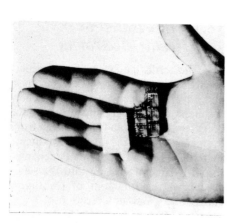

Courtesy, *Radio-Electronics* and United States Army Signal Corps.

FIG. 18-60. COMPLETE SEVEN-STAGE MICRO-MODULE SUPERHETERODYNE RECEIVER AND A LUMP OF SUGAR

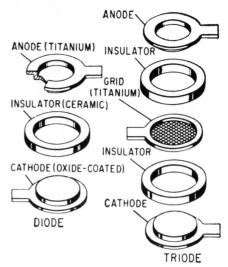

Courtesy, Electronic Components Div., General Electric Co.

FIG. 18-61. EXPLODED VIEWS OF MICROMINI-ATURE TITANIUM-CERAMIC DIODE AND TRIODE

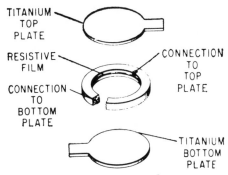

TITANIUM TOP PLATE

RESISTIVE FILM

CONNECTION TO TOP PLATE

CONNECTION TO BOTTOM PLATE

TITANIUM BOTTOM PLATE

Courtesy, Electronic Components Div., General Electric Co.
FIG. 18-62. EXPLODED VIEW OF MICROMINI-ATURE TITANIUM-CERAMIC RESISTOR

Courtesy, General Electric Co.
FIG. 18-64. MICROMINIATURE CIRCUIT UNDER A MAGNIFYING GLASS

awarded Westinghouse a 2-million-dollar development contract in the field of molecular electronics. Since that time, Westinghouse scientists have developed a transistorized, light-modulated oscillator which functions as a light-sensing device for satellite telemetry. It consists of a single wafer less than 0.5 in. in diameter and 0.01 in.

Courtesy, Electronic Components Div., General Electric Co.
FIG. 18-63. THERMIONIC INTEGRATED MICRO-MODULE (TIMM) UNITS
Clustered on the end of a clothespin, these three tiny ceramic devices take the place of more than 25 components in a conventional circuit.

thick. The following table listing the characteristics of three similar light-sensing circuits may provide a comparison of this device with vacuum-tube and transistorized circuits that perform similar functions:

	Size (cu.in.)	Weight (grams)	Input Power (watts)	Compo-nents	Solder-ed con-nections
Vacuum tube	4	26	5	16	18
Transistorized	1	7	0.75	14	15
Molecular system	0.001	0.02	0.06	1	2

It is claimed that this new concept could make possible the reduction of a transistor radio receiver, excluding the power supply and loudspeaker, to the size of a match head (Figs. 18-65, 18-66, and 18-67).[76]

According to a statement made in 1960 by Colonel William S. Heavner, Chief of the Electronic Technology Laboratory, Wright Air Development Division, molectronics is the complete answer to miniaturization, and it will eliminate the use of capacitors, resistors, and similar components. He also stated that operational molecular equipment could be available within three to five years. While he was unable to predict

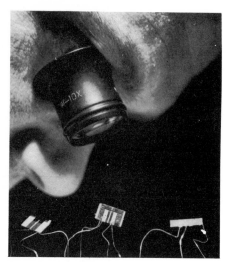

Courtesy, Westinghouse Electric Corp.
FIG. 18-65. MOLECULAR ELECTRONIC MULTI-VIBRATOR UNITS

cost differentials compared with transistors and standard components, it was his opinion that the increase in reliability and the marked decrease in size will

Courtesy, Westinghouse Electric Corp.
FIG. 18-66 MOLECULAR ELECTRONIC AMPLIFIER

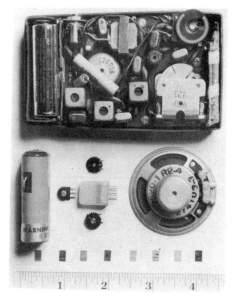

Courtesy, Westinghouse Electric Corporation.
FIG. 18-67. TODAY'S AND TOMORROW'S RADIOS
The sub-miniature components of tomorrow's thimble-size radio are shown here in comparison with the insides of a conventional 7-transistor radio. At the top of the photograph is the 7-transistor model. Below it is an equivalent molecular radio receiver which includes the battery at the left, the molecular components in the center, and the speaker at the right. The speaker is similar to the one in the conventional radio, but projects are underway to develop a speaker comparable in size to the functional blocks. The electronic circuitry portion of the molecular radio is packaged in the small module shown here between the battery and speaker. The three circular devices around it are the tuning, volume, and sensitivity controls. Just above the ruler are the eight silicon functional electronic blocks which make up the receiver and under operating conditions would be "stacked" in the module.

make molectronics competitive with these other systems regardless of cost.

Texas Instruments Inc. has announced a similar circuit-construction technique in which transistors, diodes, capacitors, resistors, and other components form an integral part of a single, tiny, semiconductor wafer. Resistors are formed by the bulk resistance of the semiconductor material, the size and shape of the material determining the resistance value. Capacitors are formed by utilizing the capacity of a large-area P-N junction. R-C (resistance-capacitance) networks are formed by combining the resistance and capacitance-forming techniques, while transistors and diodes are formed by employing diffusion techniques (Figs. 18-68, 18-69, and 18-70).

Employing these techniques, engineers have constructed a multivibrator circuit only 1/4 by 1/8 by 1/32 in.

Courtesy, Texas Instruments, Inc.

Fig. 18-69. Adder unit containing 13 solid circuit semiconductor networks (right) and equivalent printed-circuit unit

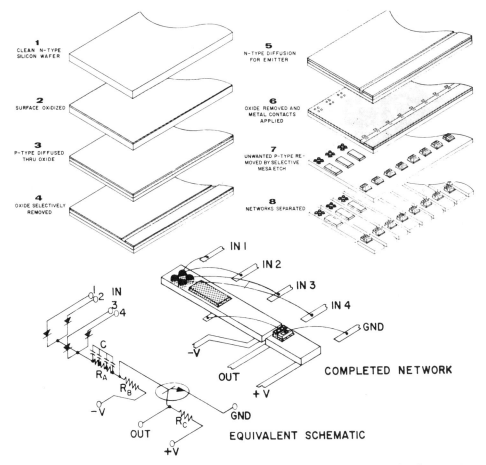

1 CLEAN N-TYPE SILICON WAFER

2 SURFACE OXIDIZED

3 P-TYPE DIFFUSED THRU OXIDE

4 OXIDE SELECTIVELY REMOVED

5 N-TYPE DIFFUSION FOR EMITTER

6 OXIDE REMOVED AND METAL CONTACTS APPLIED

7 UNWANTED P-TYPE REMOVED BY SELECTIVE MESA ETCH

8 NETWORKS SEPARATED

IN 1
IN 2
IN 3
IN 4
GND

COMPLETED NETWORK

IN 2 3 4
C
R_A
R_B
R_C
OUT
-V
+V
GND
OUT
-V
+V

EQUIVALENT SCHEMATIC

Courtesy, Texas Instruments Inc.

Fig. 18-68. Fabrication of solid circuit semiconductor network NOR logic element

that is identical to a conventional circuit consisting of 8 resistors, 2 capacitors, and 2 transistors.[77] This means that this technique permits a component density of 34 million parts per cubic foot.[78] Not to be outdone, RCA announced an integrated electronics technique that will enable its scientists to fit 100 million components into 1 cu ft of space. It is planned to use these as components for a computer that will be as compact as the human brain.[79]

Courtesy, Radio Corporation of America
FIG. 18-71. "LOGIC" CIRCUIT FOR COMPUTERS *A solid-state element made from a single chip of silicon and containing 16 insulated-gate field-effect transistors, interconnected by evaporated metal paths, is here contrasted with a large mock-up model showing details of the circuit.*

Courtesy, Texas Instruments, Inc.
FIG. 18-70. SOLID CIRCUIT DIFFUSED SILICON NOR LOGIC NETWORK (BELOW) COMPARED WITH EQUIVALENT CONVENTIONAL PRINTED CIRCUIT UNIT

A two-year research effort sponsored jointly by RCA and the Air Force has prepared a solid-state element called an insulated-gate field-effect transistor (Fig. 18-71). A semiconductor device made from silicon, it can be made to switch, amplify, or otherwise regulate its output of electric current in a manner analogous to a pentode vacuum tube by varying the input voltage on the insulated gate. Arrays of up to 850 of these devices have been produced in an area the size of a dime. Experimental microcircuits being built from these arrays include electronic switches and counters for computers, amplifiers for military and commercial communications systems, and control networks for a variety of industrial and military applications.

18.17 *Printed-circuit and other micro-miniaturized semiconductors*

The process of micro-miniaturization has also been aided by the development of another innovation, the printed-circuit transistor. This new component was developed in 1957 by Lathrop and Nall of the Diamond Ordnance Fuze Laboratories of the Army Ordnance Corps. The transistor's protective case is discarded, and a tiny wafer of P-type germanium is made an integral part of a printed circuit.

The entire process of manufacturing the transistor is a rather complex one in which arsenic is diffused into the germanium, aluminum is evaporated on the surface of the germanium, and gold, antimony and silver are also employed. A similar process can be used to make semiconductor diodes. This manufacturing technique enables 200 transistors and associated components to be squeezed into the volume of 1 cu in., a volume formerly capable of holding only 20 ordinary transistors.[80 81 82 83]

In 1959, Pacific Semiconductors announced the commercial availability of micro-miniaturized silicon diodes. Neglecting the leads, the egg-shaped diodes were 0.080 in. long and 0.035 in. in diameter, occupying a volume that was only 2 per cent of that of the average sub-miniature diode. An idea of their size can be obtained from the fact that it is possible to pack 20 million of these diodes in 1 cu ft of space.

18.18 *Printed batteries*

Another interesting innovation in printed circuitry is the recent development of the printed battery for use in transistor circuits. The development has been briefly described in a preceding section of this book. An ink, consisting of iron suspended in an electrolyte, is deposited on a paper or plastic base. The ink is subjected to a powerful magnetic field which aligns the iron particles so that they contact each other. A second layer of ink, containing nickel in place of iron, is printed on top of the first and then magnetized. The iron and nickel act as plates of a simple cell. If desired, higher voltages can be obtained by printing additional alternate ink layers on top of the original ones. The first and last layers are provided with terminals for making connection to the rest of the circuit.[84]

18.19 *Tape resistors*

A major disadvantage of the earliest printed circuits was the difficulty of incorporating satisfactory resistors in these circuits. The usual method employed was to paint or spray resistive material directly on the base. This direct-coating method made it very difficult to produce individual resistors to close tolerances.

This difficulty was largely overcome by an adhesive-tape-resistor method developed, in connection with work on the previously described Project Tinkertoy, by Davis of the National Bureau of Standards. In this technique, a gap is left in the printed circuit at each point where a resistor is required. A self-adhesive resistor is then cut from a strip and pressed into position. This provides much better control of resistance values and provides higher yields of acceptable assemblies.[85]

Tape resistors are characterized by light weight and small size, making them extremely useful for miniaturization techniques. Since they may be applied easily by hand or machine, they facilitate fast and economical production and assembly by unskilled personnel. They have good resistance to shock and vibration, can withstand temperatures as high as 170°C, and are highly reliable.

The tape resistor consists of a mixture of carbon black or graphite resin and solvent applied in the form of spray to a thin roll of asbestos paper tape (Fig. 18-72). This tape, known as Quinterra, has a width of 0.13 in. A piece 0.5 in. in length cut from this tape and connected to the terminals of the printed circuit produces a resistor the effective length of which is 0.3 in. (Fig. 18-73).

The various values of resistance, ranging from 100 ohms to 10 megohms, are obtained by changing the ratio of carbon to resin in the resistance mixture. The proportion of carbon to resin is usually between 10 and 50 per cent. Another method of changing the resistance is by using different types of carbon. For values of resistance between 100 and 5,000 ohms, graphite mixtures are used. These mixtures are stable up to temperatures of 200°C. Above 5,000 ohms, it is necessary to employ carbon black, which is less stable at high tem-

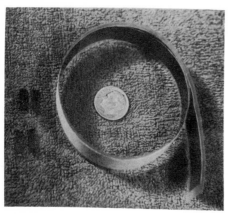

FIG. 18-72. RESISTANCE TAPE
Tape is produced in a roll, from which individual resistance elements can be cut to value and shape desired.

FIG. 18-73. EXAMPLES OF TAPE RESISTORS
Thermal time delay relay (left) using a tape resistor as the heating element: ceramic plate (right) having several resistors with leads attached.

peratures, being limited to temperatures not exceeding 170°C.

The resistor is manufactured by spraying the resistance mixture onto a moving belt of tape. A thin, easily removable polyethylene film is placed over the resistive coating for protection during storage and handling. Because of its suitability for high-temperature operation, silicone resin is used as the binder-adhesive.

After the resistors have been placed in their correct positions, the silicone resin is cured by heating the entire printed circuit. The heat causes the tape resistor to adhere to the terminals or to the ceramic plate in a firm and permanent bond. Because of the high temperature required for this curing process, the base of the printed circuit must be made of teflon glass or ceramic materials.[86] Research is currently being conducted on the problem of developing tape resistors that will cure at lower temperatures, thus permitting the use of plastic base materials.[87] Another important problem now under investigation is that of producing tape resistors within the 10- to 100-ohm range.

An additional discussion of the applications of modules, printed circuits, and tape resistors in the automatic production of electronic equipment will be found in a later chapter dealing with the topic of automation.

REFERENCES

1. Ken Purdy, "Make It Better, Lighter, Smaller." *Think,* 25:24-27, Feb. 1959.
2. Mel Mandell, "Miniaturization is Big!" *Electronics Illustrated,* 2:54, June 1959.
3. Sam Milbourne, "Miniaturization of Electronic Equipment," *Radio and Television News* (Engineering Edition), 44:10A, Dec. 1950.
4. M. Mandell, *Op. cit.,* p. 54.
5. *Miniaturization.* Standard Pressed Steel Co., Jenkintown, Pa., 1955, p.3.
6. Arthur H. Wulfsberg, "The Price of Reliability," *Collins Signal,* 7:9-10, No. 4, 1959.
7. "Miniaturization," *Design News,* 7:2, Apr. 1, 1957.
8. K. Purdy, *Op. cit.,* p. 27.
9. W. W. Hamilton, "Micro-Miniature Techniques," *Electronic Design,* 5:33, July 1, 1957
10. H. E. Marrows, "Marketing and Production Trends in the Semiconductor Industry," *Semiconductor Products,* 1:40, July 1958.

11. "Machine-Winding Coils Through the Needle's Eye," *Stanford Research Institute, Research for Industry*, 10:5, Mar. 1958.

12. "Fixed Capacitors in Transistor Circuits," *Aerovox Research Worker*, 29:1, July 1959.

13. Sam Kass, "On Tantalum Capacitors," *Semiconductor Products*, 1:39, May 1958.

14. "Automation and Miniaturization Highlight Electronics Convention," *Design News*, 10:10-11, Apr. 15, 1955.

15. Paul S. Darnell, "Miniaturized Component Design," *Radio and Television News*, (Engineering Edition), 48:11A, Sept. 1952.

16. *Mu Circuit*, Bull. AE-12, International Resistance Co., Phila., Pa., p. 1.

17. Henry A. Stone, Jr., "Component Development for Micro-Miniaturization," *Electronic Design*, 5:18, July 1, 1957.

18. "Micro-Modular Resistors," *Instrument and Apparatus News*, 7:15, July 1959.

19. "Sputtered Resistors May Permit High Component Density," *Design News*, 14:19, Sept. 14, 1959.

20. "Resistors Made on Glass with Sputtering Method," *Science NewsLetter*, Oct. 24, 1959.

21. "Microminiature Resistors," *Radio-Electronics*, 30:6, Oct. 1959.

22. "Redesign Miniaturized Loudspeaker," *Design News*, 10:8, Dec. 1, 1955.

23. "The Vanishing Hearing Aid," *Electronic Design*, 5:48-49, July 1, 1957.

24. "Miniature Hearing Aid," *Radio-Electronics*, 30:51, June 1959.

25. "Tiny Transistor-Amplifier," *Electronic Design*, 5:47, July 1, 1957.

26. K. Kilbon, "Miniaturization—The Big Trend Toward Smallness," *Radio-Age*, Apr. 1957.

27. K. Purdy, *Op. cit.*, pp. 24, 27.

28. "Look and Listen with a Sunglasses Radio," *Popular Electronics*, 11:48, Oct. 1959.

29. "News Transmitter for U.S. Satellite," *Radio and TV News*, 59:82, June 1958.

30. "Powerful Transmitter Uses Less Power," *Industrial Laboratories*, 9:28-29, June 1958.

31. "Satellite Transmitter," *Radio-Electronics*, 61:41, June 1959.

32. Arthur C. Ansley, *Value Analysis of Printed Circuits*, Arthur Ansley Manufacturing Co., New Hope, Pa., p.12.

33. Allan Lytel, "Printed Circuitry," *Military Automation*, 1:34, Jan. 1957.

34. John Diebold, *Automation*, D. Van Nostrand Co., N.Y., 1952, p. 38.

35. Eric Leslie, "IRE Stresses Human Side," *Radio-Electronics*, 30:46, June 1959.

36. John D. Cochrane, "The Age of Printed Circuitry," *Signal*, 13:47, Mar. 1959.

37. A. C. Ansley, *Op. cit.*, p. 12.

38. "Service Techs Report on Printed Boards," *Radio-Electronics*, 30:50, June 1959.

39. "Printed Boards; Roadblocks or Road Maps?," *Electronics World*, 62:50, Nov. 1959.

40. "Innovation in Plated Circuitry," *Electronics World*, 62:100, Oct. 1959.

41. "Printed-Circuitry Progress," *Radio-Electronics*, 30:91, June 1959.

42. Allan Lytel, "Printed Circuits Are Here to Stay," *Radio-Electronics*, 30:50-51, Nov. 1959.

43. A. C. Ansley, *Op. cit.*, p. 7.

44. *Ibid*, p. 8.

45. *Ibid*, p. 8.

46. *Printed Circuit Techniques*, NBS Circular 468, U.S. Government Printing Office, Washington, D.C., 1947, pp. 1-28.

47. Allan Lytel, "Printed Circuitry—Part 4," *Military Automation*, 1:213, July 1957.

48. E. D. Olson, "Fine Line Etched Wiring," *Electronic Design*, 7:38-41, Feb. 4, 1959.

49. Allan Lytel, "Printed Circuitry—Part 2," *Military Automation*, 1:84, Mar. 1957.

50. *New Advances in Printed Circuits*, NBS Mis. Pub. 192, U.S. Government Printing Office, Washington, D.C., 1948, pp. 1-5.

51. "Printed Circuit Primer," *Electronics Illustrated*, 2:29-32, Oct, 1959.

52. Lawrence P. Lessing, "Automatic Manufacture of Electronic Equipment," *Scientific American*, 193:29-30, Aug. 1955.

53. *Modulized Standard Circuits*, Aerovox Corp., New Bedford, Mass., p. 2.

54. Ralph W. Hallows, "Robot Makes Radio," *Radio Craft*, 18:20, Sept. 1947.

55. L. P. Lessing, *Op. cit.*, p. 29

56. Fred Shunaman, "Now—A Modular TV Receiver," *Radio-Electronics*, 27:37, June 1956.

57. W. H. Klippel and E. J. Lorenz, "Repairing Printed Wiring," *Radio and Television News*, 55:50, June 1956.

58. Allan Lytel, "Printed Circuits Come of Age," *Popular Electronics*, 7:49-50, Dec. 1957.

59. "New Compact Transistor Circuits," *Stanford Research Institute Research for Industry*, 11:14, July 1959.

60. "Modularized Sets Now Available," *Radio and Television News*, 56:40-41, 173, Oct. 1956.

61. M. Mandell, *Op. cit.*, p. 98.

62. T. A. Prugh and others, "The DOFL Microelectronics Program," *Proc. IRE*, 47:882, May 1959.

63. Lou Garner, "Transistor Topics," *Popular Electronics*, 11:122, July 1959.

64. "Miniature, Sub-miniature, Micro-miniature," *Signal*, 13:12-13, Mar. 1959.

65. W. Walter Watts, "Tools of the Space Age," *Signal*, 13:32, Mar. 1959.

66. "Micro-Miniature Electronic Parts," *Science Digest*, 44:92, Aug. 1958.

67. "Little Giants of Electronics," *Electronic Age*, 18:3, Spring 1959.

68. T. E. Gootee, "Micro-Modules—The Ultimate in Miniaturization," *Radio and TV News*, 60:48, Sept. 1958.

69. "New Shapes of Things to Come," *Electronic Age*, 18:10, Summer 1959.

70. "Nuvistors and Micro-Modules," *Popular Electronics*, 10:56, June 1959.

71. "Modular Circuits," *Radio-Electronics*, 30:54, Aug. 1959.

72. "Ceramic Stacked Module for Space Electronics," *Electronics World*, 62:47, Aug. 1959.

73. *TIMMS Thermionic Integrated Micro-Modules*, ETD-2052, General Electric Co., Schenectady, N.Y., 1959, pp. 1-14.

74. J. E. Beggs and others, *Thermionic Integrated Micromodules*, ETD-2044, General Electric Co., Schenectady, N.Y., 1959, pp. 1-2.
75. "What's New with Transistors?," *Electronics Illustrated*, 2:93, Aug. 1959.
76. "Breakthrough in Molecular Electronics Revealed by Air Force," *Electronics World*, 62:28. Aug. 1959.
77. *Semiconductor Solid Circuits*, Texas Instruments. Inc., Dallas, Tex., pp. 1-7.
78. L. Garner, *Op. cit.*, p. 123.
79. "New Shapes of Things to Come," *Op. cit.*, p. 10.
80. "New Method Produces Printed Circuit Transistors," *Design News*, 12:4, Dec. 15, 1957.
81. "Develop Printed Transistor," *Science Digest*. 43:92, Feb. 1958.

82. Louis E. Garner, Jr., "A Radio on Your Thumbnail," *Popular Electronics*, 8:55-56, June 1958.
83. "Army Develops Printed Transistors," *Control Engineering*, 5:31, Feb. 1958.
84. John Bjorksten, "Printed Battery," *Radio-Electronics*, 26:142, Mar. 1955.
85. *Printed Circuit Techniques: An Adhesive Tape-Resistor System*, NBS Circular 530, U. S. Government Printing Office, Washington, D.C., 1952, p. 1.
86. *Ibid*, p. 54.
87. "High-Temperature Adhesive Tape Resistor," *Radio and Television News*, (Engineering Edition), 47:14, Jan. 1952.

19 - MAGNETIC AMPLIFIERS, DIELECTRIC AMPLIFIERS, AND RELATED SOLID-STATE AMPLIFIERS

19.1 *Characteristics of the magnetic amplifier*

Another electronic device that is beginning to replace the thermionic tube in numerous special applications is the magnetic amplifier. This device is also known as an amplistat, transductor, or direct-current transformer. The magnetic amplifier consists of a saturable reactor plus a metallic-rectifier stack. It may be technically described as a variable-inductance device that controls the flow of power to a load and the operation of which depends upon the non-linear magnetization of ferromagnetic substances. It may also be defined as "a device which utilizes the saturation of a magnetic core for the purpose of securing amplification of electrical signals or control of electrical devices."[1]

A simple half-wave magnetic amplifier contains only the following four basic components:

1. A saturable iron-core reactor of low resistance and high inductance.

2. A rectifier.

3. A load resistance in series with a supply voltage. These are connected across the terminals of the reactor.

4. A signal winding which is in series with a source of variable d-c voltage and which is used to control the flow of current through the saturable reactor.[2]

19.2 *History of the magnetic amplifier*

The magnetic amplifier is not a new device. As early as 1885, American engineers employed saturable-core equipment for the control of electrical machinery. In 1901, C. F. Burgess and B. Frankenfeld developed a magnetic-amplifier device that was used for the control and distribution of industrial power. In 1916, Ernest F. W. Alexanderson of General Electric employed magnetic-amplifier principles for modulating a 72-kilowatt radio transmitter employed for trans-Atlantic communications.[3]

Some people may recall a Majestic radio receiver, manufactured during the late 1920's which indicated by the dimming of a dial light when the receiver had been correctly tuned so that it resonated with the incoming signal. This Colorama indicator circuit employed a type of magnetic amplifier in which the decrease of the plate current in the r-f and i-f amplifier circuits, which was produced at resonance by the action of the automatic-volume-control circuit, was used to increase the inductance of a saturable inductor which was connected in series with these amplifier circuits. When the inductance of this coil was increased, it offered more opposition to the flow of current, and this action produced the dimming of an indicator lamp that was connected in series with another winding of this inductor. The magnetic-amplifier principle was also employed in other power-control applications, such as in electric furnaces and the control of theatrical lighting.

Despite this early start, the magnetic amplifier was set aside in favor of its electronic counterpart and was practically forgotten until World War II. This neglect was due in large part to the fact that core materials possessing the desired magnetic properties were not available, and metallic rectifiers did not have the required degree of efficiency and reliability.[4]

The Germans are generally considered responsible for the rebirth of the magnetic amplifier. During World War II, the Nazis assigned their best scientists and expended millions of dollars to produce better magnetic amplifiers by developing better magnetic materials and producing superior selenium rectifiers with extremely-high forward-to-reverse current ratios. The German scientists eventually developed a magnetic amplifier with improved efficiency and response time, reduced weight and bulk, and a broadened field of application. By the time World War II ended, the Germans were using magnetic amplifiers in gun stabilizers, fire-control equipment, automatic pilots, ground-approach systems, and the control systems, of the V-2 and other long-range rockets and guided missiles. These devices were also used as cathode followers, replacing electron tubes in computer circuits. German engineers quickly began to apply this device to the control of high-voltage power lines, streetcar controls, and electric brakes for locomotives and trucks.

Since these developments occurred at a time when there was no shortage of electron tubes in Germany, it is prob-able that the main reason for this enormous expenditure of talent and money was an acute shortage of electronic technical personnel. This shortage made mandatory the development of dependable, maintenance-free devices.[5] Even ruggedized electron tubes have limitations because of their inherent fragility and their tendency to wear out after a relatively short period of time. This factor is particularly important in the maintenance of complex electronic equipment that sometimes contains hundreds of tubes, since investigations have revealed that the great majority of electronic-equipment failures are caused by tube failures. Since tubes were the weakest link, it appeared logical to replace them by devices that did not wear out so rapidly and could be installed and subsequently forgotten because their service requirements were negligible.[6] However, the war ended before many of these magnetic-amplifier systems could be put into service, and the Germans failed to reap full benefit from this idea.

19.3 *Saturable reactors*

A saturable reactor is basically an electromagnetic device that functions as a variable inductance (Fig. 19-1). It usually possesses the same general type of physical construction as a transformer. The core usually consists of thin laminations of a material such as silicon steel, permalloy, mu-metal, or Hipernik V, which is a 50-50 iron-nickel alloy. The shape of this core may be either rectangular or circular (toroidal).

The term *saturation* is associated with the core material. It refers to the point of maximum magnetization of the core, in which any further increases in the magnetizing force have no appreciable effect in increasing the flux density (Fig. 19-2).

FIG. 19-1. TYPICAL SATURABLE-CORE REACTOR

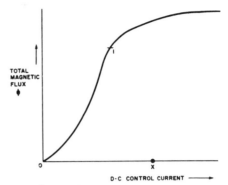

FIG. 19-2. MAGNETIZATION CURVE OF A REACTOR CORE

19.4 *Operation of a simple magnetic amplifier*

As shown in Fig. 19-3, the saturable reactor of a magnetic-amplifier circuit usually contains one or more d-c or control windings, N_c. The d-c winding contains many turns of wire and is used to control the load. There are also one or more a-c or load windings, N_L, which are connected in series with the load L, and to a source of alternating current. Thus, a pair of d-c and a-c windings resembles the primary and secondary windings of a transformer in that there is no direct connection between the two coils. They are linked only by the magnetic properties of the core on which they are wound.

As was previously stated, this core contains a special type of easily saturated material. The permeability of the core varies inversely with the strength of the applied magnetizing force. Consequently, when the amount of direct current flowing through the d-c control winding is zero, the permeability will be very high. Since the inductance of a coil is directly proportional to the permeability of its core, the inductance and the inductive reactance of the a-c coil will be very large. Since the a-c coil is in series with the load, the load current will be reduced to a low value.

When the amount of current

through the d-c coil is increased, the permeability of the core will decrease. This decreases the inductance and the inductive reactance of the a-c coil, causing the load current to increase. If the amount of direct current flowing through the d-c coil is increased until the core is saturated, there is practically no inductive reactance, and the amount of current flowing in the load circuit can become very high.

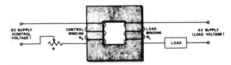

FIG. 19-3. FUNDAMENTAL SATURABLE-REACTOR CIRCUIT

If the amount of direct current is kept slightly below this saturation point, small changes in the amount of direct current can produce large changes in the amount of alternating current flowing through the load.[7] Thus, a small amount of direct current and a low-wattage potentiometer may control a current of several hundred amperes. Application has been made of this principle in the design and operation of certain types of battery chargers, theatre-light dimming systems, and electric-furnace heating controls.[8]

Since the amount of d-c energy required to control the load is less than the amount of a-c energy used to operate the load circuit, this device produces a certain amount of gain or amplification. The gain is equal to the ratio of the change in a-c output power to the change in d-c input control power.[9] Modern magnetic amplifiers can now be designed that produce power gains between ten thousand and ten million, with a signal input that is as low as 0.001 microwatts.

The coils of the saturable-core amplifier are usually wound around a shell-type or three-legged transformer core. The d-c winding is placed on the center leg, while the two outer legs hold the output a-c windings, which are wound oppositely. The opposite winding of the a-c coils cancels out any voltages that might be induced in the d-c winding. Thus, the d-c control winding can control the current in the a-c windings, while the alternating load current has no influence upon the control winding. A diagram of this type of arrangement is shown in Fig. 19-4.

19.5 *Special types of magnetic amplifiers*

Some magnetic-amplifier circuits do not contain two a-c winding coils. and others contain two coils connected in parallel rather than in series. When more than one coil is used in the input circuit, it is possible to amplify the resultant of two input voltages—an operation which is difficult to perform with conventional electronic amplifiers.[10] This permits the device to be employed in applications such as totalizing and recording on one instrument the current flowing in several independent circuits.

19.6 *Improved magnetic-amplifier circuits*

The saturable-reactor amplifier circuit shown in Fig. 19-4 may be converted into a basic and simple form of self-saturating magnetic amplifier by placing a rectifier in series with the load, as shown in Fig. 19-5. This produces a unidirectional load current which assists the control winding in producing saturation. Consequently, considerably less control power is required.

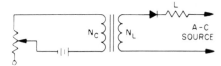

FIG. 19-5. SIMPLE SELF-SATURATING MAGNETIC AMPLIFIER CIRCUIT

While the circuit just described produces high gain, it still possesses certain defects. The single rectifier delivers an inefficient pulsating direct current to the load. There is also considerable loss of energy resulting from the tendency of the a-c load coil to induce voltages across the d-c control coil.

A circuit that is designed to

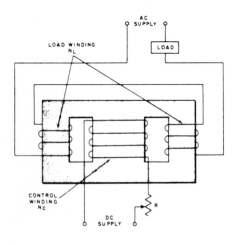

FIG. 19-4. SATURABLE-REACTOR CIRCUIT USING A THREE-LEGGED CORE

eliminate these disadvantages is shown in Fig. 19-6. The two load coils, N_{L_1} and N_{L_2} are wound in an opposed manner on the outside legs of a three-legged core, and the control coil is wound on the center leg. This tends to neutralize any transformer action on the control coil. The efficiency is increased through the utilization of both halves of the alternating-current cycle. If it is desired to control a d-c load, this can be accomplished by the addition of two more rectifiers, as shown in Fig. 19-7.

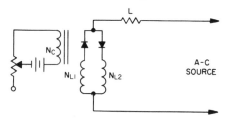

FIG. 19-6. SELF-SATURATING MAGNETIC AMPLIFIER FOR AN A-C LOAD

An additional development is the adding of an external feedback coil, N_{L_3}, which enables gains up to 10 million per stage to be obtained. Typical feedback circuits for both a-c and d-c loads are shown in Figs. 19-8 and 19-9. Negative feedback is also occasionally employed in order to improve linearity of response.

In one type of feedback circuit employed in power supplies, as a load in-

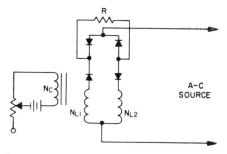

FIG. 19-7. SELF-SATURATING MAGNETIC AMPLIFIER FOR A D-C LOAD

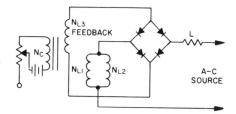

FIG. 19-8. MAGNETIC AMPLIFIER WITH FEEDBACK—A-C LOAD

crease tends to cause a drop in the voltage across the load, this change in output voltage is fed back to the control winding in such a manner as to increase the saturation of the core. This decreases the reactance of the load winding, permitting more current to flow and enabling the load voltage to increase once again to its normal value.

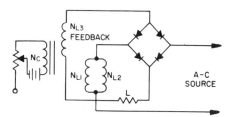

FIG. 19-9. MAGNETIC AMPLIFIER WITH FEEDBACK—D-C LOAD

19.7 Audio-frequency magnetic amplifiers

The curve representing the relationship between magnetic saturation and impedance of a magnetic amplifier closely resembles the Ip-Eg curve of an electronic amplifier. This indicates that the operating conditions of both are quite similar and that it is possible to design magnetic amplifiers to amplify audio-frequency signals with a reasonably high degree of fidelity (Fig. 19-10).

The parts of an audio-frequency magnetic-amplifier circuit are analogous to the parts of a vacuum-tube amplifier circuit. The control current cor-

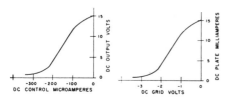

FIG. 19-10. COMPARISON BETWEEN CHARACTER-
ISTICS OF MAGNETIC AMPLIFIER (LEFT) AND
VACUUM-TUBE AMPLIFIER (RIGHT)

responds to the control-grid voltage,
the carrier current corresponds to the
plate current, and the carrier supply
corresponds to the B plus supply.

Practical audio-frequency magnetic amplifiers are usually operated
push-pull Class AB. This type of circuit
produces greater efficiency, smooths
out the rectified output pulses, and
tends to cancel out the high power-
supply carrier frequency. A single-
stage amplifier of this type is capable of
producing gains up to several thousands,
while 2-stage amplifiers with extremely high stability characteristics have
been developed whose power gains are
in the neighborhood of 10 billion.
Audio amplifiers have been constructed
that contain several such stages connected in series and that produce power

outputs up to 500 watts with excellent
linearity up to 7,000 cps.

19.8 *General applications of magnetic amplifiers*

One of the most common applications of the magnetic amplifier is in the
field of regulation and control of the
voltage, current, and frequency of industrial power installations, theatre-
dimming systems, and aircraft generating equipment (Fig. 19-11). Another
industrial application employs magnetic
amplifiers for regulating and controlling
the speed of motors and for keeping
groups of motors in step with each other.

Thus, a magnetic amplifier can
make use of feedback principles to
measure the speed of a series-wound
motor. Whenever a change in the load
or in the line voltage is likely to produce
a change in speed, the magnetic amplifier senses the change in armature
current and voltage drop and applies a
compensating correction voltage (Fig.
19-12). Magnetic amplifiers are employed
for this purpose in the pickling and
cleaning operations of the steel industry,

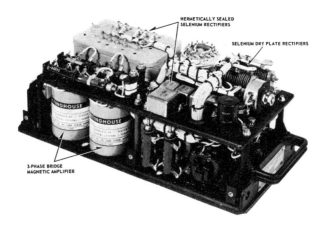

Courtesy, Westinghouse Electric Corp.

FIG. 19-11. MAGNETIC AMPLIFIER VOLTAGE REGULATOR USED IN AIRCRAFT A-C GENERATOR

in newsprint presses, and in diesel-electric locomotives.

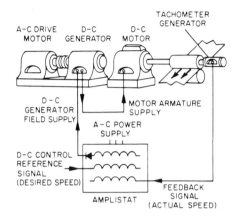

A-C DRIVE MOTOR · D-C GENERATOR · D-C MOTOR · TACHOMETER GENERATOR

D-C GENERATOR FIELD SUPPLY · MOTOR ARMATURE SUPPLY · A-C POWER SUPPLY

D-C CONTROL REFERENCE SIGNAL (DESIRED SPEED)

AMPLISTAT · FEEDBACK SIGNAL (ACTUAL SPEED)

Courtesy, General Electric Co.

Fig. 19-12. Magnetic amplifier or amplistat —motor-control system

A d-c signal applied to one or more control windings varies the magnetic permeability—and thus the impedance to the flow of a-c through an output winding—to produce an amplifying action. Metallic rectifiers usually convert output to d-c. In this system the regulated quantity (actual speed) is compared with the input quantity (desired speed), and the difference is amplified to maintain an accurate match between the two.

Magnetic amplifiers are also being employed in low-level d-c applications, such as operating motors, controllers and relays directly from thermocouples, ionization chambers, and photocells. They function as excellent d-c amplifiers with extremely-high gain and are not subject to the drift difficulties frequently encountered with electronic d-c amplifiers. Because of their flip-flop characteristics, they can also be substituted for mechanical relays and for electronic multivibrators and square-wave generators.

Many types of servo systems now employ magnetic amplifiers in place of electronic amplifiers. Examples of devices of this type that are now em-

ploying magnetic amplifiers are ship-steering servos, aircraft gas-turbine controls, automatic pilots, guided-missile controls, azimuth and elevation controls for radar and artillery, and electric computers. Other important applications of magnetic amplifiers are in arc-welding controls, ignitron-firing controls, and automatic battery-charger controls. Magnetic amplifiers, used in combination with transistors, are replacing thermionic and mechanical devices in many types of automatic-control systems.

Other recent applications. One radio-manufacturing firm has recently constructed for demonstration and publicity purposes a completely tubeless superheterodyne radio receiver employing magnetic amplifiers for the r-f, i-f, and a-f amplifier stages. A transistor was used for the oscillator stage and a crystal for the detector stage. A magnetic converter was used to supply the high-frequency carrier current for the a-c windings.

Another interesting development is a new loran receiver-indicator that is completely actuated by magnetic amplifiers except for the scope and oscillator tubes. This design reduces the number of tubes required from 32 to 2—one of which is a cathode-ray picture tube.[11]

Still another recent application is a device called the fluxgate magnetometer that is used to measure the strength of weak magnetic fields. An a-c input is applied to the control winding. The core is saturated twice during each cycle. When the core becomes unsaturated, the weak magnetic field that is being measured cuts the output winding. This produces a new a-c signal with a frequency twice that of the applied a-c signal and a magnitude proportional to the strength of the magnetic field being measured.

19.9 *Advantages and disadvantages of the magnetic amplifier*

The outstanding advantage of the magnetic amplifier is the absence of moving parts and of delicate heated filaments. The entire unit requires little more maintenance than does a transformer. Since it also requires little ventilation, it can be hermetically sealed for protection from moisture and fungus, and for high-altitude applications. These hermetically sealed units can also be operated near combustible materials with less danger of producing fires from sparks and arcs than is true of corresponding electronic and electromechanical units. Furthermore, the elimination of the need for a high-voltage power supply is an advantage with respect to the safety of the personnel involved in the operation and maintenance of the magnetic-amplifier devices.

The operating life of a magnetic amplifier is generally governed by the type of rectifier that it employs. Modern dry-disc rectifiers are now rated at 60,000 hours of operation, which is many times greater than the life expectancy of an average electron tube. In general, magnetic amplifiers are rugged and long-lived, even when subjected to high shock, vibration, and overloading. For example, the log book of the German cruiser "Prinz Eugen" reveals that not one of the various magnetic amplifiers employed on that ship for gun stabilizers and servos required servicing during a period of 10 years.

Since there is no cathode to be heated, the efficiency of a magnetic amplifier is generally higher than that of an electron-tube amplifier. Furthermore the magnetic amplifier operates almost immediately after power is applied, and no warm-up time is required. This means that fire-control units do not have to be kept continuously energized for instant use. The absence of a cathode and its accompanying filament supply also means that power-supply voltage fluctuations, which affect cathode emission, have little effect upon the operating characteristics of a magnetic amplifier.

Magnetic amplifiers can be cascaded to produce almost any desired amount of power gain. They can also be used where electronic amplifiers are unsuitable, such as applications where the input and output circuits must be electrically isolated from each other, or where the output must be proportional to the algebraic sum of several input signals. In this respect, as has been previously mentioned, they provide a simple means of combining or mixing signals that is difficult or impossible to obtain with electron tubes.

Where weight and size factors are of prime importance, magnetic amplifiers are inferior to electronic amplifiers if the available power supply has a frequency of 60 cps. On the other hand, when the frequency of the power supply is 400 cps or higher, it is possible to make the magnetic amplifier even smaller than the electronic amplifier.

The outstanding disadvantage of the magnetic amplifier is that its inductive circuits cause its time constant to be long compared with that of an electronic amplifier. The theoretical minimum time delay occuring between a change in the signal in the control circuit and the corresponding change produced in the load circuit is one-half cycle of the a-c supply frequency. Unfortunately, as the amount of amplification is increased, the amount of delay is increased proportionately and in some instances the delay may be as great as several hundred cycles.

When a low-frequency power supply is used, the speed of response is relatively slow compared with that of an electronic amplifier. When this frequency is 60 cps, the time delay may be as great as 0.1 seconds. As the frequency of the power supply is raised, the speed of response of the magnetic amplifier is increased proportionately.[12] For high-performance systems, the frequency of the power supply should be 2,000 cps or higher.

Current production units have a lag of one cycle of exciting frequency. However, with high-frequency power sources and modern materials it is now possible to obtain time constants, measured in microseconds, that are comparable with those of electron-tube circuits. For example, if the frequency of the excitation source is 3 mc, the upper frequency limit is raised to 500 kc, and the time constant is approximately 1 microsecond.

Another disadvantage results from the distortion produced in the output waveshape. This is accompanied by the generation of harmonic frequencies that produce interference with the operation of nearby equipment.

In addition, the operation of the magnetic amplifier is limited to the temperature range between $-50°$C and $100°$C. Outside this range, there is an undesirable change in the magnetic properties of the core material and in the characteristics of the dry-disc rectifiers that are associated with the magnetic amplifier.

Finally, the input impedance of the magnetic amplifier is generally of such a value that it is difficult to match it to the stage that is driving it. This necessitates the use of impedance-matching systems.

In order to reduce the effects of these disadvantageous characteristics, magnetic amplifiers are often employed in combination with electron-tube and transistor circuits. In such applications, the latter are used to provide voltage amplification in the early stages, while the magnetic amplifier is employed in the final power-output stage.[13]

19.10 *Problems associated with the power supply*

The acceptance of the audio-frequency magnetic amplifier has been held back by the necessity for using a power-supply frequency for the a-c winding that is inaudible and several times higher than the frequency of the highest frequency signal that is to be amplified. Obviously, if electron-tube circuits are used to generate these supply frequencies, the advantages associated with the employment of magnetic amplifiers are cancelled out.

There have recently been developed special types of magnetic converters that are designed to multiply the frequency of the voltage supplied by the power line until this frequency reaches the required value. As a result, there is now available an airborne, audio-frequency, magnetic amplifier designed for intercommunication purposes. It is powered by a 10-kc source, which makes use of magnetic frequency-multiplier equipment to obtain this energy from the aircraft's 1-kc power source.

It is now readily apparent that here is one of the serious weaknesses of the magnetic amplifier. In circuits involving high gain and short time constants, the excitation frequency should be as high as possible, preferably in the neighborhood of 15 to 20 kc. However, these frequencies complicate the power-supply problem and often cause a sharp drop in performance due to capacitive effects and the deterioration of core properties [14]

19.11 *Additional considerations*

The power-handling capacity of the magnetic amplifier is limited primarily by the size of the rectifiers employed. Otherwise, there is no theoretical upper limit to the power-handling capacity of a magnetic amplifier. There is also no lower limit of amplification; magnetic amplifiers are capable of amplifying signals that are too weak to penetrate the emission shot noises of a vacuum tube.

With respect to the factor of cost, magnetic amplifiers are, at present, more expensive than competing electronic amplifiers. However, once mass production is established, magnetic amplifiers will probably compete in cost not only with electronic amplifiers but also with cheaper electromechanical devices such as relays, rheostats, circuit breakers, and synchros.[15]

An additional disadvantage is the fact that the upper frequency limit of the ordinary magnetic amplifier is about 1 mc. This limit is produced by core eddy-current and winding effects. However, it may be pointed out that CGS Laboratories has recently made available a special high-frequency saturable reactor called the Increductor that is able to maintain a useful Q (figure of merit) and to operate at frequencies as high as 400 mc.[16]

Another serious problem is posed by the limited predictability of the performance of the cores of magnetic amplifiers. The differences in the magnetic properties of cores derived from different heats, or sometimes even from the same heat, are frequently appreciable when the magnetic amplifier is used for a critical application, such as a low-level amplifier.

Also considered disadvantageous is the fact that the input impedance of the magnetic amplifier cannot be increased to infinity or decreased to zero. In contrast with the electron tube, the magnetic amplifier is essentially a low-impedance device with respect to both its input and output circuits. For this reason, it is usually used for power amplification rather than for voltage gain. However, magnetic amplifiers have been designed with inputs varying from a fraction of an ohm to more than 1 megohm.

A final consideration is the fact, which is not always necessarily disadvantageous, that the magnetic amplifier circuit must always operate from an a-c power source.

19.12 *The magnistor*

Newly designed magnetic-circuit elements, such as the magnistor, are capable of amplifying signal frequencies as high as 1 mc. These magnistors also possess permanent-memory characteristics which make them particularly useful in computers, data-handling systems, automation control systems, and high-speed counters (Fig. 19-13).[17]

Courtesy, Potter Instrument Co., Inc.
FIG. 19-13. A MAGNISTOR

The magnistor differs from the conventional magnetic amplifier chiefly in its smaller size and in its use of a 10-mc carrier frequency in place of the

60 or 400-cps carrier frequency used by the ordinary magnetic amplifier.[18] Magnistors may be used in combinations to perform complex logic functions with relatively simple circuits. In certain instances, two magnistors may be used to perform functions normally requiring as many as six vacuum tubes.

There are two types of magnistors, a relatively simple transient magnistor and a more complex permanent magnistor (Fig. 19-14). In the transient magnistor, the r-f current can be varied by changing the control current, while in the permanent magnistor, a magnetic circuit of high retentivity can be "permanently" magnetized or demagnetized at will by set and reset windings, thus producing an on-off control element. It is also possible to combine the transient and permanent magnistors in one unit, known as an integrated magnistor. It then becomes a computer device which can store digital information, which can be interrogated repeatedly by another source, and which can be

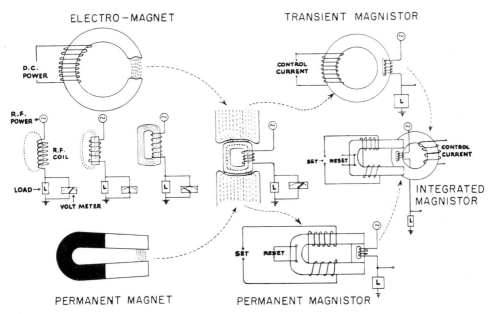

Courtesy, Potter Instrument Co., Inc.

Fig. 19-14. Evolution of the Magnistor

Evolution of the magnistor can best be approached by examining the three coil diagrams at the left. The air-core RF coil, in conjunction with a suitable load, causes the meter to register large voltage; in other words, the RF coil presents a low drop to the flow of RF current. When a slug core is inserted, increasing the number of flux lines, the indicator shows a midway position. Increasing the inductance of the coil removes some of the RF voltage from the load, and completely enclosing the core with a toroid creates a maximum of flux for a given number of ampere turns and a given ferrite structure. The toroid maximizes the absorption of power supply voltage, and the meter shows a minimum voltage. The maximum and minimum states are made use of in data processing applications concerned with off and on, zero and one, yes and no. The center diagram shows the elementary structure placed between the poles of either a permanent magnet or an electromagnet. These magnets externally create the maximum and minimum states by overcoming the coerciveness of the circulating flux resulting from the coil and reduce the inductance of the coil to that of an air-core state. This mode of operation forms the basis of either a transient magnistor or a permanent magnistor. The two together form the integrated magnistor, which combines the advantage of a magnetic circuit with that of an electrical circuit.

reset instantly at will.[19]

The transient magnistor consists of a thin ferroceramic wafer with a hole in its center. The control coil passes through this hole and is wound around the main body of the core. There is also a small hole in the outer ring of the core. The signal coil is wound through the smaller hole and is connected in series with both the load and the high-frequency signal source. As the current increases through the control coil, the flux density in the main body of the coil increases. This decreases the effective impedance of the signal coil, and the amount of high-frequency current through the load increases. Thus, variations of input current in the control circuit create corresponding proportional changes in the load current, and power gains as high as 35 db may be obtained. Since the high-frequency flux is confined to the flux material surrounding the small signal-coil hole, the input or control coil is unaffected by the high-frequency source.[20]

19.13 *The ferristor*

The ferristor is a trade name for a sub-miniature saturable reactor manufactured by the Berkeley Division of Beckman Instruments (Fig. 19-15). It consists of two windings of fine wire around a tiny core, which is then potted or encased in a half-inch cube of epoxy resin. The inner, carrier-current winding has a few hundred turns, while the outer, control winding contains between 1,000 and 4,000 turns. The core contains magnetic sheet metal with a thickness only slightly greater than 0.0001 in. The resulting unit is a component which can be employed as a very reliable magnetic amplifier.[21] The ferractor is a similar type of device manufactured by the Sperry Rand Corporation (Figs. 19-16 and 19-17).

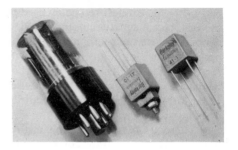

Courtesy, Berkeley Div., Beckman Instruments, Inc.
FIG. 19-15. COMPARISON BETWEEN TWO TYPICAL FERRISTORS AND A VACUUM TUBE

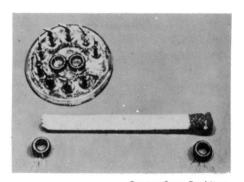

Courtesy, Sperry Rand Corp.
FIG. 19-16. TWO FERRACTOR MAGNETIC AMPLIFIERS
Each ferractor can do the work of a vacuum tube.

Courtesy, Sperry Rand Corp.
FIG. 19-17. USE OF FERRACTORS IN PRINTED CIRCUIT BOARD
Each pill box houses units similar to the one in the man's fingers, with two tiny ferractor amplifiers at the center of each pillbox.

Devices of this type function in the same manner as a conventional magnetic amplifier, current in one winding controlling the reactance of the other winding. If a carrier current is flowing in this second winding, it is modulated linearly in response to the changes in the small controlling current. This produces an amplified reproduction of the controlling current. Amplification results because the carrier-current variations are much greater than the control-current changes. The amplified input waveform may be recovered by rectifying the output and filtering out the r-f carrier. By introducing feedback circuits, this amplifier may be modified to produce oscillations and to serve as a multivibrator.[22] The core is designed so that carrier frequencies up to 10 mc are possible. This gives this magnetic amplifier the rapid response that is required for many specialized applications, such as electronic instrumentation.

If a capacitor is placed in series with the second winding and with the source of r-f energy, a ferroresonant circuit is produced. The capacitor resonates with the carrier coil at a frequency that is close to that of the applied radio-frequency current. This circuit possesses two stable states. In one state, the core is saturated, and in the other state, it is unsaturated. A suitable trigger-pulse input signal can produce the transition from one state to the other. This bistable flip-flop action can be utilized in computer and industrial pulse-counting circuits.[23]

19.14 *Cypak*

Communications experts have discovered that any combination of definite conditions or arrangements used for processing information can be described in terms of only four logic functions called AND, OR, NOT, and MEMORY.

Relays may be used to perform these functions in computers and control systems. The AND function can be accomplished by placing relay contacts in series with one another so that an output occurs only when all inputs are received. The OR function is produced by connecting relay contacts in parallel with one another. An output occurs when any input is produced. The NOT function is produced by a normally closed relay contact. An output occurs only when there is no input. Finally, the MEMORY function is accomplished by means of a latched-in relay. Output occurs after the first input and continues until the second input.[24]

Cypak is the name given to a magnetic-amplifier circuit developed by Westinghouse scientists to perform the logic functions previously performed by relays (Fig. 19-18). It obtains its name from the word "cybernetics," which in turn is based on a Greek term that is related to steering and control. The "pak" portion of the name is derived from the English word "package."

The Cypak circuit contains magnetic amplifiers, resistors, and selenium or silicon diodes (Fig. 19-19). The magnetic amplifier consists of two coils

Courtesy, Westinghouse Electric Corp.
FIG. 19-18. MARK II CYPAK CONTROL MODULE FOR A COMPUTER

Courtesy, Westinghouse Electric Corp.
FIG. 19-19. CONTENTS OF ORIGINAL CYPAK MODULE
Hand-wired and stud-mounted on an insulating board, first Cypak control element used soldered connections.

wound around a core of Hipernık V grain-oriented magnetic steel. This core provides a very sharp hysteresis loop for fast response (Fig. 19-20). The square-loop characteristics of the resulting B-H curve produce a positive, on-off switching action closely approximating the action of a relay. Either the toroidal core is unsaturated and will pass no

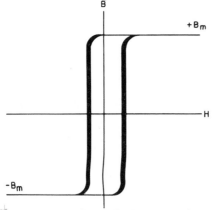

Courtesy, Westinghouse Electric Corp.
FIG. 19-20. HIPERNIK V HYSTERESIS LOOP
Cypak's core of Hipernik V grain-oriented magnetic steel provides a very sharp hysteresis loop.

signal, or else it is saturated to the point where a signal will be passed.

Unlike relays, Cypak possesses the advantage of having no moving parts, contacts, springs, or other elements subject to wear or corrosion. Consequently, a Cypak element has an estimated life of billions of open-close cycles. This life is 10 to 15 times greater than that of a conventional relay.[25]

Cypak is expected to find its greatest application in industrial control systems where a considerable amount of electrical sequencing and interlocking is involved. The high reliability it provides brings promise of integrated process and machine operations vastly superior to and more extensive than anything now known in industry. Among the industries in which Cypak has been applied are the automotive, chemical, food, lumber, machine-tool, plastic, printing, rubber, and steel industries.[26]

19.15 *The hybrid magnetic amplifier*

In a preceding section of this chapter the point was made that although the magnetic amplifier possesses the virtue of reliability, it cannot compare with the vacuum-tube amplifier in stage gain, bandwidth, and high input impedance. This often makes it necessary for the control engineer to choose between the better performance of electron-tube circuits and the greater reliability of magnetic-amplifier circuits. It was this dilemma that led to the development of the hybrid magnetic amplifier. This circuit contains a magnetic-amplifier output stage that is driven by a high-gain amplifier containing premium tubes. These tubes, similar to those used in submarine repeater telephone cables, possess life expectancies that are measured in tens of years. The tubes are used in low-level, low-plate-dissipation amplifier stages, where the rise in temperature is very low. Thus, a typical five-tube electronic servo amplifier, consisting of one rectifier, two voltage amplifier tubes and two power-amplifier tubes, could be replaced by its hybrid equivalent containing a single low-level amplifier tube plus a magnetic-amplifier stage. The reliability of this hybrid combination is greater by several orders of magnitude than that of the all-tube circuit.

Consequently the hybrid amplifier that is currently available functions as a control amplifier with characteristics superior to those obtainable by means of any single circuit method. It combines the versatility and stability of the vacuum tube with the efficiency and power-handling capacity of the magnetic amplifier, resulting in over-all power efficiency, reasonably good stability, high gain, and small size and weight. In many instances, the hybrid circuit emerges not just as a replacement for a vacuum-tube amplifier but as a means of achieving a degree of performance and miniaturization hitherto impossible. Miniaturization makes this amplifier extremely important in airborne applications.[27]

19.16 *The status of the magnetic amplifier*

The magnetic-amplifier market, which started from scratch shortly after World War II, reached an estimated level of 100 million dollars annually by 1957. By 1959, the rapidly expanding American magnetic-amplifier industry had achieved an annual sales volume of 125 million dollars, which was divided among 150 manufacturers. At that time, it was predicted that the annual volume of sales would approach the 2-billion

dollar mark before 1969. It might also be noted that while the magnetic-amplifier market was at first exclusively a military one, the commercial portion of this market now approximates 40 per cent, and this percentage is steadily increasing.

Although the magnetic amplifier is currently being employed in many diverse applications ranging from automatic pilots to high-speed motor drives, and although the number and variety of its applications are constantly increasing, this does not necessarily mean that magnetic amplifiers will replace electronic amplifiers within the near future. For one purpose the magnetic amplifier may be superior to the electronic amplifier; for another purpose it may be a poor choice. Thus, it possesses advantages for certain applications and handicaps for others. The magnetic amplifier should not be regarded as an automatic substitute for all electron tubes and relays in control and regulating circuits. Instead, it should be considered only if its advantages outweigh its disadvantages when it is compared with other types of amplifiers.

It should also be emphasized that the magnetic amplifier complements rather than competes with the vacuum tube and the transistor. There are many situations in which the magnetic amplifier, working in conjunction with these other amplifying elements, produces results that could not be effectively achieved by using only a single type of amplifying element.[28]

19.17 *The dielectric amplifier*

Another potential competitor of the electronic amplifier is the dielectric amplifier. Its principle of operation is very similar to that of the magnetic amplifier, except that it uses a non-linear capacitor in place of a non-linear inductor.

The non-linear capacitor is based upon a discovery made by Peter Debye in 1912. He discovered that the dielectric constant of certain crystalline substances could be made to vary by applying a varying d-c voltage across them (Fig. 19-21). This non-linear dielectric action has been given the rather misleading name of ferroelectricity, misleading because this type of capacitor contains no ferrous metal and possesses no ferrous characteristics. Ferroelectricity may be defined as the characteristic possessed by certain dielectric materials of changing their dielectric constants in accordance with the value of the applied voltage. The silicon capacitor, which was described in an earlier chapter, serves as a good example of a substance that behaves in this manner.

Many ferroelectric materials have been discovered. Among the most important of these are titanium dioxide, barium niobate, lead metaniobate, triglycene sulphate, and guanadine aluminum sulphate hexahydrate, which is commonly known as GASH.[29] Many of these substances also display piezoelectric properties. In 1942, Wainer and Solomon discovered that barium and strontium titanates possessed ferroelectric properties, making them suitable for use in electromechanical transducers and as dielectrics for non-linear capacitors. By using a suitable control voltage, the dielectric constants of these substances can be varied over a range of five to one.

19.18 *Operation of the dielectric amplifier*

A diagram of a simple dielectric amplifier is shown in Fig. 19-22. R1, the input resistor, should be very large in order to prevent the a-c power supply from sending current through the input circuit. The biasing voltage provided by the battery determines the value of the capacity of C, the non-linear capacitor, at the time when there is no signal. This, in turn, determines the amount of alternating current that will flow in the output circuit. The a-c power supply usually consists of a high-frequency electronic oscillator.

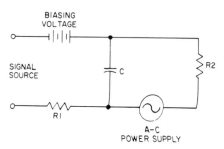

FIG. 19-22. SIMPLE DIELECTRIC AMPLIFIER

The introduction of a signal now causes the capacity of C to vary. This, in turn, changes the reactance of the output circuit and causes the output current to vary at the signal frequency. The result is a modulated wave whose carrier is the current that is provided by the high-frequency power supply, and whose envelope corresponds to the signal. Since the amplitude of the modulated wave is greater than that of the original signal, a signal gain has been obtained. It is necessary to demodulate

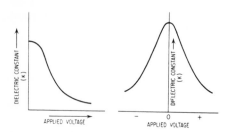

Courtesy, Cornell-Dublilier Electronics Div.
FIG. 19-21. VARIATION OF DIELECTRIC CONSTANT WITH APPLIED VOLTAGE

and filter this modulated wave in order to obtain the desired signal. A single stage of dielectric amplification is capable of providing gains as high as 1 million. The principles of the dielectric amplifier can also be applied to bridge and push-pull amplifier circuits.

19.19 Some applications of the dielectric amplifier

An interesting use of the dielectric-amplifier circuit is as a frequency doubler. This action is obtained when the bias of the dielectric amplifier is set at zero, and a signal is applied.

Experimenters have successfully employed the dielectric amplifier to replace conventional electronic amplifiers in multivibrators, relays, and sweep generators. Their present frequency range is from zero cps (direct current) to 10 mc, with every indication that the upper limit will eventually be raised to a much higher value.

19.20 Characteristics of the dielectric amplifier

The dielectric amplifier possesses many of the advantages of the magnetic amplifier, being rugged, reliable, efficient, simple, and compact, as well as requiring no warm-up time. It can develop power gains as high as 1 million per stage. Its cost is lower than that of equivalent electronic or magnetic amplifiers, and it has a high input impedance. Among its disadvantages are the need for a high-frequency power supply, its present 10-mc upper-frequency limitation, its relatively high noise level, and the fact that the capacity of the nonlinear capacitor is greatly affected by temperature variations. The device is at present in an early stage of development, but it appears to be destined eventually for large-scale use in amplifier,

frequency-multiplier, and oscillator circuits.[30]

19.21 The parametric amplifier

The parametric or variable-reactance amplifier is a descendant of the magnetic and dielectric amplifiers and is today one of the most important developments in the field of electronics. This device is also known as the junction-diode amplifier and the mavar (Modulation Amplification through Variable Reactance). Like the dielectric and magnetic amplifiers, it employs the principle of producing amplification by the varying of one of the reactive elements or parameters of a circuit. It is capable of amplifying with less noise than can be obtained by means of electron tubes, particularly in the UHF and SHF regions.

The first amplifier of this type employed germanium diodes. It was designed during World War II by Harper Q. North of General Electric in connection with developmental work on radar. The first application of the germanium parametric amplifier occurred in 1956, when the Bell Telephone Laboratories installed germanium-diode amplifiers in the transmitting modulator of a microwave-relay system.

The reactive element in the modern parametric amplifier consists of a Varicap, Semicap, or Varactor (Figs. 19-23 and 19-24). The term Varactor was suggested by Marion E. Hines of Bell Telephone Laboratories and is a combination of the words "variable" and "reactor." It refers to a silicon P-N junction diode whose capacitance depends upon the magnitude of the voltage applied across the junction. The first practical diffused-silicon diode capable of being used in an amplifier was developed in 1957 by A. E. Bakanowski and Arthur

FIG. 19-23. INTERNATIONAL RECTIFIER SEMI-CAPS—SILICON VOLTAGE VARIABLE CAPACITOR

Uhlir, Jr., of Bell Telephone Laboratories, who were members of a research group working under the direction of Robert M. Ryder.[31] When these diodes were first introduced, they sold for 150 dollars each. By the middle of 1959, the price had fallen to 35 dollars, and a year later, some types were selling for 4 dollars and a half.

In the parametric amplifier, it is the high-frequency supply or "pump" voltage, rather than the signal, that causes the reactive diode to vary at a frequency that is related to, but several times higher than, the signal frequency. This frequency is known as the pump frequency. The amount of output power delivered to the load is increased when the reactance of the variable diode is increased.

FIG. 19-24. SOME TYPICAL VARACTOR DIODE CAPACITORS

The theory of operation of this device is rather complex and will not be described here (see Chapter 31). However, it can be pointed out that there are several different types of parametric amplifiers. One type operates as a simple negative-resistance amplifier, while another type employs frequency conversion and sideband formation. The resulting effect resembles the transconductance gain produced in the mixer or converter stages of superhetrodyne radio receivers.

These amplifiers have demonstrated low-noise and high-gain performances at frequencies ranging between 1 and 6,000 mc. At present, the highest frequency at which this type of amplification has been obtained is 11,000 mc. Scientists at RCA, Zenith, and other large industrial laboratories are investigating this type of amplifier closely, and there is little doubt that the parametric amplifier will prove to be one of the most important semiconductor devices.[32][33]

In July 1959, Motorola announced the availability of the first commercial parametric amplifiers. They were being supplied in models operating at frequencies of 220 and 450 mc. Other types of parametric amplifiers are being developed for applications in radar, tropospheric transmission, the reception of signals reflected from satellites, and radio telescopes. Some of these applications of the parametric amplifier will be discussed in greater detail in later chapters dealing with radar and microwaves. Finally, mention may be made of the fact that because of their excellent high-frequency response characteristics, investigations are currently under way with regard to the possibility of employing junction diodes in digital computers that would be capable of operating 1,000 times faster than present computers.[34]

REFERENCES

1. *Aviation Electronics Technician 3 and 2 NAVPERS 10317-A.* U.S. Government Printing Office, Washington, D.C., 1959, p. 51.
2. V. J. Louden. "The Magnetic Amplifier," *General Electric Review,* 56:22, Mar. 1953.
3. E. F. W. Alexanderson, "A Magnetic Amplifier for Radio Telephony," *Proc. IRE,* 4:101, Feb. 1916.
4. J. J. W. Brown, "How Good is the Magnetic Amplifier?," *General Electric Review,* 57:53, July 1954.
5. *Magnetic Amplifiers,* NAVSHIPS 900, 172, Department of the Navy, Bureau of Ships, Washington, D.C., 1954, pp. 2-3.
6. Leo G. Sands, "The Magnetic Amplifier," *Radio-Electronics,* 25:103, Nov. 1954.
7. V. J. Louden, *Op. cit.,* p. 22.
8. "The Saturable Reactor in Industrial Electronics," *Popular Electronics,* 2:114, Apr. 1955.
9. Erwin Levey, "Saturable Reactors," *Radio and Television News,* 47:68, 150, Mar. 1952.
10. A. A. Bosschart, "The Magnetic Amplifier," *Radio-Electronics,* 22:41, Sept. 1951.
11. *Magnetic Amplifiers, Op. cit.,* p. 27.
12. V. J. Louden, *Op. cit.,* p. 24.
13. *Aviation Electronics Technician 3 and 2, Op. cit.,* pp. 63-64.
14. "Why Magnetic Amplifiers?," *Control Engineering,* 4:82, Dec. 1957.
15. *Magnetic Amplifiers, Op. cit.,* pp. 46-47.
16. *An Introduction to Increductor Controllable Inductors,* CGS Laboratories, Ridgefield, Conn., p. 4.
17. "Magnetic Device Amplifies," *Radio and Television News,* 54:108, July 1955.
18. "Transient Permanent Magnistor is Miniature Computer Element," *Military Systems Design,* 2:220, Nov. 1958.
19. *Ibid.* p. 220.
20. *Magnistor—A Basic Magnetic Circuit Element.* Mag-Tran Sales Corp. Ridgewood, N.J., pp. 2-3.
21. A. Hugh Argabrite, "Subminiature Magnetic Amplifiers." *Radio and TV News,* 58:70, Dec. 1957.
22. *Ferristors, Their Use and Application.* Data File 110, Berkeley Div., Beckman Instruments, Richmond, Calif., 1956, pp. 2-3.
23. "Introducing the Ferristor," *Popular Electronics,* 7:83, 118, July 1957.
24. *The Whys and Wherefores of Cypak,* B-6584, Westinghouse Motor and Control Division, Buffalo, N.Y., p. 2.
25. *Cypak Industrial Control Systems,* B-6738, Westinghouse Motor and Control Division, Buffalo, N.Y., pp. 3-5.
26. *Ibid.* p. 8.
27. *Progress Report—The Hybrid Magnetic Amplifier,* Industrial Control Co., Wyandanch, L.I., N.Y. 1956, pp. 1-3.
28. "Why Magnetic Amplifiers?," *Op. cit.,* p. 82.
29. "Ferroelectricity and Its Applications," *Cornell-Dubilier Capacitor,* 23:3, Sept. 1958.
30. James S. Fink, "Introducing the Dielectric Amplifier," *Radio-Electronics,* 25:92, Feb. 1954.
31. Arthur Uhlir, Jr., "Junction-Diode Amplifiers," *Scientific American,* 200:123-124, June 1959.
32. Fred Shunaman, "The Variable Reactance Amplifier," *Radio-Electronics,* 30:78-82, Feb. 1959.
33. Arthur Uhlir, Jr., *Varactors,* Microwave Associates, Inc., Burlington, Mass., 1959, pp. 2-9.
34. A. Uhlir, Jr., "Junction Diode Amplifiers," *Op. cit.,* p. 129.

20-AUDIO-FREQUENCY AMPLIFYING SYSTEMS

20.1 *Public-address systems*

A public-address system is an audio-frequency amplifying system that is employed for the amplification of speech and music over a large indoor or outdoor area. It includes the microphones, phonograph turntables, mixers, volume controls, amplifiers, volume indicators, monitoring systems, and loudspeakers required for operation (Fig. 20-1). A small public-address system may contain merely a microphone, volume control, amplifier, and loudspeaker, whereas a large system may contain two or more microphone inputs, a phonograph turntable, a radio tuner, a pre-amplifier, a mixer, a monitor, several main amplifiers, a volume indicator, a power amplifier, and several loudspeakers.

The first crude public-address system was probably the one that was set up around the year 1910 by Peter L. Jensen, who later became chairman of the board of Jensen Industries, and Edwin L. Pridham, who later became vice-president of Magnavox Corp. This system was installed in a San Francisco ball park to amplify the voice of a sports

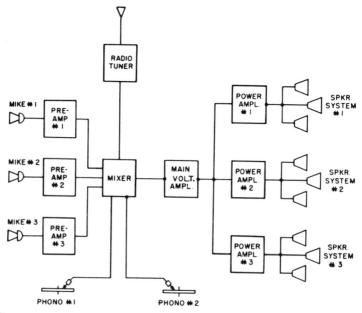

FIG. 20-1. BLOCK DIAGRAM OF LARGE PUBLIC-ADDRESS SYSTEM

announcer known as "Foghorn" Murphy. On Christmas Eve, 1915, they set up a similar installation for the convenience of 75,000 persons who were gathered to hear Christmas carols. It was the first time that such a huge crowd could hear this type of music without any straining of ears.[1]

A high-quality public-address system should possess the following characteristics:

1. A frequency range of 20 to 20,000 cps with a response curve that is flat within plus or minus 1 db.

2. Amplitude characteristics that follow the equal-loudness contour curves of the ear at their respective levels.

3. A percentage of amplitude distortion that does not exceed 2 per cent.

4. An acoustic response that is uniform over an angle of 90 deg.

5. Power capacity that is great enough to handle peaks of power with a dynamic volume range of at least 45 db.[2]

20.2 *Microphone characteristics*

The microphone is a device which changes sound waves or variations in air pressure into corresponding electrical variations. A good microphone should possess the following characteristics:

1. It should respond equally well to all variations between 30 and 15,000 cps (ideally between 20 and 20,000 cps) and should not produce harmonic distortion by generating harmonics of the original signal frequencies. The reproduction of signal frequencies between 60 and 8,000 cps will still produce fairly realistic response, and for the reproduction of speech, response from 60 to 5,000 cps is sufficient.

2. It should be capable of reprod-

ucing great variations in sound pressure or loudness without distortion.

3. It should not generate noticeable background noise, such as hiss or sputter.

A microphone that is to be used in a public-address system designed primarily for broadcasting announcements should be capable of providing crisp reproduction and a natural sound without too much distortion. The microphone need not possess a smooth or level response curve. On the other hand, if the public-address system is to be used for amplifying music, a microphone with a smooth response curve containing no peaks is required. If the microphone is to be used outdoors, it is also necessary to select one that will not be readily affected by wind, and that is capable of excluding extraneous background noise.[3]

For general public-address work, the usual choice today is between the ceramic microphone and a good-quality dynamic microphone. If care is taken to avoid damp and hot conditions, crystal microphones may also be used in lower-cost public-address installations.[4]

Microphone polar patterns. Another factor that must be considered in selecting a microphone is its polar pattern. This pattern is a graph that is drawn on polar coordinate paper, with the position of the microphone located at the center of the graph. The curve that is drawn indicates the radial distance from the microphone at which a sound of a given intensity will always produce the same output.

An omnidirectional or non-directional microphone is characterized by a circular polar pattern, which indicates that it responds equally well to sounds coming from all directions (Fig. 20-2). Microphones possessing this type of pattern are useful as general pickups for orchestras and choruses.

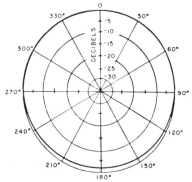

FIG. 20-2. DIRECTIVITY RESPONSE CURVE OF A
NONDIRECTIONAL DYNAMIC MICROPHONE

A bidirectional characteristic is indicated by a pattern that resembles the figure 8 (Fig. 20-3). This pattern indicates that the microphone responds well to sounds emanating from the front or back but is insensitive to the sounds originating from the sides. This type of microphone is useful for conducting interviews and also for picking up sounds of applause from an audience when this is desired.

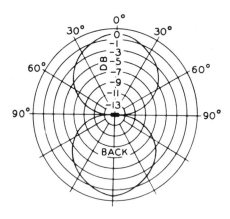

FIG. 20-3. THE FIGURE-8 RESPONSE CURVE OF A
BIDIRECTIONAL MICROPHONE

A heart-shaped or cardioid pattern indicates that the microphone has maximum sensitivity to sounds produced in front of it (Fig. 20-4). The sensitivity increases from the sides and becomes very low with respect to sounds

originating from the rear of the microphone. This type of pattern is useful in applications where it is desired to eliminate the pickup of sounds from the audience, as for example in solo performances and addresses.

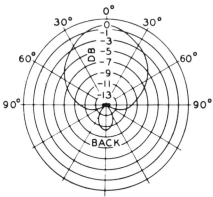

FIG. 20-4. THE CARDIOID RESPONSE CURVE OF
A UNIDIRECTIONAL MICROPHONE

20.3 *Development of the microphone*

There are many names associated with the history and development of the microphone, names such as Sir Charles Wheatstone, Philip Reis, Amos E. Dolbear, Emile Berliner, David E. Hughes, Francis Blake, Alexander Graham Bell, and Thomas A. Edison. It was Wheatstone who in 1827 first coined the term microphone. In 1861, Reis designed a contact microphone by means of which musical sounds could be transmitted. Berliner observed in 1877 that the resistance of a loose contact varied with the pressure and designed a microphone employing this principle. In 1878, Blake developed a telephone microphone that employed a block of carbon and a vibrating diaphragm, while in the same year Hughes constructed a microphone that consisted of a carbon rod resting on two carbon blocks. Hughes also revived the use of the term microphone. Dolbear developed several microphones, which were considered by many to be superior to those developed by Bell.

The early microphone or transmitter that Bell developed for his telephone system was a very clumsy affair that was used both as a telephone receiver and as a transmitter (Fig. 20-5). Conversation, even over short distances, was extremely difficult because of hissing and static produced by this device. At the request of the Western Union Company, Edison spent several years working on this problem. In 1877, he patented a microphone that contained a button of solid carbon. A few years later, he patented a modified type of microphone containing granules of hard coal. Successful tests were held over 140 miles of wire, which indicated

the superior qualities of this device with respect to articulation and volume of sound. As a result, Western Union purchased his rights to the carbon telephone transmitter for 100,000 dollars. In the words of one writer: "Bell may have been the first to invent the telephone, but it was Edison who made it possible to hear something on it."[5]

20.4 The carbon microphone

The present-day carbon microphone makes use of the fact that the resistance of a mass of carbon granules depends upon the amount of pressure applied to the carbon. Direct current is passed through the granules, which are mounted against a diaphragm to form a "button" (Fig. 20-6). Some carbon microphones contain a double button, which is connected to a center-tapped transformer in a push-pull circuit (Fig. 20-7). This arrangement makes the microphone less noisy and more sensitive and also improves its

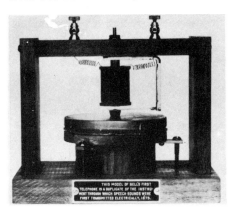

Courtesy, American Telephone & Telegraph Co.

FIG. 20-5. MODEL OF BELL'S FIRST TELEPHONE (1875)

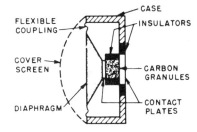

FIG. 20-6. INTERNAL CONSTRUCTION OF TYPICAL SINGLE-BUTTON CARBON MICROPHONE

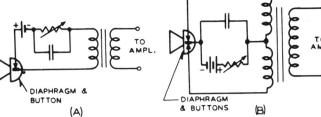

FIG. 20-7. TYPICAL CIRCUIT CONNECTIONS FOR (A) SINGLE-BUTTON AND (B) DOUBLE-BUTTON CARBON MICROPHONES

frequency-response characteristics. This double-button carbon-microphone circuit was first patented by Edwin H. Colpitts.

When sound waves strike the diaphragm, they produce a variation of the pressure exerted upon the granules. This pressure variation produces corresponding changes in the resistance of the carbon button and causes the amount of current to vary. The output of the microphone is connected to the primary winding of a transformer. The secondary winding of the transformer is connected between the grid and ground of an amplifier circuit.

The carbon microphone is substantially non-directional, and its impedance is low. The frequency of its response is between 60 and 7,000 cps, and its response curve is a peaked one. The response of this microphone to signals above 3,000 cps falls off sharply to sounds emanating at an angle that exceeds 40 deg from the microphone.[6]

The carbon microphone possesses the advantages of light weight, sturdy construction, portability, and low cost. The output of the carbon microphone is very high, since the microphone itself acts as an amplifier, and the power of the electrical output is usually greater than that of the sound input. However, the carbon microphone does possess several disadvantages. One is the steady background hiss that is produced by variations in the contact resistance of the carbon granules.[7] Another disadvantage is its poor frequency-response characteristics. A third disadvantage is the fact that it is usually necessary to use it in the vertical position. Finally, there is the need for batteries and for an audio-frequency transformer.

This type of microphone is used in amateur, portable, military, and police transmitters, and in telephone systems and other communication devices that are designed for the transmission of information rather than for entertainment. It is not used in public-address systems or commercial broadcast transmitters.

20.5 *The condenser microphone*

The first commercial model of the condenser microphone was developed by E. C. Wente in 1922. This type of microphone is basically a capacitor, one plate of which is fixed while the other acts as a diaphragm, moving as the sound waves strike it (Fig. 20-8). A polarizing d-c potential of between 150 and 300 volts is applied through a resistor to the plates of the capacitor. As the pressure of the sound waves moves the diaphragm, the capacity of the capacitor varies, producing a corresponding voltage change across the resistor.

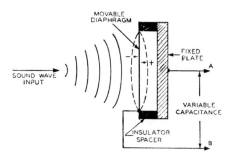

FIG. 20-8. BASIC CONSTRUCTION OF THE CONDENSER MICROPHONE

The condenser microphone is characterized by a smooth frequency response from 20 to 18,000 cps, with a variation of plus or minus 2 db. It has a rather low output, about one-hundredth that of the carbon microphone. It possesses a very high impedance, is non-directional, and has no background noise. In order to avoid losses, the first amplifier stage or pre-amplifier is usually mounted together with the microphone on the microphone stand (Fig. 20-9).

The advantages of the condenser microphone are high fidelity, excellent frequency response, and freedom from background noise. The disadvantages are its lack of portability and ruggedness, high cost, great weight and size, need for an associated bulky battery or power supply, sensitivity to moisture, and very low output level (Fig. 20-10). Its uses are restricted to studio and nonportable work. This microphone has been largely displaced by dynamic, velocity, and crystal-type microphones for broadcast and public-address-system applications.[8] In recent times, there has been an attempt made to encourage its use and to restore its popularity.

Courtesy. Capps and Company, Inc.

FIG. 20-10. A CONDENSER MICROPHONE

20.6 *The crystal microphone*

The heart of the cellular or bimorph type of crystal microphone consists of a bimorph unit containing two squares of Rochelle salt crystals cemented together (Fig. 20-11). The pressure of the sound waves produces a strain across the axis of the crystals, and the resulting piezoelectric effect generates a voltage that corresponds to the sound waves. A second type of crystal microphone frequently employed is the diaphragm type (Figs. 20-12 and 20-13). It contains a single piezoelectric crystal to which a diaphragm is attached. The response of the diaphragm type of crystal microphone is higher than, but not as flat as, the response of the bimorph type.

The crystal microphone is normally non-directional. It possesses a flat res-

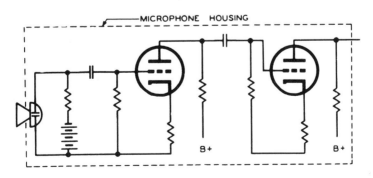

MICROPHONE HOUSING

B+   B+

FIG. 20-9. CIRCUIT DIAGRAM OF A CONDENSER MICROPHONE AND ITS ASSOCIATED PRE-AMPLIFIER
The pre-amplifier is included in the microphone housing.

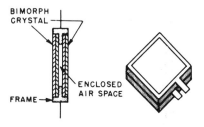

FIG. 20-11. BASIC CONSTRUCTION OF A CRYSTAL SOUND CELL

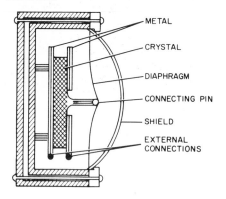

Courtesy, The Turner Co.

FIG. 20-12. CUTAWAY VIEW OF THE DIAPHRAGM-TYPE CRYSTAL MICROPHONE

ponse from 50 to 15,000 cps, and because of its high impedance, it may be connected directly to the grid and ground of an amplifier circuit (Fig. 20-14). The crystal microphone possesses many advantages. Among these are the following:

1. It is light and simple in construction.

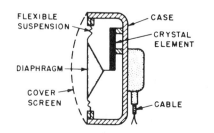

FIG. 20-13. INTERNAL CONSTRUCTION OF A TYPICAL DIAPHRAGM-ACTUATED CRYSTAL MICROPHONE

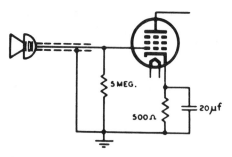

FIG. 20-14. HOW A CRYSTAL MICROPHONE IS CONNECTED TO AN AMPLIFIER

2. It possesses a fair-to-good frequency response.

3. It cannot be overloaded by loud sounds.

4. It develops a moderately high level of output.

5. It requires no battery.

6. It produces little background noise.

7. It will work in any position.

Among the disadvantages of the crystal microphone is the fact that the crystal is affected by humidity and sunlight and may be damaged by temperatures above 55°C or 130°F. The microphone is not sensitive to sounds of low intensity, the value of its output voltage is relatively low, and it possesses a high output impedance which increases the chances of picking up hum in the microphone cable. Because of this latter characteristic, the microphone cable should not have a length greater than 30 ft. The crystal microphone is the type that is most widely used in public-address system installations.[9]

In recent years ceramic microphones have been developed that possess better response characteristics than crystal microphones. Their properties are generally similar to those of the crystal types except that they are not as susceptible to damage as a result of being subjected to extremes of temperature and humidity.[10]

20.7 *The dynamic microphone*

In the dynamic or moving-coil microphone, the diaphragm is connected to a moving coil that is suspended in a magnetic field (Fig. 20-15). It is basically a miniature dynamic loudspeaker that is operated in reverse. Sound waves cause the diaphragm to move the coil, thus generating an alternating voltage (Fig. 20-16). This microphone has uniform frequency response from 20 to 10,000 cps and may be operated in reverse as a dynamic loudspeaker. Its response pattern (Fig. 20-17) is non-directional except for high-frequency sounds. Because the output of this microphone is both low-voltage and low-impedance, it is necessary to feed the output to the primary winding of a transformer. The secondary winding of this transformer is then connected to the grid circuit of the first amplifier stage.

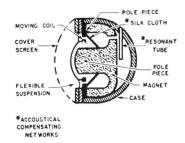

FIG. 20-15. INTERNAL CONSTRUCTION OF A TYPICAL DYNAMIC MICROPHONE

The dynamic microphone possesses the following advantages:

1. It produces no background noise.

2. In addition to possessing a low noise level, i. can be handled and moved during operation without producing an undesirable noise output.

3. It possesses a high output level.

4. It is dependable and rugged.

5. It requires no batteries.

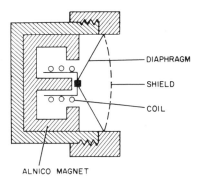

Courtesy, The Turner Co.

FIG. 20-16. CUTAWAY VIEW OF A DYNAMIC MICROPHONE

6. It possesses excellent frequency response and sensitivity.

7. It is characterized by light weight and small size.

8. It is not affected by wind, temperature, or humidity.

9. It has very little tendency to be overloaded by loud sounds.

The main disadvantage of the dynamic microphone is the falling off of its frequency response to sound fre-

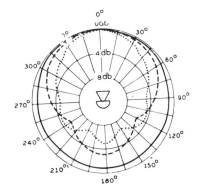

LEGEND:—
1000 CPS ——————
3000 CPS – – – – –
5000 CPS ··········

FIG. 20-17. DIRECTIVITY RESPONSE CURVES OF A NONDIRECTIONAL DYNAMIC MICROPHONE
At 1,000 cps the response is almost circular, becoming less circular as the frequency increases.

quencies above 1,000 cps as the angle of incidence of the sound departs from 90 deg. It is widely employed in public-address systems that are installed outdoors in stadiums, ball-fields, and racetracks.[11]

20.8 *The ribbon microphone*

The ribbon microphone, which was perfected by RCA scientists in 1931, is sometimes called the velocity microphone because, unlike the pressure-operated microphones that have been previously described, this type of microphone is actuated by the velocity component of the sound waves. It consists of a corrugated aluminum or duralumin ribbon that is hung between the poles of a magnet (Fig. 20-18). The velocity component of the sound waves causes the ribbon to move, thus generating an alternating voltage. This alternating signal is transferred to the primary winding of a step-up transformer that is located within the microphone housing. The high-impedance output of the secondary coil is then connected through a shielded cable to the input of the first amplifier stage.

This type of microphone has excellent frequency-response characteristics from 20 to 15,000 cps, provided that the sound source is at a distance that is greater than 2 ft from the microphone. A type of distortion that emphasizes the lower frequencies occurs if the sound

source is closer than 2 ft. The response is bidirectional, since the sound waves that strike the ribbon broadside will cause it to vibrate, while the sound waves that approach from the side will have little effect upon the thin edge of the ribbon (Fig. 20-19).[12]

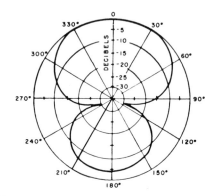

FIG. 20-19. TYPICAL FIGURE-8 DIRECTIONAL RESPONSE CURVE OF RIBBON MICROPHONE

The ribbon microphone possesses the following advantages:
1. Low impedance.
2. Simple in construction and portable.
3. Lack of background noise.
4. Excellent response characteristics.
5. Good bidirectional characteristics.

When the microphone is used outdoors, it must be protected from puffs of wind which tend to move the ribbon and to produce noise. Another disadvantage is the fact that the person who is speaking must stand at least 2 ft away from the microphone. This reduces the strength of the output.[13] It is a rather fragile device and may be permanently damaged by a sudden intense puff of wind or breath that is strong enough to stretch the diaphragm beyond its normal range.

Because of its "figure-8" type of directional pattern, this microphone

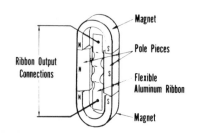

FIG. 20-18. BASIC CONSTRUCTION OF A RIBBON MICROPHONE

can be used to minimize undesired reverberation, noise, and feedback in public-address systems. It is also very suitable for use as a lapel microphone for on-the-street broadcasts.[14]

20.9 The cardioid microphone

The cardioid microphone houses two units, one a dynamic-type microphone and the other a ribbon-type microphone (Fig. 20-20). When their outputs are properly phased by acoustical means, this combination produces a cardioid or heart-shaped response pattern (Fig. 20-21). There is a very low response to sounds emanating from directly behind the microphone or from the sides of the microphone. Consequently, this microphone is sometimes

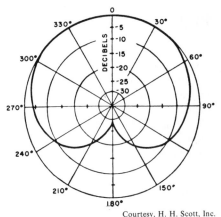

Courtesy, H. H. Scott, Inc.

FIG. 20-21. CARDIOID TYPE OF DIRECTIONAL RESPONSE

employed in broadcasting studios to eliminate acoustic feedback and noises produced behind the microphone by the audience.

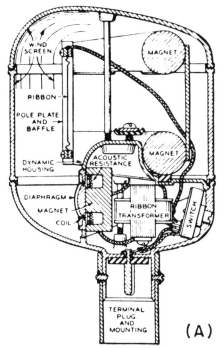

(A)

(B)

Courtesy Altec Lansing Corp.

FIG. 20-20. TYPE 639 CARDIOID MICROPHONE
The drawing shows how the ribbon element (above) and the dynamic element (below) are assembled to operate either as a nondirectional, bidirectional, or cardioid directional microphone. Any of these three effects may be selected by changing the setting of the switch (lower right).

20.10 *Pre-amplifiers*

Since many microphones, tuners, tape recorders, and phonograph pickups produce a relatively low voltage output, a voltage amplifier called a pre-amplifier or control amplifier is generally employed ahead of the main amplifier (Figs. 20-22 and 20-23). This pre-amplifier is a Class A audio-frequency amplifier of moderate gain, with low hum and noise output.

Its purpose is to amplify the output of the microphone or other transducer to a level that is suitable to drive the output or power-amplifier stage. It may be mounted on the same chassis as the main amplifier, or it may be mounted on a separate chassis. Since mixers and volume controls introduce noise, these components are usually placed after the pre-amplifier rather than before it.

The pre-amplifier that is associated with a high-quality amplifying system usually contains a compensated gain control and two frequency-compensating circuits with accompanying controls that raise or reduce the bass or treble components of the signal (Fig. 20-24). One control is called a turnover control, and its purpose is to boost the bass level to compensate for the reduction in bass level that is produced when a disc recording is made.

The second control, called the roll-off control, performs a different function. It de-emphasizes the high-frequency signals which were emphasized during the production of the disc recording. This was done in order to make the level of the high-frequency signals much higher than that of the scratch and surface noise. The action produced by these controls is known as equalization, and it will be considered in detail in a later chapter.

20.11 *Phonograph players*

Many public-address systems possess a phonograph-player unit which consists of a turntable, a tone arm, and a pickup cartridge (Fig. 20-25). The function of the turntable is to provide unwavering, quiet rotation of the record in order to produce maximum

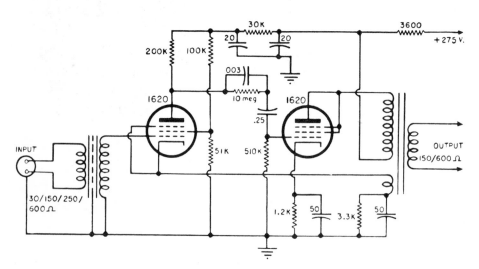

Fig. 20-22. Schematic circuit diagram of a magnetic microphone pre-amplifier

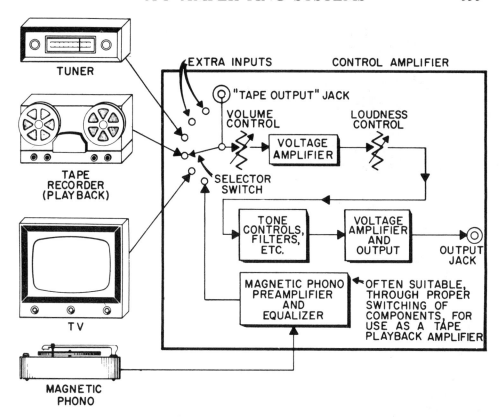

FIG. 20-23. BASIC FUNCTIONS OF A CONTROL AMPLIFIER

fidelity of reproduction. The important characteristics of a turntable are quality of construction, speed of rotation, and type of drive used.

20.12 Turntable speeds

The common turntable speeds required for the playing of modern records are $33\frac{1}{3}$, 45, and 78 revolutions per minute (Fig. 20-26). Recently two new speeds, 16 rpm and 8 rpm have been developed. The 16-rpm speed has been employed in automobile phonographs, and both speeds are now being employed in record players that are used in connection with "Talking Books" for the blind that are produced by the American Foundation for the

Blind and the Library of Congress.

At the speed of 8 rpm, fidelity is sacrificed at the expense of long playing time.[15] A 7-in. record operating at 8 rpm plays for a total of 4 hours, 2 hours on each side, while a 12-in. record plays for a total of 10 hours. The 8-rpm record loses some of its high-frequency res-

Courtesy, H. H. Scott, Inc.

FIG. 20-24. SCOTT MODEL 121-C PRE-AMPLIFIER

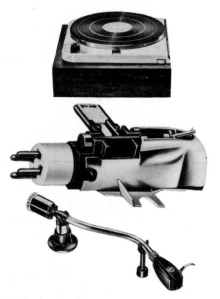

Courtesy, (a) Thorens; (b) and (c) Sonotone

FIG. 20-25. PARTS OF THE PHONOGRAPH (A) TURNTABLE; (B) CARTRIDGE; (C) TONE ARM

ponse characteristics, since its frequency range is from 100 to 5,000 cps, but this is not important for the understanding of speech in which a 5,000-cps maximum response provides adequate reproduction. A noteworthy advantage of both of these lower speeds is the accompanying reduction of surface

Courtesy, Garrard Sales Corp

FIG. 20-26. THREE-SPEED PHONOGRAPH TURN-TABLE

noise. Reducing the speed from 33 1/3 to 16 rpm reduces the surface noise by 4 db, and reducing the speed to 8 rpm reduces the noise by another 3 db.

20.13 *Wow and flutter*

There are various types of turntable drives employed, among them the rim drive, the belt drive, and the direct drive. Irregularities in the drive mechanism produce low-frequency variations in turntable speed. These variations produce a type of low-frequency distortion known as wow (Fig. 20-27). When the audible tone variations occur at a rate higher than 10 per second, this higher pitched type of disturbance is sometimes called flutter.

The human ear is extremely sensitive to both wow and flutter. For this reason, it is more important for a turntable to rotate at a steady speed than at an accurate speed. Speed deviations of as much as 3 per cent from the correct speed are usually neither perceptible nor annoying. However, extremely small variations in the speed of steady rotation, ranging as low as 0.1 per cent to 0.5 per cent, produce sufficient amounts of wow and flutter to be perceptible and annoying to most persons.[16]

There is only one way of reducing the amount of wow and flutter to low levels. This method is through excellent design of the turntable driving mechanism. The turntable disc should be so heavy that it is practically immune to vibration or to momentary changes in driving speed. The motor should be well balanced and mechanically isolated in order to keep vibration from reaching the turntable disc.[17] Cheap turntables and automatic changers nearly always produce a certain amount of wow, since their parts are not precision-tooled on a lathe but are roughly stamped out on a die-press.

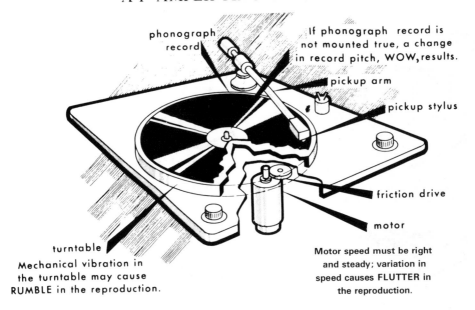

phonograph record

If phonograph record is not mounted true, a change in record pitch, WOW, results.

pickup arm

pickup stylus

friction drive

motor

turntable

Mechanical vibration in the turntable may cause RUMBLE in the reproduction.

Motor speed must be right and steady; variation in speed causes FLUTTER in the reproduction.

FIG. 20-27. THE TURNTABLE—WOW, RUMBLE, AND FLUTTER

20.14 *Rumble*

If the public-address system possesses speakers that are capable of responding to frequencies below 50 cps, a low-pitched type of distortion called rumble may sometimes be noted when a two-pole, shaded-pole motor is used to drive the turntable. Rumble may also be produced by an unbalanced rotor in the motor, poor turntable bearings, poor records, and tone-arm or stylus resonance. A 30-cps motor-produced rumble may be eliminated by using a high-quality, four-pole motor, or by using a hysteresis synchronous motor. Other types of rumble may be reduced by using a special LRC rumble filter that contains a series capacitor and resistor and a shunt inductor. It is designed to attenuate frequencies below 50 cps.[18] The main objection to the use of a rumble filter is the fact that it removes some of the desired bass sounds from the output of the phonograph system.

Numerical specifications on turntable performance are helpful as general guides but should not be compared too closely with one another, since methods of measurement are not standardized. Generally, a rumble figure of −40 db and a speed variation of 0.2 per cent offer a presumption of reasonably good quality.

20.15 *Acoustic feedback*

Another source of trouble is acoustic feedback from the loudspeaker to the phonograph pickup (Fig. 20-28). It is produced when low-frequency sounds emanating from the speaker reach the turntable and cause the turntable to vibrate. This, in turn, vibrates the pickup, which produces a high-voltage signal that is amplified and comes out of the speaker at a very high level. The volume continues to build up, and both the amplifier and the speaker may be damaged.

The problem is a severe one today

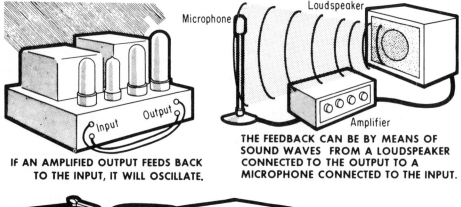

IF AN AMPLIFIED OUTPUT FEEDS BACK
TO THE INPUT, IT WILL OSCILLATE.

THE FEEDBACK CAN BE BY MEANS OF
SOUND WAVES FROM A LOUDSPEAKER
CONNECTED TO THE OUTPUT TO A
MICROPHONE CONNECTED TO THE INPUT.

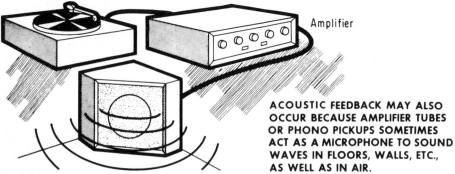

ACOUSTIC FEEDBACK MAY ALSO
OCCUR BECAUSE AMPLIFIER TUBES
OR PHONO PICKUPS SOMETIMES
ACT AS A MICROPHONE TO SOUND
WAVES IN FLOORS, WALLS, ETC.,
AS WELL AS IN AIR.

FIG. 20-28. ACOUSTIC FEEDBACK

because of the recent development of loudspeaker systems that are capable of producing strong low-frequency sounds. The solution to this problem lies in isolating the entire turntable mechanism by placing it on soft springs designed to absorb and dampen these vibrations.[19]

20.16 *Rim drive*

The most satisfactory type of drive for general-purpose applications is the rim drive. This type of drive contains a rubber disc that is connected to the motor shaft and makes contact with the rim of the turntable. As the rubber disc turns, the turntable revolves. When the player is not in use, the disc should not be allowed to press against the turntable

rim; otherwise wow distortion produced by the flattening of the rubber disc will occur.

20.17 *Turntables vs. record changers*

The development of the 33 1/3-rpm long-playing record has led to a reconsideration of the desirability of using record changers in phonograph-playing equipment. Before the advent of the long-playing record, the record changer provided the only means of presenting a lengthy and continuous program of recorded music without the necessity of having to get up to change discs (Fig. 20-29). Since a long-playing disc will play a single side for almost a half hour, the need for a record changer is consi-

FIG. 20-29. TYPICAL RECORD CHANGER—THE GARRARD RC88

derably reduced and even questionable.

There is little doubt that the turntable provides maximum flexibility and the best possible reproduction and is the logical choice for the perfectionist. Audio experts point out the following advantages in favor of the turntable versus the record changer:

1. The major function of the record-playing device is to rotate the record accurately and quietly. The addition of clutch arrangements to couple the motor with the changer mechanism adds an irregular friction factor which causes the speed of rotation to fluctuate and which compromises this major function.

2. The mechanics of a record changer requires the use of a short pickup arm. This produces tracking error and distortion.

3. The stacking of records on the changer may injure the records.

4. Loading records on a changer is frequently a complex job.

5. Most record players do not turn the record over. It is usually simpler to perform this operation by hand on a manual turntable than to remove the record from a changer, turn it over, and then reload the changer.

6. The stylus is designed to contact the record groove at an angle of 90 deg.

As the records pile up on a changer, the stylus contacts each succeeding record with a different angle of incidence and with a different amount of stylus pressure. This increases the amount of wear on both the record and the stylus and produces distortion.

7. In most changers, the center spindle remains stationary while the record rotates. This may ream out the center hole and make it egg-shaped. This, in turn, will cause the record to produce a wavering sound.

8. The absence of the complex changer mechanism that is employed by record changers saves both space and money. There is an additional saving in repair and maintenance charges, since in general, the greater the number of automatic devices that are found in a piece of equipment, the greater is the probability that something will go wrong with that piece of equipment.[20][21]

20.18 *Phonograph pickups*

The phonograph pickup serves two important functions. The first is the conversion of the side-to-side wiggles of the groove into lateral movements of the stylus. The second function is to serve as a transducer by converting this stylus movement into corresponding electrical signal voltages. It is therefore a type of transducer which changes mechanical movement into electrical output (Fig. 20-30).

The most important characteristics of a good pickup are its frequency response, needle pressure, and output level. In order for the stylus to follow or track the grooves with ease, the pickup should possess relatively small mass and low inertia, and the spring that returns the stylus to its center position should possess compliance or be sufficiently yielding. It is also necessary for the pickup to exert just enough downward

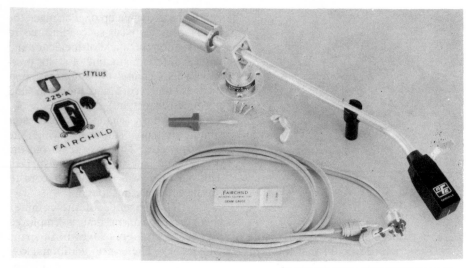

FIG. 20-30. FAIRCHILD 225A CARTRIDGE (LEFT) AND MODEL 500 CURVED TONE ARM

pressure on the stylus to prevent the stylus from climbing up the side walls of the record grooves. This pressure should be kept as low as possible, since low pressure increases record life and reduces both the resonance effects and a peculiar rasping sound effect called needle talk that is produced by direct acoustical radiation from the pickup. Other and desirable features to look for in a pickup are constant voltage output over a wide frequency range, low pickup of hum from stray magnetic fields, and the development of minimum voltages from vertical movements. Since the recorded characteristics of a monaural record are in a lateral direction, this latter voltage represents no useful information.[22]

20.19 *The tone arm*

The tone arm or pickup arm is the name given to the unit that supports the pickup cartridge while the stylus moves from the starting grooves to the finishing grooves of the record. The name tone arm is derived from the fact that in the days of the acoustical phonograph, long before electrical methods of reproduction were developed, this arm actually conveyed the sound waves that were produced in the sound box to the horn. When these arms were redesigned to carry the pickup, the old name was retained.[23]

The behavior of this arm affects the quality of reproduction of the recorded sound. The arm bears the same relationship to the cartridge as a loudspeaker baffle or enclosure does to the loudspeaker that it houses. The ideal arm should be rigid enough to avoid twisting, must be light enough to glide easily over warped· records, and must possess enough inertia to hold the cartridge still while the stylus vibrates. It should allow the spiral groove to carry the pickup across the record without causing the stylus to press harder against one groove than the other and without exerting enough pressure to wear or deform the groove. Finally, it must also hold the pickup tangent to the groove at every point on the record.[24] In the words of one writer, it must combine the rigidity of a brick wall with the delicate touch of a feather.[25]

20.20 *Tracking error*

A common source of trouble and distortion that involves the tone arm is known as tracking error. When a record is made, the cutting stylus is suspended from a horizontal bar that runs across the record. Consequently, the stylus follows a true radial path that is tangent to every groove and is always at right angles to the line of motion of each groove.

The stylus that is employed for playback is not suspended from an overhead bar but is held in a tone arm that pivots at one end. This causes the stylus to make a curve, rather than a straight track, in moving from the outside of the record toward the center. With a straight tone arm, it is impossible to produce correct tracking at more than one radius on the record. As a result, the stylus may be off its correct position by as much as 15 deg. This tracking error produces harmonic and intermodulation distortion and causes rapid wearing of the record.

Solutions. One solution to this problem is to use a very long pickup arm (Fig. 20-31). The fact that the arc traced by this long arm closely resembles a straight line tends to reduce the tracking error. However, this long arm causes the entire phonograph assembly to oc-

cupy an excessive amount of space and to require an unduly large enclosing cabinet.

A second solution is to employ a short pickup arm. In this arm, improved tracking may by obtained either by curving the head or by mounting the pickup at a slight angle (Fig. 20-32). Either of these methods produces tracking that is correct at two different radii during the playing of the record. As a consequence, the deviation from correct tracking will be considerably reduced throughout the playing of the entire record.[26]

20.21 *Resonance effects*

Tone arms tend to produce low-frequency mechanical-resonance effects. The two factors involved in this type of mechanical resonance are mass, which is a function of weight, and compliance, which is springiness or the opposite of stiffness. The behavior of mass and compliance in producing mechanical resonance is comparable to that of inductance and capacitance in producing electrical resonance. At some frequency at which the mass and compliance reactions are opposite and equal to each other, mechanical re-

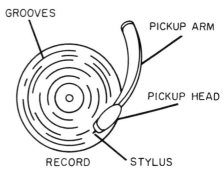

FIG. 20-32. EFFECT OF A CURVED PICKUP ARM
When the arm is curved and the reproducing head is offset from the pickup arm, the tracking angle will be maintained at 90 deg.

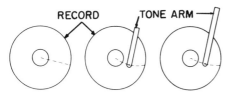

FIG. 20-31. REDUCING TRACKING ERROR BY USING A LONGER PICKUP ARM

sonance will occur. An unavoidable and undesirable resonance effect is produced as a result of the interaction of the mass of the tone arm with the compliance of the pickup movement. If this resonance effect occurs within the range of recorded frequencies, the arm will vibrate violently, and the music or voice will sound distorted. In fact, the pickup may even jump out of the groove.

If resonance occurs at a frequency of 30 cps, it will increase the noises produced by turntable rumble. The resonance effect can be reduced to a point where it will be relatively unimportant if a careful choice of a high-compliance pickup and arm combination is exercised. However, undesirable vibrations may be set up by harmonics that are generated in a poorly designed tone arm. This effect is intensified if the arm possesses a uniform cross-section throughout its length. This type of resonance may therefore be reduced or eliminated by the use of a tapered arm.

20.22 *Viscous damping*

Viscous damping is a feature that is associated with certain types of pickup arms. The pivot bearings employ a special viscous fluid that produces a fixed amount of controlled resistance to the motion of the tone arm. Its primary purpose is to serve as a safety precaution against the stylus being dropped on the record with undue force. When the arm is dropped, it descends at a slow rate. Viscous damping also performs the function of damping tone-arm resonance. It does this job well with flat records, but when it is employed with warped or off-center records, it offers the same drawback as high-inertia arms in that it tends to produce increased and uneven wear.[27]

20.23 *Classification of pickups*

Phonograph pickups may be classified into two basic groups: amplitude-responding and velocity-responding types (Fig. 20-33). Amplitude-responding pickups deliver an output that is proportional to the side-to-side distance that the stylus is moved by the record grooves. On the other hand, velocity-responding pickups deliver an output that is proportional to the speed of the stylus as it follows the modulations of the grooves. Velocity-responding cartridges include the dynamic, magnetic, and variable-reluctance types, while amplitude-responding cartridges include crystal, ceramic, condenser, and strain-gauge types.[28] The operating principles of most of these pickups are very similar to those of the corresponding types of microphones (Fig. 20-34).

20.24 *Velocity-responding pickups*

The operation of all dynamic, magnetic, and variable-reluctance cartridges is based upon the principle that a voltage is induced across a coil when it is moved through a stationary magnetic field or when it is kept stationary in a varying magnetic field. The magnitude of the induced voltage is proportional to the strength of the field, the number of turns of the coil, and the rate of relative motion between the coil and the field.

In considering cartridges, it should be noted that one of the most important characteristics of a cartridge is its compliance. This term, which was briefly mentioned in a previous section of this chapter is the opposite of stiffness, and indicates how readily the stylus can move. If the compliance is low, this will produce reduced high-frequency response, poor transient re-

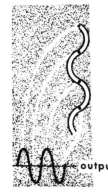
In a Velocity Pickup, Movement produces output. Maximum and minimum points correspond with fastest movement.

output

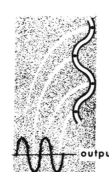
In an Amplitude Pickup, the output voltage depends on the Position of the stylus, so the audio output is a replica of the groove.

output

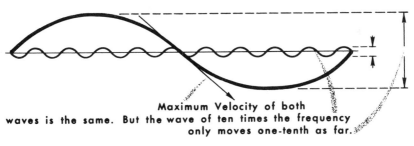

Maximum Velocity of both waves is the same. But the wave of ten times the frequency only moves one-tenth as far.

FIG. 20-33. VELOCITY AND AMPLITUDE PICKUPS

sponse, and excessive record wear.

The compliance of a cartridge is a function of the structure of the stylus and the mass of the system. In general, for high-quality reproduction, the amount of mass supported by the tip of the stylus should not exceed 1 milligram. Other factors to be considered in selecting a cartridge are its frequency response and whether it tends to resonate mechanically within the audio-frequency portion of the spectrum.[29]

20.25 *Dynamic pickups*

A common type of dynamic or moving-coil pickup contains a coil which is attached to the stylus (Fig. 20-35). This coil is surrounded by a fixed magnetic field. Motion of the stylus causes the coil to move and to induce a corresponding voltage that is proportional to the velocity of the stylus. Because of the low mass of the moving system, the high-frequency response is very good, and the frequency-response curve is flat from 25 to 12,000 cps. The use of low-impedance coils with few turns reduces the problem of hum pickup.

Among the disadvantages is the fact that the output is low. This usually necessitates the use of a step-up transformer and a considerable amount of pre-amplification. Other disadvantages are the relatively delicate construction of this cartridge and its tendency to over-accentuate the high frequencies. This latter characteristic means that it is frequently necessary to provide correction by means of a special pre-amplifier or a special network.

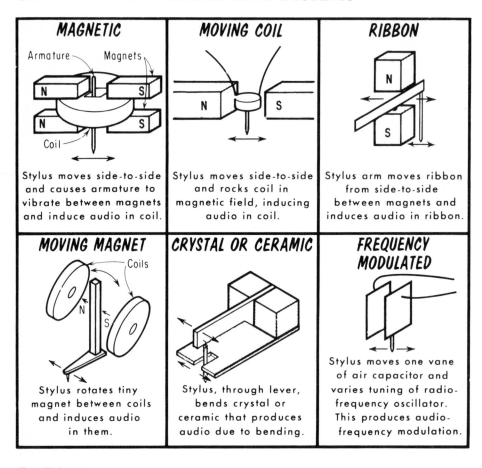

MAGNETIC

Armature ⌐   Magnets ⌐

N   S

N   S

Coil ⌐

Stylus moves side-to-side
and causes armature to
vibrate between magnets
and induce audio in coil.

MOVING COIL

N   S

Stylus moves side-to-side
and rocks coil in
magnetic field, inducing
audio in coil.

RIBBON

N

S

Stylus arm moves ribbon
from side-to-side
between magnets and
induces audio in ribbon.

MOVING MAGNET

⌐ Coils

N

S

Stylus rotates tiny
magnet between coils
and induces audio
in them.

CRYSTAL OR CERAMIC

Stylus, through lever,
bends crystal or
ceramic that produces
audio due to bending.

**FREQUENCY
MODULATED**

Stylus moves one vane
of air capacitor and
varies tuning of radio-
frequency oscillator.
This produces audio-
frequency modulation.

FIG. 20-34. ACTION OF CUTTERS AND PICKUPS

Until fairly recently, the high cost
of dynamic cartridges limited their
applications to broadcasting and recording studios. During the last few
years, the development of new manufacturing techniques has brought the
price down, and an increasing number
of home sound-reproducing installations now employ dynamic pickups.

20.26 *Magnetic pickups*

A common type of magnetic pickup contains a magnet which is attached
to the stylus. When the stylus moves,
the magnet moves past a stationary coil

of wire and induces a voltage across it.
This type of pickup is rather expensive,
produces low output, and requires a
stage of pre-amplification. It also possesses the undesirable characteristic of
high moving mass. Consequently, it is
seldom employed in modern cartridges.

In 1958, the Phillips Laboratories
announced the development of a mag-
netodynamic pickup operating on a
principle similar to that of the magnetic
pickup. The movable magnet consists of
a rod of Ferroxdun, a ferrite material,
1/2 in. in length and 1/32 in. in diameter.
The rod is magnetized in an unconventional manner, with the poles on oppo-

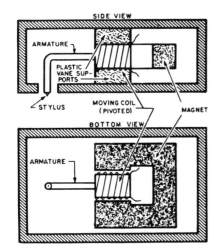

FIG. 20-35. INTERNAL CONSTRUCTION OF A TYPICAL MOVING-COIL DYNAMIC PICKUP

site sides of the rod along its length. Movement of the stylus is transmitted to this rod, and an audio-frequency voltage is developed across a pair of coils located nearby. It is claimed that this pickup possesses a frequency response that is flat from 10 to 20,000 cps within plus or minus 2 db.[30]

20.27 Variable-reluctance pickups

Closely related to the magnetic pickup is the variable-reluctance type, which is now the most widely sold type

of high-fidelity pickup. It was developed in 1948 by Bachman and was first manufactured by General Electric.

The term reluctance refers to the magnetic counterpart of electrical resistance (Fig. 20-36). Thus, the reluctance of iron is low, while that of air is very high. An increase in reluctance tends to decrease the amount of magnetic flux.

The stylus of this pickup is mounted on an armature of magnetic material (Fig. 20-37). The fixed end of the armature is located near an Alnico V bar magnet. The other end is placed half way between the Mumetal pole pieces of two coils whose windings are connected in series with each other. As the stylus follows the modulations of the record grooves, it approaches one pole piece. This reduces the reluctance of the magnetic circuit involving the bar magnet, armature, and coil. The result is an increase in the amount of magnetic flux through one coil and a decrease in the amount of flux through the other. Consequently, voltages are induced across each coil that are proportional to the velocity of the stylus. Since the coils are connected in series, a push-pull addition action results.

This type of pickup is unusually compliant, permitting the stylus to follow the swings of the record grooves and making for accurate tracking and

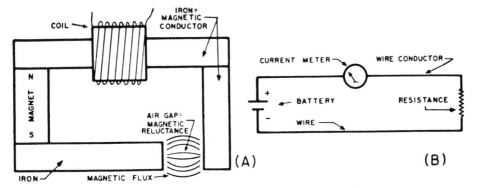

FIG. 20-36. SIMPLE MAGNETIC CIRCUIT (A); ANALOGOUS ELECTRICAL CIRCUIT (B)

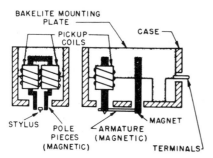

FIG. 20-37. BASIC INTERNAL CONSTRUCTION OF A VARIABLE RELUCTANCE MAGNETIC PICKUP

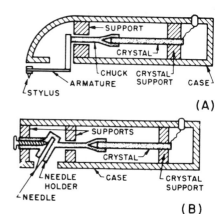

FIG. 20-38. INTERNAL CONSTRUCTION OF TWO TYPES OF CRYSTAL PICKUPS
(A) Low-noise type; (B) removable-needle type.

low wear on the stylus and record. Since lateral motion of the stylus is the only way of producing an output, vertical stylus motion produces no effect. This eliminates noises caused by vertical stylus motion in grooves that have been damaged by scratches. Both the magnetic pickup and the variable-reluctance pickup are stable and immune to climatic changes. They possess flat frequency-response characteristics of better than 30 to 15,000 cps throughout a long life, when equalization circuits are employed to compensate for the non-linear characteristics that cause them to accentuate the treble and diminish the bass.

They are susceptible to hum produced by strong alternating fields such as those generated by the turntable motor. This hum may be reduced by surrounding the cartridge with a Mu-metal shield and by connecting the two coils in a hum-bucking arrangement which tends to cancel externally induced hum.[31]

20.28 *Crystal pickups*

Crystal pickups have the advantages of being relatively inexpensive and of possessing a high output level (Figs. 20-38 and 20-39). They also possess a high output impedance which enables them to be connected directly to the grid of the main amplifier. Consequently, there is no necessity for employing a pre-amplifier stage. As is true of the crystal microphone, the crystal pickup is easily damaged by high temperature and high humidity. Most crystal pickups employ Rochelle salt elements and are permanently damaged by temperatures that exceed 105°F. They also lose their bass response in moist climates. The bass response is also affected adversely by the fact that the crystal acts electrically in a manner resembling that of a capacitor whose value is approximately 0.001 μfd. It therefore provides a much higher impedance to signals of lower frequency than to those of higher frequency. Another disadvantage is the falling off of the treble response at frequencies above 5,000 cps. The crystal type of pickup is the type most frequently encountered in phonograph players associated with public-address systems.

In recent years, the crystal pickup has been improved by substituting a P-N crystal of ammonium dihydrogen phosphate in place of the less durable crystal of Rochelle salt. This type of P-N crystal is not damaged by high temperature or humidity.

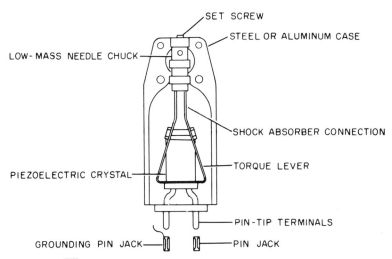

SET SCREW

STEEL OR ALUMINUM CASE

LOW-MASS NEEDLE CHUCK

SHOCK ABSORBER CONNECTION

TORQUE LEVER

PIEZOELECTRIC CRYSTAL

PIN-TIP TERMINALS

GROUNDING PIN JACK

PIN JACK

Courtesy, Shure Brothers, Inc.

FIG. 20-39. CONSTRUCTION DETAILS OF THE LEVER-TYPE CRYSTAL PICKUP

20.29 *Ceramic pickups*

Another recent improvement in crystal pickups has been the employment of ceramic electrostrictive materials containing barium titanate in place of the Rochelle salt piezoelectric element (Fig. 20-40). Like the previously described P-N crystal, the barium titanate element is practically unaffected by extremes of temperature and humidity. Another advantage is its strong, wide, and uniform frequency response, which covers a range of 20 to 20,000 cps with a deviation of 2 db. Consequently, it requires little or no preamplification and only a relatively simple, low-frequency equalization circuit.[32]

Another recent development has been the production of ceramic electrostrictive materials in which zirconium dioxide has replaced the oxide of titanium. Such zirconia-containing ceramic crystals, which possess excellent high-temperature characteristics, are now being employed in phonograph pickups and as the generating and receiving crystals in sonar equipment.[33]

A major asset of all piezoelectric and electrostrictive pickups is their insensitivity to magnetically induced

FIG. 20-40. SONOTONE MODEL 9T CERAMIC CARTRIDGE
The cartridge has a flat response, plus or minus 1 db, over the entire audible recording range of 20 to 17,000 cycles with smooth roll-off to 20,000 cycles. High compliance reduces tracking pressure to 2 to 4 grams for professional tone arms.

hum. They also require very little in the way of pre-amplifiers or elaborate equalization circuits. Since the ceramic pickup possesses nearly all of the advantages and none of the disadvantages characteristic of the Rochelle salt crystal, it is beginning to challenge the hitherto unquestioned supremacy of the magnetic pickup for high-fidelity applications.[34] [35]

20.30 *Magnetostriction pickup*

The torsional magnetostriction pickup has recently appeared on the market. It is claimed that this type of pickup possesses substantially uniform characteristics over the frequency range of 30 to 10,000 cps. This range can be extended to 15,000 cps by using a transformer. An additional claimed advantage is the low needle-point mass and the subsequent low needle pressure required to operate the device.[36]

20.31 *Capacitance or condenser pickup*

In the Weathers capacitance or condenser pickup, the movement of the stylus varies the size of a small capacitor that is connected across an electronic oscillator circuit. As the stylus moves, the resulting changes in capacity produce variations in the frequency of the oscillator, thus producing a frequency modulated signal. This signal is then demodulated by means of a circuit that is similar to the discriminator circuit of an FM receiver.[37] The operation of the discriminator circuit will be described in a later chapter.

The condenser pickup is characterized by the highest compliance, lowest moving mass, and lowest stylus-tracking force of any of the pickups currently available.[38] It provides smooth response

up to 25,000 cps, which is beyond the range of audibility. However, because it is expensive and complicated, it is restricted mainly to professional applications.

20.32 *Strain-gauge pickups*

Examples of an interesting type of pickup that is occasionally encountered are the Pfanstiehl and the Capehart strain-gauge pickups. Their operation is based upon a principle that is employed in industry to measure the bending of girders. A piece of a special type of wire is placed across the pickup head, and a system of levers connects the stylus to the middle of the wire. Movement of the stylus causes the wire to stretch one way and then the other, causing the resistance to vary. A direct current is sent through the wire, and the variations in this current are proportional to the stretching of the wire, which in turn is related to the movement of the stylus.

20.33 *The phonograph stylus*

Contrary to the popular notion, the point of the stylus does not rest upon the bottom of the record groove (Fig. 20-41). Instead, it rides on the side walls; the undulations of the grooves cause the stylus to move back and forth and thus reproduce the recorded material. Wearing of either the grooves or the needle affects the fit and usually produces distortion (Fig. 20-42).

An ideal stylus should be cone-shaped with a highly polished hemispheric tip. It should contact the walls of the record groove only at two small areas on the side of the groove. Many substances, ranging from cactus to diamonds, have been used as the needle or stylus of phonograph pickups. Despite advertising claims, there is no such thing as a permanent needle. All need-

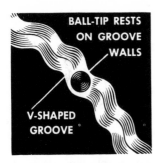

BALL-POINT CONTACT INSURES TOP
PERFORMANCE, PROTECTS GROOVE

Courtesy, The Tetrad Co.

Fig. 20-41. Position of the stylus in the groove

les, including diamond-pointed needles, will wear out eventually.

The reason for this wearing out becomes apparent when it is realized that because of the small contact area of the stylus tip, a 6-gram tone arm may produce a pressure of 25,000 psi. The temperature at the point of contact may be as high as 1,800°F. The effect of this is to wear down the stylus sides into

WEAR-FLAT DISTORTS MUSIC
CHISEL EDGE DAMAGES GROOVE

Courtesy, The Tetrad Co.

Fig. 20-42. Worn stylus in a record groove

flat sections, which become wider and longer, until sharp cutting edges are formed. These cutting edges are probably the single greatest cause of damage to records.[39]

With the advent of automatic record changers, needles made of steel, bamboo, cactus, thorn, and fiber have become obsolete, since their maximum life is one play and they must be changed for each new record.

Many of the needles used today in inexpensive 78-rpm record players have metal-alloy points that are usually plated with osmium and indium. The playing life of this type of needle is between 50 and 500 plays. In fact, according to one writer, this estimate is far too generous. He claims that when a metal stylus is used to play a relatively soft vinyl, 12-inch, long-playing record, it will become worn and will begin to damage the record grooves before the end of the first playing of the record.[40]

The needle that is most in use today has a point that consists of natural or synthetic sapphire. According to some experts, this needle is good for between 250 and 1,000 plays. However, there are other experts who claim that this estimate is also too generous and that a sapphire needle should be replaced after 10 to 30 hours of use. This would correspond to the playing of between 15 and 30 long-playing records.[41][42]

The best and most expensive type of needle has a diamond point. Its cost is about ten times that of a sapphire-pointed needle, ranging between 10 and 20 dollars, but since it lasts 10 to 20 times as long as a sapphire needle does, the cost per play is probably less than that for a sapphire needle (Figs. 20-43 and 20-44).

There are several additional advantages associated with the use of a diamond stylus. First, it does not deposit

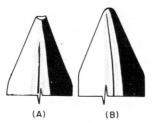

(A)　　　　(B)

FIG. 20-43. STYLUS WEAR CAUSED BY USED RECORDS
(A) Sapphire; (B) diamond.

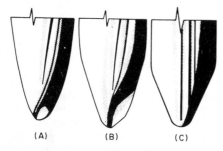

(A)　　　　(B)　　　　(C)

FIG. 20-44. STYLUS WEAR INDUCED BY PLAYING TIME
(A) Worn osmium stylus after 15 hours of playing time; (B) sapphire stylus showing wear at the tip after 30 hours of playing time; (C) diamond stylus showing no wear after several hundred hours of playing time.

abraded stylus dust in the grooves. Dust that is deposited by other types of styli tends to produce surface noise and additional abrasion. Second, there is tremendous heat generated at the point of contact between a stylus and a record. Since diamond is an excellent conductor of heat, it tends to transfer this heat away from the delicate groove surfaces.[43]

In 1957, Walco Products announced the development of an automatic electric diamond-grinding machine designed to form and polish jewels to a cone-shaped tip for diamond phonograph needles. It is expected that this application of automation will reduce the cost of diamond styli by 40 per cent.[44]

In any event, no matter what type of stylus is employed, experts do not recommend adhering too closely to any rules based upon the number of hours of playing time to be expected from a stylus of a given type. Instead, it is suggested that the stylus be periodically inspected with the aid of a low-cost microscope that is now available at a cost of approximately 4 dollars (Fig. 20-45). This will enable the user to detect excessive stylus wear and to replace the stylus before it has had a chance to damage valuable records.

FIG. 20-45. 50-POWER MICROSCOPE FOR CHECKING THE CONDITION OF A STYLUS

20.34 *Radio tuners*

Radio tuners make it possible to feed a broadcast program into a public-address system. A tuner is essentially a special type of AM or FM radio receiver that does not contain the final audio-frequency amplifier stages and the loudspeaker (Fig. 20-46). The audio-frequency output of the tuner is fed into the high-impedance phonograph-input section of the public-address system. The output of a tuner does not generally require the use of a stage of pre-amplification.[45]

FIG. 20-46. PILOT MODEL FA-540 FM-AM TUNER

The quality of an audio system employing an AM tuner is usually limited. This is due to the fact that since AM broadcasting stations are assigned to narrowly adjacent channels, they tend to interfere with each other when high-frequency notes are used to modulate the carrier wave. This generally prevents the transmission of tones that are higher than 5,000 cps—a limitation set by the Federal Communications Commission—which is not present in FM transmission. Consequently, an FM tuner generally permits a frequency range that may reach or exceed 15,000 cps.

However, it should be pointed out that it is not true that all AM broadcasting stations must cut off at audio frequencies exceeding 5,000 cps. Where AM stations are not likely to produce interference with each other, they may maintain flat response up to 15,000 cps. Unfortunately, the usual telephone lines that are employed to feed radio-network programs cut off sharply at frequencies above 5,000 cps for reasons of design and in order to minimize the production of whistles caused by inter-station interference.

An FM tuner may possess one major disadvantage—a tendency to drift or detune itself. This disadvantage is eliminated in tuners that are equipped with an AFC (automatic frequency control) circuit designed to prevent this detuning action.[46]

In selecting a tuner, its sensitivity rating provides a good indication of the ability of the tuner to bring in stations clearly and without noise. This rating is usually given in units of microvolts, and the lower the number of microvolts, the more sensitive is the tuner. A useful control that is present in some AM tuners is a selectivity switch. This switch enables adjustment of the tuner for best reception of either local or distant stations. When listening to a powerful local station, the use of this switch to reduce selectivity and sensitivity will produce better quality of reception. Adjustment of this switch for reception of distant weaker stations increases the sensitivity and reduces the audio-frequency bandwidth, thus reducing the amount of interference between adjacent channels.[47]

20.35 Mixers and loudness controls

When several microphones, phonograph turntables, and tuners are feeding into the same public-address system, it is necessary to control the volume of the output of each device after any necessary pre-amplification has been accomplished. The blending of these various outputs is then performed by means of a mixer circuit (Fig. 20-47). The mixer is then followed by an attenuator or master volume control.

There are many types of mixing circuits, and the type which is used is a very important consideration, since some types of mixers fail to eliminate interaction between the various input channels. As a result, cross-talk distortion may result. The most satisfactory types of mixers employ constant-impedance attenuation, which is produced by a network of volume controls arranged to form a pattern resembling the letters T, H, or L. These attenuators are therefore known as T-pads, H-pads, and L-pads (Fig. 20-48).

Some loudness controls are compensated to correct for the discrepancies in human hearing that were discovered by Fletcher and Munson. These Bell Telephone Laboratories scientists discovered that people tend to hear sounds in the middle frequencies more easily than either the low or the high tones. They also discovered that as the sound level is lowered, people hear

MIXER
MIC. NO. 1
INPUT
PREAMP. NO. 1
MIC. NO. 1
GAIN CONTROL
MASTER
GAIN
CONTROL
MIC. NO. 2
INPUT
PREAMP. NO. 2
MIC. NO. 2
GAIN CONTROL
PHONO
INPUT
PHONO
GAIN CONTROL

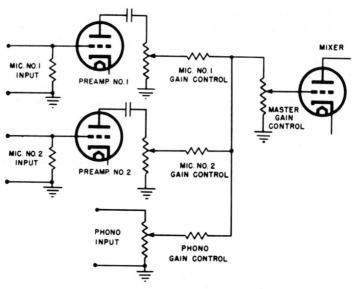

FIG. 20-47. HIGH-LEVEL MIXING CIRCUIT
The microphone inputs and the phonograph input are combined in the grid of a mixer tube.

even less of the low and high-frequency sounds in proportion to the audible mid-frequency sounds. The results of these studies have been graphically summarized in a series of curves known as Fletcher-Munson curves (Fig. 20-49). The compensated loudness control makes use of the data provided by these curves, and by means of an arrangement of resistors and capacitors, it accentuates the lows and highs at the expense of the middle frequencies when the volume of sound is reduced. This prevents the loss of these lows and highs when

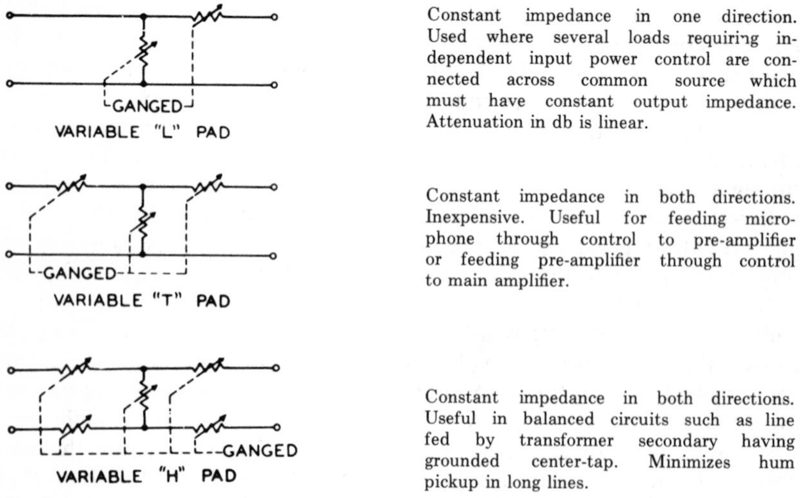

GANGED
VARIABLE "L" PAD
Constant impedance in one direction. Used where several loads requiring independent input power control are connected across common source which must have constant output impedance. Attenuation in db is linear.
GANGED
VARIABLE "T" PAD
Constant impedance in both directions. Inexpensive. Useful for feeding microphone through control to pre-amplifier or feeding pre-amplifier through control to main amplifier.
GANGED
VARIABLE "H" PAD
Constant impedance in both directions. Useful in balanced circuits such as line fed by transformer secondary having grounded center-tap. Minimizes hum pickup in long lines.

FIG. 20-48. VARIOUS TYPES OF PAD ATTENUATORS

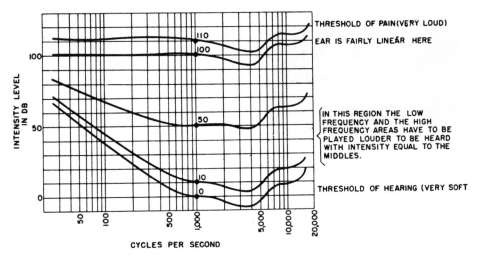

FIG. 20-49. FLETCHER-MUNSON CONTOUR LINES OF EQUAL LOUDNESS FOR NORMAL EARS
The curves show how much louder than the 1,000-cps note other frequencies must be in order to be heard equally as loud as the 1,000-cps note.

the volume is lowered to reasonable levels.[48]

20.36 *The main amplifier and the power amplifier*

The purpose of these amplifier stages is to increase the output of the mixer to a level which is high enough to drive the loudspeakers (Fig. 20-50 and 20-51). The selection of the amplifier circuit to be employed depends upon the amount of power output desired.

the fidelity requirements, the degree of portability, and cost considerations. The power output is usually rated in terms of the number of watts of undistorted output, that is, an output whose harmonic distortion is below 5 per cent. The final power amplifier may be operated either Class A, AB, or B, depending upon whether the amplifier is a small or a large one.

A basic characteristic of most audio amplifiers is that the amount of non-linear distortion increases as the power

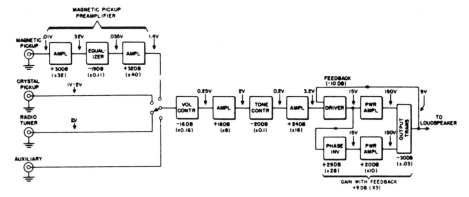

FIG. 20-50. BLOCK DIAGRAM OF A TYPICAL COMMERCIAL AUDIO AMPLIFIER

FIG. 20-51. TYPICAL COMMERCIAL AUDIO AMPLIFIER

level rises. In high-quality amplifiers, this distortion increases very gradually as the power output is raised to the rated power level, and the distortion is negligible over this range. If the amplifier is operated above its rated output range, the amount of harmonic distortion begins to increase more and more rapidly until it reaches an unacceptable level.

A satisfactory amplifier frequency response is one that is flat with a deviation of 1 db between 25 and 15,000 cps at full rated output (Fig. 20-52). This covers the frequency range that is audible to the average individual, although there are some people who possess extreme frequency ranges of hearing and can hear sounds from 18 cps to slightly over 20,000 cps. A top-quality, high-fidelity amplifier should possess a flat response with a deviation of 0.5 db between 20 and 20,000 cps (Fig. 20-53). It should also possess a harmonic-distortion figure that is below 2 per cent and preferably ranging around 0.5 per cent. If the amplifier is to be used for voice work only, it need be flat only within 2 db from 100 to 8,000 cps, and distortion levels of up to 10 per cent can be tolerated.

A much-more sensitive gauge of distortion is the intermodulation

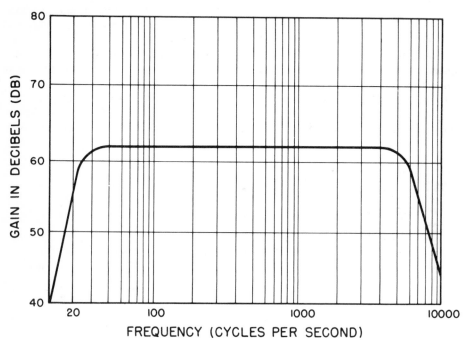

FIG. 20-52. TYPICAL GAIN VERSUS FREQUENCY RESPONSE CURVE

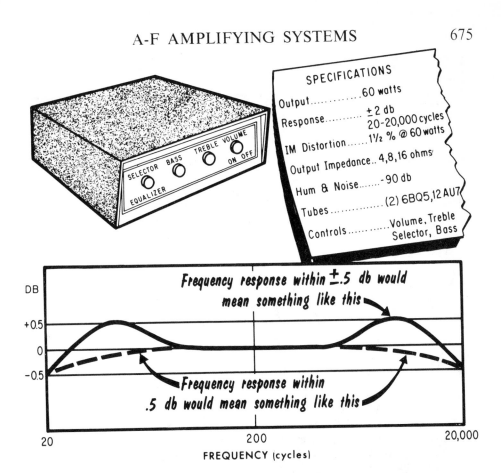

FIG. 20-53. MEANING OF AMPLIFIER FREQUENCY RESPONSE CURVES

method. Two signals, whose frequencies are 60 and 2,000 cps respectively, are fed into the amplifier at the same time (Fig. 20-54). Measurements are then made of the amount of interaction or intermodulation between them. An objectionable effect of intermodulation distortion is the production of beat notes whose frequencies are equal to the differences in frequency between the tones causing them (Fig. 20-55). The most objectionable beats are those caused by two high-frequency tones that are close together and that produce a spurious low-frequency tone.

A satisfactory amplifier will produce no more than 8 per cent intermodulation distortion at its rated power. If the amount of intermodulation distortion is kept below 3 per cent, its effect is not discernible.

Mention may also be made of the fact that most of the commercial high-fidelity amplifiers that are produced today employ variations and modifications of an excellent amplifier circuit that was first produced by D.T.N. Williamson in 1947 (Fig. 20-56).

20.37 Impedance matching

When a generator or other source of energy is connected to a load, the impedances are said to be matched when the impedance of the load is so adjusted that it equals the impedance of the

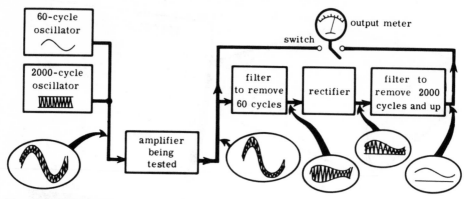

FIG. 20-54. TEST SET-UP FOR MEASUREMENT OF INTERMODULATION DISTORTION

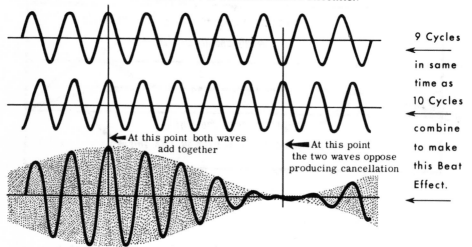

FIG. 20-55. EFFECT PRODUCED BY INTERMODULATION DISTORTION

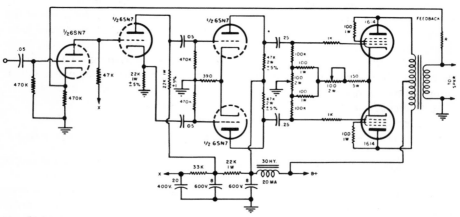

FIG. 20-56. THE WILLIAMSON AMPLIFIER CIRCUIT

power source. Proper matching of impedances is important in public-address systems. Without this matching, it is impossible to obtain maximum power output and reduction of distortion. Therefore, it is necessary to make certain that the impedance of the loudspeaker is matched to the impedance of the final power amplifier.

In order to accomplish this impedance match, each amplifier is usually equipped with an output transformer whose secondary coil is tapped (Fig. 20-57). If a high-fidelity response is desired, this output transformer should have a heavy core in order to prevent magnetic saturation by the relatively large plate currents produced by the final power-amplifier stage. A skimpy transformer, with an undersized core and inadequate copper content in its windings, will saturate with only a few watts of audio power. This limits the power output and produces unequal amplification over the desired frequency range.

In addition, each loudspeaker has a line transformer whose primary is tapped. By selecting suitable impedance taps on the output transformer and on

the line transformer, the audio-frequency signal may be transferred from the amplifier to the loudspeaker with maximum efficiency (Fig. 20-58).

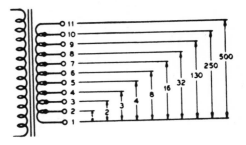

FIG. 20-58. TYPICAL UNIVERSAL OUTPUT TRANSFORMER SHOWING THE IMPEDANCE AVAILABLE BETWEEN EACH TAP AND THE COMMON TAP

20.38 Sound reproducers

Sound reproducers are sound transducer devices that are designed to convert electrical energy into sound energy (Fig. 20-59). They are essentially electromagnetic motors that push air out with each forward stroke and pull air back with each backward stroke.

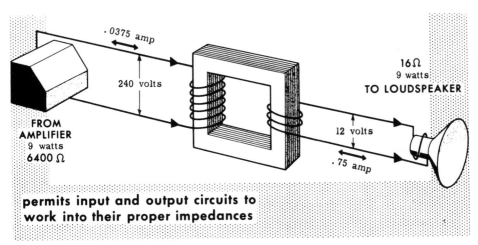

permits input and output circuits to work into their proper impedances

FIG. 20-57. IMPEDANCE MATCHING TRANSFORMER

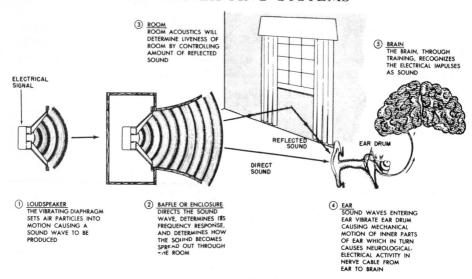

③ ROOM
ROOM ACOUSTICS WILL DETERMINE LIVENESS OF ROOM BY CONTROLLING AMOUNT OF REFLECTED SOUND

⑤ BRAIN
THE BRAIN, THROUGH TRAINING, RECOGNIZES THE ELECTRICAL IMPULSES AS SOUND

ELECTRICAL SIGNAL

REFLECTED SOUND

EAR DRUM

DIRECT SOUND

① LOUDSPEAKER
THE VIBRATING DIAPHRAGM SETS AIR PARTICLES INTO MOTION CAUSING A SOUND WAVE TO BE PRODUCED

② BAFFLE OR ENCLOSURE
DIRECTS THE SOUND WAVE, DETERMINES ITS FREQUENCY RESPONSE, AND DETERMINES HOW THE SOUND BECOMES SPREAD OUT THROUGH THE ROOM

④ EAR
SOUND WAVES ENTERING EAR VIBRATE EAR DRUM CAUSING MECHANICAL MOTION OF INNER PARTS OF EAR WHICH IN TURN CAUSES NEUROLOGICAL-ELECTRICAL ACTIVITY IN NERVE CABLE FROM EAR TO BRAIN

FIG. 20-59. ACOUSTIC CIRCUIT FROM LOUDSPEAKER TO HEARING

The first device capable of converting electrical signal energy into acoustical signal was developed around 1875 by Alexander Graham Bell and Thomas A. Watson. They discovered that if two sets of coils and spring-steel rods were placed in series with a battery, when one spring was set into motion by impulses sent along the wire, the other piece of spring metal would vibrate in a similar manner and would produce a sound. It is interesting to note that this invention of a sound reproducer preceded the invention of the sound recorder or phonograph. This device is the ancestor of the modern magnetic earphone, the telephone receiver, the magnetic loudspeaker, the magnetic microphone, and all sound-powered telephone equipment.

For high-fidelity applications, a loudspeaker should, as a minimum, possess a frequency response that is flat from 30 to 15,000 cps. It should also be capable of handling the peak amount of power delivered by the power-amplifier stage without producing an undue amount of distortion.

20.39 The magnetic telephone receiver

The terms *telephone receiver, earphone, headphone,* or *headset,* are used to designate a transducer device which converts electrical energy into sound energy and which is held against the ear when used. A magnetic telephone receiver contains two coils which are wound on pole pieces attached to the poles of a magnet (Fig. 20-60). When there is no signal, the pole pieces attract a steel diaphragm with a steady pull. When the signal current passes through the coils, a varying magnetic field is set up. This causes the diaphragm to move and thus creates sound waves.

The resistance of this device is comparatively high. The frequency response is poor, with a resonant peak occurring around 1,000 cps. This type of sound reproducer is generally employed in telephone equipment, military radio-communications systems, a-c bridge circuits, signal tracers, and hearing aids.

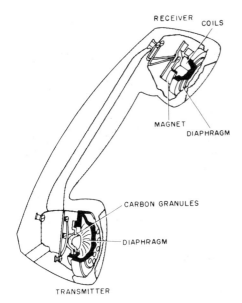

RECEIVER COILS

MAGNET
DIAPHRAGM

CARBON GRANULES

DIAPHRAGM

TRANSMITTER

Courtesy, American Telephone & Telegraph Co.

FIG. 20-60. MODERN HAND-SET TELEPHONE
The carbon chamber in the transmitter is bowl shaped and into it protrudes a thimble-like projection of the diaphragm so that it will operate at any angle its user holds it. Special alloys developed by telephone research have made possible the small but powerful magnet in the compact receiver.

Another type of headset that is sometimes encountered utilizes crystal headphones. This type of receiver contains neither coils nor magnets. The electrical energy is converted into the mechanical energy of a vibrating diaphragm by means of a piezoelectric crystal. These crystal earphones possess very good frequency response.

20.40 *Magnetic loudspeakers*

This type of loudspeaker is simply a modification of the magnetic telephone receiver (Fig. 20-61). The varying current which passes through the coil causes a metal armature to move back and forth. A paper cone is attached to this armature. When the armature is set into motion, the paper cone moves, thus

creating sound waves. In other words, this loudspeaker, like other loudspeakers, is basically a type of air pump that alternately pushes and pulls the air that is in front of it and behind it. In this manner, it creates compressions and rarefactions of the air, which the ear interprets as sound. The larger the cone. the lower are the frequencies of the signals that it can reproduce.

The magnetic loudspeaker possesses low efficiency and a low range of frequency response. Its main advantage is its extremely low cost. Because of the poor quality of its frequency response, the magnetic loudspeaker has been largely replaced by the dynamic one.

20.41 *The electromagnetic dynamic loudspeaker*

The electromagnetic dynamic or electrodynamic loudspeaker was invented by Sir Oliver Lodge. In 1913, Peter L. Jensen and Edwin L. Pridham were issued a patent for a moving-coil dynamic loudspeaker. According to Jensen, they accidentally stumbled on this device in the course of trying to develop an improved type of telephone receiver. At first, they tried to use it in telephone and similar communications applications. There it proved to be a failure, because it was too bulky. No one was interested in it until it was employed in connection with the amplification of the human voice in a public-address system. However, it was the development of the radio receiver that gave this type of loudspeaker its biggest boost.[49] It took many years to perfect this type of speaker, and it was not until 1928 that Bell Telephone Laboratories demonstrated a practical electromagnetic loudspeaker to the public. It is no exaggeration to state that this development revolutionized the techniques of sound reproduction.

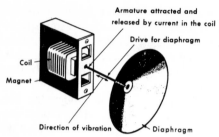

FIG. 20-61. The magnetic or moving-iron speaker

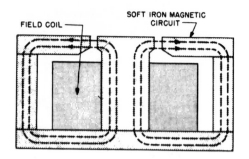

FIG. 20-62. Magnetic field set up by field coil carrying current
The magnetic field magnetizes the iron circuit and produces flux in the air gap only during that period in which current flows through the coil.

This device is a cone type of loudspeaker in which the flow of direct current through a field coil produces an electromagnetic field. The field coil sometimes serves a dual purpose by acting as a choke coil in the filter circuit of the amplifier power supply. The audio-frequency signal that is to be reproduced is sent through a nearby voice coil which is attached to the paper cone.

This voice coil consists of a number of turns of copper or aluminum wire wound around a thin but strong cylinder of paper, dural, or glass. The voice coil is suspended and positioned in correct relationship to the magnetic field by means of a device called a spider. The paper cone is suspended at its outer edges by means of rubber, cloth, or leather suspensions attached to the rim of the frame.[50] There is no need for a heavy metal diaphragm or armature. When the changing current passes through the voice coil, the voice coil moves back and forth in the electromagnetic field of the field coil (Figs. 20-62 and 20-63).[51]

Since the direct current that is required to excite the field of this speaker is obtained from the power supply of the amplifier, if the filtering is inadequate, a hum may be induced from the field coil to the speaker voice coil. A hum-bucking coil may be used to re-

duce this effect. It consists of a coil of a few turns that is wound around a pole piece and is connected in series with the voice coil. Hum voltages are also induced across this coil, but the coil is wound in such a manner that the hum voltages that are induced across it oppose and cancel the hum voltages that are induced across the voice coil.

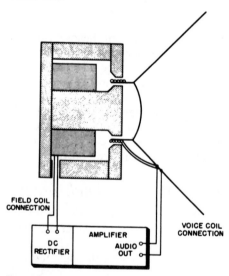

FIG. 20-63. Basic construction of an electrodynamic loudspeaker
Note the connection of the field coil to a source of direct current.

The electromagnetic loudspeaker is usually quite bulky, although compact models have been designed. The voice coil possesses great freedom of movement and can reproduce very low frequencies. The frequency range is adequate for the reproduction of signals produced by ordinary broadcast receivers, since a good cone-type speaker can produce a smooth, low-distortion response from 70 cps to 12,000 cps. As was previously mentioned, the loudspeaker has a tendency to pick up hum and needs transformer coupling from the last amplifier stage.

The electromagnetic loudspeaker and the permanent magnet dynamic loudspeaker are the two types most frequently found in radio receivers and public-address systems. These dynamic loudspeakers may also be operated in reverse as dynamic microphones.

When more than one speaker is used in a public-address system, it is necessary to pay attention to two factors, impedance matching and phasing. The presence of additional speakers changes the total impedance of the speaker load. It is therefore necessary to compensate for this by connecting to different taps of the matching transformer.

Phasing is the term that is used to indicate that the diaphragms of all of the speakers in the system are working in the same direction at the same moment (Fig. 20-64). If the phasing is not correctly adjusted, and the speakers are out-of-phase with each other, partial cancellation of sound will result, and the dispersion and frequency-response characteristics of the speaker system will be affected adversely (Fig. 20-65).

20.42 *Permanent-magnet dynamic loudspeakers*

The characteristics and operating principles of this type of loudspeaker are very similar to those of the electromagnetic type, except that in the permanent-magnet (PM) loudspeaker, a strong permanent magnet has replaced the field coil as a producer of the magnetic field (Figs. 20-66 and 20-67). The substitution of a permanent magnet for the electromagnet reduces the consumption of electrical power but increases the weight of the speaker.

The cost of a small PM speaker is approximately 10 per cent greater than that of the electromagnetic (EM) type. Larger PM speakers, such as those used in large radio receivers and in medium-powered public-address systems, cost approximately 50 per cent more, while very large PM speakers, such as those used for theatres and large public-address-system installations, may cost twice as much as electromagnetic units.

Various types of magnetic alloys are now being employed by loudspeaker manufacturers. Among the most popular alloys for making magnets are alnico, alni, alcomax, and ticonal.

PM speakers are preferred to EM speakers in low and medium-powered public-address installations because they do not require a source of field excitation. This reduces the amount of cabling required. Although PM speakers have a higher initial cost, in the long run, PM speakers have been found to be the most economical.

20.43 *Selecting a cone-type loudspeaker*

There are seven characteristic factors that should be considered in the selection of a cone-type speaker for an installation in which high fidelity is of great importance. They are: (1) fundamental resonance frequency, (2) transient response, (3) strength of speaker field, (4) power-handling capacity,

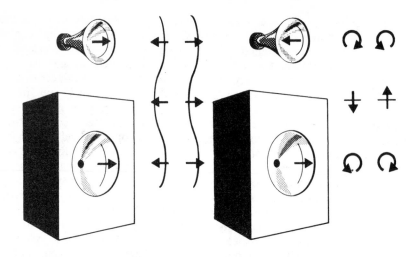

UNITS IN PHASE   UNITS OUT OF PHASE

(A)   (B)

FIG. 20-64. THE IMPORTANCE OF PHASING
(A) Units in phase—the sound waves combine; (B) units out of phase—unnatural air movement.

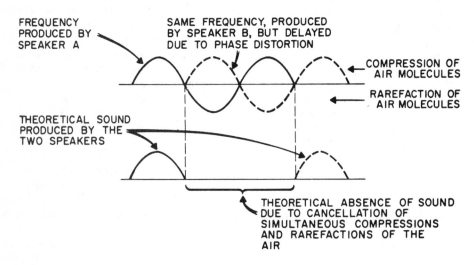

FIG. 20-65. CANCELLATION OF SOUND DUE TO PHASE DISTORTION

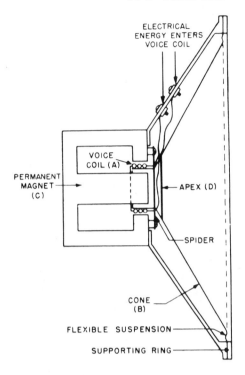

ELECTRICAL
ENERGY ENTERS
VOICE COIL

VOICE
COIL (A)

PERMANENT
MAGNET
(C)

APEX (D)

SPIDER

CONE
(B)

FLEXIBLE SUSPENSION

SUPPORTING RING

Fig. 20-66. Permanent   magnet   dynamic
loudspeaker

(5) conversion efficiency, (6) break-up action, and (7) size of diaphragm.

Resonance. The resonance phenomenon is due to the fact that the cone and voice coil possess mass and are moving on an elastic suspension (Fig. 20-68). This combination tends to have a natural resonant frequency to which it gives a pronounced peaked response. This produces transient distortion and gives a false coloration to the tone quality by upsetting the proper balance of the various sound frequencies. In addition, the speaker responds poorly to sounds below this resonant frequency. Consequently, a speaker should be chosen whose resonant frequency is below that of the lowest frequency that the audio system is designed to reproduce.

Transient response. Closely related to this resonant phenomenon is a similar type of transient-response distortion called hangover, which causes the blending and slurring of one tone with the following tone (Fig. 20-69). The speaker cone overshoots its mark and keeps vibrating after a sudden boom or clang in the music. This inertial hangover effect can be reduced by the damping action of a stiff cone and by a high concentration of magnetic energy around the voice coil (Fig. 20-70).[52] Any remaining hangover effect can then be eliminated, as has been previously described, (1) by damping the amplifier-output circuit and reducing the impedance of the output circuit through the use of inverse feedback; (2) by using low-impedance triode output tubes in place of pentodes and beam-power tubes possessing high plate resistances; and (3) by using large output transformers.

Magnetic field strength. A strong magnetic field is a third essential factor. Such a field produces a greater volume of sound for the same amount of power input and causes the bass response to be improved. An undersized magnet or field coil will limit the amount of power that the speaker can handle, producing severe distortion at power levels exceeding a few watts (Fig. 20-71).

The magnetic strength of the speaker is usually specified in gauss, and a high-quality speaker will have a magnetic flux whose strength is over 10,000 gauss. It should be noted that, in comparing speakers, a comparison of magnet weights is generally an acceptable guide only between models of a given brand, rather than between different brands of loudspeakers. This is due to the fact that differences in design may make a smaller magnet assembly produced by one manufacturer more efficient than a larger magnet assembly

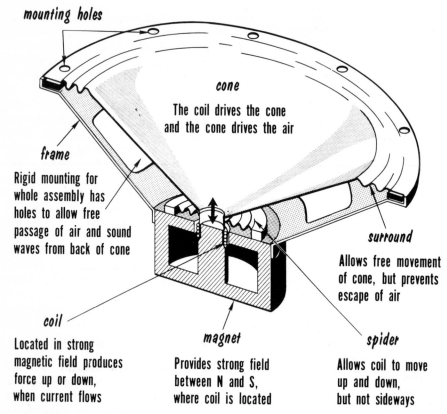

mounting holes

cone

The coil drives the cone
and the cone drives the air

frame

Rigid mounting for
whole assembly has
holes to allow free
passage of air and sound
waves from back of cone

surround

Allows free movement
of cone, but prevents
escape of air

coil

Located in strong
magnetic field produces
force up or down,
when current flows

magnet

Provides strong field
between N and S,
where coil is located

spider

Allows coil to move
up and down,
but not sideways

Fig. 20-67. Parts of a PM dynamic loudspeaker and their functions

produced by a different manufacturer.[53] Another factor responsible for differences in magnet size is the difference in the densities of the magnetic alloys that are used by different manufacturers.

Power rating. Power-handling capacity refers to the amount of power that the loudspeaker can accept without being damaged or without producing an excessive amount of distortion. In general, with all factors equal for a given listening level, the greater the power-handling ability of the speaker, the less the distortion that will be produced. It should also be noted that the dynamic range of certain recorded compositions may produce power peaks several times greater than the normal

rating of the amplifier. The loudspeaker should be capable of handling these surges without being damaged or without producing annoying distortion.

The two factors which determine the power-handling ability of a cone-type speaker are the size of its diaphragm and the construction of its voice coil. The ability of the voice coil to handle power is limited by the rise in its operating temperature. Since, all other factors being equal, a PM speaker tends to run cooler than an EM speaker (because the PM speaker contains no field coil to contribute heat), the PM speaker is generally capable of handling more power than a comparable EM unit is.

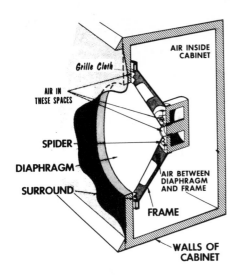

FIG. 20-68. SOURCES OF RESONANCE
All elements identified here can cause resonance.

Conversion efficiency. The next factor, conversion efficiency, indicates the ratio of the output of acoustical watts to the input of electrical watts. If this conversion efficiency is high, there is a reduction of the power demands

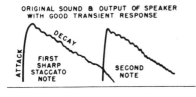

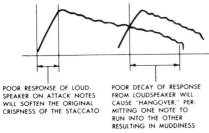

FIG. 20-69. TRANSIENT RESPONSE OF LOUD-SPEAKER

made upon the amplifier, and an amplifier with a lower rating may be used.

Break-up. An ideal cone moves back and forth like a piston does—in one piece. At high frequencies, many cones tend to vibrate in segments, and complex patterns of vibration travel through the diaphragm. This result is known as break-up (Fig. 20-72). Break-up produces an intermodulation-distortion effect in which the bass frequencies distort the treble frequencies, resulting in the production of a rough, grating sound. Break-up can be reduced by several schemes, one of which is to divide the cone into smaller segments. Another method is to employ a dual-speaker system with separate high-frequency and low-frequency speakers and a dividing network to separate the low frequencies from the highs. Proper design and selection of materials for the diaphragm will also minimize cone break-up (Fig. 20-73).

Size of diaphragm. The final factor to be considered in selecting a speaker is the area of the diaphragm. In general, the larger the diaphragm, the better, since a larger diaphragm produces a greater volume of sound output and also responds better to the lower end of the audio-frequency spectrum (Fig. 20-74).[54]

20.44 *Horn-type loud-speakers*

A horn is essentially an impedance-coupling device for transforming acoustical energy at high pressure and low velocity at the throat of the horn into acoustical energy at low pressure and high velocity at the mouth of the horn (Fig. 20-75). The horn-driving mechanism usually consists of a type of PM unit in which the voice coil is connected

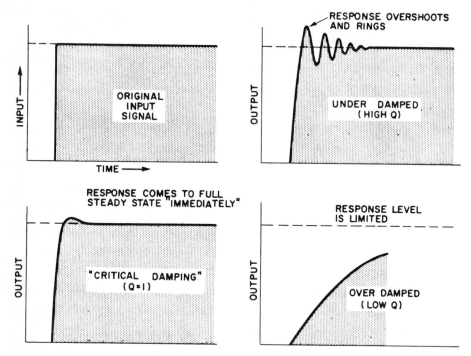

FIG. 20-70. DAMPING ACTION AND THE HANGOVER EFFECT
Proper damping will make the loudspeaker respond to a signal without excessive overshoot and without loss of output.

to a diaphragm instead of to a cone (Fig. 20-76). The horn is therefore used to match the relatively high impedance of the driving mechanism to the low impedance of the air. Most horns are of the flared or exponential trumpet type, although there are some horns of the hyperbolic and conical types (Fig. 20-77). The term exponential refers to the fact that the cross-sectional area of

the horn is proportional to an exponent or power of the distance along the horn (Fig. 20-78).[55] The horn therefore possesses a flared shape resembling that of a trumpet. It was first developed by A. G. Webster, who obtained a patent for it in 1919.

The exponential type of horn is a type of high-pass filter and readily transmits all frequencies above but none

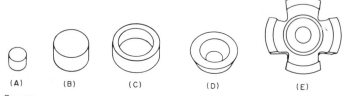

FIG. 20-71. SHAPES AND SIZES OF THE PERMANENT MAGNET
Shapes and sizes are determined by the performance and cost objectives of the loudspeaker; (A) $\frac{1}{2}$-oz slug from 2-in. speaker; (B) 8-oz slug from 12-in. speaker; (C) 6-oz ring magnet from compression driver unit; (D) 12-oz cored slug; (E) 24-oz "W" magnet from coaxial type speaker.

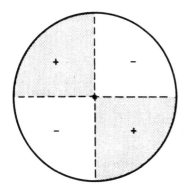

FIG. 20-72. DIAPHRAGM BREAK-UP
The sections marked "plus" may move in one direction and the sections marked "minus" may move in the other as the diaphragm vibrates back and forth.

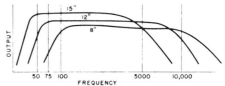

FIG. 20-74. FREQUENCY RESPONSE CURVES OF VARIOUS SIZES OF SPEAKERS

below a certain cutoff frequency. The horn also possesses the ability to focus sound into a beam which can be made as narrow as 30 deg. Since horns are very directional, a second type of horn known as the multicellular horn is often provided with internal deflecting vanes (Fig. 20-79). These vanes divide the horn into many smaller cells and help distribute the higher-frequency sound energy in directions away from the axis of the horn.

In a third type of horn, called the folded or re-entrant horn (Fig. 20-80), the axis along which the area expands is neither a straight line nor a curved

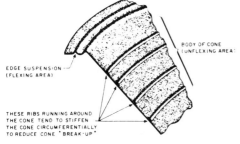

FIG. 20-73. REDUCING CONE BREAK-UP
Cone break-up may be minimized by the application of stiffening ribs as well as by proper diaphragm weight, shape, and stock.

line. The horn folds back upon itself, with a given section expanding along the exterior of the section preceding it. This design obviously conserves space. The folded-horn principle is also used with certain types of enclosures for conventional cone-type loudspeakers, and this application will be described more fully in the sections of this chapter dealing with loudspeaker baffles and enclosures.

There are additional methods of dispersing the sound energy emanating from a horn. In the diffraction horn, the driving element is mounted vertically and the mouth is a narrow vertical slit (Fig. 20-81). The acoustic lens accomplishes sound dispersion by means of a series of perforated screens placed at the mouth of the horn (Fig. 20-82). Finally, the reciprocating-flare horn uses an ingenious patented combination of flares in the vertical and horizontal planes to produce an even sound-dispersal pattern (Fig. 20-83).[56]

20.45 *Comparison of cone speakers and horns*

Cone-type speakers possess low sound-conversion efficiencies, between 5 and 15 per cent, and can handle up to 25 watts of power. Horn-type speakers can handle up to 50 watts of power per unit and possess excellent high-frequency-response characteristics and great directivity. Their efficiencies may range as high as 30 per cent (Fig. 20-84). This increased efficiency means that the

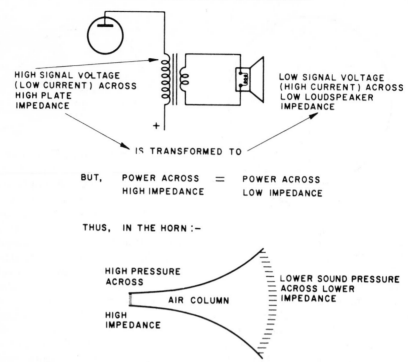

HIGH SIGNAL VOLTAGE
(LOW CURRENT) ACROSS
HIGH PLATE
IMPEDANCE

LOW SIGNAL VOLTAGE
(HIGH CURRENT) ACROSS
LOW LOUDSPEAKER
IMPEDANCE

IS TRANSFORMED TO

BUT,   POWER ACROSS   =   POWER ACROSS
        HIGH IMPEDANCE   LOW IMPEDANCE

THUS,   IN THE HORN :-

HIGH PRESSURE
ACROSS

AIR COLUMN

HIGH
IMPEDANCE

LOWER SOUND PRESSURE
ACROSS LOWER
IMPEDANCE

FIG. 20-75. ANALOGY SHOWING THE IMPEDANCE TRANSFORMATION FUNCTION OF A HORN

amplifier does not have to operate on as high a power level in order to produce a given volume of sound as when a cone-type speaker is used. The reduced amplifier power level is usually accompanied by reduced distortion (Fig. 20-85).

On the other hand, the cone-type speaker possesses better low-frequency-response characteristics and much less directivity. A horn-type speaker that is capable of reproducing low-frequency sounds is a very bulky object indeed. For example, a horn that is capable of

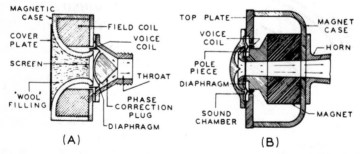

MAGNETIC
CASE
COVER
PLATE
SCREEN
"WOOL"
FILLING

FIELD COIL
VOICE
COIL

THROAT

PHASE
CORRECTION
PLUG
DIAPHRAGM

(A)

TOP PLATE
VOICE
COIL

POLE
PIECE
DIAPHRAGM

SOUND
CHAMBER

MAGNET
CASE

HORN

MAGNET

(B)

Courtesy, Jensen Manufacturing Co.

FIG. 20-76. PERMANENT-MAGNET DRIVER UNITS USED WITH HORN LOUDSPEAKERS
(A) Curved diaphragm; (B) straight-ring diaphragm

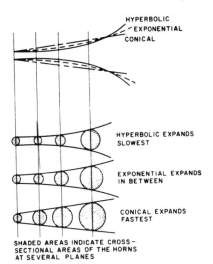

HYPERBOLIC
EXPONENTIAL
CONICAL

HYPERBOLIC EXPANDS
SLOWEST

EXPONENTIAL EXPANDS
IN BETWEEN

CONICAL EXPANDS
FASTEST

SHADED AREAS INDICATE CROSS-
SECTIONAL AREAS OF THE HORNS
AT SEVERAL PLANES

FIG. 20-77. COMPARISON OF THE RATES OF
EXPANSION OF HYPERBOLIC, EXPONENTIAL, AND
CONICAL HORNS HAVING THE SAME THEORETICAL
CUTOFF FREQUENCY

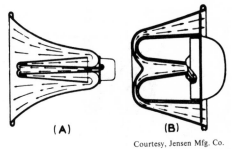

(A)   **(B)**

Courtesy, Jensen Mfg. Co.

FIG. 20-80. TYPES OF RE-ENTRANT HORNS
(A) Trumpet folded twice; (B) trumpet folded once.

reproducing 40 cps must have a mouth with a diameter of at least 5 ft, with a very slow rate of flare from the small end or throat to the mouth.[57] This explains the reason why most horns in use are designed solely for the reproduction of the middle and higher ranges of audio frequencies.

20.46 *Multi-speaker systems*

A dual-speaker system is generally employed for high-quality systems that are designed to reproduce music (Fig. 20-86). This type of speaker system contains a large and heavy cone-type speaker called a woofer, which responds to frequencies as low as 20 cps. One of the largest woofers ever made for home

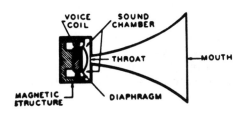

VOICE COIL   SOUND CHAMBER

THROAT

MOUTH

MAGNETIC STRUCTURE   DIAPHRAGM

FIG. 20-78. EXPONENTIAL HORN

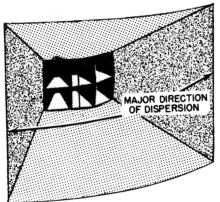

MAJOR DIRECTION OF DISPERSION

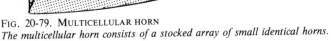

FIG. 20-79. MULTICELLULAR HORN
The multicellular horn consists of a stocked array of small identical horns.

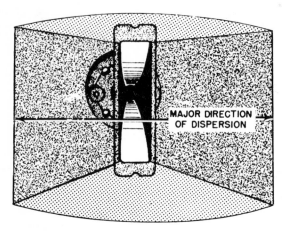

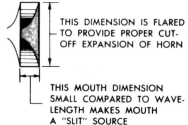

HORN EXPANDS UNIFORMLY IN VERTICAL DIRECTION, IS UNFLARED IN HORIZONTAL DIRECTION

MAJOR DIRECTION OF DISPERSION

THIS DIMENSION IS FLARED TO PROVIDE PROPER CUT-OFF EXPANSION OF HORN

THIS MOUTH DIMENSION SMALL COMPARED TO WAVE-LENGTH MAKES MOUTH A "SLIT" SOURCE

Fig. 20-81. Diffraction horn

use is a 30 in. unit manufactured by Electro-Voice. Its polystyrene cone is capable of responding to frequencies as low as 18 cps. The dual system also contains a small, lightweight cone-type or multicelled horn-type speaker called a tweeter, which responds well to frequencies as high as 20,000 cps (Figs. 20-87 and 20-88).

Since a horn-type tweeter is also very directional, it is usually constructed so that it consists of many separate cells that point in different directions over an angle of 100 deg. The tweeter

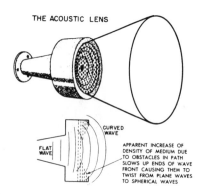

THE ACOUSTIC LENS

CURVED WAVE

FLAT WAVE

APPARENT INCREASE OF DENSITY OF MEDIUM DUE TO OBSTACLES IN PATH SLOWS UP ENDS OF WAVE FRONT CAUSING THEM TO TWIST FROM PLANE WAVES TO SPHERICAL WAVES

Fig. 20-82. Conversion of a plane wave-front into a curved wavefront by an acoustic lens

may be mounted either directly above the woofer or coaxially in the mouth of the woofer (Figs. 20-89, 20-90, and 20-91).[58] The Altec-Lansing 604B is an excellent example of this type of coaxial speaker.

The high-frequency sound output of a cone-type tweeter is also extremely directional. Because of this, it is usually necessary to arrange two or more of these speakers in an arced array in order to cover the listening area with a reasonable degree of uniformity (Fig. 20-92).

When a dual-speaker system is employed, the low frequencies are fed to the woofer and the high frequencies are fed to the tweeter by means of a crossover or frequency-dividing LC filter network (Figs. 20-93 and 20-94). The crossover frequency is generally between 400 and 5,000 cps, depending upon the kind of tweeter and woofer employed. The crossover frequencies that are most-commonly used are 400, 800, 1,000, 2,000, and 5,000 cps (Figs. 20-95 and 20-96).[59] When all other factors are equal, a lower crossover frequency is preferred in high-fidelity systems because it tends to produce a better quality of sound reproduction.

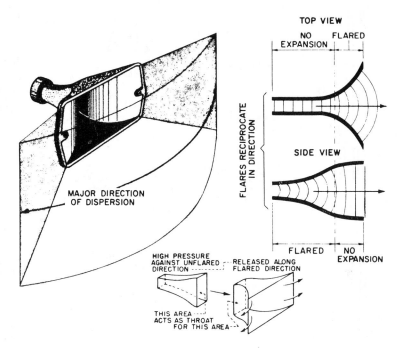

FIG. 20-83. RECIPROCATING FLARE HORN
This horn builds up high pressure against walls in unflared direction; pressure is then released into front flared section to produce uniform wide angle dispersion.

In addition to providing extended range, the use of multiple-speaker systems produces a flatter and smoother over-all response. The physical separation of the various frequency ranges makes it impossible for the heavier thrusts of the lower notes to interfere with the smaller and weaker vibrations of the higher-frequency sounds. The net result is maximum range plus maximum

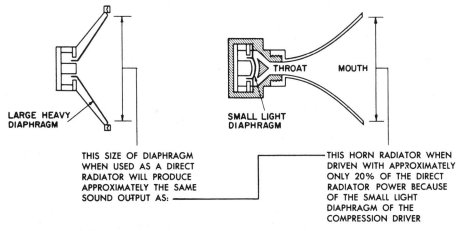

FIG. 20-84. COMPARATIVE EFFICIENCIES OF CONE AND HORN-TYPE SPEAKERS

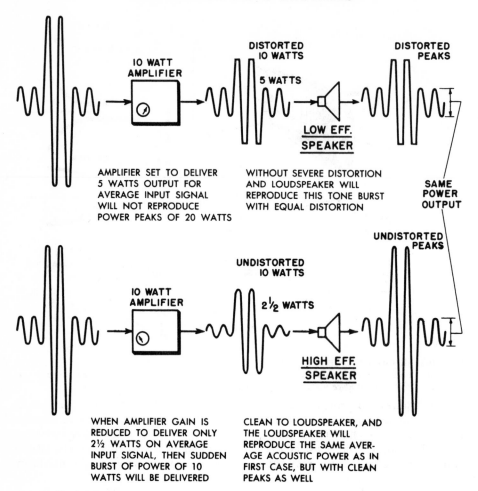

FIG. 20-85. AMPLIFIER GAIN SETTING IN A HORN-TYPE SPEAKER
A low-efficiency speaker requires a high amplifier gain setting, thus producing distortion on the peaks. A high-efficiency speaker permits a low amplifier gain setting, producing less overdriving of the amplifier on the peaks.

clarity. Mention has been made previously of the fact that this separation of the lows from the highs also reduces the amount of speaker break-up and keeps the percentage of intermodulation distortion to a very low value.[60] Since the efficiency of such a system is relatively high, ranging in the neighborhood of 25 per cent, a much-better frequency response and higher power capacity without distortion are possible.

It might be noted that there has also been developed a triaxial type of speaker system containing three separate units: a low-frequency cone-type woofer, a mid-range unit called a squawker, and a high-frequency tweeter (Figs. 20-97 and 20-98). In addition, there is also a four-way speaker system in which the reproduced sound spectrum is divided between four separate drivers. The crossover frequencies are 200, 600,

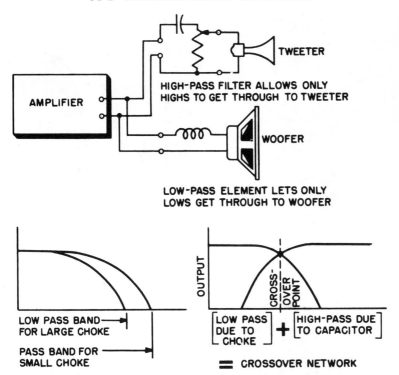

FIG. 20-86. DUAL-SPEAKER SYSTEM

Courtesy, (a) Electro-Voice, Inc; (b) Jensen Manufacturing Co.

FIG. 20-87. CONE-TYPE WOOFER (LEFT), CONE-TYPE TWEETER (RIGHT)

Courtesy, University Loudspeakers, Inc.

FIG. 20-88. HORN-TYPE TWEETER

Courtesy, Altec Lansing Corp.

FIG. 20-90. COAXIAL SPEAKER WITH A MULTI-CELLULAR-HORN TWEETER

Courtesy, Jensen Manufacturing Co.

FIG. 20-89. COAXIAL SPEAKER WITH A CONE-TYPE TWEETER

Courtesy, University Loudspeakers, Inc.

FIG. 20-91. TYPICAL COAXIAL LOUDSPEAKER

and 3,500 cps, and the frequency range is from 32 cps to beyond the range of hearing.

Another interesting recent devel-opment is an electronic crossover net-work (Fig. 20-99). The electronic cross-over follows the pre-amplifier stage. After the signal has been amplified and passed through a filter, one output is

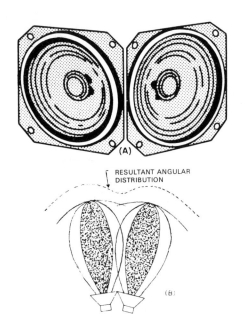

RESULTANT ANGULAR
DISTRIBUTION

(B)

FIG. 20-92. CONE-TYPE TWEETERS ARRANGED IN
AN ARC ARRAY TO IMPROVE ANGULAR RADIATION

fed to a low-power frequency amplifier and woofer, while the other is fed to a high-frequency power amplifier and tweeter. This system requires additional power-amplifier components, but it possesses compensating advantages related to flexibility of operation and reduction of intermodulation distortion.[61]

20.47 *Dual-cone speaker*

One of the recent developments in dual-speaker systems is a patented device called the Diffusicone (Fig. 20-100). This is one of a group of speakers known as dual-cone speakers, which employ a single magnet and voice coil to drive two cones of different resonances. The Diffusicone represents an economical compromise between a single-cone unit and a full dual-speaker system containing a crossover network.[62]

It contains a large cone to take care of the lows and an auxiliary diaphragm at the apex of the speaker to handle the highs. The rim of the inner section is folded back to form a dual horn. The section that is folded back contains holes designed to produce an even dispersal of the higher-frequency sounds (Fig. 20-101). Each portion of the speaker acts independently. No crossover network is necessary because there is a mechanical crossover effect which operates at a frequency of 1,000 cps to divide the incoming signal between the two cones.[63]

20.48 *Biflex speaker*

A somewhat similar type of speaker is called the Biflex (Fig. 20-102). The compliance of the cone is such that it serves as a mechanical crossover. At frequencies below 1,000 cps, the stiffness of the cone is such that its inner and outer sections are coupled into a single larger integral unit. At frequencies above 1,000 cps, the two sections of the cone are uncoupled and the inner section operates independently. It is claimed that this speaker possesses an efficient frequency range that far exceeds that of any other type of single-voice-coil speaker and is equal to or exceeds that of the majority of two- or three-way units.

20.49 *New developments in loudspeakers*

While the art of designing loudspeakers has progressed considerably since the first sound reproducer was designed by Bell, the fundamental operating principles of the conventional loudspeaker are practically identical with those of Bell's receiver. We still employ diaphragms and cones which vibrate and displace air, thus producing

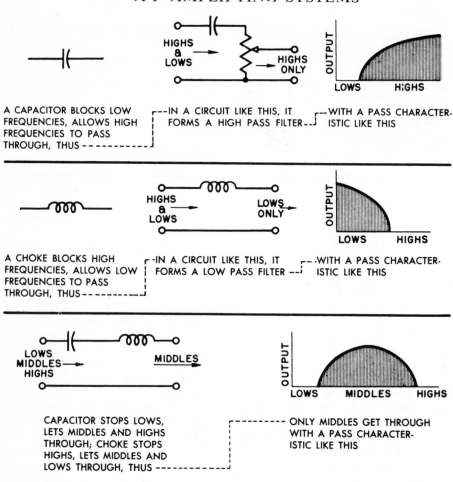

A CAPACITOR BLOCKS LOW FREQUENCIES, ALLOWS HIGH FREQUENCIES TO PASS THROUGH, THUS ----------

---IN A CIRCUIT LIKE THIS, IT FORMS A HIGH PASS FILTER---

---WITH A PASS CHARACTERISTIC LIKE THIS

A CHOKE BLOCKS HIGH FREQUENCIES, ALLOWS LOW FREQUENCIES TO PASS THROUGH, THUS ----------

-IN A CIRCUIT LIKE THIS, IT FORMS A LOW PASS FILTER --

--WITH A PASS CHARACTERISTIC LIKE THIS

CAPACITOR STOPS LOWS, LETS MIDDLES AND HIGHS THROUGH; CHOKE STOPS HIGHS, LETS MIDDLES AND LOWS THROUGH, THUS ----------

---------- ONLY MIDDLES GET THROUGH WITH A PASS CHARACTERISTIC LIKE THIS

FIG. 20-93. OPERATING PRINCIPLES OF A CROSSOVER NETWORK

sound. All these devices suffer to some extent from transient distortion, which results from the fact that inertia tends to cause the cone to keep vibrating after the signal has stopped, thus producing spurious sounds.

Another fault of present-day speakers is the fact that if one wishes to cover the entire audio-frequency spectrum, he must employ more than one speaker. The solution to both of these problems lies in the development of an inertialess speaker that is capable of covering the entire audio-frequency spectrum. The operating principles of such a speaker would have to be quite different from those of Bell's electromagnetic reproducer. The Ionophone and the electrostatic or capacitive loudspeaker represent attempts to solve these problems through application of entirely different operating principles.

A third weakness of today's loudspeaker is the relative weakness of the sound output. The Stanford Airstream Modulator is designed to overcome this weakness and to produce sounds of extremely high intensity.[64]

20.50 *The Ionophone*

The Ionophone is a true inertialess speaker that was developed in 1951 by Klein, a French physicist (Figs. 20-103 and 20-104). It consists of a quartz-glass exponential horn, 2 in. in length, connected to a larger exponential horn. A fine platinum wire is placed at the smaller end. The application of radio-frequency energy to this wire produces ionization of the air. When this r-f energy is modulated by an audio-signal, the variations in ionization produce varying air pressures corresponding to sound waves. Thus, sound waves are set

Courtesy, Electro-Voice, Inc.

FIG. 20-94. MODEL X 36 CROSSOVER NETWORK

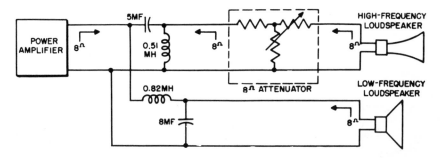

FIG. 20-95. DESIGN OF A PRACTICAL FREQUENCY-DIVIDING NETWORK WITH A CROSSOVER FREQUENCY OF 2,500 CPS

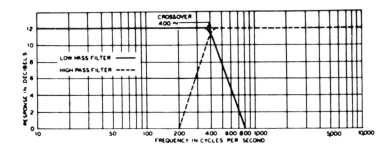

FIG. 20-96. IDEAL FREQUENCY-RESPONSE CURVE OF A DUAL-RANGE LOUDSPEAKER SYSTEM WITH CROSSOVER POINT AT 400 CPS.

Courtesy, (left) University Loudspeakers, Inc; (right) Jensen Manufacturing Co.

FIG. 20-97. TWO TYPICAL 15-IN. TRIAXIAL SPEAKERS

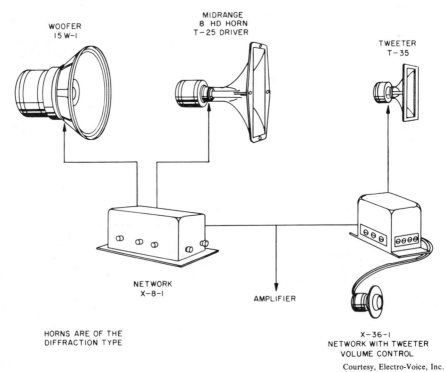

Courtesy, Electro-Voice, Inc.

FIG. 20-98. THREE-WAY MULTI-SPEAKER SYSTEM WITH CROSSOVER POINTS AT 800 AND 3,500 CPS

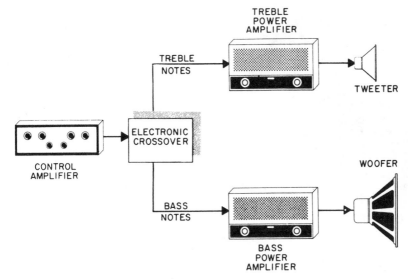

FIG. 20-99. LOCATION OF ELECTRONIC CROSSOVER IN AN AMPLIFYING SYSTEM

up directly in the air without the need for employing the conventional diaphragm found in ordinary tweeters. The Ionophone was probably the first sound-producing transducer to be completely free from moving parts.

This speaker works better as the frequency of the audio signal is increased, and it is an excellent ultrasonic transducer, operating at frequencies as high as 1 mc. Commercial models of this device have been produced by the Telefunken Company of Hanover, Germany and it is now being manufactured in the United States.[65] As might be expected,

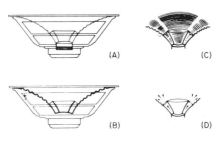

Courtesy, University Loudspeakers, Inc.
FIG. 20-101. HIGH FREQUENCY DISPERSION IN A DIFFUSICONE SPEAKER
(A) Aural dome over voice coil maximizes use of higher frequencies; (B) specially flared diaphragm affixed to center portion of dome; (C) outer horn, actually a radial projector, sends sound waves off on extreme angles from speaker axis; (D) apertures in radial projector diffract very high frequencies.

Courtesy, University Loudspeakers, Inc.
FIG. 20-100. TWO-WAY 8-IN. DIFFUSICONE DIFF-AXIAL SPEAKER

Courtesy, Altec Lansing Corp.

FIG. 20-102. BIFLEX LOUDSPEAKER

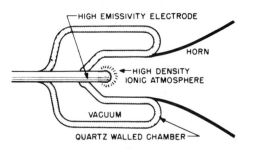

FIG. 20-103. THE IONOPHONE
A dielectric field placed around the quartz cylinder heats the quartz, which in turn heats the high-emissivity electrode. The ionic atmosphere boiled off from the electrode is modulated by a surrounding modulated r-f field and pulses accordingly to place the air into motion.

it is comparatively expensive and also requires a very large horn if it is to be used to cover the entire audio range.

The special characteristics of this type of speaker suggest interesting possibilities. Radio receivers intended to be used with this speaker can be designed without the usual stages of detection and audio amplification, since the radio frequencies or intermediate frequencies can, if they are amplified sufficiently, serve as a source of excitation for the loudspeaker. This elimination of the detector stage would serve two purposes. It would eliminate one source of distortion, and it would also eliminate the need for the oscillator cir-

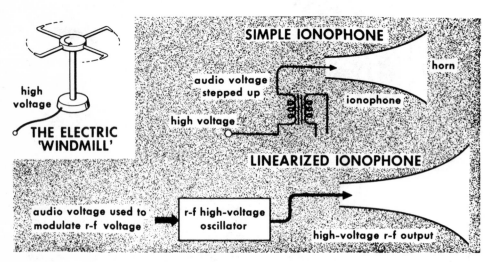

FIG. 20-104. SIMPLE AND LINEARIZED IONOPHONES

cuit that is now required to provide the high-frequency excitation for this novel type of speaker.[66]

20.51 *The Ionovac*

In 1957, the DuKane Corporation of St. Charles, Ill., developed a modified version of the Ionophone. This device, called the Ionovac, is now being manufactured by Electro-Voice (Fig. 20-105). It is designed for use in high-fidelity audio-amplifier systems. The electric field is created by an oscillator operating at a frequency between 17 and 25 mc (Figs. 20-106, 20-107, and 20-108). This oscillator is modulated by audio-frequency or ultrasonic signals to produce corresponding pressure waves and sound waves in the air. Its response curve is flat within 5 db from 2,000 to 20,000 cps and does not deviate much from this level at considerably higher frequencies. It is capable of producing air-pressure waves at frequencies from 1,000 cps to 500 kc. The lower frequency limit of 1,000 cps is set by the dimensions of the horn.[67]

Courtesy, Radio-Electronics
FIG. 20-105. IONOVAC LOUDSPEAKER
The "unit" is the small quartz tube in the foreground. A small stylus is inserted into the narrow part of the tube and a 20-mc rf current is applied between its point and a collar around the tube's neck, ionizing the air around the point. By modulating the rf with audio frequency, sound waves are produced as the ionization of the air varies.

20.52 *The corona-wind loudspeaker*

Another type of inertialess loudspeaker that converts electrical energy directly into sound energy without any moving parts is the corona-wind loudspeaker or CWLS, invented by Tombs, a New Zealand engineer (Fig. 20-109). It makes use of the corona-wind effect and the resulting movement of ionized air away from a high-voltage discharge point (Fig. 20-110).

A high difference of potential is applied between two sharply pointed opposed electrodes, while a smooth ring is placed around the positive electrode (Fig. 20-111). This ring tends to behave like a control grid and controls the amount of corona current and corona wind. When a signal voltage is applied between this control grid and the positive electrode, a pulsating wind is produced which becomes a source of sound. Two of these units can be connected in a push-pull arrangement designed to minimize distortion.

The device possesses no audible resonant frequency, and its frequency response is smoother than that of cone-type speakers. It is claimed that in its perfected form the speaker will have a response that is essentially flat from zero cps to beyond the upper limit of audibility.[68] It requires no coupling mechanism or transformer. When it is used as a full-range reproducer, it requires baffling in order to preserve the low-frequency response.[69]

20.53 *The electrostatic speaker*

An electrostatic speaker, unlike the ionic and corona speakers, is not a truly inertialess speaker, but it comes very close to it. It is fundamentally nothing more than a capacitor, one

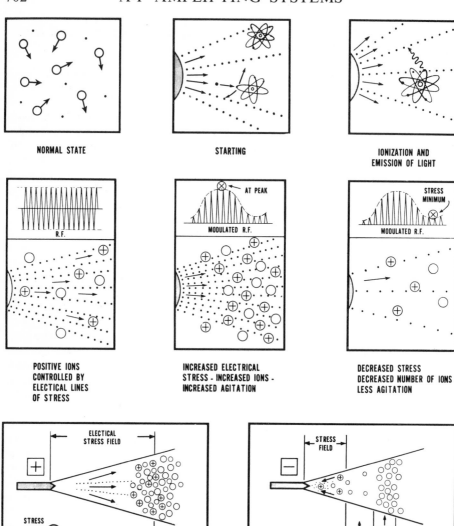

FIG. 20-106. OPERATION OF THE IONOVAC

Courtesy, DuKane Corp.

plate of which is a moving metallic diaphragm (Figs. 20-112 and 20-113). It may be considered to be a condenser microphone that is operating in reverse. Its principle of operation was developed in 1879 by Dolbear, who employed it in a simple condenser or capacitance telephone system.

An early type of electrostatic speaker was the Oscilloplan, which was developed in 1927 by a German scientist named Vogt. It required a polarizing voltage of 2,500 volts across its plates. This high voltage tended to produce

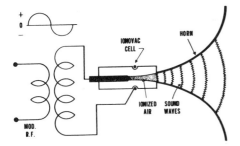

Courtesy, DuKane Corp.

FIG. 20-107. DIAGRAM OF THE IONOVAC

sparking, which affected the acoustic quality of the output.

The success of the present-day electrostatic speaker is primarily due to the development of new plastic materials with high physical strength and good electrical-insulating properties. When coated with a thin layer of metal, this plastic makes an ideal diaphragm for an electrostatic speaker.

The diaphragm is usually mounted between two metallic screens, and a d-c polarizing voltage of 250 volts is applied between the diaphragm and the screen. When an audio-frequency signal voltage is superimposed, the forces of electrostatic attraction and repulsion cause the entire diaphragm to vibrate and to produce sound waves. Because the diaphragm is so light, it responds well to transient signals and to high-frequency signals. The push-pull operation pro-

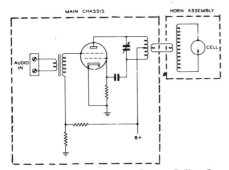

Courtesy, DuKane Corp.

FIG. 20-108. SIMPLIFIED SCHEMATIC OF IONO-VAC

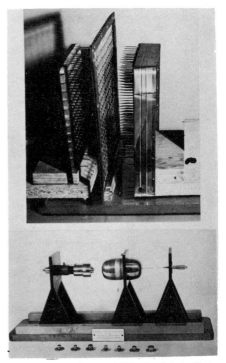

Courtesy, Aldshir Manufacturing Co. Inc.

FIG. 20-109. EARLY MODELS OF THE CORONA LOUDSPEAKER

duced by the two metallic screens and the fact that the diaphragm is pushed with equal force at every point on its surface tend to reduce distortion (Fig. 20-114).[70] Another advantage is associated with the fact that the diaphragm can be made very large, up to several feet square. Furthermore, electrostatic speakers do not require critically designed enclosures for operation.

The electrostatic speaker was first extensively employed in Germany for high-frequency tweeter units. However, full-range electrostatic speakers are now available. Recently, both Philco and Columbia have employed electrostatic tweeter units on some of their radio-phonographs (Figs. 20-115 and 20-116).[71]

The Acoustical Manufacturing Company of Huntingdon, England, has

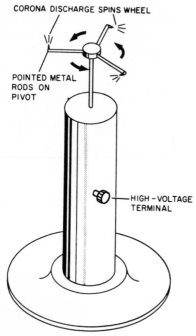

Courtesy, *Radio-Electronics*

FIG. 20-110. CORONA-WIND EFFECT
The wheel spins exactly as if air were jetting out of each point.

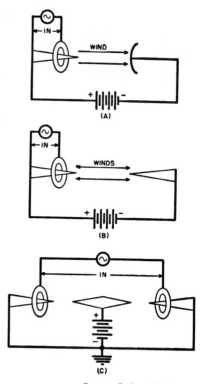

Courtesy, Radio and Television News

FIG. 20-111. OPERATING PRINCIPLES OF THE CORONA LOUDSPEAKER.
(A) Simplest form of "Corona" triode speaker which produces steady "background" wind; (B) advanced form in which winds are balanced on no signal; (C) a push-pull version of the original "corona loudspeaker."

produced an electrostatic speaker called the Acoustical. This speaker has a virtually-distortionless response from 40 cps to well above the range of human hearing.[72] In the United States, Pickering has developed two commercial Isophase electrostatic speakers (Fig. 20-117). One is for the range from 400 cps up, and the second, a smaller one, is for the range from 1,000 cps up.[73] The same company has also developed two experimental electrostatic units, one a tweeter and the other a woofer. The crossover point is 400 cps, and the manufacturer claims that the response of the speaker is flat from 25 to 25,000 cps, and that the speaker system can reproduce sound accurately up to 35,000 cps.

Like most newly developed devices, the electrostatic speaker possesses certain disadvantages. When an electrostatic tweeter is teamed up with a dynamic-loudspeaker woofer, there is a pronounced difference in the impedance characteristics of the two units. This is due to the fact that the impedance of any capacitive device is inversely proportional to the frequency, while the impedance of an inductive component, such as a conventional voice-coil type of loudspeaker, is directly proportional to the frequency. This effect produces problems in matching the two units to the same amplifier (Fig. 20-118).[74][75]

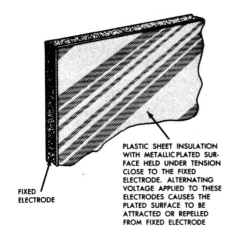

FIXED
ELECTRODE

PLASTIC SHEET INSULATION
WITH METALLIC PLATED SUR-
FACE HELD UNDER TENSION
CLOSE TO THE FIXED
ELECTRODE. ALTERNATING
VOLTAGE APPLIED TO THESE
ELECTRODES CAUSES THE
PLATED SURFACE TO BE
ATTRACTED OR REPELLED
FROM FIXED ELECTRODE

FIG. 20-112. BASIC STRUCTURE OF THE ELEC-
TROSTATIC SPEAKER

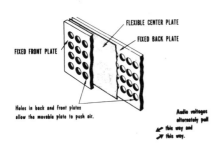

FLEXIBLE CENTER PLATE

FIXED BACK PLATE

FIXED FRONT PLATE

Holes in back and front plates
allow the movable plate to push air.

Audio voltages
alternately pull
◄ this way and
► this way.

FIG. 20-113. ELECTROSTATIC SPEAKER DIA-
PHRAGM

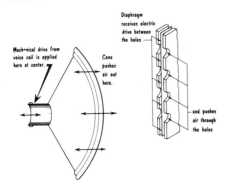

Diaphragm
receives electric
drive between
the holes

Mechanical drive from
voice coil is applied
here at center.

Cone
pushes
air out
here.

...and pushes
air through
the holes

FIG. 20-114. COMPARISON BETWEEN THE DYNA-
MIC MOVING-COIL SPEAKER AND THE ELECTRO-
STATIC SPEAKER
*Unlike the moving coil speaker's diaphragm, the
electrostatic speaker's diaphragm is driven almost
uniformly.*

In addition, the impedance of the electrostatic speaker is entirely capacitive. When the speaker is matched to the amplifier, this effective capacitance is approximately 3 μfd. This capacitance may cause the amplifier to break into oscillation.[76] The sound-conversion efficiency of the electrostatic speaker is low, which limits the acoustic power it can deliver. Finally, there may be a high inherent noise level due to corona hiss produced on the surface of the diaphragm.

20.54 *Electrostrictive speakers*

Electrostrictive speakers are very similar to electrostatic speakers. They employ the principle of electrostriction, which involves the contraction of a material when a voltage is applied across it. Loudspeakers have been constructed in which a paper cone is attached to an electrostrictive disc of barium titanate (Fig. 20-119). When an audio-frequency voltage is impressed across the disc, the disc vibrates and these vibrations can be conveyed directly to the cone. This device can be connected directly to the output stage of an audio-frequency amplifier.[77] [78]

20.55 *The Stanford air-stream modulator*

The Stanford airstream modulator or SAM is a compressed-air loudspeaker and amplifier that is capable of being heard over a distance of between 1.5 and 4 miles. It was developed for the Signal Corps by Vincent Salmon of the Stanford Research Institute and is intended for use in military applications such as amphibious landings. It is also being used by acoustic experts as a source of noise for experiments in reducing the offensive effects of loud

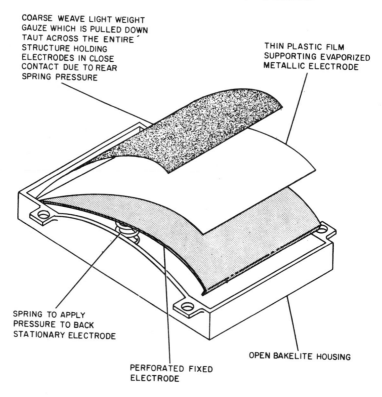

COARSE WEAVE LIGHT WEIGHT GAUZE WHICH IS PULLED DOWN TAUT ACROSS THE ENTIRE STRUCTURE HOLDING ELECTRODES IN CLOSE CONTACT DUE TO REAR SPRING PRESSURE

THIN PLASTIC FILM SUPPORTING EVAPORIZED METALLIC ELECTRODE

SPRING TO APPLY PRESSURE TO BACK STATIONARY ELECTRODE

PERFORATED FIXED ELECTRODE

OPEN BAKELITE HOUSING

FIG. 20-115. ONE FORM OF ELECTROSTATIC SPEAKER

noises produced by jet planes and in studies of the effects of sonic fatigue upon metal structures.

This device is of the modulated-airstream type, and its operation is analogous to the production of sound by human beings. This operation depends upon the controlled emission of a stream of compressed air. The airstream is caused to vary by means of a quick-acting valve that is operated by an amplifier and is controlled by the sounds made by the person who is speaking. These air fluctuations are then sent to an acoustic horn where they are changed into sound. The compressor and air-pipes correspond to human lungs and bronchial tubes; the valve corresponds to the human vocal cords and larynx; the amplifier controls the modulation in a manner analogous to that of the central nervous system; and the horn is analogous to the human mouth.[79][80] The device requires 10 watts of air power and 10 watts of electric-control power; it possesses an efficiency of 80 per cent of the theoretical maximum.

Toward the end of 1958, engineers at RCA announced that they had developed a similar type of instrument that was capable of producing the loudest controlled noise in the world. Called the compressed air loudspeaker, it can be heard at a distance of 10 miles. It will be used to study the effects of high noise intensities, such as those produced by jet engines, upon sensitive electronic equipment.[81]

Researchers have been working for over 50 years on the problem of de-

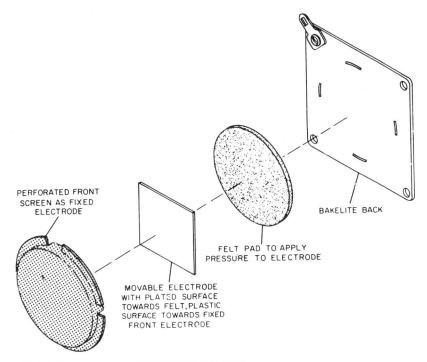

PERFORATED FRONT
SCREEN AS FIXED
ELECTRODE

BAKELITE BACK

FELT PAD TO APPLY
PRESSURE TO ELECTRODE

MOVABLE ELECTRODE
WITH PLATED SURFACE
TOWARDS FELT, PLASTIC
SURFACE TOWARDS FIXED
FRONT ELECTRODE

FIG. 20-116. SECOND FORM OF ELECTROSTATIC SPEAKER

signing a modulated-airstream speaker. The SAM and the RCA compressed air loudspeaker represent the latest but not the only attempts to solve this problem. Edison, Chichester Bell, and C. A. Parsons developed compressed air loudspeakers and amplifiers. Edison called his device the Aerophone, while Parsons named his the Auxetophone. Gibson and Dennison of the Victor Company combined this system with the phonograph, and in 1904, scientists working for the Pathe Company attempted to couple it with motion pictures to produce sound motion pictures. However, poorly designed mechanisms prevented these compressed-air devices from producing satisfactory results, and they were commercial failures.

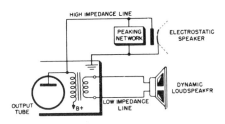

HIGH IMPEDANCE LINE

PEAKING
NETWORK

ELECTROSTATIC
SPEAKER

DYNAMIC
LOUDSPEAKER

OUTPUT
TUBE

B+

LOW IMPEDANCE
LINE

Courtesy, Pickering and Co., Inc.

FIG. 20-117. PICKERING ISOPHASE ELECTRO-STATIC SPEAKER

FIG. 20-118. COMPARISON BETWEEN CONNEC-TIONS OF ELECTROSTATIC AND DYNAMIC SPEAKER

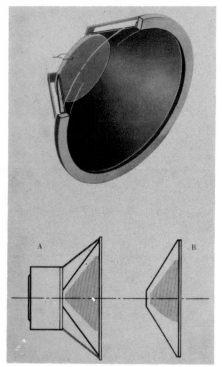

Courtesy, *Radio-Electronics* and Mullenbach Div., Electric Machinery Mfg. Co.

FIG. 20-119. STRUCTURE OF A CAPADYNE ELEC-TROSTRICTIVE LOUDSPEAKER

Comparison of conventional loudspeaker (A) with new, light-weight loudspeaker using ceramic driver element (B) Ceramic disc removes need for heavy magnets and coils.

During the early 1940's, Dilks developed a fairly successful modulated airstream speaker called the Vocal-Aire, which produced a volume of sound greater than that of 25 conventional speakers of the same physical size. Its major weakness was its poor fidelity, since its frequency range was from approximately 250 to 5,000 cps, which was satisfactory for the reproduction of speech but not for musical reproduction.[82]

20.56 *Baffles*

The low-frequency-response characteristics of a loudspeaker are dependent upon the type and size of baffle or enclosure used. All cone-type speakers require baffles, which may consist of an open-back box, a large piece of wall board, or a reflex cabinet (Figs. 20-120 and 20-121).

The purpose of the baffle is to improve speaker efficiency and performance by loading the speaker cone and by preventing a collision between the sound waves produced by the front of the cone and the sound waves produced by the rear. Such collisions tend to cancel out the low-frequency sound waves. This effect is particularly marked at frequencies where the wavelength of the sound is much greater than the dimensions of the loudspeaker. It should be noted that a baffle is a necessary evil that is used to avoid cancellation of sound waves and that it does not improve the quality of the original sound produced by the loudspeaker.[83]

In order to prevent the baffle from resonating, the cone should be mounted off-center. In addition, the baffle should be made of a material that possesses substantial mass and will not vibrate too readily.

20.57 *The flat or plane surface baffle*

The simplest type of baffle is the plane-surface baffle (Fig. 20-122). The speaker is mounted within a large plane surface, wall, or closet. This type of baffle is quite popular, but it requires a considerable amount of space since its dimensions determine the frequency below which a loss in bass radiation will occur. Thus, in order to obtain good frequency response down to 50 cps, the distance from the speaker to the edge of the baffle would have to be 11 ft. Additional disadvantages are a tendency towards boominess at the resonant

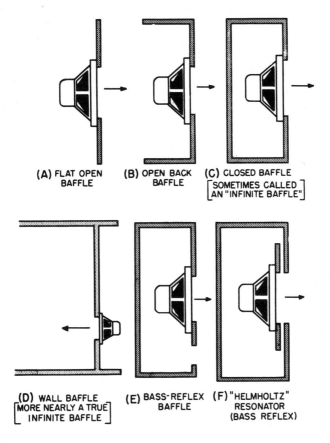

(A) FLAT OPEN BAFFLE   (B) OPEN BACK BAFFLE   (C) CLOSED BAFFLE [SOMETIMES CALLED AN "INFINITE BAFFLE"]

(D) WALL BAFFLE [MORE NEARLY A TRUE INFINITE BAFFLE]   (E) BASS-REFLEX BAFFLE   (F) "HELMHOLTZ" RESONATOR (BASS REFLEX)

FIG. 20-120. FORMS OF DIRECT RADIATOR BAFFLES
The face of the diaphragm feeds directly into open space.

frequency of the speaker and a dropping off of the low-frequency response as the listener approaches the plane of the baffle.

20.58 *The infinite baffle*

A second type of baffle is the infinite baffle. This consists of a large, rigid, enclosed cabinet lined on the inside with absorbing material designed to absorb nearly all of the sound emitted from the back of the loudspeaker (Fig. 20-123). Theoretically, this produces infinite separation between the front and back waves. The enclosure must be rigid in order to reduce vibrations from its surfaces which could affect the quality of the sound. The shape is relatively unimportant, although square shapes should be avoided. The total volume should be at least 10 cu ft, and a volume of 15 cu ft is preferable in order to eliminate undesirable resonant-speaker effects. The enclosure possesses low efficiency, since half of the audio output of the speaker is absorbed by the lining of the baffle and converted into frictional heat. Another disadvantage is the fact that the baffle provides no acoustic assistance to help couple the loudspeaker to the air of the room.[84]

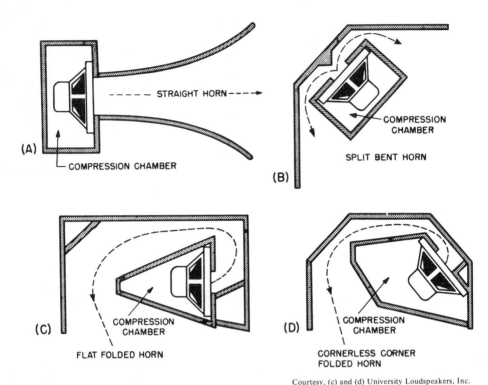

- - - - - STRAIGHT HORN - - - →

(A)

└─ COMPRESSION CHAMBER

COMPRESSION
CHAMBER

SPLIT BENT HORN

(B)

COMPRESSION
CHAMBER

(C)

FLAT FOLDED HORN

COMPRESSION
CHAMBER

(D)

CORNERLESS CORNER
FOLDED HORN

Courtesy, (c) and (d) University Loudspeakers, Inc.

FIG. 20-121. FORMS OF INDIRECT RADIATOR BAFFLES
The horn element is interposed between the listening area and the diaphragm. The compression chamber seals off the rear of the diaphragm.

20.59 *The bass-reflex baffle*

No one person's name is associated with the development of the bass-reflex

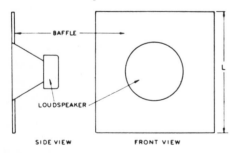

BAFFLE

L

LOUDSPEAKER

SIDE VIEW   FRONT VIEW

FIG. 20-122. THE PLANE-SURFACE BAFFLE
In order to prevent the sound waves that are set up in the rear of the speaker from interfering with those from the front, a plane-surface baffle may be placed in the plane of the cone as shown

type of enclosure. In 1930, A. L. Thuras of Bell Telephone Laboratories was awarded a patent for a system employing a cabinet that contained an opening with short internal pipes. However, most of the developmental work seems to have been accomplished by scientists of RCA, and the first commercial bass-reflex cabinet was brought out by that organization in 1938. Interestingly enough, the name bass-reflex was derived from a similar type of enclosure bearing that name that was brought out later by Jensen Manufacturing Co.[85]

A baffle of the bass-reflex type contains a hole called a port or vent. This port is usually located below the loudspeaker opening (Fig. 20-124). It is basically nothing more than a Helm-

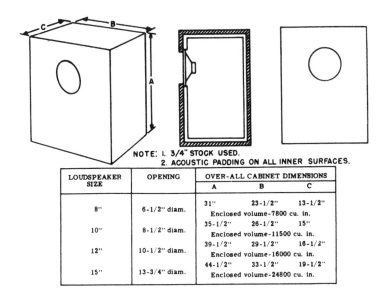

NOTE: 1. 3/4" STOCK USED.
2. ACOUSTIC PADDING ON ALL INNER SURFACES.

LOUDSPEAKER SIZE	OPENING	OVER-ALL CABINET DIMENSIONS		
		A	B	C
8"	6-1/2" diam.	31" 23-1/2" 13-1/2" Enclosed volume-7800 cu. in.		
10"	8-1/2" diam.	35-1/2" 26-1/2" 15" Enclosed volume-11500 cu. in.		
12"	10-1/2" diam.	39-1/2" 29-1/2" 16-1/2" Enclosed volume-16000 cu. in.		
15"	13-3/4" diam.	44-1/2" 33-1/2" 19-1/2" Enclosed volume-24800 cu. in.		

FIG. 20-123. CONSTRUCTION DETAILS AND DESIGN DATA FOR INFINITE-BAFFLE CABINETS

holtz resonator—a cavity with a communicating duct to free air. The low-frequency sound waves radiated from the back of the speaker are phase inverted or shifted in phase by 180 deg. They leave the part in phase with the low-frequency sound waves produced at the front of the speaker. For this reason, the baffle is sometimes called an acoustic phase inverter.

Since an absorbent lining inside the baffle tends to absorb the higher-frequency sounds, the low-frequency response is accentuated considerably. The characteristics of this type of baffle may be varied by using a sliding panel

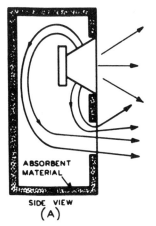

SIDE VIEW
(A)

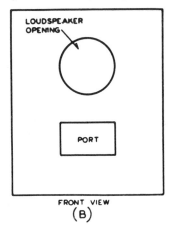

FRONT VIEW
(B)

FIG. 20-124. DIAGRAM OF A BASS-REFLEX BAFFLE
The sound waves emerging from the rear of the speaker travel through the port and are in phase with those coming from the front of the diaphragm

to change the area of the vent. In this manner, the enclosure may be tuned or acoustically matched to the speaker for maximum efficiency and minimum distortion. The resonant effects produced by the air cavity of the enclosure also tend to cancel the natural resonance of the speaker, thus reducing the bass peak produced by speaker resonance and also smoothing the response curve.

The position of the vent or port is not too critical. In general, it should be fairly close to the speaker, but not closer than 4 in. (Fig. 20-125). The dimensions of the enclosure should resemble those of a cube and the ratio between any two dimensions should not exceed 3 to 1.[86] This type of baffle is inexpensive and simple to construct and produces excellent results. Consequently, it is probably the most popular and most widely used type of baffle.

20.60 *The labyrinth cabinet*

The labyrinth cabinet, which was developed by Stromberg-Carlson, is another type of phase-inverter baffle. It is essentially a folded resonant tube that is lined in such a manner that it absorbs all frequencies above 150 cps (Fig. 20-126). The length of the tube is such that it is a quarter of the wavelength of the resonant frequency of the loudspeaker system (Fig. 20-127). It therefore acts as a high impedance to that frequency, thus damping it. The tube is one-half wavelength for double that frequency, and it then acts as a phase inverter, reinforcing the sounds in a manner analogous to that of the bass-reflex baffle. Its principal advantage is that it occupies less space than the bass-reflex baffle does. Its main disadvantage is its low efficiency.

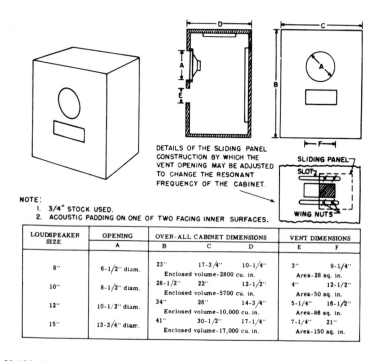

DETAILS OF THE SLIDING PANEL CONSTRUCTION BY WHICH THE VENT OPENING MAY BE ADJUSTED TO CHANGE THE RESONANT FREQUENCY OF THE CABINET.

SLIDING PANEL

SLOT

WING NUTS

NOTE:
1. 3/4" STOCK USED.
2. ACOUSTIC PADDING ON ONE OF TWO FACING INNER SURFACES.

LOUDSPEAKER SIZE	OPENING	OVER-ALL CABINET DIMENSIONS			VENT DIMENSIONS	
	A	B	C	D	E	F
8"	6-1/2" diam.	23"	17-3/4"	10-1/4"	3"	9-1/4"
		Enclosed volume-2800 cu. in.			Area-28 sq. in.	
10"	8-1/2" diam.	28-1/2"	22"	12-1/2"	4"	12-1/2"
		Enclosed volume-5700 cu. in.			Area-50 sq. in.	
12"	10-1/2" diam.	34"	26"	14-3/4"	5-1/4"	16-1/2"
		Enclosed volume-10,000 cu. in.			Area-86 sq. in.	
15"	13-3/4" diam.	41"	30-1/2"	17-1/4"	7-1/4"	21"
		Enclosed volume-17,000 cu. in.			Area-150 sq. in.	

FIG. 20-125. CONSTRUCTION DETAILS AND DESIGN DATA FOR BASS-REFLEX CABINETS

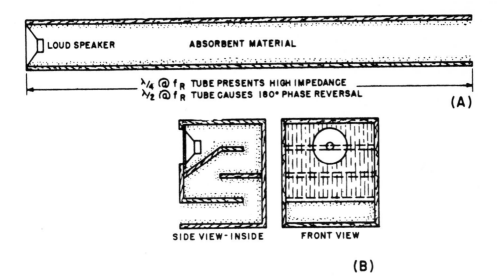

FIG. 20-126. PRINCIPLE OF THE LABYRINTH CABINET
(A) Method of coupling the back of a loudspeaker cone to the air through a resonant tube; (B) labyrinth cabinet formed by folding the resonant tube.

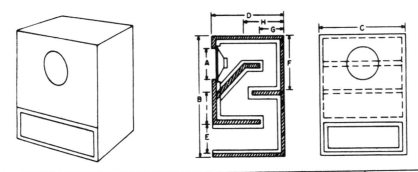

LOUDSPEAKER SIZE	SPEAKER OPENING	OVER-ALL CABINET DIMENSIONS			PARTITION POSITIONING					MATERIAL
	A	B	C	D	E	F	G	H	I	
8"	6-1/2" diam.	17"	14"	11-1/2"	3"	9-1/2"	2-1/2"	5"	3-3/4"	1/2" plywood 1/2" felt padding
10"	8-1/2" diam.	21-3/4"	17"	14"	4-1/2"	10-1/2"	4"	5"	3"	3/4" plywood 3/4" felt padding
12"	10-1/2" diam.	27-3/4"	21"	16-3/4"	6"	13-1/2"	5-3/4"	6-1/4"	5"	3/4" plywood 1" felt padding
15"	13-3/4" d. cm.	35"	25"	21"	7"	18"	6-1/2"	7-1/2"	4"	3/4" plywood 1" felt padding

NOTE: ACOUSTIC PADDING ON ALL INNER SURFACES

FIG. 20-127. CONSTRUCTION DETAILS AND DESIGN DATA FOR LABYRINTH CABINETS

20.61 *The folded horn*

A type of baffle that is becoming widely used is the folded-horn type that was developed by Paul Klipsch in 1940. The high-frequency sounds are radiated from the front of the speaker cone, while the lower-frequency sounds are radiated from a horn coupled to the rear of the cone (Figs. 20-128 and 20-129). Mention has previously been made of the fact that a horn can function as an acoustical equivalent of an impedance-matching transformer. This arrangement therefore serves as a device to couple the low impedance that is offered by the air to sounds of low frequency to the high impedance of the speaker cone. A well-designed folded horn is extremely efficient, has a good low-frequency response that is superior to that of a bass-reflex enclosure, and reproduces frequencies as low as 20 cps from standard commercial loudspeakers. A well-designed horn may also possess an efficiency of 40 to 50 per cent compared with the efficiency of 10 per cent of a direct radiator.

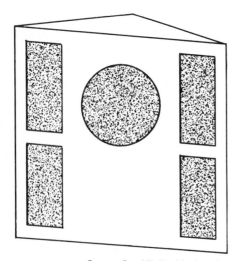

Courtesy, G. and H. Wood Products Co.

FIG. 20-128. A CORNER FOLDED HORN

In order to improve its operation, this type of enclosure is usually placed in a corner of a room so that the floor and the walls form an extension of the folded throat structure of the horn (Fig. 20-130). Unfortunately, the excellent bass response of this enclosure is achieved at the expense of the mid-range frequencies beyond 400 cps, producing thinness and lack of realism in this frequency range. Another disadvantage is the structural complexity of folded horns and the relatively high cost of factory-built models.[87]

20.62 *Planning and installation of public-address systems*

In considering the power requirements of a public-address system, it is necessary to evaluate a number of factors, such as the average level of background noise, whether the system is to be used outdoors in a stadium or indoors in an auditorium, and the effect of draperies and the clothing of the audience in absorbing sound energy.

Another acoustical factor to be considered is the placement of sound-absorbing materials so as to produce a desired amount of reverberation, or echo, and reverberation time. The reverberation time is defined as the number of seconds required for the sound intensity to decay to one-millionth of its original value, a decrease corresponding to 60 db (Fig. 20-131). According to an equation derived by Sabine many years ago:

$$T = 0.05\frac{V}{A}$$

in which T is the reverberation time in seconds, V is the volume of the room in cubic feet, and A is the total number of sabines or units of absorption in the room.[88]

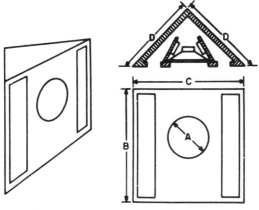

LOUDSPEAKER SIZE	SPEAKER OPENING	CABINET DIMENSIONS		
	A	B	C	D
12"	10-1/2" diam.	32"	32"	22-1/2"
15"	13-3/4" diam.	32"	36"	24-1/2"

FIG. 20-129. CONSTRUCTION DETAILS AND DESIGN DATA FOR A CORNER FOLDED HORN

It is the opinion of most authorities that the optimum reverberation time for a room is 0.75 seconds.[89] Of course, the value of the optimum time would also depend upon the size of the room and the type of program being reproduced by the system (Fig. 20-132). If it is a slow-moving organ selection, a long reverberation time might lend additional majesty and grandeur to the performance. On the other hand, if a staccato instrument solo is being reproduced, a large amount of reverberation would blur the individual sounds and would produce confusion (Fig. 20-133).

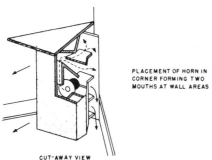

WALLS NOT INTEGRAL TO THE HORN CONSTRUCTION BUT ESSENTIAL TO HORN OPERATION

TOP VIEW

PLACEMENT OF HORN IN CORNER FORMING TWO MOUTHS AT WALL AREAS

CUT-AWAY VIEW

Courtesy, Klipschorn

FIG. 20-130. FOLDED HORN DESIGNED TO BE COMPLETELY CORNER LOADED BY THE WALLS OF THE CORNER OF A ROOM

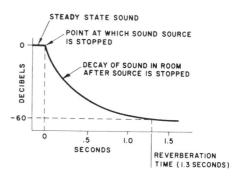

FIG. 20-131. GRAPH SHOWING MEANING OF THE TERM REVERBERATION TIME

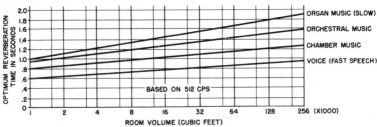

FIG. 20-132. OPTIMUM REVERBERATION TIMES IN ROOMS OF VARIOUS SIZES

The reverberation time of a room can usually be adjusted by adding or subtracting sound-absorbing materials such as draperies, upholstered furniture, and heavy carpets until the desired value is reached (Figs. 20-134 to 20-137). It should not be forgotten that the human body is an excellent absorber of sound. Consequently, the reverberation time of an auditorium filled with people is quite different from that of the same auditorium empty. Draw drapes can be used to compensate for this effect, since the absorption of sound produced by the drapes is halved when they are hanging flat rather than pulled together in folds.[90] For a recording session, proper microphone placement can also be used to control reverberation time (Fig. 20-138).

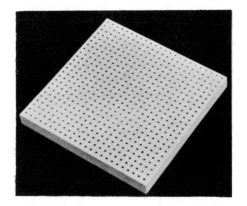

Courtesy, Johns-Manville

FIG. 20-134. SOUND ABSORBER OR INSULATOR (ACOUSTICAL TRANSITE)

In placing loudspeakers, an attempt should be made to place every member of the audience in line with some loud-speaker, since higher-frequency sounds do not travel effectively around obstacles. Ideally, the speakers should be mounted in a high position and directed down at the audience so that the

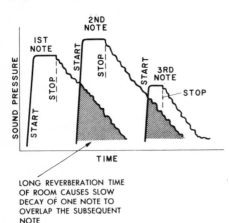

FIG. 20-133. EFFECT PRODUCED BY EXCESSIVELY LONG REVERBERATION TIME

LONG REVERBERATION TIME OF ROOM CAUSES SLOW DECAY OF ONE NOTE TO OVERLAP THE SUBSEQUENT NOTE

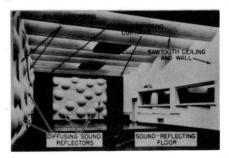

Courtesy, Johns-Manville

FIG. 20-135. ACOUSTICAL TREATMENT OF AN NBC STUDIO

MATERIAL		128 CPS	512 CPS	4096 CPS
ABSORBANT MATERIALS	FIBREGLASS (1" THICK)	.17	.91	.77
	ACOUSTIC CELOTEX (1")	.25	.99	.50
	WOOL CARPET ON PAD	.20	.35	.40
	DRAPERIES			
	HUNG FLAT — LIGHT WEIGHT	.04	.11	.38
	MEDIUM WEIGHT	.05	.13	.37
	HEAVY WEIGHT	.05	.35	.37
	DRAPED TO 1/2 WIDTH — LIGHT WEIGHT	.06	.40	.58
	MEDIUM WEIGHT	.07	49	.62
	HEAVY WEIGHT	.14	.55	.62
REFLECTIVE MATERIALS	CONCRETE UNPAINTED	.01	.02	.03
	BRICK WALL UNPAINTED	.02	.03	.06
	WOOD FLOOR	.04	.03	.02
	LINOLEUM ON SOLID FLOOR	.04	.04	.02
	PLASTER ON METAL LATH AND WOOD STUDS	.04	.04	.04
	GLASS	.04	.03	.02

INDIVIDUAL OBJECTS	TOTAL ABSORPTION UNITS		
MOHAIR TYPE UPHOLSTERED CHAIR	2.5	4.5	4.8
ALL WOOD CHAIR	.18	.24	.37
ADULT PERSON, STANDING	2.5	4.2	5.00
ADULT PERSON IN UPHOLSTERED CHAIR	3.0	4.5	5.2
CHILD	1.8	2.8	3.5

FIG. 20-136. SOUND ABSORPTION PROPERTIES OF VARIOUS MATERIALS

persons directly below the loudspeakers will not be appreciably closer to the sound source than the rest of the audience.[91]

A final factor to be considered is the relationship between the speakers and the microphones. The speakers should be placed in positions so that it

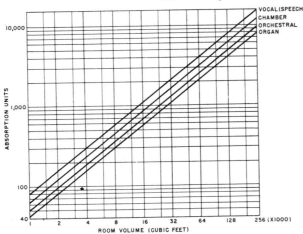

FIG. 20-137. TOTAL NUMBER OF ABSORPTION UNITS REQUIRED FOR A GIVEN ROOM VOLUME FOR DIFFERENT TYPES OF PROGRAM MATERIAL

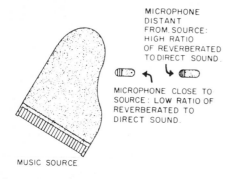

MICROPHONE DISTANT FROM SOURCE: HIGH RATIO OF REVERBERATED TO DIRECT SOUND.

MICROPHONE CLOSE TO SOURCE: LOW RATIO OF REVERBERATED TO DIRECT SOUND.

MUSIC SOURCE

FIG. 20-138. HOW MICROPHONE PLACEMENT CONTROLS REVERBERATION TIME IN RECORDING

is very difficult for their sound output to reach the microphones. If this precaution is not observed and the gain control is set at a high level, the sound energy that is fed back by the speakers to the microphones will be reamplified. The end result will be the production of audible oscillations, ringing sounds, whistles, howls, and squeals that will make the voice of the speaker almost unintelligible.[92]

An interesting method of reducing this type of feedback howl has been developed by Manfred R. Schroeder of Bell Telephone Laboratories. In this feedback squelching arrangement, a frequency-shift modulator shifts the frequency of the sound output of the system by approximately 5 cps, an amount which is inaudible in speech and in most types of music. As a result of these shifts in frequency, the reverberations do not reinforce each other but tend rather to cancel each other. It is claimed that this new method permits increasing the gain of an indoor public-address system to double that of a conventional system before any indications of instability are developed.[93]

20.63 Industrial applications of sound systems

Industrial establishments now comprise one of the largest groups of purchasers of public-address and intercommunication systems. Since today's industrial organizations are run chiefly on verbal messages, their success is dependent to a large degree on the rapid and accurate transmission of the spoken word.

On the production line, these systems keep the plant superintendent in immediate voice contact with production-line foremen. The resulting closer coordinating of over-all plant effort helps reduce idle or down time. Music broadcast over plant public-address systems creates a relaxed, cheerful, and pleasant atmosphere, relieves monotony and fatigue, and reduces accidents and rejects. The same system can be used to provide management with a direct channel to all employees, resulting in improved employee-employer relations and better control in emergency situations. Industrial intercommunications systems link offices, laboratories, manufacturing areas, and warehouses, help locate roving personnel, integrate the functions of administration and operating departments, and provide on-the-spot control of shipping and warehousing activities.[94]

REFERENCES

1. Peter L. Jensen, "Reminiscing About Stereo," Radio and TV News, 61:112, Feb. 1959.
2. A. C. Matthews, High-Fidelity, Consumers Research, Inc., Washington, N. J., p. 6.
3. Norman H. Crowhurst, "Outdoor Public Address Systems," Radio and TV News, 59:29, June 1958.
4. Louis E. Garner, Jr., "How to Plan a P.A. System," Popular Electronics, 8:73, Apr. 1958.
5. C. B. Wall, "Incandescent Genius," Reader's Digest, 64:154, Apr. 1954.

6. F. S. Goucher, "The Carbon Microphone: An Account of Some Researches Bearing on Its Action," *Bell System Technical Journal*, 15:197, Apr. 1936.

7. C. J. Christensen and G. L. Pearson, "Spontaneous Resistance Fluctuations in Carbon Microphones and Other Granular Resistances," *Bell System Technical Journal*, 15:197, Apr. 1936.

8. W. C. Jones, "Condenser and Carbon Microphones—Their Construction and Use," *Bell System Technical Journal*, 10:46, Jan. 1931.

9. C. B. Sawyer, "The Use of Rochelle Salt Crystals for Electrical Reproducers and Microphones," *Proc. IRE*, 19:2020, Nov. 1931.

10. Norman H. Crowhurst, "Microphones for Tape Recorders," *Radio and TV News*, 59:46, May 1958.

11. E. C. Wente and A. L. Thuras, "Moving-Coil Telephone Receivers and Microphones," *Bell System Technical Journal*, 10:565, Oct. 1931.

12. E. Eugene Garnes, "Which Mike Should I Use?" *Popular Electronics*, 9:75, July 1958.

13. Harry F. Olson, "On the Collection of Sound In Reverberant Rooms with Special Reference to the Application of the Ribbon Microphone," *Proc. IRE*, 21:655, May 1933.

14. Harry F. Olson and Richard W. Carlisle, "A Lapel Microphone of the Velocity Type," *Proc. IRE*, 22:1354, Dec. 1934.

15. Norman Eisenberg, "The Fourth Speed," *Popular Electronics*, 7:63-66, Aug. 1957.

16. "Wow and Flutter," *Better Listening*, 3:21, Jan. 1957.

17. "How to Choose the Right Turntable," *Popular Science*, 169:174, Oct. 1956.

18. Adelore F. Petrie, "Rumble Filters for Hi-Fi Systems," *Radio and TV News*, 58:42-43, Aug. 1957.

19. "Shakeproof Your Hi-Fi Turntable," *Hi-Fi Lowdown*, 1:5, Summer 1958.

20. N. H. Crowhurst, "Turntables Versus Record Changers," *Radio and Television News*, 55:45, Feb. 1956.

21. Hans Fantel, "What You Should Know About Record Players," *Popular Electronics*, 3:72-76, Sept. 1955.

22. Ken Fehling, "DuMont High Fidelity," *DuMont Service News*, 5:75. Oct. 1955.

23. N. H. Crowhurst, "Buying a Tone Arm," *Radio and Television News*, 57:51, Jan. 1957.

24. Hubert Luckett and Martin Mann, "How to Choose the Right Tone Arm," *Popular Science*, 169:176. Dec. 1956.

25. Hubert Luckett, "Hi-Fi Buyer's Guide: Tone Arms," *Popular Science*, 174:215, Feb. 1959.

26. *Ibid*, p. 52.

27. *Ibid*, pp. 53, 143.

28. Julian D. Hirsch, "Modern Phonograph Cartridges—Part 1," *Radio-Electronics*, Apr. 1957.

29. John G. Dodgson, "Magnetic Cartridges for Stereo," *National Radio Institute News*, 19:9, 12, Feb. 1960.

30. "Record Grooves Wiggle Magnet," *Popular Electronics*, 9:69, July, 1958.

31. J. D. Hirsch, *Op. cit.*, pp. 37-38.

32. Herman Burstein, "The Ceramic Cartridge and Equalization," *Radio and Television News*, 55:44, May 1956.

33. "The Dioxide Forms of Zirconium," *Advanced Materials Technology*, 2:11, Sept. 1959.

34. Herbert Reid, "New Trends in Transducers," *Better Listening*, 2:5-6, Sept. 1956.

35. Bud Tomer, *Why a Ceramic Cartridge?*, Bull. E-325, CBS-Hytron, Danvers, Mass., pp. 1-4.

36. *Magnetostriction*, International Nickel Co., N.Y. 1956, p. 6.

37. N. H. Crowhurst, "Choosing a Phono Pickup," *Radio and Television News*, 55:37, Jan. 1956.

38. Julian D. Hirsch, "Modern Phonograph Cartridges—Part 4," *Radio Electronics*, 28:38, July 1957.

39. E. J. Marcus, "Diamond Styli for Hi-Fi," *Popular Electronics*, 3:91, Oct. 1955.

40. J. G. Dodgson, *Op. cit.*, p. 12.

41. *Ibid*, p. 12.

42. "Sapphire vs. Diamond," *Radio-Electronics*, 29:47, Oct. 1958.

43. *Ibid*, p. 91.

44. "Diamond Needles Produced Automatically," *Radio and TV News*, 58:105, Sept. 1957.

45. Oliver Read, "The Recording and Reproduction of Sound—Part 10," *Radio News*, 38:48, Dec. 1947.

46. Herbert Reid, "How to Buy Your Hi-Fi Tuner," *Popular Electronics*, 5:60, Oct. 1956.

47. Norman H. Crowhurst, "Which Way to High-Fidelity?," *Radio and TV News*, 59:45. Feb. 1958.

48. "What is a Loudness Control?," *Better Listening*, 2:4, Dec. 1956.

49. P. L. Jensen, *Op. cit.*, p. 112.

50. Joseph Marshall, "Inside the Hi-Fi Loudspeaker," *Popular Electronics*, 11:86, Oct. 1959.

51. J. D. Seabert, "Electrodynamic Speaker Design Considerations," *Proc. IRE*, 22:738, June 1934.

52. "Transients," *Hi-Fi Lowdown*, 1:20, Summer 1958.

53. Larry Nielson, "A Guide to Buying Loudspeakers," *Better Listening*, 3:7, Mar. 1957.

54. Robert Lanier, "How to Choose Loudspeakers—Part 1," *Better Listening*, 2:5-6, 11-12, Mar. 1956.

55. C. R. Hanna and J. Slepian, "The Function and Design of Horns for Loud-speakers," *Trans. AIEE*, 43:393, Feb. 1924.

56. *Speaking About Loudspeakers*, University Loudspeakers, Inc., White Plains, N.Y., 1956, pp. 18-19.

57. R. Lanier, *Op. cit.*, p. 6.

58. "New Trends in Loudspeakers," *Radio-Electronics* 20:35, Oct. 1948.

59. "Crossover Network," *Better Listening*, 3:4, Sept. 1957.

60. Herbert Reid, "Why Multiple Loudspeakers?" *Better Listening*, 3:14, Jan. 1957.

61. "The Electronic Crossover," *Hi-Fi Lowdown*, 1:4, May 1958.

62. H. H. Fantel, "Two are Better Than One," *Popular Electronics*, 4:54, June 1956.

63. *Speaking About Loudspeakers, Op. cit.*, p. 15.

64. Hugh Gernsback, "Wanted—Inertialess Speakers," *Radio-Electronics*, 24:33, Oct. 1953.

65. "Space Sound," *Radio-Electronics*, 25:69, Aug. 1954.

66. E. Aisberg and M. Bonhomme, "Ionophone Circuitry," *Radio-Electronics*, 23:33, Dec. 1951.

67. "Ionic Cloud Tweeter Demonstrated," *Radio and TV News*, 57:102, May 1957.

68. Gerald Shirley, "The Corona Loudspeaker," *Radio and Television News*, 56:57, Oct. 1956.
69. Gerald Shirley, "Loudspeakers of the Future," *Radio-Electronics*, 28:44-45, Nov. 1957.
70. Werner W. Diefenbach, "Electrostatic Speaker," *Radio-Electronics*, 24:66, Apr. 1953.
71. "New Electrostatic Speakers," *Radio-Electronics*, 25:61, Oct. 1954.
72. "Electrostatic Loudspeaker," *Radio-Electronics*, 27:8, Aug. 1956.
73. Jean Shepard, *Isophase, A New Kind of Sound*, Pickering and Co., Plainview, N.Y. pp. 2-6.
74. *N. H. Crowhurst*, "Buying a Loudspeaker?," *Radio and Television News*, 55-58, June 1956.
75. Warren Philbrook, "Electrostatic Loudspeakers," *Radio and TV News*, 59:38, June 1958.
76. C. G. McProud, "The Speaker You'll be Hearing," *Popular Science*, 169:168, Oct. 1956.
77. "Ceramic Loudspeakers," *Radio-Electronics*, 30:6, Mar. 1959.
78. Rufus P. Turner, "Electrostrictive Ceramics," *Radio-Electronics*, 30:32, Sept. 1959.
79. "Louder Loudspeaker," *Science Digest*, 38:97, Oct. 1955.
80. "SAM Gets Around," *Stanford Research Institute Research for Industry*, 11:8, May 1959.
81. "Device Creates World's Loudest Noise," *Science Digest*, 45:92, Jan. 1959.
82. William P. Vogel, Jr., "The Horn That Shouts Like a Man," *Popular Science*, 153:129, July 1948.
83. G. A. Briggs, "All About Audio and Hi-Fi—Part 9," *Radio and TV News*, 59:64, Mar. 1958.
84. H. H. Fantel, "No Confusion....Just Baffling! " *Popular Electronics*, 4:84-85, Feb. 1956.
85. P. G. A. H. Voigt, "All about the Reflex Enclosure—Part 1," *Radio-Electronics*, 30:38, Feb. 1959.
86. George L. Augspurger, "Reflex Enclosures—How They Work," *Electronics World*, 61:86, June 1959.
87. H. H. Fantel, "Horns—Folded and Loaded," *Popular Electronics*, 4:79, Apr. 1956.
88. Wallace C. Sabine, *Collected Papers on Acoustics*, Harvard University Press, Cambridge, Mass., 1922.
89. J. L. Smith, "Testing the Properties of Loudspeakers," *Radio and TV News*, 60:124-125, Aug. 1958.
90. "The Listening Room," *Hi-Fi Lowdown*, 1:9-12, Summer 1958.
91. Norman H. Crowhurst, "Outdoor Public Address Systems," *Radio and TV News*, 59:30-31, June 1958.
92. Louis E. Garner, Jr., "How to install a PA System," *Popular Electronics*, 8:63, May 1958.
93. "Reduce PA Howl," *Radio-Electronics*, 30:52, Oct. 1959.
94. *How RCA Sound in Industry Gets Things Done*, RCA Engineering Products Division, Camden, N.J., pp. 1-9.

21 - RECORDING SOUND ON DISCS

Disc recording is a method of recording sound by means of modulated grooves which are cut into a revolving disc. The modulated grooves are produced by means of a recording-head cutter that is equipped with a stylus.

21.1 *History of disc recording*

There were many unsuccessful attempts made to reproduce sound by mechanical means before the first successful phonograph was invented. In 1857, a French scientist named Scott developed a Phonautograph, which recorded sound as a wavy, spiral line on a rotating cylinder that had been coated with lampblack. However, this device could not reproduce the sounds that had been recorded.

In 1877, while he was experimenting with an automatic telegraph repeater, Edison invented a device that could both record and reproduce sound (Fig. 21-1). It consisted of a spiral, grooved

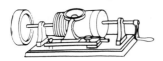

Courtesy, Record Div., Radio Corporation of America
FIG. 21-1. EDISON PHONOGRAPH. 1877

metallic cylinder coated with tin foil, a mouthpiece for the incoming sounds, a funnel for the outgoing sounds, a diaphragm, a needle, and a crank to rotate the cylinder. There was little trouble in obtaining a patent on this invention, since, for the first time in its history, the Patent Office found that there were no primary claims on any device bearing even the slightest resemblance to this one.

The idea of using wax as an improved sound-recording medium was conceived in 1881 by Chichester Bell and Charles Tainter. In 1888, an improved commercial model of the phonograph was brought out that employed a wax cylinder, called a phonogram, on which the sound was recorded as elevations and depressions in the record grooves. This was known as vertical engraving, or the hill-and-dale method of recording. This phonograph, called a graphophone, bore a close physical resemblance to the office dictaphone machines of today (Fig. 21-2).[1]

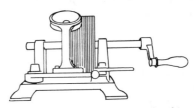

Courtesy, Record Div., Radio Corporation of America
FIG. 21-2. BELL-TAINTER GRAPHOPHONE. 1881

During that same year, Emile Berliner and Eldridge Johnson brought out a radically different type of phonograph which was first called the phonautogram and later called the gramophone (Fig. 21-3). This device employed a flat disc upon which the sound was recorded by means of a lateral-engraving process.[2] In addition, Berliner developed an etching process by means of

721

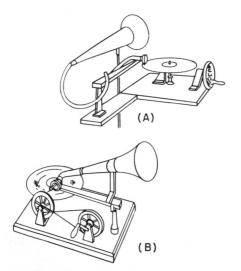

Courtesy, Record Div., Radio Corporation of America

FIG. 21-3. BERLINER PHONOGRAPHS
(A) 1888 model—phonautogram; (B) 1895 model—gramophone.

which these records could be manufactured in large quantities from a master record. This later evolved into an electroplating process, similar to the one that is now used in the production of records. Some additional innovations provided by Johnson were spring-wound motors, a governor to provide constant turntable speed, and a radial tone arm. Johnson possessed the imagination to foresee the commercial possibilities of the phonograph. This was in sharp contrast to Edison, who once stated: "I don't want the phonograph used for amusement purposes. It is not a toy."[3]

In October 1889, Laurie Dickson demonstrated to Edison a primitive device called the kinetophone. This device featured Dickson speaking on a phonograph record that was synchronized with his image on a motion picture—the first "talking picture."

In 1901, Johnson acquired the Berliner patents and founded the Victor Talking Machine Company to produce

his machines (Fig. 21-4). This company is the ancestor of one of the important divisions of today's giant corporation, the Radio Corporation of America.

In 1906, the traditional horn disappeared into the cabinet in a new model phonograph that was called the "Victrola" (Fig. 21-5).[4] Meanwhile, Edison continued his investigations in this, his favorite invention, and continued to make various improvements, ultimately acquiring more than 80 patents relating to the phonograph. His efforts proved to be rather lucrative, since by 1910, the annual sales of phonographs and records had reached a volume of 7 million dollars. Even after the expiration of his basic patents on the phonograph, he received a considerable amount of income from the sale of records.

Courtesy, Record Div., Radio Corporation of America

FIG. 21-4. VICTOR PHONOGRAPH WITH MORNING GLORY HORN

The next important development in recording was not made until 1925, when electrical recording was introduced as a result of research conducted by Bell Telephone Laboratories and

Courtesy, Record Div., Radio Corporation of America

FIG. 21-5. VICTROLA PHONOGRAPH, 1910

General Electric. A patent on the electrical recording of sound was granted to Harrison of the Western Electric Company, a subsidiary of the Bell system. The recording horn was replaced by a microphone, and the energy that actuated the stylus now became electrical energy instead of sound energy (Fig. 21-6). This process extended the frequency range of the records and produced recordings of higher quality.[5] Shortly afterwards, electrical reproduction replaced acoustical reproduction, and the jewel stylus came into use.

In 1927, the first automatic record changers were produced. These improvements were the last important developments in disc recording until 1948, when the 78-rpm records began to be supplanted by 33 1/3-rpm long-playing and 45-rpm records.[6]

21.2 *Types of disc recordings*

There are two main types of disc records, pressed and instantaneous. The category of pressed records includes popular entertainment records,

electrical transcriptions used by broadcasting companies, and the majority of commercial records. Instantaneous types of records are usually made at home or in the studios which specialize in their production. They are made on specially prepared discs and consist of a ridged base made of paper, glass, fiber, or aluminum and coated with a lacquer-like varnish.

Courtesy, Record Div., Radio Corporation of America

FIG. 21-6. TECHNIQUES OF RECORDING, OLD (TOP) AND NEW

21.3 *Recording equipment*

A recording unit consists of a microphone, an amplifier, a cutting head, an arm, a feed mechanism, a turntable, and a drive motor.

21.4 *Recording microphones*

The type of microphone to be selected depends upon the intended application. For the recording of music, both the velocity type and the cardioid type will prove satisfactory. For voice recording, the crystal and dynamic types are preferred. Non-directional microphones are usually preferred for general use. Directional models are helpful where feedback is bothersome or in a reverberant room. Some of the newer microphones feature both directional and non-directional response within the same unit.

21.5 *Amplifiers used in recording*

A suitable recording amplifier should possess the following desirable characteristics:

1. The amplifier possesses low hum and noise levels.

2. The volume control does not need to be all the way up for normal recording conditions, thus leaving a margin of gain in reserve.

3. The amplifier possesses sufficient output to drive the cutting head without serious distortion at full modulation or full-volume level.

4. The amplifier contains provisions for connecting a radio or a phonograph pickup, if it is desired to record from the radio or to re-record from another turntable and pickup.[7]

21.6 *Equalizers*

Electrical circuits that are used to modify the frequency-response characteristics of a sound-transmission or sound-reproduction system are called equalizers. The most familiar type of equalizer is the ordinary tone control. An equalizer is frequently incorporated in a recording amplifier in order to counteract a peak in the cutting-head response and produce a better over-all recording characteristic. Once a recording system has been adjusted by the manufacturer to provide the most faithful playback possible, the indiscriminate use of equalizers by the average person is to be discouraged.

21.7 *Recording heads and cutters*

A recording head converts electrical energy into the mechanical energy that is required to cut grooves into the disc. The recording head holds a cutting needle or stylus which is shaped like a miniature lathe. The electrical impulses that pass through the cutting head cause the needle to vibrate from side to side, cutting corresponding waveforms in the spiral grooves of the recording blank (Fig. 21-7).

Cutting heads are of two general types, magnetic and crystal. Magnetic heads are usually mounted vertically, while crystal heads are mounted horizontally. There are both good and bad

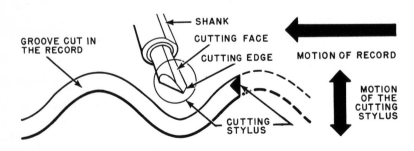

FIG. 21-7. GROOVE PATTERN PRODUCED BY CUTTING STYLUS

cutting heads in each type. Where cost is not an important consideration, the magnetic type is preferred, owing to its stability, ruggedness, wide frequency range, and ability to handle high volume without distortion. Crystal cutters have been quite extensively used in medium and low-priced recorders. Their range is good and they can handle a considerable volume of sound satisfactorily.[8]

The following is a list of some of the qualities required of a good cutting head. It must be able to handle high volume, clearly and efficiently. The frequency range must be wide over the entire audible sound spectrum, that is to say, it should be comparatively flat, emphasizing neither treble, bass, nor medium frequencies, but rather passing all of these frequencies in their proper proportions.

21.8 *Vertical-engraving characteristics*

The term vertical engraving is sometimes known as hill-and-dale recording. With this system, the cutting stylus does not move from side to side but travels along a straight line in the vertical plane and moves up and down in this vertical plane (Fig. 21-8). It is not used as widely as lateral engraving, but it does permit the production of recordings of very high quality.

The vertical-engraving system was the one first used by Edison. Under ordinary conditions, vertical recording tends to produce more distortion than lateral recording does. Because of the geometry of the cutting stylus, depression of the cutter requires more force than lifting it. This tends to pro-

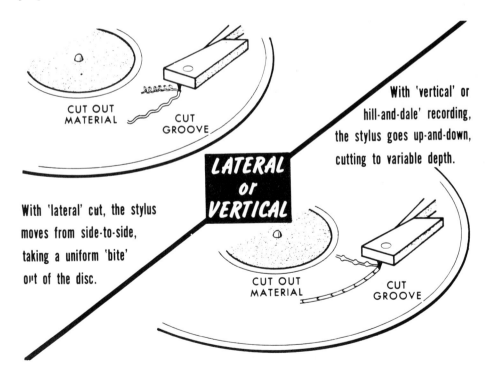

CUT OUT MATERIAL   CUT GROOVE

With 'vertical' or hill-and-dale' recording, the stylus goes up-and-down, cutting to variable depth.

LATERAL or VERTICAL

With 'lateral' cut, the stylus moves from side-to-side, taking a uniform 'bite' out of the disc.

CUT OUT MATERIAL   CUT GROOVE

FIG. 21-8. COMPARISON BETWEEN LATERAL AND VERTICAL ENGRAVING

duce second-harmonic and similar types of distortion. In contrast, in the lateral-recording system, the cutter removes a constant amount of material, and there is no inherent distortion. However, in recent times, feedback cutters have been developed which compensate for the factors producing vertical-engraving distortion. It is therefore now possible to record vertically with as little distortion as by recording laterally.[9]

21.9 *Lateral-engraving characteristics*

This term refers to the manner in which the disc is cut. With this system, which was developed by Berliner, the depth of the cut made on the surface of the disc is kept constant while the recording stylus moves from side to side, cutting an undulating groove. Today, most recordings are made by means of this lateral system, since it is the simplest.

21-10 *Constant-amplitude characteristics*

When the undulations that are cut in a record are all of the same amplitude, regardless of the frequency being recorded, the recording is said to be constant-amplitude recording (Fig. 21-9). Under this system, if the sound pressure at the microphone remains the same while the frequency is varied, the amplitude of the undulations cut in the record will remain the same.

21.11 *Constant-velocity characteristics*

With constant-velocity recording, the velocity of the cutting stylus remains the same when the frequency of the recorded sound is varied, provided the amplitude of the sound remains constant

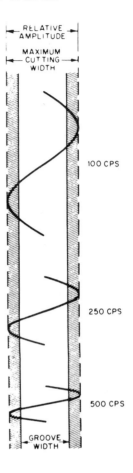

FIG. 21-9. CONSTANT-AMPLITUDE   RECORDING

(Fig. 21-10). There is an inverse relationship between the amplitude of the modulations and the frequency of the recorded sound. The amplitude of the wave is twice as great at 100 cps as it is at 200 cps. At low frequencies, the amplitude of the undulations may be great enough to cause overcutting in which one groove cuts completely over into an adjacent groove (Fig. 21-11). Another undesirable effect, referred to as echo, occurs at slightly lower amplitudes when the groove is cut close enough to an adjacent groove to deform the wall of that adjacent groove.

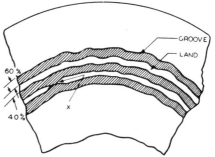

FIG. 21-11. GROOVE OVERCUTTING

In lateral recording if the proportion of groove to land exceeds 60 to 40, groove overcutting may result, as indicated by point X.

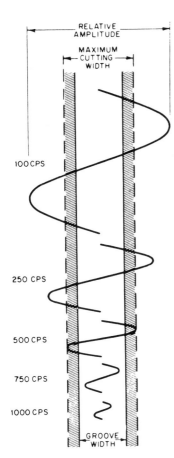

FIG. 21-10. CONSTANT-VELOCITY RECORDING

21.12 *Turnover*

In order to eliminate the undesirable effects of over-cutting and echo, special recording circuits have been designed which permit constant-velocity recording above a pre-determined frequency, while all frequencies below this value are cut constant-amplitude. The frequency at which the recording characteristic changes from constant-velocity to constant-amplitude is known as the turnover or crossover point. This point is usually between 200 and 800 cps (Fig. 21-12).

In order to prevent distortion, the sound-recording system through which the record is played usually contains an equalization circuit that is designed to compensate for this recording characteristic. The subject of equalization will be considered again later in this chapter.

21.13 *The cutting stylus*

The cutting stylus is mounted in the cutting head. It cuts the coating of the disc in accordance with the sound being recorded. It operates somewhat in the manner of a lathe, and its cutting end is shaped somewhat like such a tool. It is a precision instrument and requires a high degree of skill in its manufacture. The stylus cuts a groove approximately 0.002 in. deep, and only the tip is subject to wear. The ability of the stylus to cut a clean, well-polished groove determines to a great extent the quality of the record produced. The most common defect which results from a poorly formed stylus is excessive surface noise during playback. Cutting styli are very delicate and must be handled with extreme care. The life of such a stylus depends upon the properties of the material used for its tip, and the surface of the recording blanks with which it is used. Styli are made with steel, alloy, and sapphire tips.

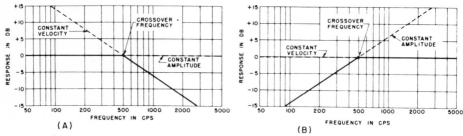

FIG. 21-12. COMPARISON OF AMPLITUDE (A) AND VELOCITY (B) RESPONSE TO A STANDARD 500-CPS CROSSOVER RECORDING CHARACTERISTIC

The steel stylus. Steel styli have a much shorter life than either the alloy or sapphire types. During its first few minutes of use, a steel stylus will cut a recording with very little surface noise. Because it wears rapidly, it produces increasingly greater surface noise and must be discarded after about 30 minutes of use.

The alloy-type stylus. Alloy styli are superior to steel in wearing qualities and are quite popular. The alloys used vary in hardness, and some alloy styli will last as long as a sapphire stylus. The use of a very hard alloy results in the creation of considerably more surface noise than is experienced with sapphire styli. One of the most widely used alloys is known as Stellite. Styli tipped with Stellite produce records that are almost as quiet as those made with sapphire. The tip will last for about 2 hours of cutting, after which the stylus may be returned to the manufacturer for re-sharpening.

The sapphire stylus. Sapphire styli are the most widely used cutting styli. Synthetic and natural gems are employed in the manufacture of sapphire styli. The natural gems are more expensive and last a little longer. A synthetic gem will retain its shape for about 6 hours of cutting time, while a natural gem will last for about 8 hours. The sapphire stylus is excellent for recording wide ranges of frequency and volume. One of

its main disadvantages is that it fractures quite easily and must therefore be handled with extreme care.

The heated stylus. A relatively recent development in connection with the microgroove recording of long-playing records has been the use of a sapphire stylus that is heated by a glowing coil of wire. The wire is heated by the application of electric current at a potential of 6 volts. The effect of this heating process is to improve the cutting action of the stylus so that it does a cleaner and better job. This process, first developed by Columbia Records, has made it possible to reduce phonograph-record surface-noise levels and to improve frequency response.[10]

21.14 *Recording discs*

Recording discs must possess a number of specific qualities which are extremely difficult to obtain. Any deviation from these qualities results in an inferior recording. The qualities desired are the following:

1. The recording blank must be very rigid. If the blank is not rigid, an effect called rumble will result. Rumble occurs when the blank flexes as a result of vertical vibration of the stylus and cutting head. The flexing of the blank amplifies these vibrations and they are heard as a rumbling sound.

2. The surfaces of the disc must be

capable of being cut cleanly. Some materials can be cut by a stylus and will leave a very smooth lustrous groove. Other materials cannot be cut cleanly and tend to leave a groove whose walls contain tiny irregularities which manifest themselves as surface noise during playback.

3. The material which forms the surface of the disc must be free from abrasive substances. A disc that is not free from such substances will produce high-frequency background hiss when it is played back.

4. The surface of the disc must be completely flat and free from irregularities. If the surface is not flat, the stylus may leave the surface of the blank and produce a defect called skip. Irregularities may also cause changes in turntable load during recording. These changes often• cause slight turntable-speed changes which result in wow or tone flutter during playback.

5. The surface of the disc must cut readily; otherwise the high-frequency signals will be attenuated.

6. The surface material should be such that it does not cause excessive stylus wear. It must also retain its shape and other properties for as long a period of time as possible.

In order to satisfy all of these requirements, it has been necessary to form recording discs by using a rigid base material and coating this base with another material. Discs are manufactured with a glass or aluminum base that is coated with a semi-plastic varnish. Fiber and paper are also used as base materials but are inferior to glass and aluminum.

21.15 *Recording turntables*

The selection of the correct recording turntable is very important (Fig. 21-13). It is impossible to turn out good

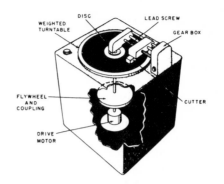

FIG. 21-13. CONSTRUCTION OF A TYPICAL DISC-RECORDING TURNTABLE

recordings with a poor turntable. The turntable should not introduce wow, nor should it slow down under the pressure of the cutting head. Wow is greatly reduced in a turntable that possesses great mass. The drive-motor should have adequate power so that it will not slow down under the load of the cutter, and it should have a rating of at least one-thirtieth of a horsepower.[11]

21.16 *Feed mechanisms*

As the turntable revolves and the stylus cuts the groove, the cutting head must be moved across the record at a constant rate. There are three main types of feeding mechanisms used to accomplish this. They are the fan-type, the overhead feed-type, and the underbed feed-type. Of the three types of mechanisms, the fan-type produces the poorest results.

21.17 *Disc size and turntable RPM*

The diameter of the disc and the speed of the turntable determine the rate at which the surface of the disc passes the stylus. As the stylus moves towards the center of the disc, the rate at which the disc passes the stylus decreases, as does the linear distance from the beginning to the end of a single cycle of a tone. This makes it necessary for the stylus to move from side to side at ever sharper angles. During playback, the needle must track these sharp bends, and as a result, there is a gradual attenuation of response, which is greatest for the high frequencies. Because this "pinch" effect produces a loss in the high-frequency response as the diameter decreases, limitations are imposed on the minimum diameter of a recording. Since the linear velocity of the surface of the disc passing the stylus is greater at 78 rpm than at $33\frac{1}{3}$ rpm, a smaller minimum diameter is permissible for 78-rpm records. The diameter of the innermost groove for acceptable response characteristics is 7.5 in. for $33\frac{1}{3}$ rpm records, and 3.75 in. for 78-rpm records.[12][13]

21.18 *Long-playing microgroove records*

Long-playing (LP) records, which were developed by Peter Goldmark of the Columbia Broadcasting System in 1945 and introduced to the public in 1948, have a playing time of 25 minutes per side for a 12-in. record instead of 5 minutes. Their speed of rotation is $33\frac{1}{3}$ rpm. The width of an LP groove is one-third that of a conventional record groove. These records require the use of an extremely-light pickup arm which applies a pressure of only $\frac{1}{5}$ oz. and employs a stylus the diameter of which is only 1 mil or 0.001 in. This is in sharp contrast with the 3-mil stylus that is used with a 78-rpm record.[14]

This method of recording was not commercially practicable until the advent of two fairly recent developments: improved reproducers which could trace a record with very low forces

at the point of the stylus and rim-driven turntable motors that could provide rumble-free and wow-free slow-speed operation.[15] Tracking and groove wear are essentially the same with an LP record as with a conventional one.

The LP records are made of vinylite plastic. This material is far superior to shellac with respect to low noise level and makes it possible to produce recordings with improved dynamic range and with a frequency range of 30 to 15,000 cps.

It may be of some interest to note that the basic idea of the LP record is not a new one. In 1926, the Edison Phonograph Company produced 12-in. discs that were capable of playing for 22 minutes on each side. These were also called long-playing records. During that same year, Western Electric demonstrated a sound-motion-picture film that employed 16-in. discs that rotated at $33\frac{1}{3}$ rpm and operated in synchronization with the projected motion pictures.

In 1931, RCA demonstrated and made commercially available LP records operating at a speed of $33\frac{1}{3}$ rpm and capable of playing 15 minutes on each side. Due to the limitations of the reproducing equipment then available, these records did not gain acceptance and their manufacture was soon discontinued.

21.19 *Commercial manufacture of disc records*

The sounds produced in the studio by the singer or orchestra are first recorded on magnetic tape that is running at a speed of 15 ips (inches per second) (Fig. 21-14). This tape can be edited, cut, and respliced so as to eliminate minor mistakes made during the recording session. The tape is then run through a magnetic reproducing device,

FIG. 21-14. RECORDING ON TAPE

FIG. 21-15. MAKING THE LACQUER MOTHER
After careful editing by combining and balancing the tracks, a master tape is made as it will sound on the record—two track for stereophonic, single track for monophonic. The master tape is played and the sound used to modulate a spiral groove cut on a nitrocellulose lacquer disc surface. After visual inspection, under a microscope, the lacquer mother is shipped to the factory.

and the resulting electrical signals are used to cut grooves in a nitrocellulose-lacquer-coated aluminum disc that is called the lacquer mother (Fig. 21-15).

When the record is being cut, a variable-pitch control is manually operated by a technician. This control determines the pitch of the spiral track or the number of grooves per lateral inch cut by the stylus. For loud music, the operator spreads the grooves apart in order to prevent the stylus from cutting across from one groove to the adjacent groove. The grooves are placed close together for soft music.

21.20 *Recording curves and equalization*

Another recording consideration is the recording curve. As has been previously mentioned, high-frequency sounds tend to produce relatively slight motion of the stylus, while low-frequency sounds of the same intensity tend to produce violent fluctuations of the stylus. In order to prevent this effect, the low-frequency sounds are weakened or attenuated, while the high-frequency sounds are accentuated (Fig. 21-16). This recording characteristic also tends to reduce the tendency of strong low-frequency sounds to cause the recording stylus to cut over into adjacent grooves, and it also helps the recorded sounds to override the disc surface noise (Fig. 21-17). Naturally, for effective reproduction, a good phonograph should be designed to reverse this process by boosting the low frequencies and attenuating the high frequencies (Fig. 21-18).[16]

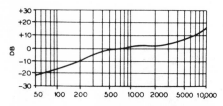

FIG. 21-16. RECORDING CHARACTERISTIC FOR A CONSTANT-AMPLITUDE RECORDING
The transitional point is at 500 cps. At 10,000 cps it rises to 16 db.

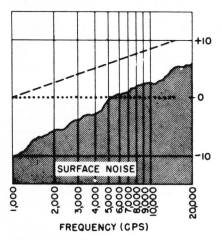

FIG. 21-17. RECORDED TREBLE PRE-EMPHASIS TO OVERRIDE SURFACE NOISE

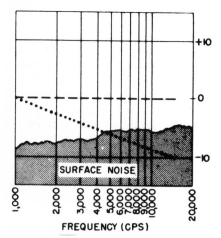

FIG. 21-18. PLAYBACK CURVE USED TO COMPENSATE FOR TREBLE BOOST

In the past, various recording companies have employed differing degrees of attenuation and accentuation during the process of manufacturing their records, resulting in many different recording and playback curves (Figs. 21-19 and 21-20). In 1954, a standard recording curve known as the RIAA (Recording Industries Association of America) or Ortho (Orthophonic) curve was adopted by the record industry (Fig. 21-21). Practically all records made since the beginning of 1955 have been recorded in accordance with this RIAA curve. In newer types of record players, it is only necessary to set the bass and treble equalizers to the RIAA position for proper compensation of these recent records.[17] [18]

21.21 *Final processing of the record*

After the lacquer mother has been cut, a chemical process similar to silvering a mirror is used to deposit a thin layer of silver out of an ammoniated silver nitrate solution upon the surface of the lacquered disc (Fig. 21-22). This layer is then covered with a thin layer of nickel and a layer of copper (Fig. 21-23). An alternative procedure is to coat the lacquer mother with gold by a cathode-sputtering process in which an electrical discharge at a potential of 3,000 volts is used to deposit a thin layer of gold on the disc within an evacuated container. This gold disc is then plated with nickel and copper. The lacquer mother disc is separated from the metal disc and is filed in a vault.

The metal disc, now called a master disc, is a negative of the original lacquer disc, containing ridges instead of grooves. The master record is far too valuable to be used directly for the pressing of a large number of records. The master is therefore used to make

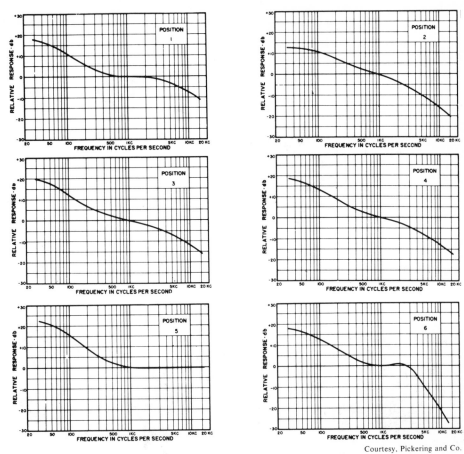

FIG. 21-19. TYPICAL COMPENSATING CURVES

Courtesy, Pickering and Co.

Courtesy, Pickering and Company

FIG. 21-20. PICKERING RECORD COMPENSATOR

metal molds (Fig. 21-24). A mold is formed by coating the master disc with a thin layer of nickel, followed by a thick layer of copper. The two sections are then separated to form a master and a mold. The mold is nickel-plated, and when the two sections are separated, a mold and a stamper are formed (Figs. 21-25 and 21-26). These stampers are also negative, and are placed in a stamping press to produce the final vinylite disc record that is sold to the public (Fig. 21-27). Meanwhile, the master discs are stored in a vault for safekeeping.[19][20][21]

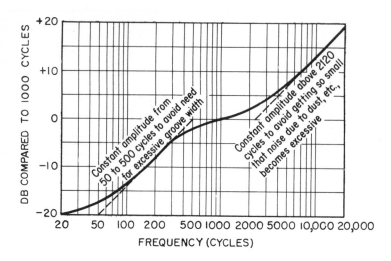

FIG. 21-21. STANDARD RECORDING CURVE OF RECORDING INDUSTRY ASSOCIATION OF AMERICA (RIAA)

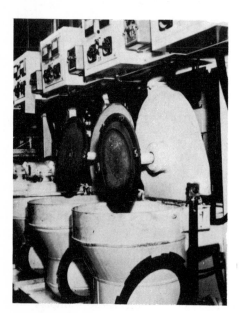

Courtesy, Record Div., Radio Corporation of America

FIG. 21-22. TREATMENT OF THE LACQUER MOTHER

After inspection, the lacquer disc is meticulously cleaned with detergent solution and placed in a chamber which automatically sequences a series of sprays, producing a mirror bright silver on the music surface.

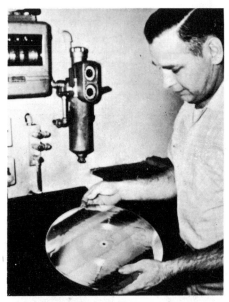

Courtesy, Record Div., Radio Corporation of America

FIG. 21-23. MAKING THE METAL MASTER

The silvered disc is first electroplated with 0.001 in. of a special, fine-grained, low-stress nickel coating, followed by a heavy copper electrodeposit in high-speed electroforming tanks to form a metal master whose silver surface is a negative of the lacquer disc.

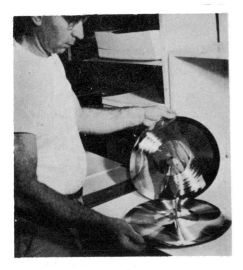

FIG. 21-24. MAKING THE METAL MOLD

After separation from the lacquer, the master is treated with a solution to prevent adhesion of but not otherwise interfere with further electrode-position. It is then plated with nickel followed by copper to produce a mold, a metal record, which can be separated from the master.

FIG. 21-25. MAKING THE NICKEL STAMPERS

The mold is audio tested to insure against flaws in the sound track grooves before being used to generate the nickel stampers by the same process by which the mold itself was produced from the master.

FIG. 21-26. CENTERING THE STAMPER

The stamper is microscopically centered in order to locate and punch an accurate center. It is then punched to fit the record press dies.

FIG. 21-27. PRESSING THE RECORD

The plastic, labels, and stampers converge at the record press. The ground compound is airveyed to a hopper above an automatic preform heater-extruder. Two stampers are mounted on cored dies in the press, one on the upper die and one on the lower die. After placing two labels upside down on the stampers, a metered amount of hot plastic from the extruder is placed on the low stamper and the press closed. The press is automatically controlled through a heating and cooling cycle while the plastic is welded and cooled under almost one ton per square inch pressure. After removal from the press, the record is edged with a hot knife edger and placed on a spindle.

REFERENCES

1. Oliver Read and James Riley, "Evolution of the Phonograph—Part 1," *Radio and Television News*, 54:58, Nov. 1955.
2. Oliver Read and James Riley, "Evolution of the Phonograph—Part 2," *Radio and Television News*, 54:56, Dec. 1955.
3. Donald C. Hoefler, *Hi-Fi Manual*, Fawcett Publications, Greenwich, Conn., 1954, p. 7.
4. *The Story of RCA Victor Phonograph Records*, Form 3E3191, RCA Victor, Camden, N.J., pp. 1-3.
5. "From Talking Machine to Color TV," *Electronic Age*, 18:22, Summer 1959.
6. *The 50-Year Story of RCA Victor Records*, Radio Corporation of America, New York, 1953, pp. 15-31.
7. J. C. Hoadley, "Small Recording Studio—Microphone, Recorder, Turntable, and Pick-up," *Radio-Craft*, 18:27, Feb. 1947.
8. Oliver Read, "The Recording and Reproduction of Sound—Part 4," *Radio News*, 37:65, June 1947.
9. Norman H. Crowhurst, "Single-Groove Stereo Discs," *Radio-Electronics*, 29:55-56, Jan. 1958.
10. "Notes on the Development of Hot Stylus Recording," *Audio Record*, 6:1, Oct. 1950.
11. J. C. Hoadley, "A Small Recording Studio—The Technique of Making a Phonograph Record," *Radio-Craft*, 18:34, Apr. 1947.
13. J. C. Hoadley, "A Small Recording Studio—Speed, Needle, and Record-cut Considerations," *Radio-Craft*, 18:32, June 1947.
14. M. Harvey Gernsback, "Microgroove Phonograph Records," *Radio-Electronics*, 40:30, Oct. 1948.
15. Vincent J. Liebler, "Notes on the Development of the LP Record," *Audio Record*, 4:1, Nov. 1948.
16. "How Hi-Fi Records are Made," *Popular Science*, 165:125-127, Nov. 1954.
17. Leon Fields and R. M. Johnson, "Why We Equalize Our Hi-Fi," *Popular Electronics*, 5:98-99, Aug. 1956.
18. Joseph Marshall, "Inside the Preamplifier—Part 2," *Popular Electronics*, 10:45-47, Mar. 1959.
19. *The Story of RCA Victor Phonograph Records*, *Op. cit.*, pp. 4-7.
20. Elliott H. Kane, "Making a Phonograph Record," *Science Digest*, 38:71, Sept, 1955.
21. *How RCA Victor Makes High Fidelity Phonograph Records*, Radio Corporation of America, Camden, N.J., pp. 2-3.

22 - MAGNETIC RECORDING, OPTICAL RECORDING AND OTHER METHODS OF SOUND RECORDING

22.1 *Magnetic recording*

The term *magnetic recording* refers to a method of recording sound by means of magnetic variations produced on a magnetic recording medium. Its development dates back to the first electromagnet produced by Sir Humphry Davy in 1820. Eleven years later, Michael Faraday succeeded in generating electricity by moving a coil of wire through a magnetic field. In 1862, the first patent was granted for the recording of sound on wire. In 1888, Oberlin Smith wrote an article on magnetic recording in which the suggestion was made that such a device could utilize either a fine steel wire or a cord that was impregnated with steel dust.[1] In the issue of *Electrical World* of September 8, 1888, Smith described a machine for spinning metallic dust into a cotton cord and predicted that the Lord's Prayer might be recorded on only a few feet of this type of string.

The Telegraphone. Valdemar Poulsen patented the Telegraphone, the first practical and workable magnetic recorder, in Denmark, in 1898. This device produced magnetic recordings of poor quality on heavy steel piano wire. In Poulsen's machine, an electromagnet was connected in series with a battery and a microphone. The electromagnet was moved along a length of wire in such a manner that one magnetic pole surrounded the wire. When sound entered the microphone, the resulting variations in current produced a fluctuating magnetic field. The message was recorded on the wire in the form of a continuous series of transverse magnetizations varying in polarity and strength. In order to play back the recording, the electromagnet was connected to a telephone receiver, and the magnet was moved along the wire.

The development of the Telegraphone, a completely unique and original invention, was seriously hampered by the poor quality of the wire then available, the tendency of the wire to twist, and the lack of suitable amplifiers. Poulsen later replaced the wire by a bulky and cumbersome steel tape. The device created quite a sensation in its day. Acclaimed as the electrical marvel of its age, it was awarded the Grand Prix at the Paris Exposition of 1900 (Fig. 22-1). It worked well enough to convince some executives of the DuPont Corporation. They had twenty of these machines installed for use as dictating machines in their Wilmington offices. But, eventually cylinder-type dictating machines won out over magnetic wire because the cylinders were simpler and did not become snarled as the wires so often did.

737

Courtesy, Ampex Data Products Co.

FIG. 22-1. IMPROVED VERSION OF THE FIRST TELEGRAPHONE

Note the microphone at far right for recording and the receiver for listening to the playback. Unlike the prototype which had a single length of wire stretched on a flat surface, the continuous wire is here closely wound on a large drum. The single record-reproduce head is traveled along the rotating drum by a screw-thread arrangement.

Further developments. Magnetic recording made very small progress during the next 30 years. In 1907, Poulsen developed the employment of d-c bias in magnetic recording. In 1914, Marconi employed the principle of magnetic recording in his Magnetic Detector, which he had developed for the detection, recording, and reproduction of wireless signals.[2]

During the 1920's, the United States Naval Research Laboratories experimented with the use of magnetic recording for transmitting telegraph signals at a high rate of speed. Eventually, difficulties associated with the handling of the wire caused the project to be abandoned. However, as a result of these investigations, in 1921 W. L. Carlsen and G. W. Carpenter of the United States Naval Research Laboratories discovered the principle of a-c bias in magnetic recording. They were granted a patent for this technique in 1927.

During the same period of time, Louis Blattner formed a motion-picture company in England that attempted to produce talking pictures by employing magnetic recording for the synchronized sound. In 1927, J. A. O'Neil was issued a United States patent for a process in which recorded tape was manufactured by applying a fluid coating to a paper tape.

By the early 1930's, there were commercial models of magnetic recorders being sold in Germany under the names of Blattnerphone and Textophone. The Blattnerphone, whose development was based upon earlier work conducted in Germany in 1924 by Stille, was adopted by the British Broadcasting Company in 1930 and was used for many years afterwards.

In 1932, Bell Telephone Laboratories developed a steel tape recorder called the Mirrophone, which was used for announcing weather and time signals over the telephone. Meanwhile, a machine was developed in Germany that was called the Magnetophone and that used a plastic tape coated with ferromagnetic material. In 1937, Acoustic Consultants and Brush Development Company produced a magnetic recorder called the Soundmirror.

In 1940, Marvin Camras succeeded in recording sound by magnetizing fine wire. He perfected a practical wire recorder that employed a-c biasing and erasing. Camras, who now holds over 200 patents in the field of magnetic recording, is sometimes called the father of modern magnetic recording. The wire recorder that he developed during the early 1920's did not differ greatly from the one constructed by Poulsen in 1898, except that it utilized electron tubes, permitting amplification of the signal, and also employed a high-frequency bias signal to overcome distortion produced by the non-linearities of the magnetic medium.[3]

When the Allied armed forces entered Germany in 1945, it was discovered that the Germans had developed magnetic recorders far superior to our own. These recorders had enabled Hitler to deliver many of his battlefront speeches while he was actually hiding in safety hundreds of miles away. The German recorders used plastic tape that was coated with a thin layer of fine particles of iron oxide. Our present-day magnetic recorders are descendants of these German machines (Figs. 22-2 and 22-3).

Courtesy, Berlant-Concertone

FIG. 22-2. TYPICAL TAPE RECORDER—THE BERLANT 31-11

Courtesy, North America Philips Co.

FIG. 22-3. TYPICAL   TAPE   RECORDER—THE NORELCO

22.2 Operation of a magnetic recorder

Sound waves that are picked up by the microphone are converted into electrical energy, amplified, and fed into a magnetic recording head which converts the electrical energy into corresponding varying magnetic fields (Figs. 22-4 and 22-5). Magnetic tape or wire, moving at a constant speed, is then brought into contact with the recording head. This tape consists of a relatively thick base with a thin layer of iron oxide coating it (Fig. 22-6). In some instances, the thickness of the oxide layer may only be 0.0006 in. According to an estimate made by the DuPont Corporation, approximately 60 per cent of the tape sold employs a Mylar polyester film base, while the remaining 40 per cent employs an acetate base.

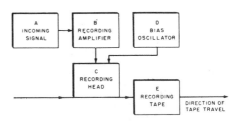

FIG. 22-4. MAGNETIC-RECORDING PROCESS

The recording head is an electromagnet consisting of a coil of fine wire wrapped around soft-iron laminations (Fig. 22-7). It is this transducer that converts the electric signal into a corresponding magnetic signal by applying the magnetizing force to the oxide-coated tape (Fig. 22-8). The head can also be used to reverse this process and convert the signals on the magnetized tape into corresponding electric signals. The magnet is almost circular, and its two poles are very close together, being separated by a gap of approximately

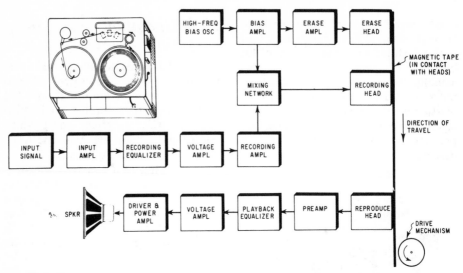

FIG. 22-5. COMPONENT PARTS OF A TYPICAL MAGNETIC TAPE RECORDING SYSTEM

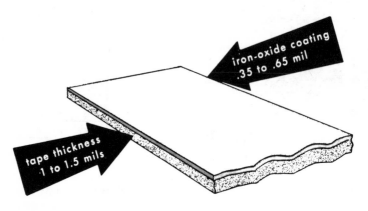

FIG. 22-6. CONSTRUCTION OF MAGNETIC TAPE.

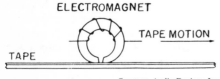

Courtesy, Audio Devices, Inc.

FIG. 22-7. MAGNETIC-RECORDING HEAD

0.001 in. (Fig. 22-9).[4] In general, the slower the tape speed, the narrower must be this gap for good high-frequency response.

The magnetization of the ferromagnetic material on the tape is proportional to the instantaneous amplitude of the audio signal (Fig. 22-10). Thus, a strong audio-frequency current produces a strong magnetic field, while a weak current produces a weak field. A high-frequency current causes each pole of the electromagnet to change through one complete cycle of polarity very rapidly, while low-frequency current causes a slower change of polarity.

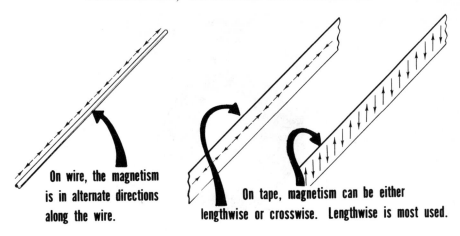

On wire, the magnetism is in alternate directions along the wire.

On tape, magnetism can be either lengthwise or crosswise. Lengthwise is most used.

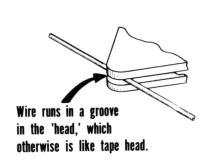

Wire runs in a groove in the 'head,' which otherwise is like tape head.

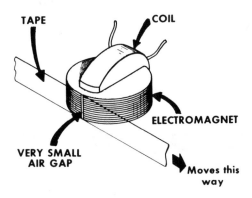

TAPE COIL

ELECTROMAGNET

VERY SMALL AIR GAP

Moves this way

FIG. 22-8. TAPE AND WIRE RECORDING

In this manner, magnetic patterns proportional to the audio waveshape are formed upon the tape (Fig. 22-11). These patterns correspond to the acoustical patterns of the original sound waves. During playback, the tape or wire is passed at constant speed in direct contact with a magnetic pickup head (Fig. 22-12). The magnetic flux on the tape or wire passes through the head and generates corresponding proportional electrical impulses in a pickup coil. These voltages are then amplified and fed to a loudspeaker (Fig. 22-13). The loudspeaker converts the electrical energy back into sound waves that correspond to the original sound.

The fidelity of the response is greatly affected by the speed of the tape (Fig. 22-14). In general, the higher the speed, the greater the fidelity. A tape speed of 15 ips (inches per second) is used for high-fidelity reproduction; a speed of 7.5 ips is used for ordinary reproduction; and a speed of 3.75 ips is used for economical reproduction that is generally accompanied by a considerable loss of high-frequency response (Fig. 22-15).

The early tape recorders discovered by the Allies when they entered Germany, and the first commercial tape

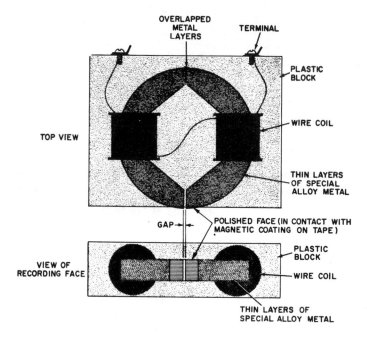

FIG. 22-9. SIMPLIFIED CONSTRUCTION OF A MAGNETIC HEAD

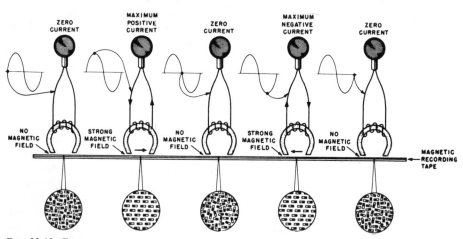

FIG. 22-10. EFFECT OF MICROPHONE CURRENT ON MAGNETIC RECORDING TAPE

recorders that were made in the United States, were full-track 30-ips machines that employed 1/4-in. tape. Although they possessed a degree of fidelity that was better than anything that had been previously developed, they cannot be compared with present-day machines.

As recording and playback heads were improved, the tape speeds dropped to 15 ips and then to 7.5 ips. As additional improvements were made, these speeds dropped to 3.75 ips, and some machines even feature a speed of 1.875 ips.

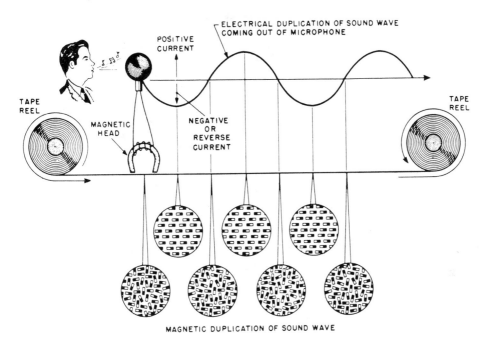

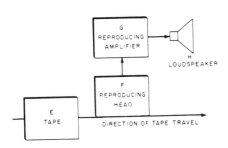

FIG. 22-11. MOTION OF TAPE PICKS UP EACH SUCCESSIVE VARIATION OF THE SOUND WAVE

FIG. 22-12. MAGNETIC-REPRODUCING PROCESS

Meanwhile, dual-track heads were developed to make it possible to record more material on the same amount of tape. This development also provided the two channels that were needed for stereo magnetic recording. Additional improvements in the art made it possible to take the next significant step—recording four channels on regular tape. This is now known as four-track or quarter-track tape (Fig. 22-16). Simultaneously, several manufacturers brought out adapters and heads that could be used to convert any recorder to a four-track system.[5]

The magnetic patterns may be erased by using a high-frequency electric current to demagnetize the tape without affecting it any other way (Figs. 22-17 and 22-18). The same tape can thus be used over and over again hundreds of times. If the recorded material is not erased, it lasts indefinitely and may be replayed thousands of times without noticeable wear or increase of surface noise.[6] Because of these characteristics, tape now has little competition in the field of making temporary recordings.

It is interesting to note that an ultrasonic signal with a frequency between 30 and 100 kc is used to provide the high-frequency signal for demagnetizing. The same signal is also used to provide a bias that is needed to over-

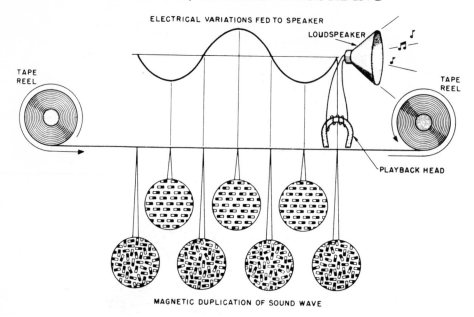

FIG. 22-13. MAGNETIC VARIATIONS IN THE TAPE CAUSE SOUND TO BE PRODUCED BY THE SPEAKER

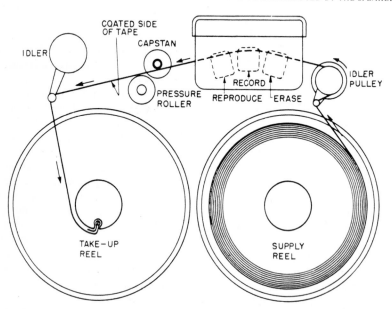

FIG. 22-14. MECHANICAL COMPONENTS OF TYPICAL TAPE RECORDER

come the non-linearity of the magnetization curve of the magnetic tape or wire. When this high-frequency bias is mixed in a linear manner with the signal to be recorded, the signal encounters only the straight-line portion

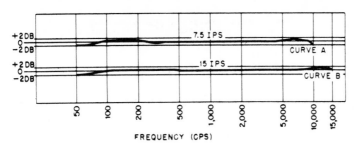

Courtesy, Berlant-Concertone

FIG. 22-15. TAPE RESPONSE OF THE BERLANT 31-11 TAPE RECORDER AT 7.5 IPS (CURVE A) AND 15 IPS (CURVE B)

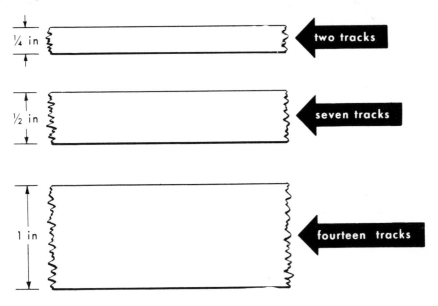

FIG. 22-16. WIDER RECORDING TAPE CAN ACCOMMODATE MORE TRACKS

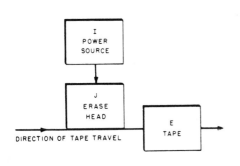

FIG. 22-17. MAGNETIC ERASURE PROCESS

of the recording-characteristic curve.

22.3 *Biasing of magnetic amplifiers*

Since every magnetic medium is essentially non-linear in nature, the amount of magnetization resulting from the magnetizing field produced by a signal is not directly proportional to the strength of that signal (Fig. 22-19). Unless corrected, this characteristic produces very bad distortion (Fig. 22-20).

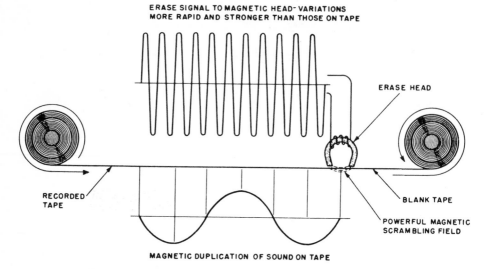

FIG. 22-18. ERASING THE RECORDED TAPE

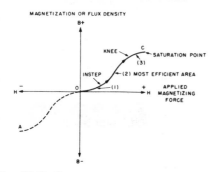

FIG. 22-19. SIMPLE MAGNETIZATION CURVE FOR IRON

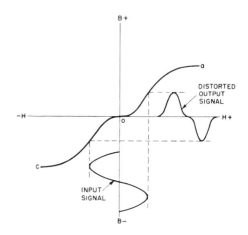

FIG. 22-20. DISTORTED SIGNAL ON DEMAGNETIZED TAPE WITH NO BIAS CURRENT APPLIED

One solution to this problem is to use d-c bias in which a constant biasing magnetic field is produced by a steady biasing current. This method, which was employed in Poulsen's early magnetic recorders, tends to produce considerable background noise and hiss on the tape.

A better solution to this problem is the employment of an a-c biasing field that is produced by an ultrasonic alternating current with a frequency at least 3.5 times greater than that of the highest audio frequency to be recorded (Fig. 22-21). The reason for

the employment of such a high frequency for biasing purposes is to prevent the formation of undesired whistling sounds by the beating of the biasing signal against the harmonics of the audio signal that is being recorded. These bias frequencies usually range from 40 kc in home recorders to 80 kc in professional recorders. The amount of bias current employed

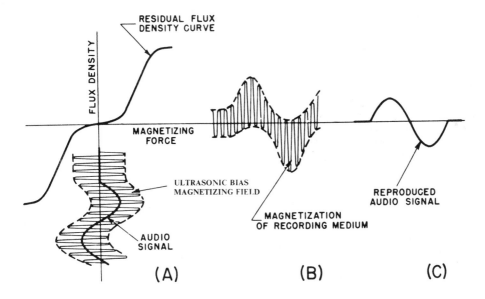

FIG. 22-21. USE OF AN ULTRASONIC BIASING FIELD TO REDUCE DISTORTION IN MAGNETIC RECORDING

is relatively large, its strength being several times greater than that of the signal being recorded. As was mentioned earlier in this chapter, this technique of employing high-frequency a-c bias was first developed during the middle 1920's by Carlsen and Carpenter of the United States Naval Research Laboratories.

The employment of alternating bias produces a linear recording characteristic (Fig. 22-22). Consequently, when a high-quality magnetic recording is played through a good sound system, it is almost impossible to distinguish the recording from a direct pickup. This fact explains why commercial broadcasting stations now use magnetic recordings for the rebroadcasting of programs, and why the making of a magnetic recording is generally the first step in producing a disc recording.

Some magnetic-recording devices contain three heads (Fig. 22-23). The first one is used to erase any previous magnetization, the second applies a

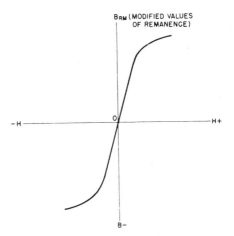

Courtesy, Armour Research Foundation
FIG. 22-22. STRAIGHT-LINE RECORDING CHARACTERISTIC RESULTING WHEN HIGH-FREQUENCY BIAS IS USED

field that corresponds to the sum of the bias and audio signal currents, and the third has a signal voltage induced in it by the moving tape when the device is set to play back the recorded sound (Fig. 22-24).

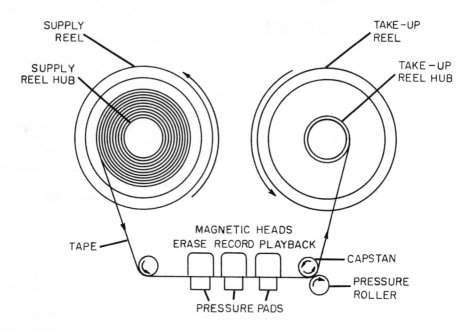

FIG. 22-23. ARRANGEMENTS OF THE HEADS IN A TAPE RECORDER

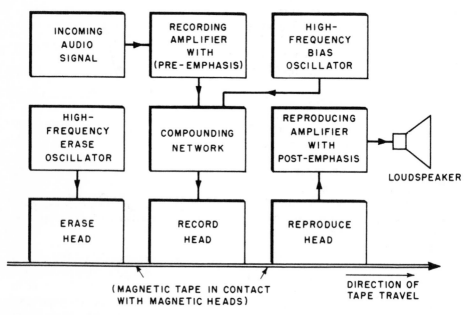

FIG. 22-24. BASIC ELECTRONIC AND ELECTROMECHANICAL COMPONENTS OF A MAGNETIC RECORDING SYSTEM

22.4 *Advantages and disadvantages of magnetic recording*

Among the advantages claimed for magnetic recording over commercial disc recording are that magnetic recording is relatively simple, does not require a high degree of proficiency and skill, requires no needles, introduces no needle-tracking problems, accommodates a maximum amount of sound in a minimum amount of space, introduces no external mechanical noise, possesses a very low-noise level, produces no discriminating frequency losses, can provide flat frequency response between 50 and 15,000 cps, and produces records which cannot warp, are compact and difficult to break, and may be erased, edited, cut out, or altered (Fig. 22-25). Accelerated aging tests of magnetic tape indicate a probable useful life of at least 100 years. The fact that magnetic recording can produce records that can be played thousands of times and that can play a continuous eight-hour program was responsible for the decision of the Muzak Company, one of the largest background-music concerns, to replace disc recordings by magnetic tapes.

On the other hand, there is at present no practical, low-cost commercial method of turning out magnetic recordings quickly and easily in large quantities at a price that will compete with disc recordings. Considerable progress towards solution of this problem has been made by Camras and Herr, who have each independently developed a promising method of duplicating magnetic-tape recordings by placing the recorded tape and a blank tape in contact with each other in a high-frequency magnetic field.[7]

The Ampex Corporation has also

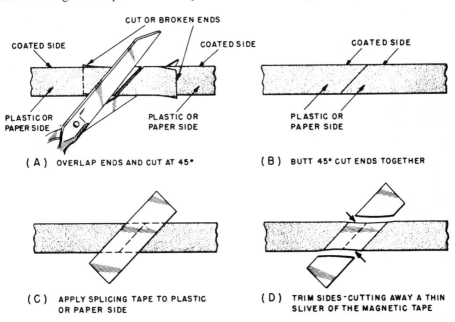

(A) OVERLAP ENDS AND CUT AT 45°

(B) BUTT 45° CUT ENDS TOGETHER

(C) APPLY SPLICING TAPE TO PLASTIC OR PAPER SIDE

(D) TRIM SIDES - CUTTING AWAY A THIN SLIVER OF THE MAGNETIC TAPE

FIG. 22-25. SPLICING MAGNETIC TAPE

developed a tape-duplicating system. The tape which is to be duplicated is placed in a master unit, while reels of blank tape are placed in ten slave units. A button is pressed, and all of the reels begin moving at either 30 or 60 ips. The output of the master unit is fed simultaneously to all of the slave units, and within minutes, ten copies have been produced.[8] Similar types of tape duplicators have been developed by other manufacturers (Fig. 22-26).

Courtesy, Ampex Corp.

FIG. 22-26. A MODERN TAPE-COPYING MACHINE

Among the other disadvantages of magnetic recording is the fact that the tape reels and capstans are not heavy enough to produce much of a flywheel action. Consequently, any slight variation in motor speed will produce very unpleasant results. Tape has a tendency to stretch and to dry out after a few years. In addition, since the tape is wound upon itself on reels, there is a tendency for a strong signal to print through onto the adjacent tape layers directly above and below it.

22.5 *Magnetic data recording*

For many years, one of the major obstacles impeding the solution of important scientific, industrial, and military problems was the lack of a simple and effective method of quickly recording data obtained from experiments and processes or telemetered from remote locations. Prior to 1950, such data were usually stored by means of ink-chart recorders, recording oscillographs, disc recorders, and optical film recorders. None of these devices proved to be satisfactory. They were too complicated and inconvenient for ordinary use, and the reliability, frequency response, and reproducibility of results left much to be desired.

With the development of magnetic-tape recording, a method of recording data became available that possessed the desired degree of compactness, simplicity, convenience, speed, economy, frequency response, reproducibility, and reliability. It was discovered that magnetic tape possesses enormous data-storage capacity per linear inch and that a 1-in. width could satisfactorily record up to 14 parallel channels of information.

According to one source, the following is a list of the desirable characteristics of magnetic tape that make it a uniquely suitable medium for data-handling and recording applications:

1. Data is reproduced in live electrical form.
2. Data may be reproduced many times for various analyses.
3. Data time bases may be expanded or contracted easily, as much as 200 to 1 in a single step on the same machine.
4. Data is available immediately with no time wasted on developing or processing operations between recording and reproducing.
5. Data reduction by automatic means is greatly facilitated.
6. Data output is readily adaptable to computer input.

7. Data capacity is greater than for any other recording medium, facilitating storage and shipment.

8. Data may be identified by simultaneously recorded voice commentary.[9]

In 1948, the Raytheon Manufacturing Company modified an Ampex Model 301 tape recorder and used it for recording audio-frequency telemetered signals produced in connection with Project "Hurricane" at the Naval Air Missile Test Center. By 1950, several magnetic-recording systems had been developed specifically for instrumentation applications in testing aircraft, guided missiles, and satellites.

Each of these systems contained transducers and sensory elements that converted physical parameters such as acceleration, temperature, stress, pressure, vibration, radiation, and micrometeorite erosion into corresponding electrical-analog signal voltages (Fig. 22-27). These signals were then amplified and recorded directly on adjacent tracks of a multiple-track multichannel tape recorder (Figs. 22-28 and 22-29).

22.6 Applications of magnetic data recording

It did not take long for scientists and engineers who were working in other fields to recognize the usefulness of the technique of magnetic recording of data, since any type of information which can be converted into electrical terms can also be faithfully recorded and reproduced on magnetic tape. These recordings possess the advantages of low inherent distortion, wide frequency range, wide dynamic range, long life, ease and rapidity of playback with no time lost in processing, and provision for simultaneous recording on many channels. Consequently, tape recorders are widely employed today in science and industry. Most of these applications come under the headings of telemetery, shock and vibration analysis, electronic computers, and automatic control.

The tape recorders that are employed for these applications are usually designed with extreme care. They may use a special type of tape in which the magnetic material is covered with a plastic coating. This prevents the oxide layer from contacting the recording and playback heads and depositing oxide on them.

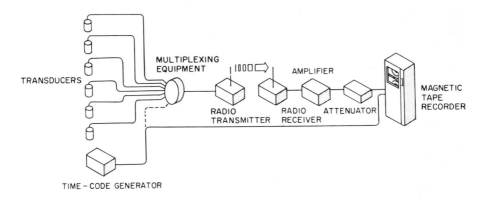

Courtesy, Ampex Data Products Co.

FIG. 22-27. DATA ACQUISITION BY MAGNETIC TAPE

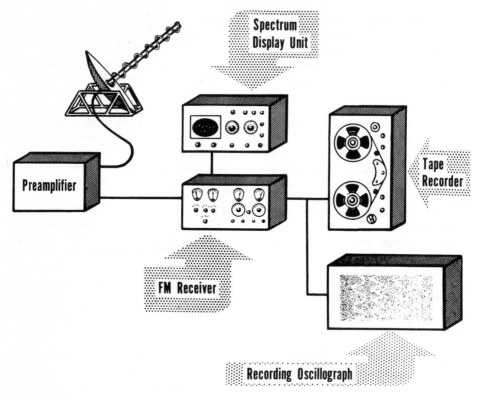

FIG. 22-28. BASIC DATA-RECEIVING STATION

Courtesy, Ampex Data Products Co.

FIG. 22-29. COMPLETE TELEMETRY GROUND STATION EQUIPPED WITH INSTRUMENTATION RECORDERS

Under normal conditions, ordinary audio-frequency tape recorders cannot be used for these types of recording applications. One reason for this is the fact that the ordinary recorder is designed to distort and pre-emphasize the extremely low and high ends of the frequency spectrum in order to compensate for the fact that the energy content of speech and music signals is not uniformly distributed over this spectrum.[10] In addition, instrumentation recorders possess precision drive systems and are as free from wow and flutter as the art permits (Fig. 22-30). Since some data frequencies may approach 100 kc, special record and playback heads have been designed which have a very low loss to 100 kc. The bias frequency has been upped to 350

Courtesy, Ampex Data Products Co.
FIG. 22-30. AMPEX FR-600 SOLID-STATE MAGNETIC TAPE RECORDER FOR INSTRUMENTATION APPLICATION

kc in order to avoid the production of beat signals. Some magnetic-tape instrumentation recorders are able to record over a frequency range extending from zero cps up to several megacycles.

Certain applications require a special type of recorder with a frequency response that accurately preserves waveshapes from a frequency of several cycles per second all the way down to direct current. The problem is solved in one type of recorder by causing the low-frequency signal that is to be recorded to modulate an FM carrier wave. The modulated signal is then recorded on tape. During playback, the original information is restored by means of a demodulating discriminator circuit. Such FM multi-track recorders have been put to great use in missile and earth-satellite research, in seismic explorations, in the study of shock and vibration, and in the investigation of the motions of ships at sea, where low-frequency information from a number of different sources must be recorded simultaneously and stored for future analysis.[11]

When a quantitative analysis of frequencies and energy content is desired, the taped data can be fed directly to an electronic wave analyzer. This type of device reduces highly complex waveshapes to their component frequencies, eliminating the tedious graphic methods of wave analysis that were previously employed with visually recorded data.

Another important point is the fact that tape is the only recording medium that readily provides the ability to alter the time base of the recorded events. Thus, the frequencies involved may be multiplied or divided upon playback; events may be recreated either faster or slower than they actually occurred (Fig. 22-31).[12]

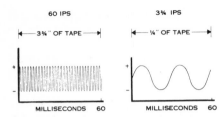

FIG. 22-31. TIME-BASE ALTERATION OF A 480 CPS SINE WAVE

22.7 Types of magnetic data-recording systems

The four major types of systems employed for magnetic data recording are: (1) direct recording, (2) FM recording, (3) pulse-duration modulation, and (4) digital recording.

Direct recording. In the direct-recording system, the signal is recorded directly on the tape in an essentially unmodified form, except for the addition of high-frequency bias to minimize distortion resulting from the non-linearity of the magnetic coating and the pre-emphasis of the higher frequency signals to provide constant-flux recording characteristics (Fig. 22-32).[13]

This system possesses several disadvantages. It is unable to record very low frequencies, and serious distortion can be overcome only by reducing the recording level by a considerable amount with a consequent deterioration of the signal-to-noise ratio of the recording. Its normal amplitude accuracy is

only within 30 per cent, or plus or minus 3 db. On the other hand, it does possess wide dynamic range, ability to handle moderate overloads, and an extremely wide frequency spectrum ranging from 50 to 100,000 cps.[14]

This system is employed most frequently for the recording of certain types of frequency-multiplexed sub-carrier signals telemetered from aircraft, missiles, and satellites. It is also used to record high-frequency vibrations and noise produced during the testing of jet and rocket engines and for audio and communications monitoring.[15]

Frequency-modulation recording. An alternative to the direct-recording system is the employment of an FM carrier system. One or more FM carrier waves is modulated by the electric signals carrying the information (Fig. 22-33). Thus, the data are converted into carrier-frequency deviations that are proportional to the amplitude of the signal. The modulated carrier waves may then be recorded directly on the tape. Since this relatively-high-frequency signal is recorded at saturation levels, the non-linearity of the tape coating produces no effects and bias is not required (Fig. 22-34).[16]

The FM carriers may also be transmitted to a receiver, which separates the carrier by filtering, demodulates the signals, extracts the information, and records the information on tape.

The tape recording is then placed

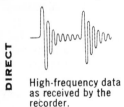

| High-frequency data as received by the recorder. | No coding or modulation are used. | Rate-of-change of the data amplitudes is recorded directly as a magnetic-signal level on the tape. |

FIG. 22-32. DIRECT RECORDING

FM-CARRIER

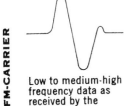

Low to medium-high frequency data as received by the recorder.

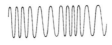

Carrier oscillation is frequency-modulated by the data.

Modulated carrier is amplified, limited and then recorded on tape at near-saturation level.

WIDEBAND

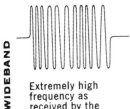

Extremely high frequency as received by the recorder.

Carrier oscillation is frequency-modulated by the data.

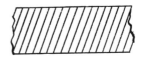

Modulated carrier is recorded transversely across the entire width of the tape. The recorded signal is similar to the FM-Carrier signal above, except that much higher frequencies are accommodated.

Courtesy. Ampex Data Products Co.

FIG. 22-33. FM-CARRIER AND WIDEBAND RECORDING

in a playback unit which converts the information into digital form. These data are then fed into computer circuits of automatic-data-reduction equipment which carry out the computations required to analyze the data (Fig. 22-35). When desired, the output of the recorder can be fed into scanning instruments

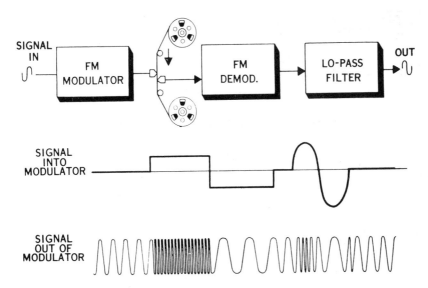

Courtesy. Ampex Data Products Co.

FIG. 22-34. BASIC FM SYSTEM

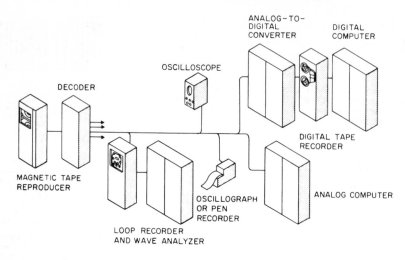

FIG. 22-35. DATA REDUCTION FROM MAGNETIC TAPE

such as oscilloscopes and galvanometers, into writing instruments such as oscillographs and pen recorders, and into translating instruments such as card-punch and tape-punch machines whose outputs can be used to plot graphs or to control machines.[17]

A modified version of this FM recording system is known as frequency-division multiplex (Fig. 22-36). In this system, a number of individual FM carriers are used. After each carrier is modulated by its own signal, all these signals are mixed and recorded, using

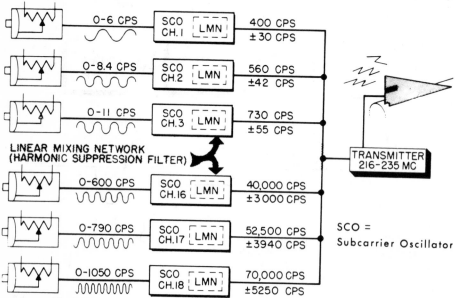

FIG. 22-36. FREQUENCY-DIVISION MULTIPLEXING AN FM-FM SYSTEM

the direct-recording process. In this manner, the linearity and great width of the direct-recording process are used to permit the simultaneous recording of many channels of information on a single tape track.

The FM recording process makes very stringent demands upon the tape-transport system, since any speed variations will introduce an undesired modulation of the carrier frequency, thus producing considerable noise and distortion. Consequently, for FM recording applications in which the maximum in accuracy and signal-to-noise ratio are required, it may be necessary to add an electronic flutter-compensation system.[18] Other disadvantages associated with this system are its failure to utilize the tape as effectively as the direct-recording system does and its need for more complex electronic circuitry. Its nominal dynamic amplitude accuracy is 5 per cent, or plus or minus 0.5 db.[19]

Frequency-modulation recording provides the most practical method of performing time-base expansion or contraction. It is used when a high degree of accuracy and stability is required, such as for the recording of vibrations and other data of medium frequencies. It is also used for the recording of d-c and low-frequency data such as those obtained from strain-gauge transducers, thermocouples, accelerometers, and potentiometers.[20]

Pulse-duration modulation. While the FM system of data recording has been widely used and displays excellent characteristics, a newer system is finding increasing use. This system employs a type of time-division multiplexing and is called pulse-width modulation (PWM) or pulse-duration modulation (PDM) (Fig. 22-37). It produces signals consisting of a sequence of pulses of meaningful duration. A keyer or modulator converts each instantaneous varying-amplitude voltage reading into a corresponding constant-amplitude signal of varying pulse length. Thus, each pulse possesses a time duration that is proportional to the amplitude of the corresponding signal.

When this system operates, a rotating or solid-state commutator samples as many as 88 channels of information within a second (Figs. 22-38, 22-39, and 22-40). The output of this commutator consists of a train of pulses

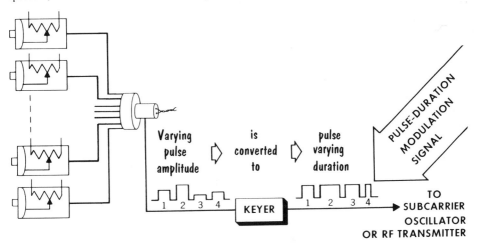

Varying pulse amplitude ⟹ is converted to ⟹ pulse varying duration

1 2 3 4   **KEYER**   1 2 3 4

PULSE-DURATION MODULATION SIGNAL

TO SUBCARRIER OSCILLATOR OR RF TRANSMITTER

FIG. 22-37. A BASIC PDM SIGNAL

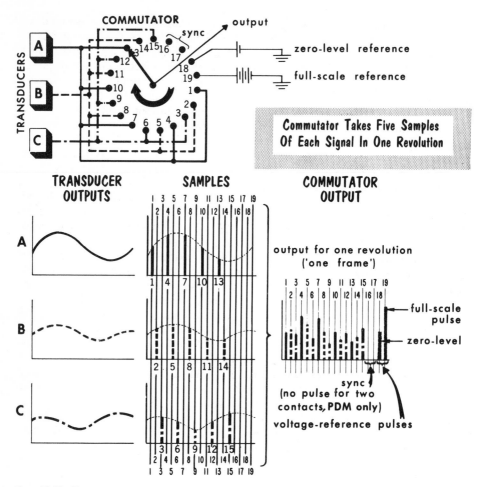

FIG. 22-38. SAMPLING TECHNIQUE AND THE FUNCTIONARY OF THE ROTATING COMMUTATOR IN TIME-DIVISION MULTIPLEXING OF THREE SIGNALS

of varying amplitudes. This train then goes to the keyer, where the amplitude of each pulse is converted into a pulse whose duration is proportional to its amplitude.

The output of the keyer may be transmitted via a telemetry link, or it may be applied to a recording module, where the received pulses are differentiated and converted into short positive and negative spikes that define the beginning or leading edge and the end

or trailing edge of each pulse (Fig. 22-41). This is then recorded as a sequence of precisely timed positive and negative impulses that mark the beginning and end of each pulse. These spikes possess sufficient magnitude to saturate the tape; consequently, the recorded signal is relatively free from errors or dropouts when it is reproduced.

The reproducing mechanism employs a de-keyer in which the reproduced spikes trigger a multivibrator.

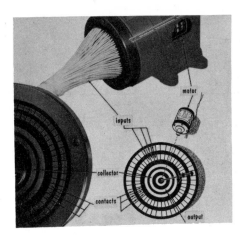

FIG. 22-39. CONSTRUCTION OF A MOTOR-DRIVEN COMMUTATOR SWITCH

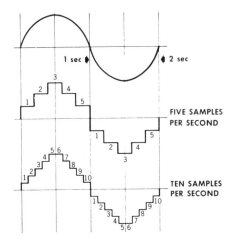

FIG. 22-40. SAMPLING A SIGNAL

This, in turn, produces an output pulse train resembling the original output that the keyer delivered to the recording module. This pulse train is then demodulated, decommutated, and filtered to produce the original data of varying amplitudes (Fig. 22-42).[21]

This system is less susceptible than the FM system is to wow and flutter. It uses tape very economically and can record a large number of channels of information. Thus, one PDM recorder can record 80 channels of information on a single track, or almost 1,200 channels of information on a 14-track tape. Another advantage is its high system accuracy: better than within 1 per cent over all. It also possesses a high signal-to-noise ratio and converts easily to digital coding.

Its major disadvantages are the limited frequency response of each channel, the less efficient utilization of the tape than with the FM technique, and the increased complexity of the auxiliary electronic equipment required.[22] [23] In general, PDM is employed for telemetric applications which require a large number of time-shared channels of narrow data bandwidth. It is therefore employed most frequently when a large number of d-c or low-frequency data channels are to be recorded on one track of tape.[24]

Digital recording. Digital recording refers to the recording of pulses that represent encoded binary digits (Fig. 22-43). The information is conveyed

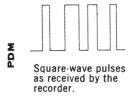

Square-wave pulses as received by the recorder.

The square waves are transformed into "spikes" that define beginnings and endings of pulses.

Positive and negative spikes are recorded on the tape.

Courtesy, Ampex Data Products Co.

FIG. 22-41. PDM RECORDING

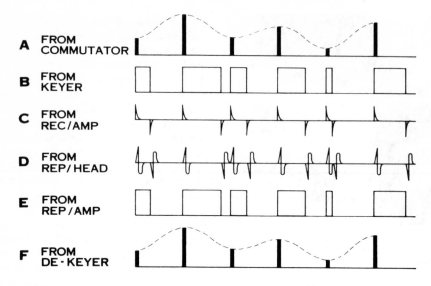

A FROM COMMUTATOR

B FROM KEYER

C FROM REC/AMP

D FROM REP/HEAD

E FROM REP/AMP

F FROM DE-KEYER

Courtesy, Ampex Data Products Co

FIG. 22-42. SIGNALS AT VARIOUS POINTS IN PDM

CHARACTER		BINARY CODED REPRESENTATION
0	=	0000
1	=	0001
2	=	0010
3	=	0011
4	=	0100
5	=	0101
6	=	0110
7	=	0111
8	=	1000
9	=	1001

560
0101 0110 0000

Courtesy, Ampex Data Products Co.

FIG. 22-43. BINARY-CODED DECIMAL SYSTEM

either by means of the presence or absence of a pulse or by the polarity of the pulse. In this system, the signal is divided into a number of slices. The amplitude of each slice is measured and is converted into binary digits or bits (Fig. 22-44).

Current practice involves the recording of 100 to 400 pulses per inch, while the recording of 1,000 pulses per inch is feasible. Pulses may be recorded at saturation level either serially along the length of the tape or in parallel across the tape (Fig. 22-45). Thus, with the aid of multi-track heads, a complete number may be represented by a series

of pulses that are simultaneously recorded in a line across the tape at right angles to the direction of tape travel (Fig. 22-46). Consequently, all of the pulses representing a number may be recorded at one instant and recovered in a similar manner for convenient entry into a digital computer.[25][26] As has been mentioned, it is also possible to record the digits serially as a sequence of pulses along a single track (Figs. 22-47, 22-48, and 22-49).

The digital-recording technique, which is sometimes known as pulse-code modulation (PCM), was invented in 1939 by A. H. Reeves of the American Telephone and Telegraph Company. The major advantage of this system is its ability to override noise, since noise can rarely obliterate a pulse or simulate a pulse where one is absent. It therefore possesses the advantage of great inherent accuracy. A typical system of this sort may possess an accuracy of within 0.1 per cent and is capable of recording and reproducing less than 2 errors in 10 million pulses. Other advan-

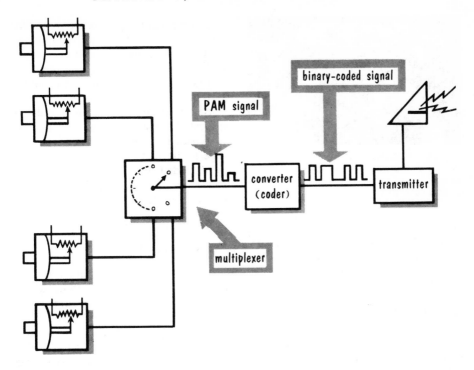

FIG. 22-44. A BASIC DIGITAL PCM SYSTEM

tages associated with this type of system are its insensitivity to variations in tape-transport speed, the simple recording and reproducing circuitry involved, and the fact that the recorded information is in the correct form to be fed into a

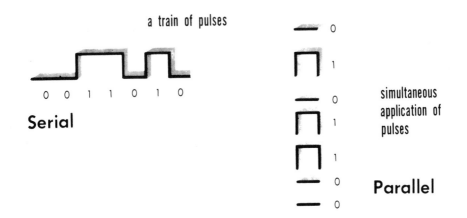

FIG. 22-45. SERIAL AND PARALLEL DIGITAL RECORDING

Courtesy, *Industrial Science and Engineering*

FIG. 22-46. DIGITAL HEAD ASSEMBLY OF A MAGNETIC TAPE RECORDER DESIGNED TO RECORD SIX TRACKS OF WEATHER INFORMATION

additional features to insure reliability. Among these features are redundancy, in which the same information is recorded twice on parallel but separate tracks, and a parity check involving a system by which an odd number of pulses is always fed in, and trouble is indicated only when an even number of pulses is recorded. A final disadvantage is the fact that unless the data to be recorded have been digitized at the source, a special, complex analog-to-digital transducer must be employed.[28]

digital computer. PCM is therefore used to record the outputs of digital measuring devices or transducers and the output pulses produced by analog-to-digital converters.[27]

Naturally, this system also possesses certain disadvantages. The first is poor tape economy, which is only one-eighth that of the PDM system and one-thirtieth that of the FM system. It also requires tape of extremely high quality for good reliability and may also require

22.8 *Magnetic tape in computers*

It is necessary for computers and automatic data processers to store large amounts of reference information which must be readily available. Many of these devices employ magnetic tape to store binary code impulses and to provide a high-capacity memory. For large storage capacity, nothing has yet been found that excels magnetic tape wound on

Pulses received by recorder are digital level-change type.

Record current changes when the binary sign changes.

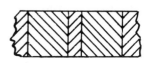

Signals are recorded at tape-saturation level.

Courtesy, Ampex Data Products Co.

FIG. 22-47. PCM RECORDING

Digital pulse input as received by the record amplifier from computer or other digital device.

Record-current polarity changes each time a pulse signifying a "one" is to be recorded. This is non-return-to-zero recording.

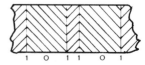

Signals are recorded at tape-saturation level to obtain maximum output.

Courtesy, Ampex Data Products Co.

FIG. 22-48. DIGITAL NON-RETURN-TO-ZERO (NRZ) RECORDING

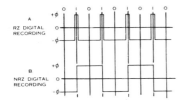

FIG. 22-49. COMPARISON BETWEEN RZ AND NRZ DIGITAL RECORDING SYSTEMS

reels.[29] As many as 20,000 records of 80 digits each may be stored on a single 12-in. reel.

Tape is also used to supply numbers, equations, and programming information. Furthermore, since most computers can process information at a much faster rate than the data can be fed in or taken out of it, magnetic tape is being employed in the input, output, and auxiliary storage sections to speed up the rate of processing. The surface has barely been scratched with respect to exploring the potential applications of magnetic recording in computers.

Another fact that should not be overlooked is that when data have been recorded on tape, particularly when they have been recorded in the form of binary digits, they are in a form that enables them to be fed easily into the input section of an automatic-data-processing system.

22.9 *Control applications of magnetic tape*

Magnetic tape is also ideally suited for automation techniques and the automatic control of machines, machine tools, and processes. Like the roll that controlled the old-fashion player piano, magnetic tape can be used to provide a complex and sensitive program of guidance (Fig. 22-50).

Any machine function that can be regulated electrically can be controlled by tape. Taped signals can open valves,

FIG. 22-50. TAPE-CONTROLLED NUMERICAL PROFILER

determine positions, regulate movements, control timing, and actuate servomechanisms that control the relative movements of cutting tools and work. Manufacturers such as Convair, Lockheed, and Martin, who have employed tape-recorded control systems, have listed many reasons for its adoption. The following are the reasons that are listed most frequently:

1. The simplification of the trained-labor problem. Highly skilled workers may be replaced by less highly trained machine operators.

2. The control system possesses greater capacity for working long hours at close tolerances than human workers possess.

3. The increased output that is obtainable because of this control system.

4. The high degree of versatility that is obtainable at low cost.

5. The improved product quality and uniformity that is obtainable through the elimination of errors and failures made by tired or careless workers.[30]

The tape recordings used for machine control can be made in several different ways. In the manual method, a skilled operator machines a sample part while the tape records the various machine motions and switching operations. This technique has been utilized in a device developed by John Coolidge of Borg-Warner to control the application of a porcelain enamel coating to bathtubs.[31]

In the tracing method, a tracer head is mounted in place of the tool, and a template or sample is mounted in place of the workpiece. The tape then records machine motions and switching operations as directed by the tracer control and the operator.

In the line-drawing method, a photoelectrically controlled device follows the lines of the original drawing, recording the motions on tape.

The most advanced and most complex method of preparing a tape is the dimensional method. It uses points plotted from the original drawings, which are then interpolated by a computer and translated into servo signals which are recorded on tape.[32] This latter method makes it possible to create machined shapes such as machined turbine blades that are impossible to produce under manual control of the machine.[33]

The Martin Company is now using blueprint information coded on tapes to control a milling machine designed for training out large precision-built structural parts for the Martin Matador Missile and the Seamaster seaplane. Control tapes can be produced in a very short time and can then be shipped to different plants equipped with similar machines.[34]

It is fairly obvious that this magnetic-tape technique will soon have a serious impact upon the logistics of replacement parts, the assurance of uniformity and reliability in production, and the adaptability of industry to rapid mobilization in the event of a national emergency. It is not hard to visualize a time in the not-too-distant future when machines in factories located in various parts of the country will be controlled by a tape recording from one central headquarters and when an installation located overseas or in a remote area will be able to produce a badly needed spare part within minutes by connecting a machine tool to a telephone line or radio receiver. In the field of process control, taped signals can be used to operate motors, valves, thermostats, and pressure controls, and to repeat any pattern of temperature, pressure, agitation, etc., of a process sequence that has previously achieved a successful result. A loop of magnetic tape can also be used to make a continuous correction in flowing or cycling processes. It can pick up a measurement at one point of the cycle and then apply a correction at another point later in the process. The magnetic tape is then erased.[35]

Magnetic tape can also be used to simulate all types of environmental and operational conditions. For example, it can be used to agitate tables that subject components to the exact vibrations produced in missiles, airplanes, and vehicles. As an illustration, the ground-based launcher of the Polaris missile is programmed by tapes recorded on a variety of ships at sea.

At the Buick plant's experimental laboratory, a tape recording has been made of the operation of an automobile engine on a given trip. This tape is then fed into a device which controls an engine on the test stand, operating the engine as though it were being driven on that trip. Thus, engines can be "driven" thousands of miles through traffic under varying road conditions without leaving the laboratory.[36] A similar device is used in the laboratories of Esso Research and Engineering Company to eliminate the human-factor variations in testing fuels and lubricants.[37] [38]

Magnetic recording can also be employed in factories that are not automated. The Westinghouse Electric Corporation and the Dictaphone Corporation have developed a magnetic-recording system called AIMO or Audibly Instructed Manufacturing Operation (Fig. 22-51). It substitutes aural instructions for work drawings, written instruction sheets, or shop blueprints. Production workers obtain their instructions from a tiny transistorized amplifier and earphone. The instructions are transmitted by a tape recorder and are received by means of an inductive pickup coil. One work step is given at a time, and when the worker desires the next series of instructions, he presses a button. The machine then transmits the next set of instructions and stops once more. It is claimed that this device can increase production by 20 to 100 per cent, that it reduces the time required to train new workers, and that it reduces the errors to approximately that point that would be achieved

if the job had been memorized.[39] The La Belle Teleguide is a similar type of device that employs both magnetic tape and 35-mm slides (Fig. 22-52).

Courtesy, La Belle Sales Corp.
FIG. 22-52. LA BELLE TELEGUIDE
This tool employs 35-mm slides and magnetic tape for the guidance of workers on intricate assemblies.

Another interesting application of magnetic recording is its employment on production lines where the material being inspected for flaws cannot be physically rejected at the inspection position. This problem is solved by recording a rejection impulse on tape. The tape is designed to produce a time delay that is just long enough so that the article to be rejected has a chance to come out of the processing machine. At that moment, the taped signal operates a deflector gate and the defective article is sent to the scrap heap.[40]

22.10 *Other applications of tape recorders*

In the fields of psychiatry, psychological research, and noise reduction, the effects produced upon the listeners are very important. Tape recorders are capable of producing sounds with a high degree of realism, especially when multi-track stereophonic tape record-

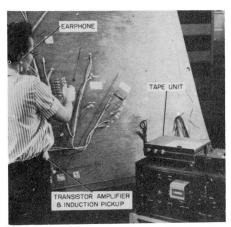

Courtesy, Dictaphone Corp.
FIG. 22-51. AUDIBLY INSTRUCTED MANUFACTURING OPERATIONS (AIMO) SYSTEM

ings are used. Tape recordings have been found to be extremely useful in isolating and reducing noise in vehicles and machines and in comparing the acoustical properties of materials and buildings. They have also been used to explore the subjective factors involved in exposure to two different types of noise spectra, such as those produced by both propeller and jet aircraft.

Medical applications. Tape recordings have proved valuable in training medical students to recognize and diagnose noises of special medical significance. This is very important in the teaching of cardiology, which depends to a great extent upon training the doctor's perception and appreciation of low-frequency sounds. Some medical instructors have solved this problem by developing a library of tape recordings of all tapes of heart sounds. These recordings are played during the lectures.

FIG. 22-53. PHYSIOLOGICAL MONITORING AND RECORDING SYSTEM
Equipment in right rack amplifies physiological signals and displays selected waveshapes on the oscilloscopes. Data are recorded on the Ampex FR-100 (center) and can be reproduced for further study with the small analog computer (left).

They are also looped into endless tapes and played constantly until the student has had plenty of time to become familiar with each individual type of sound.[41]

Another application (Fig. 22-53) of tape recording is in the study of nerve and brain functions. Tape recordings are used to record the voltage changes occurring with each nerve impulse and thus help to chart the relations between nerve endings and the brain (Fig. 22-54). Tape recordings of electrical shocks transmitted through connecting muscles have aided the study of degenerative muscular ailments. In addition, special brain-wave tape recorders are being used by medical research workers to record amplified electrical potentials generated by the brain (Figs. 22-55). These encephalographic recordings make it possible to study the waveforms, their time relationships, and their places of origin.[42]

Time Compresser. A fascinating application of magnetic recording is the Time Compresser, developed in 1950 by Fairbanks, Everitt, and Jaeger of the University of Illinois. This device can take a 45-minute speech or musical concert and compress it into 30 minutes without dropping a single syllable or note and without changing the pitch. The mechanism involves a continuously rotating loop of recording tape upon which sound is temporarily stored and four pickup heads mounted in a revolving drum. This arrangement is used to

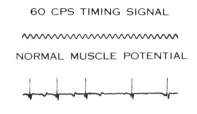

60 CPS TIMING SIGNAL

NORMAL MUSCLE POTENTIAL

ENERVATED MUSCLE POTENTIAL

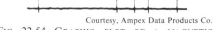

FIG. 22-54. GRAPHIC PLOT OF A MAGNETIC RECORDING OF MUSCLE IMPULSES

FIG. 22-55. RECORDING BRAIN WAVES ON MAG-NETIC TAPE
Electrical potentials from brains of retarded children are amplified, recorded, and studied on paper graphs from a multi-channel oscillograph. Of chief interest are the wave form, time relationships, and exact origin, all useful for planning surgery to correct convulsive and motor-nerve disorders.

discard portions of the incoming signal and to push the retained portions together smoothly. As each pickup in turn touches the loop of tape, it records that portion of the sound on a permanent tape. As that pickup leaves the loop, the next pickup comes around to record. The sound that is located on the loop between the two pickups and is untouched by either pickup is left out. This machine can also be operated in reverse as a time expander.[43][44]

Mention has previously been made of the fact that one of the important properties of magnetic-tape recording is its ability to alter the time base, enabling an event that was recorded on one time scale to be recreated on a compressed or an expanded time scale (see Fig. 22-31). Thus, a fast transient or a high-frequency signal may be recorded and played back at a speed a thousand times slower (Fig. 22-56). Conversely, a very-low-frequency signal, as low as a

fraction of a cycle-per-second, can be recorded and then played back at a much higher speed (Fig. 22-57). When the frequencies of these signals are thus multiplied by a constant factor, they can be analyzed by commercial spectrum-analyzing equipment.[45]

FIG. 22-56. 1:8 TIME BASE EXPANSION

Ipsophone. Another ingenious application of magnetic recording is the Ipsophone, which has found extensive use in Switzerland. This is an automatic telephone-answering device that records messages on magnetic tape and plays them back later when called for. The Ipsophone swings into action when no one lifts the receiver after the third ring. A recorded voice asks the caller to leave a recorded message with the device. When the subscriber comes home, he can obtain the recorded messages by dialing the Ipsophone number and responding correctly to a series of code digits. Swiss department stores and banks have found this device useful for recording after-hour orders and taking important messages after closing time. Many press agencies, including the British news agency Reuters, are now using the Ipsophone to record messages from foreign correspondents all over the world.[46]

Military applications. The United States Army has developed a magnetic-tape playback unit called the Talk-back. It is intended for use in psycho-

FIG. 22-57. 16:1 TIME-BASE CONTRACTION

logical warfare and is designed to talk enemy troops into surrendering. It is dropped from a high-flying airplane. The combination of a barometric switch and timer causes the device to go into operation at an altitude of 4,000 feet. The magnetic equipment drives an amplifier which produces a volume of sound 250 times greater than that produced by the average home-television receiver. The equipment continues to deliver the message for 5 minutes during its descent from 4,000 feet to the ground.

Another military application is the incorporation of magnetic-tape recordings in a new Target Classification Trainer System for sonar operators. This device is used to train sonar operators to distinguish between the signals produced by a school of porpoises and those produced by a submarine. The magnetically recorded signal can be used not only to simulate different types of targets but also to simulate the bearing of the targets.

Educational applications. The tape recorder has also become a valuable tool in the field of education. A complete list of educational applications of magnetic tape is too long to be included in this book, and it is suggested that the interested reader consult some of the articles and pamphlets that have been published on this topic. [47] [48]

However, mention will be made of one or two recent developments in this field. The first is the language laboratory that is designed to improve language instruction in secondary schools and colleges (Figs. 22-58, 22-59. and 22-60). This system provides each student with earphones, a microphone, and an amplifier, which enable him to listen to taped lessons and to respond to them. The teacher can then monitor the lessons and check on the progress of each individual.

Courtesy, Dictaphone Corp.

FIG. 22-58. ELECTRONIC LANGUAGE LABORATORY

Courtesy, Dictaphone Corp.

FIG. 22-59. CONTROL CENTER OF ELECTRONIC LANGUAGE LABORATORY

A second innovation is the RCA Hear-See system (Fig. 22-61). This involves television tape recording, which will be explained in detail shortly. The system contains a recorder that can tape a program from a telecast and also contains a tape player that is capable of reproducing the pictures and sound of television programs. It can use a library of pre-recorded programs to bring lessons conducted by master teachers to schools throughout the nation. It also enables both the educator and the home viewer to tape educational programs

Courtesy, Monsanto Chemical Co.

FIG. 22-60. ELECTRONIC LANGUAGE LABORATORY IN OPERATION

Control console switches link instructor with one or more of 30 students in new Notre Dame language laboratory while speech samples are produced by phonograph and tape recorders in foreground.

from the air and build a permanent library of worthwhile shows.[49]

Mention may also be made of the "talking magazine" which appeared in 1959 on Tokyo news-stands. It had magnetically treated pages called Synchrosheets, which when placed in a Synchroreader machine produced sounds illustrating the text material. These Synchrosheets, which bear the printed matter, are coated on the reverse side with a ferrite magnetic material similar to that employed on recording tape. The Synchroreader machine

Courtesy, Radio Corporation of America

FIG. 22-61. HEAR-SEE TAPE PLAYER

Magnetic tape player for television can play prerecorded black-and-white television selections from magnetic tape through any standard television receiver.

contains three playback heads that resemble those found in a conventional tape recorder. The three heads are equally spaced on the rim of a metal turntable that is located under the Synchrosheets. As the turntable rotates, the heads scan the page from left to right. Simultaneously, the turntable assembly is moved down the length of the sheet. In this manner, every portion of recorded material on the sheet is scanned and played back. Y. Hoshino of the Tokyo Institute of Technology, who is the inventor of this device, plans to use it for educational applications such as the teaching of music and languages and to produce entire textbooks in printed sound.[50][51] It has also been suggested that this device might prove helpful in more advanced technical books and publications. Thus, a student of electronics might be able to look at a complex circuit diagram or at a picture of a complicated electronic device and listen simultaneously to an explanation given by the designer or by the author in his own words.[52]

22.11 *Faxtape*

The Ampex Corporation has developed Faxtape, a system for recording facsimile signals on magnetic tape (Fig. 22-62). The input to the Faxtape recorder is the output signal produced by a facsimile transmitter. This signal is used to frequency-modulate a carrier wave and is then recorded on tape. Upon playback, the Faxtape recorder reproduces a voltage pattern that is identical with the original signal. It then either feeds it to a local facsimile receiver or retransmits it to receivers at distant points.

The use of this system makes it possible to store graphic information and to transmit it at high speeds. It is also useful for overseas radio transmission of facsimile, since Faxtape makes it

Courtesy, Ampex Data Products Co.
FIG. 22-62. AMPEX FAXTAPE MAGNETIC RECORDER AND REPRODUCER FOR FACSIMILE

possible to utilize the most favorable periods of transmission.

In another interesting application of facsimile on tape, a large corporation has placed all of its blueprints on microfilm. When desired, the original microfilm can be projected, scanned, and recorded on magnetic tape. These signals can then be transmitted via land line or radio to any plant. This makes possible rapid non-photographic reproduction of blueprints at any one of the company's widespread network of plants.[53]

22.12 *Magnetic recording of television programs*

A long-sought dream of the television industry, the recording of both picture and sound, has become a reality. This development promises to produce major changes not only in the television industry but also in other fields such as the motion-picture industry. There are at present two different major successful systems, one developed by the Ampex Corporation and the other by RCA.

The Ampex system. The Ampex Videotape system was the one employed in 1951 in the first successful demonstration of the recording of television on magnetic tape. In November 1956, the Columbia Broadcasting System employed Videotape for the first magnetically recorded telecast of an entire regularly scheduled television program.

The current model of the Videotape device employs a tape with a width of 2 in. and a speed of 15 in. per second (Fig. 22-63). A 12.5-in. reel of this tape can record a 64-minute black-and-white television program with no apparent difference in quality from that of the original live program. For video-recording applications, this device must be capable of recording frequencies as high as 4 megacycles. In order to do this at normal tape speeds, a special head assembly is used which contains four magnetic-recording heads that rotate at a speed of 14,400 rpm across the tape. These heads record across the tape instead of along the length of the tape. This produces a relative effective tape speed of 1,500 in. per second, which is sufficient to record and reproduce the full 4-megacycle bandwidth. The accompanying sound is recorded in the conventional longitudinal manner along the edge of the tape.[54][55]

The RCA system. The RCA process was first successfully demonstrated in 1953 (Figs. 22-64 and 22-65). It employed a tape with a width of 0.5 in. and required a tape speed of 20 fps (feet per second). Because of this high tape speed, a one-hour program required four 20-in. reels of tape. The tape employed for recording monochrome programs contained two tracks,

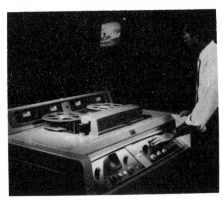

Courtesy, Ampex Data Products Co.

FIG. 22-63. AMPEX VIDEOTAPE RECORDER AND REPRODUCER

one for the video signal and the other for the audio.

Courtesy, Radio Corporation of America

FIG. 22-64. EARLY RCA TELEVISION TAPE RE-CORDER
Laboratory equipment on which the first public demonstration of tape recording of both black-and-white and color television was made.

Courtesy, Radio Corporation of America

FIG. 22-65. MAGNETIC TAPE FOR RECORDING TELEVISION PICTURES IN BOTH COLOR AND BLACK-AND-WHITE, DEMONSTRATED BY BRIG. GENERAL SARNOFF FOR THE FIRST TIME, DECEMBER 1, 1953.

Since the RCA system was also designed to record color-television programs, a special tape was developed for this purpose. This color tape originally contained six tracks: one each for the three primary color signals, blue, green, and red; one track for the synchronizing signal; one track for high-frequency signals; and one track for audio signals.[56] In May 1955, the National Broadcasting Company used the RCA system to transmit successfully the first recorded color-television program over commercial television-network facilities.[57] In October 1957, the National Broadcasting Company used the RCA system for the first nationwide, on-the-air transmission of a color-television program.

In recent years, this tape has been

improved so that it now consists of 1-mil Mylar, 2 in. in width. A tape speed of 15 ips is used, so that a standard tape reel of 4,800 ft provides 64 minutes of playing time. Four tracks are recorded on the tape, the first for the video signal, the second for the sound, the third for control signals that operate a servo system, and the last for recording cueing information required for editing the tape.[58]

RCA has also demonstrated the previously mentioned Hear-See tape player for home use. It will take a reel of tape containing a recorded television program and play it back through the home-television receiver. Another accompanying unit enables the user to tape-record a television program that is being received at home. In this way it makes it possible to build a library of favorite programs.[59]

In 1957, RCA and Ampex entered into a patent-exchange agreement which made it possible to standardize Videotape parameters for both color and monochrome television transmission.[60]

The DeForest system. A third system of recording television on tape was patented by Lee DeForest. He solved the problem of excessive tape speed by scanning a 1/2-in. tape with rapidly moving magnetic styli, while the tape itself moves at a relatively slow speed. One hundred and twenty-five of these styli are mounted on the rim of a disc that has a radius of 10 in. The disc rotates across the surface of the tape at 125 rps. As one stylus leaves the tape, another begins the scan. Consequently, there is no interruption in either the recording or the playback processes.[61]

22.13 Future applications and effects of Videotape

The general acceptance of tape by the television industry will affect the manner in which television programs are produced. There is little doubt that it will eventually supplant the use of film. Major shows will probably be taped first to detect flaws, and improvements will be added where necessary. This should make it possible to obtain both the spontaneity of live television and the smooth and finished quality of film.

Immediate playback has proved especially valuable to performers. According to television announcer Dennis James: "One Videotape playback is worth ten rehearsals," while actor-producer Peter Lawford states: "Tape is the reason so many film stars have consented to appear in television . . . . It gives them a feeling of security such as they have in motion pictures."[62]

Although there is no technical reason why the use of tape should cause a loss of quality in live television programs, several leading television critics have begun to complain about the undesirable effects that tape has already produced. They state that many television programs are now acquiring the qualities of motion picture programs. They also point out the very human tendency to use tape to simulate or to improve upon reality and insist that actors are not likely to give the same type of performance when they know that a program is being taped and that their performance can be revised or altered later if deemed necessary to do so.

Another application of video recording will be to help television networks overcome the time differential between the east and west coasts. Taped recordings of programs produced at one end of the network can be shown at convenient hours at the other end.[63]

Video recording should affect motion-picture production by eliminating unnecessary retakes. It will not be necessary for the director to wait until the film is processed the following day in order to see what he has taken. With the aid of video recording, the director can see immediately whether or not the scene has been correctly recorded.

It is also expected that within the near future Videotape recording and playback installations will be available at a cost which will be within the reach of many school systems. Lloyd S. Michael, Superintendent of the Evanston Township High School in Illinois, has stated: "This equipment will make it possible for schools to receive, store, reproduce and transmit any television program over a simple wire distribution system to as many television receivers as may be connected to it. The day for the common use of this new technological marvel in our schools is literally tomorrow."[64]

A somewhat different type of application of Videotape is its use by the Yonkers Raceway in Yonkers, New York. All races are recorded on tape, which can be played back for the judges before the photo-finish still pictures can be developed.

It is extremely likely that eventually a home recorder and playback system for tape television pictures, such as the previously described RCA Hear-See system, will become commercially available at a reasonable price. This will make it possible for the owner of such a device to pick up a tape recording of a full-length motion picture from a tape-rental library and to play this recording through his own home-television receiver.

22.14 *Optical sound-on-film recording*

The first use of film as an electrical recording medium dates back to 1902. During that year, Duddell recorded on film the electrical waveforms produced by a vibrating-mirror oscillograph. These recordings were later reproduced by means of a light beam and a photocell.

The basic technique of recording sound by optical means on film was developed by de Forest, and in 1924 he was awarded a patent for this invention. Theodore W. Case and E. I. Sponable also made important contributions to the sound-on-film system.

There are two general methods for recording sound optically on motion-picture film (Fig. 22-66). One method produces sound by use of a variable-density sound track that has a constant width (Fig. 22-67). The other, which is the most commonly used method, employs the variable-area or variable-width track (Fig. 22-68). Here the density remains fixed while the width of the track varies in accordance with the sound.

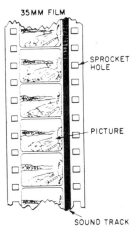

FIG. 22-66. POSITION OF THE SOUND TRACK

Variable-density recording depends primarily upon the action of a light valve, consisting of a loop or slit of duraluminum ribbon which is illuminated by a glow lamp (Fig. 22-69). The amount of audio current governs the

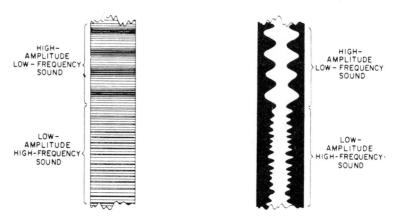

FIG. 22-67. VARIABLE-DENSITY SOUND TRACK   FIG. 22-68. VARIABLE-AREA SOUND TRACK

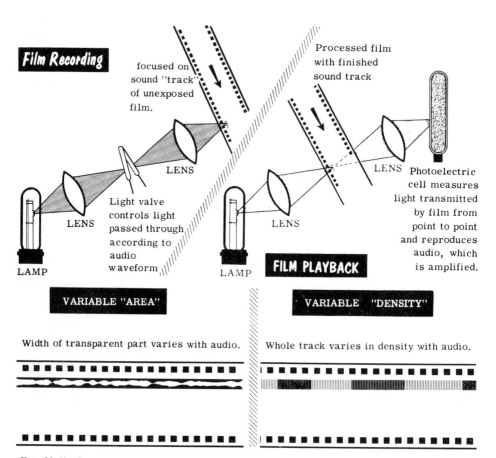

FIG. 22-69. OPTICAL FILM RECORDING AND PLAYBACK

width of the slit, which in turn limits the amount of the light that strikes the film. In this manner, the density of the sound track is controlled.

In another variation of this technique, the width of the slit is kept constant, while the brightness of the glow lamp varies with the audio signal. In this manner, the optical density of the sound track becomes a recording of the variations in the sound waves.

In the variable-area method, recording is accomplished by means of an oscillograph or mirror galvanometer, the mirror of which is actuated by variations in the amplified audio-frequency signals. This throws a strong beam of variable light on to a moving film. The variations of light correspond to the sound-wave variations. These variations are recorded as heavy jagged lines that closely resemble a series of mountain peaks.[65]

Since immediate playback is impossible, because it is necessary to develop the film, a variation of this technique, called the Philips-Miller system, is sometimes employed. In this system, a stylus that resembles the one used in disc recording is used to cut a variable-area track on the film.

When either type of sound film is played on a motion-picture projector, the sound track passes over a narrow slit in a metal plate (Fig. 22-70). The

light from a small incandescent lamp called an exciter lamp is focused on the same slit. The light passes through the sound track and strikes the cathode of a phototube. The varying sound track produces a variation in the intensity of the light reaching the cathode of the photocell. The resulting changing output of the phototube is amplified and is then converted into sound by means of a loudspeaker (Fig. 22-71).

The optical method of recording sound produces good high-frequency response, the problem of wear is negligible, and the film record may be easily duplicated by simple direct-contact printing. However, the processing requires skilled techniques, making it relatively expensive. Furthermore, the sound cannot be monitored immediately, since the film must be processed before the sound can be played back. For these reasons, Fairchild Camera, Eastman Kodak, RCA, and other manufacturers of 8-mm and 16-mm motion-picture equipment for home use are making sound-film projectors and cameras that are designed to employ magnetically recorded sound tracks (Figs. 22-72 and 22-73).[66]

It is claimed that magnetic-sound-on-film is capable of producing a considerable increase in sound quality over presently available 16-mm optical sound tracks. Generally, between one and

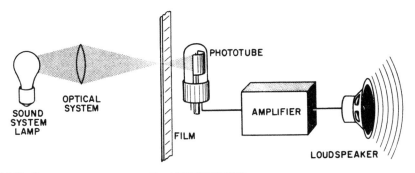

FIG. 22-70. REPRODUCTION OF AN OPTICAL FILM RECORDING

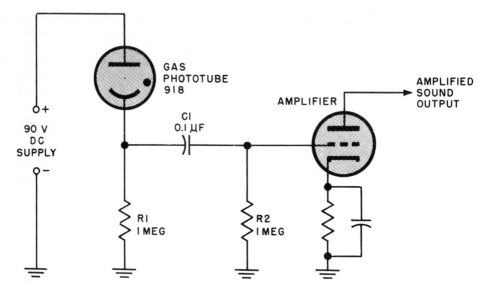

FIG. 22-71. TYPICAL PHOTOTUBE CIRCUIT FOR SOUND REPRODUCTION

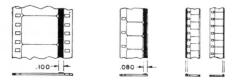

FIG. 22-72. MAGNETIC SOUND TRACKS ON 35-MM, 16-MM, AND 8-MM FILM

two additional octaves of high-frequency response are made possible, with a marked improvement in signal-to-noise ratio and reduced distortion.[67]

22.15 Visible speech—the audiospectrograph

Potter and his colleagues at Bell Telephone Laboratories have succeeded in translating the spoken word into readable pictures. Their visible-speech machine displays the spectrum of component frequencies found in speech sounds. Vibrations of the voice are unravelled through electronic circuits and are then reassembled as luminous spectral patterns which travel across a screen. Each syllable possesses a distinctive shape and intensity (Fig. 22-74). By reading these spectral patterns, it is possible to recognize differences in the speech of individuals and minor differences in dialects.

Visible speech is still in its infancy, but educators of the deaf are now evaluating it. Indications are that the deaf can learn to read the patterns, and by

FIG. 22-73. MAGNETIC SOUND 16-MM MOTION PICTURE PROJECTOR AND RECORDER

Courtesy, Bell Telephone Laboratories
FIG. 22-74. SOUND SPECTROGRAM

comparing these patterns with their own voice patterns, can improve their diction. Patterns of visible speech also provide a means of analyzing and recording sound in the study of phonetics and languages. Ornithologists are also making use of the audiospectrograph to gain new understandings of the songs of birds and their "language". It is also quite possible that, eventually, visible speech may make possible visual telephony for the deaf.[68]

Similar types of sound or sonic analyzers have proved useful in diagnosing causes of troubles involving noise and vibration in complex machines such as jet engines, air-conditioning units, electric motors, and automobile-axle assemblies. In 1956, McKusick of Johns Hopkins reported the use of this technique to provide a refined analysis of heart sounds. The instrument produces a tracing which shows both the rhythm of the heart sounds and a spectral analysis of these sounds. There is little doubt that much useful information can be extracted from this detailed analysis of murmurs and valve sounds.[69]

22.16 *Thermoplastic recording*

In 1959, the General Electric Company announced that William E. Glenn had invented a promising new electronic recording system called thermoplastic recording or TPR. This system permits the high-density storage

of color or black-and-white video signals, analog or digital data, photographic images, and printed matter. It combines the processing speed and versatility of magnetic recording with the storage capacity of photography (Fig. 22-75).

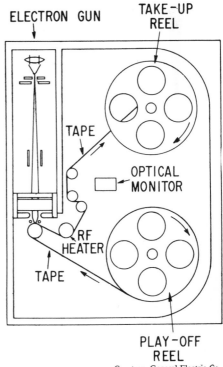

Courtesy, General Electric Co.
FIG. 22-75. SCHEMATIC OF TPR RECORDER

According to Guy Suits, director of research of General Electric, TPR can concentrate 100 times as much information in a given space as magnetic recording can. Theoretically, it could record in color the equivalent of 24 volumes of the Encyclopedia Britannica on a reel the size of a spool of thread, requiring only a minute per volume. It does not require the chemical processing needed by photographic film and can be erased and re-used as desired.

In the recording technique, an electron beam is used to develop a pattern of electrical charges on the surface of a high-melting-point film that is coated with a transparent conducting coating (Fig. 22-76). This coating has a thin film of low-melting-point thermoplastic film on its surface (Fig. 22-77). When the film is heated to the melting point of the thermoplastic, electrostatic forces depress the surface where the charges occur. If the film is then cooled, the deformations are frozen into its surface. The time required for this is 0.01 seconds. Reproduction is accomplished by optical means employing diffraction principles. The signal can be made to appear on a screen resembling a motion-picture screen, or it can activate a photoelectric pickup to produce electrical signals. Erasure can be accomplished by using a radio-frequency field to heat the film area that is to be erased to a temperature well above its melting point. Surface tension then smooths out the deformations.[70]

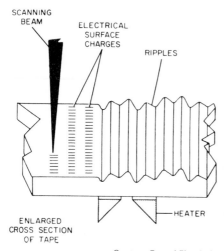

Courtesy, General Electric Co.

FIG. 22-76. HOW INFORMATION IS STORED ON THERMOPLASTIC TAPE

An electron scanning beam, modulated by information to be stored, "writes" upon the moving tape by depositing a pattern of electrical charges. The tape then passes over a heating element, which softens its surface to the melting point and allows the charges to form actual microscopic ripples. These information-bearing ripples are frozen into place as the tape cools. The entire recording process takes less than 1/100th of a second. The tape produces images in black-and-white or color without chemical processing. It may also be erased and re-used.

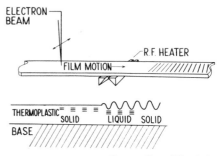

Courtesy, General Electric Co.

FIG. 22-77. MECHANISM FOR THERMOPLASTIC RECORDING AND CROSS-SECTION OF TPR TAPE

REFERENCES

1. Leon Wortman, "What About Tape Recorders?," *Popular Electronics,* 3:86-87, Sept. 1955.
2. H. M. Tremaine, "Magnetic Recording—1914 Style," *Radio and TV News,* 60:90, July 1958.
3. Paul J. Weber, *The Tape Recorder as an Instrumentation Device,* Ampex Corp., Redwood City, Calif., 1958, p. 5.
4. Leon Wortman, "Live Sound to Magnetic Tape," *Popular Electronics,* 3:85, Oct. 1955.
5. Mark Mooney, Jr., *Four Track Recording Developed,* Nortronics, Inc., Minneapolis, Minn., pp. 1-2.
6. A. C. Shaney, "Magnetism—Elements of Tape Recording," *Radio-Craft,* 19:30, Nov. 1947.
7. "Magnetic Tape Contact Prints," *Radio-Electronics,* 21:52, Feb. 1950.
8. "Tape Duplicators Improved," *Ampex Playback,* 2:3, Oct. 1956.
9. *Magnetic Tape Instrumentation,* DC—3170, Minneapolis-Honeywell Regulator Co. Beltsville, Md., 1960, p. 4.
10. D. W. Halfhill, "Recording Techniques," *Instruments and Control Systems,* 32:386, Mar. 1959.

11. Robert Endall, "Magnetic Tape Data-Recording Systems," *Radio and Television News*, (Engineering Edition), 47:3-6, 30, Mar. 1952.
12. P. J. Weber, *Op. cit.*, pp. 8-9.
13. *Magnetic Tape Instrumentation, Op. cit.*, pp. 2, 4.
14. P. J. Weber, *Op. cit.*, p. 22.
15. *Magnetic Tape Instrumentation, Op. cit.*, p. 4.
16. *Ibid*, p. 8.
17. "Tape In Space," *Ampex Readout*, 1:8-10, Aug. 1958.
18. *Magnetic Tape Instrumentation, Op. cit.*, p. 10.
19. P. J. Weber, *Op. cit.*, pp. 23-27.
20. *Magnetic Tape Instrumentation, Op. cit.*, pp. 4, 8.
21. *Ibid*, p. 11.
22. P. J. Weber, *Op. cit.*, pp. 27-33.
23. *Magnetic Tape Instrumentation*, Ampex Corporation, Redwood City, Calif., 1957, p. 10.
24. *Magnetic Tape Instrumentation*, DC-3170, *Op. cit*, pp. 4, 11.
25. *Ibid*, p. 4.
26. *The Role of Magnetic Tape in Data Recording*, Bull. 1001, Davies Labs, Beltsville, Md., 1956, p. 2.
27. *Magnetic Tape Instrumentation*, DC-3170, *Op. cit.*, pp. 4, 12.
28. P. J. Weber, *Op. cit.*, pp. 33-39.
29. Marvin Camras, "Tape Recording Today," *Industrial Research*, 1:67, Jan. 1959.
30. "The Whys of Recorded Information Control," *Control Engineering*, 5:113-115, Sept. 1958.
31. John Jipp, "Tape Recording Today," *Industrial Research*, 1:63-64, Jan. 1959.
32. *Record-Playback Control*, GEA-6092, General Electric Co., Schenectady, N.Y., 1954, p. 5.
33. *Data Recording, Machine Control and Process Regulation by Magnetic Tape Recording*, Ampex Corporation, Redwood City, Calif., 1954, p. 9.
34. "Taped Blueprints Control Machine," *Electronic Design*, 5:10, June 1, 1957.
35. P. J. Weber, *Op. cit.*, p. 71.
36. "Feedback Fact," *Control Engineering*, 3:292, Sept. 1956.
37. J. Jipp, *Op. cit.*, pp. 64-66.
38. "Rock'n Roll Can Reduce Gas Mileage!," *Ampex Readout*, 1:13, Jan. 1959.
39. "Electronics Speeds Hand Assembly," *Radio-Electronics*, 29:77, Aug. 1958.
40. James R. Cornelius, "Magnetic Tape Recorder Aids Industry," *Radio-Electronics*, 26:62, June 1955.
41. J. Scott Butterworth, "Tape Recording in Cardiology," *Audio Record*, 8:5, Jan. 1952.
42. "Rx for Modern Medicine," *Ampex Readout*, 1:3, Nov. 1958.
43. Arthur R. Wildhagen, "The Time Compressor," *Audio Record*, 9:2, Apr. 1953.
44. "Time Compressor," *Radio and Television News*, 49:96, June 1953.

45. P. J. Weber. *Op. cit.*, pp. 65-66.
46. "The Telephone That Answers Itself," *Audio Record*, 6:4, Apr. 1950.
47. *The Tape Recorder in the Elementary Classroom*, Minnesota Mining and Mfg. Co., St. Paul, Minn. 1955, pp. 1-52.
48. "The Tape Recorder at Goucher College," *Audio Record*, 13:2, Dec. 1957.
49. "Magnetic Magic," *Electronic Age*, 18:25, Autumn 1959.
50. Edward Nanas, "Listen to a Printed Page," *Electronics Illustrated*, 2:36-39, Feb. 1959.
51. Edward Nanas, "Voices from Printed Books," *Science Digest*, 45:12-14, Apr. 1959.
52. James Kreis, "Synchroreader—The Page That Talks Back!," *DeVry Tech. News*, 20:6, Aug. 1959.
53. J. Jipp, *Op. cit.*, p. 68.
54. "TV Programs on Magnetic Tape," *Radio and Television News*, 56:92, July 1956.
55. Mike Bienstock, "They're Putting TV on Tape," *Popular Electronics*, 7:49, Nov. 1957.
56. "Pictures on Tape," *Radio and Television News*, 51:55, Feb. 1954.
57. "Color Telecast from Magnetic Tape," *Radio Age*, 14:13, July 1955.
58. Julian L. Bernstein, "Taping a TV Program," *Radio-Electronics*, 30:40, July 1959.
59. "Electronic Gifts from RCA Research," *Radio Age*, 15:11-12, Oct. 1956.
60. Gordon L. Longfellow, "Videotape Magnetic Recording," *Military Automation*, 1:319, Nov. 1957.
61. "Picture Recording on Tape," *Radio-Electronics*, 28:170, Jan. 1957.
62. *The Show is on Videotape*, Minnesota Mining and Mfg. Co., St. Paul, Minn., p. 13.
63. "Ribbons of Tape Work Television Revolution," *Chemical News*, 6:3, Nov. 1959.
64. Lloyd S. Michael, "New Directions in Secondary Education," *University of Kansas Bull. of Education*, 14:87, May 1960.
65. Oliver Read, "The Recording and Reproduction of Sound—Part 3," *Radio News*, 37:62, May 1947.
66. "16-mm Motion Picture Sound Camera," *Science Digest*, 46:91, Aug. 1959.
67. R. F. Dubbe, *Laminated Magnetic Tapes for Motion Picture Film*, Sound Talk Bull. No. 33, Minnesota Mining and Mfg. Co., St. Paul, Minn., p. 4.
68. L. O. Schott, "A Playback for Visible Speech," *Bell Lab. Record*, 26:333, Aug. 1948.
69. Victor A. McKusick, "Heart Sounds," *Scientific American*, 194:128-130, May 1956.
70. *Thermoplastic Recording*, GP.146, General Electric Research Laboratory, Schenectady, N.Y., 1960, pp. 2-20.

23-HIGH-FIDELITY AND STEREO-PHONIC REPRODUCTION

23.1 *Confusion concerning high-fidelity reproduction*

The term high-fidelity as applied to sound-reproducing equipment is one which has been handled rather loosely in recent years. During the middle 1930's, the Radio Manufacturers Association (now Electronics Industries Association) limited the use of this term to equipment which could reproduce sound frequencies up to 7,500 cps—standards which are now quite obsolete. In recent years, the Federal Trade Commission investigated the possibility of setting up standards of high-fidelity, but soon abandoned this effort.

Consequently, there are today no definitions for high-fidelity that are accurate and complete. There is no one set of accepted standards to differentiate equipment that is high-fidelity from that which is not. As a result, there is nothing to prevent a manufacturer, for example, from attaching the description high-fidelity, as was done in a recent advertisement, to a portable three-speed phonograph and radio-receiver combination that was contained in a lightweight carrying case whose dimensions were $12\frac{1}{2}$ in. by $9\frac{1}{2}$ in. by $4\frac{1}{2}$ in. According to this advertisement, the combination, which sold for $29.95, contained a tone chamber that was scientifically designed for "stereoscopic sound."

The validity of this claim to high-fidelity reproduction becomes extremely doubtful when it is pointed out that a top-quality audio transformer for use in high-fidelity equipment cannot be manufactured for much less than the price of this complete radio-phonograph combination. In general, high-fidelity audio equipment is not cheap. In order to obtain the desired effects, near perfection of each component of the system is required. When a manufacturer uses the term high-fidelity in describing the performance of a device containing a wafer-thin cabinet enclosing a 5-in. speaker and a two-tube audio-amplifier system, he is helping to eliminate whatever meaning may still remain in what started out to be a meaningful term. This fact was illustrated recently when one manufacturer came out with a "high-fidelity" piano.

This confusion is compounded by the fact that a person can adapt his hearing to a certain quality of sound. Eventually, despite the fact that the sound is highly distorted or deficient in frequency response, it may eventually appear preferable to him over undistorted, full-range audio reproduction. H. A. Chinn and Philip Eisenberg noted this phenomenon in a report based on their findings that listeners to broadcast-radio programs generally preferred a narrow frequency range to a medium frequency range by a margin of two to one and preferred a narrow frequency range to a wide frequency range by a margin of four to one.[1]

Some of the leaders of the recording industry have shown concern about the eventual effects of the misuse of the term high-fidelity. The president of the British Industries Corporation remarked after examining many phonographs at a trade show that: "It is with concern and apprehension that I found that many of these units are not really high-fidelity; not all are capable of reproducing sound with the lifelike qualities which genuine high-fidelity imparts."

At the same time, the president of the Magnavox Company stated: "Growing public interest in the faithful reproduction of sound in phonograph, television and radio sets must not be nipped in the bud by the careless use of the term high-fidelity."[2]

23.2 Meaning of high-fidelity

The term high-fidelity is practically equivalent in meaning to high quality. It is a relative term which possesses different meanings under different conditions and therefore induces difficulties when one tries to draw the line of quality below which

it cannot be applied. Since no universally accepted objective standards for high-fidelity reproduction exist, an attempt has been made to define high-fidelity in terms of the effects produced upon the listener. An ideal high-fidelity system possesses *presence,* a term which means that it should be capable of reproducing music or voice with such a degree of realism that the listener cannot distinguish the quality of the reproduced signal from that of the original concert-hall performance.

In order to be capable of achieving a quality of performance approaching this subjective standard, a reproducing system must possess certain minimum characteristics. The system should possess a frequency-response curve that is flat and well-balanced within plus or minus 1 db from 20 to 20,000 cps, with no sharp peaks in the curve (Fig. 23-1). The amplifier should contain a push-pull output stage and should have a minimum power rating of 25 watts with a maximum of 2 to 3 per cent intermodulation distortion and less than 2 per cent harmonic distortion.[3][4] A power rating of 15 watts might be considered acceptable if the listener is satisfied with less than thunderous volume.

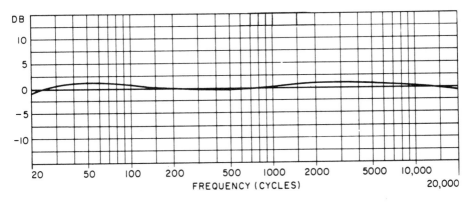

FIG. 23-1. FREQUENCY CHART OF AN AMPLIFIER SYSTEM WITH A RESPONSE OF 20 TO 20,000 CPS, ± 1 DB

The pickup on the tone arm should be of the ceramic or variable-reluctance type and should preserve the true wave-form at all frequencies, while the turn-tables should not contribute noticeable wow, flutter, or rumble. The output section should contain a dual-range or coaxial-speaker system that is capable of reproducing sounds over the entire audio range.

However, it should be pointed out that these standards have not been universally accepted by the sound-reproduction industry and that many experts state that they are far from certain that all of the significant factors that make up high-fidelity have been discovered. In addition, many of the methods of measuring these factors, such as the distortion factor, have not yet been standardized. Consequently, in the final analysis, the quality of the desired audio reproduction must be considered to be a matter of individual preference.

It may be of some interest to note that in 1959 the Institute of High Fidelity Manufacturers decided to formulate standards that would make possible direct comparison of the adver-tised characteristics of high-fidelity components. The Institute stated that while these standards would not be binding on any manufacturer, it hoped they would meet industry-wide ac-ceptance.[5][6]

The first set of standards, designed for the measurement of tuners, was a 24-page booklet listing testing and measuring procedures. Following this were measuring standards for stereo and monophonic amplifiers and pre-amplifiers, standards for turntables and record changers, and finally standards for loudspeakers and phono cartridges.[7]

Early in 1959, an organization known as the High Fidelity Consumer's Bureau of Standards was created in New York City. This Bureau, which claims to be an independent, bias-free organi-zation that admits no manufacturers to membership, has established two sets of performance standards, one for minimum true high-fidelity and the other for premium quality high-fidelity. In a manner similar to that of other testing bureaus, they plan to place their silver or gold seal of approval on equip-ment sent to them by manufacturers if these devices measure satisfactorily up to one or the other of the standards.[8]

23.3 History of high-fidelity reproduction

Although it is only a few years since high-fidelity reproduction at-tracted the attention of the public, many of the engineering fundamentals of high-fidelity sound transmission, re-cording, and reproduction were de-veloped nearly 30 years ago. Edwin Armstrong's FM station transmitted high-fidelity musical programs during the early 1930's. Some record com-panies, such as Victor, produced long-playing 33 1/3 rpm records during this same period of time. These were full-frequency-range recordings available for those who were willing to pay the high prices and who possessed the re-quired record-playing equipment. Some engineering laboratories and recording studios possessed equipment that com-pares very favorably with what is being produced today.

However, this high-quality audio reproduction was limited to a small esoteric group. In general, the public knew little about these developments and apparently cared even less. The sound-reproducing equipment that gained public acceptance was the type that produced a syrupy tone with a boomy bass. An extremely popular feature of this equipment was a tone control designed to narrow the frequency range and attenuate the high frequencies in order to reduce the annoyance of needle scratch.

There are several factors responsible for the present-day acceptance of and demand for high-fidelity reproducing equipment. The motion-picture industry contributed its share. The quality of the sound produced by the sound systems of many theatres made the public realize the limitations of home-reproducing equipment. World War II caused many laymen to become familiar with electronic amplification and was responsible for much research and development in this area.

In 1946, the shifting of the FM broadcast-frequency band encouraged many stations to broadcast programs simultaneously on both AM and FM. The listening public soon became aware of the higher quality of audio reproduction associated with FM reception.

The introduction of the variable-reluctance phonograph cartridge in 1947 gave momentum to the high-fidelity movement. Diamond and sapphire-tipped styli replaced the old-fashioned steel needle. In 1948, Columbia initiated the long-playing LP microgroove record, and plastic records replaced shellac. These developments were accompanied by improvements in other system components, such as the introduction of dual-speaker systems, the development of the Williamson amplifier, and the production of high-quality tape recorders. The most recent improvement, stereophonic sound, will be discussed in a following section.

At present, the high-fidelity market is the fastest growing and most profitable end of the consumer-electronics business, and there are those who predict that before long the sales volume of high-fidelity equipment will be as important to the industry as that of home television equipment is at present.

Progress in the art and science of high-fidelity reproduction is still being made. The developments within the immediate future seem to lie in the direction of designing lower-priced equipment with less distortion and a wider frequency range than is found in today's equipment. Stereophonic sound will probably become available in the medium-priced field. When this happens, monaural sound will be outdated and will go the way of the spring-wound acoustic phonograph. The day is probably not far off when the term high-fidelity will prove to be insufficiently descriptive—and the era of the perfect-fidelity sound-reproducing system will have begun.

23.4 *Stereophonic and binaural sound*

The visual perception of depth is based upon the fact that each eye "sees" a slightly different picture. When the signals from these two different pictures are transmitted to the brain, the brain is able to extract depth information from the difference between the two images.

Similarly, each ear "hears" a slightly different sound. When these two signals are transmitted to the brain, the brain is able to use the differences between the two sounds to compute the distance and direction of the source of sound.[9] It is an interesting fact that neither depth nor direction can be computed with low-frequency sounds. Consequently, there are few directional or stereo effects that are noticeable below 2,000 cps, and practically none below 600 cps.[10]

In a conventional monaural or monophonic sound-reproducing system, the sounds are picked up by a single microphone or group of microphones (Fig. 23-2). The signals are fed

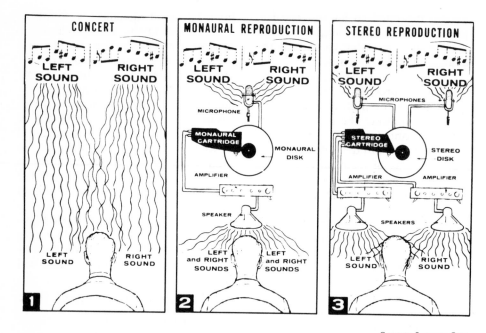

Courtesy, Sonotone Corp.

FIG. 23-2. HOW STEREO RECREATES ORIGINAL PERFORMANCE

Part 1 shows the effect generally found when you attend a live performance. Part 2 diagrams the effect of mono record. Both ears receive the same sounds from one source, even with multiple speakers. Part 3 demonstrates the recreation of the original live performance by stereo. The left sounds are reproduced on the left side and the right sounds on the right side. The different sounds mix together in a manner quite similar to Part 1.

to a single-channel amplifying system which, in turn, feeds a single speaker or group of speakers. Since the resulting sounds correspond to what the listener would have heard originally had he used only one ear, his brain will not be able to attach depth or direction to these sounds.[11]

Stereophonic or stereo sound is an attempt to duplicate in the field of sound recording the effects that are produced visually by a three-dimensional stereoscopic motion picture or by stereoscopic slides. The word *stereo,* derived from the Greek, means solid or three-dimensional space.

When it is properly reproduced, stereophonic sound creates an aural perspective and produces a feeling of presence and an illusion of depth. It causes the ear to reject distortion and to seem to hear a wider range of frequencies. Consequently, a stereophonic-system employing components of mediocre quality may sound as good as or even better than a monaural or monophonic system employing excellent components. The most common type of stereophonic recording is binaural or two-channel recording.

Although the terms binaural and stereophonic are frequently used interchangeably to denote any method of adding auditory perspective to the reproduction of sound, experts in the field differentiate between the two. Binaural is used to denote a system in which two closely spaced microphones are positioned in such a manner that they simulate the sound-pickup characteristics of a pair of human ears (Fig. 23-3). The system employs two separate audio-amplifying channels, one for each ear, and the sound is reproduced through a pair of binaural earphones.

On the other hand, stereophonic is used to designate a system in which widely spaced microphones are used (Figs. 23-4, 23-5). While it will function with two channels, three channels will provide more satisfactory results, and theoretically, an infinite number of channels would be required to obtain results that could be deemed perfect (Fig. 23-6). The sound is reproduced through loudspeakers, one loudspeaker for each channel. While two-channel stereophonic systems are widely used (Fig. 23-7), many theatres may use as many as seven channels in their systems.

In 1959, the Magnetic Recording Industry Association formulated the following definition of the word *stereophonic*. It is intended to provide Better Business Bureaus and other agencies with a yard-stick against which to measure fraudulent claims.

"Stereophonic: A technique of transmitting sound which employs two or more complete transmission channels for the purpose of creating in the listening environment the sense of auditory perspective inherent in the source environment. Each channel must include a separate microphone, amplifier, and loudspeaker, and may have one channel of a multi-channel recorder and reproducer interposed as a time-storage device."[12]

23.5 *Channel separation*

Channel separation and channel isolation are terms that are employed in connection with stereo reproduction. They are used to denote the amount of isolation between the channels of a system. Ideally, the amount of separation should be infinite, and when a tone is introduced into only one channel of a stereo system, it should produce no output in the other channel. In actual practice, a channel separation of 15 db, in which a signal in one channel produces a signal that is 15 db lower in the

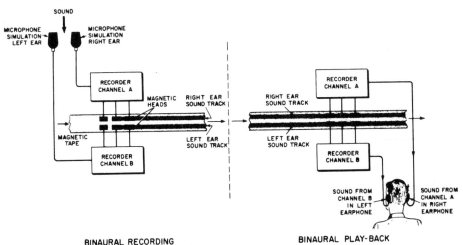

BINAURAL RECORDING   BINAURAL PLAY-BACK

FIG. 23-3. BINAURAL TAPE RECORDING AND PLAYBACK

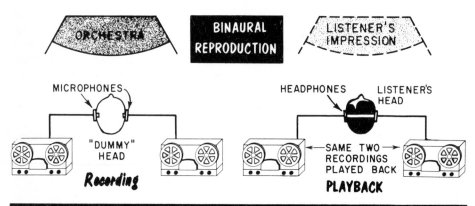

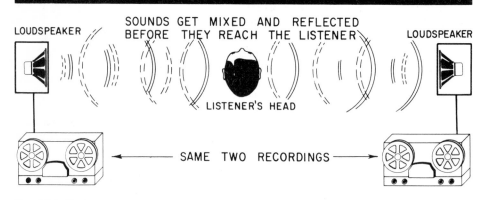

FIG. 23-4. COMPARISON BETWEEN BINAURAL REPRODUCTION AND STEREO TWO-CHANNEL SOUND

other channel, is considered sufficient for the production of excellent stereophonic effects.[13]

23.6 History of stereophonic reproduction

The concepts of binaural and stereophonic reproduction date back to the early tinfoil stage of sound recording. A primitive attempt to demonstrate stereo sound reproduction was made at the Paris Exposition of 1881, when engineers employed two telephone circuits for the transmission of programs from the stage of the Paris Opera. One circuit was used for each ear, truly

binaural transmission.[14]

Since that time, nearly 400 patents have been issued that are related to stereo sound recording and reproduction. For example, in 1901, a device called the Polyphone was patented. It attempted to achieve realism and depth through the use of two vibrating needles that played through two separate horns.

The first public stereophonic demonstration was provided by Peter L. Jensen and Edwin L. Pridham in 1919. This system was installed in a San Francisco nightclub with the unlikely name of the "Hoo Hoo House". A five-piece orchestra was placed on the second floor, and microphones were

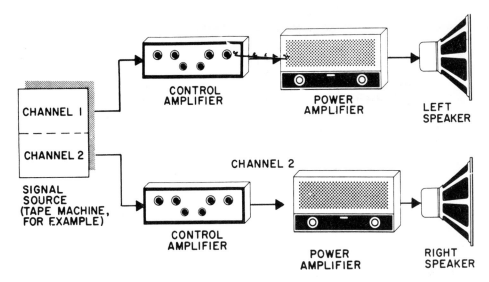

FIG. 23-5. BASIC ELEMENTS OF A TWO-CHANNEL STEREO SYSTEM

attached to each of the five instruments. Each microphone was connected to an individual amplifier, which was then connected to a corresponding speaker on the main floor. The speakers were arranged in the same manner as the musicians. It is reported that the stereophonic effect was so startling that the audience forgot to dance.[15]

In this manner, the management

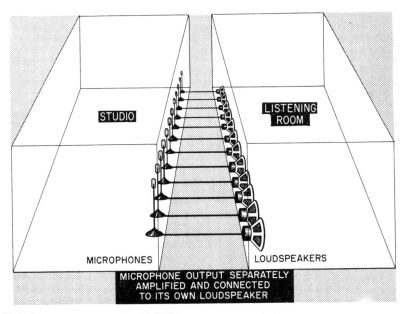

FIG. 23-6. IDEALIZED STEREOPHONIC SYSTEM

Courtesy, Bogen-Presto Div., Siegler Corp.

FIG. 23-7. MODEL 3D-12 STEREOPHONIC TWO-CHANNEL AMPLIFIER

was able to operate two dance floors simultaneously with music provided by a single band. However, the musician's union stopped this two-for-the-price-of-one plan after three nights, and stereophonic sound died shortly after its birth.[16] It is interesting to note that it is only recently that any attempts have been made to incorporate these principles within commercial public-address systems and to conduct experiments with public-address-system stereo effects.[17]

In 1925, radio station WPAJ in New Haven, Conn., broadcast a public demonstration of binaural sound via two AM transmitters operating on two different frequencies, 1110 kc and 1320 kc. At the Chicago World's Fair that was held during the early 1930's, the Bell Telephone Laboratories demonstrated binaural sound to the public. The sound was picked up by two separate microphones. Each microphone was placed over an ear of a dummy figure. The output of each microphone was amplified separately and the output was then fed into the corresponding split earphones of the listener. The results achieved by the use of these two channels of amplification were both realistic and startling.

In 1933, A. D. Blumlein, an engineer employed by Electrical and Musical Industries, Ltd., was issued a British patent for a single-groove stereo disc that employed a combination of vertical and lateral recording. During the same year, Bell engineers, under the direction of Harvey Fletcher, used a three-channel stereophonic transmission system to transmit a performance of the Philadelphia Symphony Orchestra in Philadelphia to Constitution Hall in Washington, D.C.[18] In 1936, I. S. Rafuse and A. C. Keller of the Bell Telephone Laboratories patented a vertical-lateral stereo disc-cutter system.[19]

A great deal of the progress made in the field of stereo sound was accomplished by the motion-picture industry. In pictures such as Walt Disney's "Fantasia," which was produced in 1940, the sound-recording systems employed widely separated microphones. The output of each microphone was amplified separately and recorded optically on a separate sound track. These sound tracks produced signals that ultimately drove separate speakers, producing a three-dimensional illusion.

Similar techniques are employed in the Cinerama and Cinemascope systems. However, these types of stereo sound reproduction are applicable only to large installations such as motion-picture theatres. For normal home use, two channels or binaural sound reproduction is all that can be conveniently accommodated.

Experimental work in binaural reproduction has been carried on by radio stations such as WQXR in New York City. These stations transmit two signals, one AM, and the other FM. There are two microphones in this studio, which are separated by the approximate thickness of a human head (Fig. 23-8). The signal from one microphone is fed to the FM transmitter, while the signal from the other microphone is fed to the AM receiver. Reception then requires two receivers, one an FM receiver and the other an AM receiver.

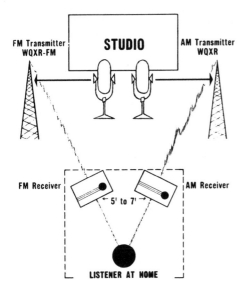

Courtesy, St. Regis Publications, Inc.

FIG. 23-8. WQXR MODEL SETUP FOR BINAURAL LISTENING

Ideally, in a true binaural system the signal from each receiver is fed into a separate earphone, and each earphone is placed over one ear. This prevents one ear from hearing sound intended for the other ear. In actual practice, a reasonably satisfactory stereophonic effect may be achieved by the use of two properly placed separate loudspeakers. A more complete description of stereo broadcasting will be found in a later portion of this chapter.

Binaural sound may be recorded either on dual-track magnetic tape or on special LP records. Since it is a relatively simple matter to convert magnetic tape to multiple-channel recording, commercially manufactured, magnetic-tape stereo recording and reproducing systems were available for many years before commercial stereo-disc systems appeared on the market (Fig. 23-9).

In 1954, commercial stereo tapes became available, largely because tape manufacturers needed a product that would compete with disc recordings

and which could provide something that could not be obtained readily on discs. While tape stereo became popular among well-to-do fans, the stereo-tape catalogue remained very small. It is an acknowledged fact that the present stereo boom did not really begin until stereo discs became available.

23.7 Cook binaural disc records

In an early type of binaural disc-recording system that was developed in 1952 by Emory Cook of Cook Laboratories, the sound is recorded on an LP disc that has two bands of grooves. One band begins in the conventional manner at the outside of the disc. The second band begins approximately midway within the central blank area (Fig. 23-10). The playing time of such a disc is about 13 minutes. In order to play this disc, a rather expensive dual pickup arm or binaural arm with two cartridges and styli is required (Fig. 23-11). The output from each pickup is then fed to a separate amplifier and speaker.[20] One disadvantage of this system is the fact that the great compliance of a modern pickup makes it easy to misplace one of

Courtesy, Bell Sound Div., Thompson Ramo Wooldridge, Inc.

FIG. 23-9. STEREOPHONIC TAPE RECORDER

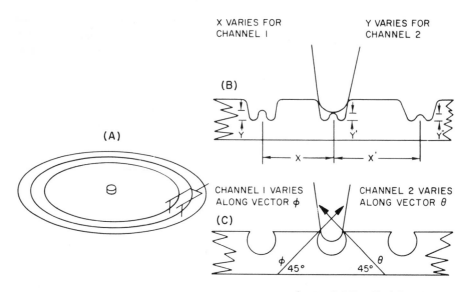

FIG. 23-10. SOME METHODS OF RECORDING STEREO SOUND ON DISCS
(A) Experimental stereo disc using two pickup cartridges; (B) and (C) two experimental single-stylus stereo disc systems that have been successfully demonstrated.

FIG. 23-11. COOK BINAURAL RECORD BEING PLAYED BY A DUAL ARM

the styli by the width of a single groove. The two channels are then no longer in synchronization.[21] Another disadvantage is associated with the fact that the

Cook record has low efficiency in the utilization of record surface, since the playing time of a Cook record is less than half that of a standard monaural LP record. This recording system may be deemed a commercial failure, and today Cook stereo discs are no longer being manufactured in this country.

23.8 *Vertical-lateral systems*

Several single-groove stereo-disc systems have been developed in Europe, all using a technique called vertical-lateral recording (Fig. 23-12). A typical illustration is the Teledec system, developed by London Records, in which vertical recording is used for one channel and lateral recording for the other (Fig. 23-13). Other European stereo-disc systems are the Stereosonic system developed by British Electrical and Musical Industries, and the German MS system.[22]

LATERAL RECORDING

VERTICAL RECORDING

Courtesy, Sylvania Electric Products, Inc.

FIG. 23-12. METHODS USED FOR MONO-DISC RECORDING

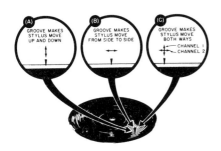

FIG. 23-13. DIFFERENT FORMS OF STYLUS MOVEMENT USED IN DISC RECORDING
(a) Vertical; (b) lateral; (c) experimental single-groove stereophonic.

One disadvantage of the vertical-lateral system is the fact that vertical recording has always been accompanied by a greater amount of inherent distortion than lateral recording. However, this distortion can now be compensated for through the use of a feedback cutter developed by London Records. Other disadvantages of this system are its incompatibility with monaural or monophonic recordings, and the tendency on the part of the turntable to produce an audible vertical rumble.

23.9 *Westrex 45/45 system*

At the present time, it appears that a system called the Westrex 45/45 stereo-disc or Vector-disc system developed in 1957 by the Westrex Company, is the one most likely to be accepted by the recording industry. As a matter of fact, in 1958 a decision was reached by the Record Industry Association of America (RIAA) to adopt the 45/45 system as standard.[23]

According to several writers, the rapid development and acceptance of the Westrex system was primarily due to the fact that Sidney Frey, the head of Audio Fidelity, Inc., a small record-manufacturing firm, pressed commercial copies of a Westrex master and issued them to equipment manufacturers for tests. This opened the gates, and most of the other record manufacturers plunged into this field. If not for this action, the introduction of commercial stereo discs might well have been postponed for several years.[24]

In this system, the walls of the record grooves are at right angles to each other and at an angle of 45 deg. to the record surface (Fig. 23-14). It is basically a vertical-lateral system that has been turned through 45 deg. Only one cutting stylus is used, and it records one stereo channel on each groove wall (Figs. 23-15 and 23-16). The records are simple to make, and its proponents claim that the system is completely compatible with monophonic records and record-playing machines. Of course, a special type of cartridge and pickup are necessary in order to obtain two stereo signals from the record.

The pickup contains one stylus which is coupled to two pickup assemb-

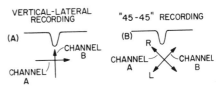

Courtesy, Sylvania Electric Products, Inc.

FIG. 23-14. METHODS USED FOR STEREO-DISC RECORDING
Note that each channel in the "45-45" system contains both horizontal and vertical components.

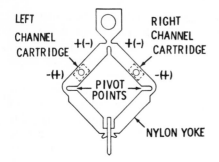

FIG. 23-15. PRINCIPLE OF OPERATION OF A STEREO CUTTING STYLUS
This figure shows a method used to couple cartridges to a common stylus. The common stylus can move in either a vertical or lateral direction, or in combinations of vertical and lateral directions, depending upon the relative acoustical phase of each signal reaching the individual microphones. The direction and depth of stereo information is in the vertical movement.

lies, each one designed to respond only to its own angle of modulation (Fig. 23-17). Originally a stylus with a standard 1-mil tip was used. Practical experience has led to the use of a tip with a 0.7-mil radius, and a recent survey has shown that a further decrease in tip

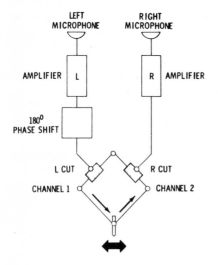

FIG. 23-16. STEREO RECORDING SYSTEM

radius to about 0.5 mils is considered desirable.[25]

It will be brought out shortly that although in this compatible system a stereo cartridge will play monaural or monophonic discs, the reverse is not necessarily true. If a monaural cartridge is used to play a stereo disc, the record grooves may be damaged by the greater stiffness of the monaural stylus and the greater size of the stylus tip.

The pickup may be of any of the conventional types such as variable-reluctance, magnetic, dynamic, crystal, or ceramic varieties (Fig. 23-18). The over-all performance level of the magnetic stereo cartridge seems to be somewhat superior to that of the ceramic stereo cartridge. However, the magnetic stereo cartridge is considerably more expensive than the ceramic type. It must be kept in mind that the design of any stereo cartridge demands a fresh approach, since it consists of more than merely tying two monaural mechanisms together to one stylus (Fig. 23-19).[26]

A leading manufacturer of stereo reproducing equipment has pointed out in a recent advertisement that since a stereo record is far more difficult to reproduce faithfully than a monophonic disc, the stereo pickup and the stereo arm should satisfy the following requirements:

Stereo cartridge

1. Small dynamic mass
2. High vertical and lateral compliance
3. Low distortion
4. Good channel response
5. Wide frequency range
6. The same frequency response in a vertical direction as in a lateral direction
7. The same dynamic mass and

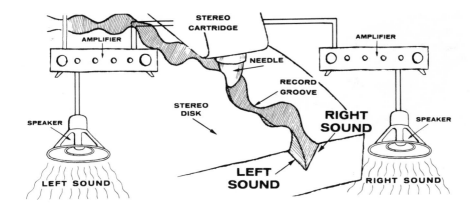

Courtesy, Sonotone Corp.

FIG. 23-17. 45/45 STEREO GROOVE

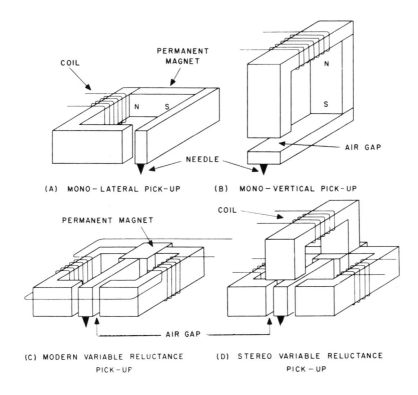

Courtesy, Sylvania Electric Products Inc.

FIG. 23-18. COMPARISON BETWEEN VARIOUS TYPES OF VARIABLE-RELUCTANCE PICKUPS
As the needle varies the air gap in each of the variable reluctance pick-ups, there is a corresponding change in magnetic flux that governs the voltage generated in the coils. This voltage is then fed to the playback amplifiers reproducing the recorded sound.

Courtesy, Radio-Electronics

FIG. 23-19. TYPICAL STEREO CARTRIDGE

compliance in both vertical and lateral operation

8. Inherently linear generating elements

9. Complete independence of the two generating elements

Stereo pickup arm

1. Maintenance of perfect stylus contact with both sides of the record groove

2. Vertical force of 4 grams or less, in order to prevent the stylus from distorting the record

3. Use of ball bearings for all vertical and horizontal motions

4. Absence of resonances in the audio range[27]

Critics of the 45/45 system state that it results in a record with a deteriorated dynamic range and a poor signal-to-noise ratio, because it is necessary to record at a level that is 3 to 6 db lower than that employed for conventional LP's in order to prevent distortion produced by the vertical component of the groove-cutting force. They state that it is not a truly compatible system, since it is necessary to connect the dual output leads of the pickups in parallel before a monaural record can be played. They also maintain that a conventional high-fidelity

pickup cannot possibly play a stereo disc and give high-fidelity monophonic reproduction.[28]

A fact that must also be considered is that most monophonic cartridges are heavily damped vertically. Due to this poor vertical compliance, they may damage the stereo disc. Because of the increased space occupied by the 45/45 grooves, the playing time of this record is less than that of a conventional LP. Finally, the design of many turntables causes them to produce a vertical rumble that is not picked up by a lateral monaural cartridge but is detected by a stereo cartridge. This problem can be solved by using a rumble suppressor or filter that reduces the effect of vertical rumble. According to the proponents of this system, the very-low frequencies—which are subdued along with these rumble effects from the vertical channel—are not required for stereo reproduction. They claim that because of their longer wavelengths, the signals of these low frequencies are always recorded in phase and are effectively reproduced by the lateral channel.[29] [30]

23.10 *Columbia compatible system*

In 1958, Peter Goldmark of CBS Laboratories announced the development of the Columbia Compatible Stereophonic Record. It resembles the Westrex 45/45 system, but avoids some of its disadvantages by putting most of the information into the lateral signal fed to the cutter, leaving only a small percentage of the total signal for the vertical component.

The operation of this system can be described in a technical manner by stating that it is a single-groove stereo system in which the vector sum of the right and left channels is recorded laterally, while the vector difference is simultaneously recorded vertically. Because of these characteristics, sound may be recorded at a level comparable with that of a monaural LP record.

It is claimed that this system produces a completely compatible stereo record. It can be played back perfectly with an ordinary monaural LP cartridge, with any 45/45 setup, or even with a European vertical-lateral cartridge. Critics of this system have expressed the opinion that it seems to introduce a slight loss in quality and some loss in stereo illusion.[31][32]

23.11 *Minter stereo disc*

Another interesting stereo system was developed in 1958 by Minter of Components Corporation and Electro-Sonic Laboratories. This is a compatible Minter Stereo Disc (MSD) multiplex system employing lateral recording. It is played back by means of a conventional lateral monaural cartridge. One channel, containing the vector sum of the two stereo channels, is recorded in the conventional lateral manner. The second channel, containing the vector difference of the two stereo channels, is produced by using this difference signal to frequency-modulate an ultrasonic 25-kc carrier. The modulated carrier is then recorded laterally in the same groove. In order to recover this information, the playback cartridge must have good frequency response up to 30 kc, and the amplifying system must also contain a demodulator or detector circuit.[33][34]

Its proponents point out that this system is completely compatible with monaural systems, and that it is simpler than other systems to the point of the stylus, which is where at least 90 per cent of all of the troubles in disc reproduction occur. Since it is a lateral system, there is no vertical-rumble problem. The playing time is about the same as that of a conventional LP record. The major drawback seems to be the fact that it entered the competition somewhat too late, after the Record Industry Association of America and the major record manufacturers, such as RCA, Victor, Capitol, Decca, and Columbia Records had decided to adopt the 45/45 system as standard.

23.12 *Present status of stereo disc recording*

Although many experts feel that binaural recording possesses a great future, relatively little material of high musical quality has as yet been made available in binaural form. Commercial stereo discs began to appear on the market during the middle of 1958 at prices ranging from $3.95 to $6.95, and many old-line manufacturers indicated that they planned to incorporate stereo disc players in future high-fidelity phonograph models. In fact, one juke-box manufacturer has developed a model capable of accommodating stereo discs. Some experts are of the opinion that stereo is setting the stage for a boom in the record industry that will exceed that produced by the development of the LP record.[35] Several leading experts have predicted that within a few years the changeover to stereo will be virtually complete and the monophonic record will join the 78-rpm record in history.[36][37]

Undoubtedly, this trend will be accelerated by the development of equipment that will reduce the size and cost of stereo reproduction. One interesting development in this direction is CBS's new two-way amplifying system, which permits what is basically a single amplifier to handle simultaneously two stereo channels and to maintain an adequate amount of isolation between the two channels.

23.13 *Stereo tapes*

Stereo magnetic-tape recordings also seem to possess a bright future (Fig. 23-20). At the present time, two-channel, 7.5 ips (inches per second) stereo-tape recordings seem to be superior in quality to stereo discs (Fig. 23-21). Stereo tape also possesses the advantage that it can go easily to three-channel stereo instead of two—a development which is not forseeable with disc at the present time. However, good stereo-tape playback equipment is very expensive, and a 7.5 ips, two-track tape may cost between $8.95 and $18.95 for a reel containing a single symphony, compared with approximately $4 for the discs containing the same music. Furthermore, tape is relatively inconvenient to use, since it must be initially threaded through the guides, rollers and heads of the machine and then rewound after each playing.

23.14 *RCA stereo tape cartridges*

In an attempt to make the use of a stereo tape recording as simple as that of a disc recording, and to lower the cost barrier, RCA and Bell Sound have developed a four-channel, bi-directional stereo-tape system. The tape, which is completely enclosed in a polystyrene cartridge or magazine, plays at a speed of 3.75 ips (Fig. 23-22)

It is claimed that the tape contained in a plastic magazine only 7 in. long and 5 in. wide plays up to an hour of stereo music. When the cartridge is slipped into the machine, one set of two stereo tracks plays in one direction. After all the tape has run through in one direction, an automatic switch functions, the tape is turned over without rewinding, and the other set of tracks is played. The prices range from $4.95 for a 22-minute recording to between $6.95 and $9.95 for a 60-minute tape.[38][39]

Since the quality of frequency response of magnetic tape is related to its speed, some experts have questioned the quality of frequency response obtainable with this 3.75-ips tape compared with that of conventional 7.5-ips tape. Some engineers maintain that the slow speed reduces the signal-to-noise ratio and makes it difficult to obtain strong undistorted music at frequencies above 8,000 cps. Another writer agrees with this criticism and claims that the response drops off sharply after 8,000 to 10,000 cps, which certainly falls below what could be regarded as high-fidelity performance, and which also falls far short of the type of response that can be obtained from the more conventional, two-channel, 7.5-ips stereo tape.

A different writer points out that this equipment requires the use of a playback head with an extremely narrow gap of 0.1 mils that is very sensitive to

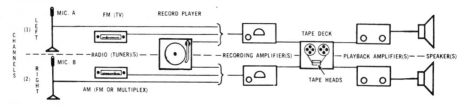

Courtesy, The Nortronics Co., Inc.

FIG. 23-20. TYPICAL STEREO TAPE RECORDING PLAYBACK SYSTEM

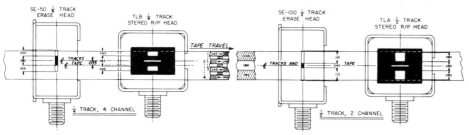

Courtesy, The Nortronics Co., Inc.

FIG. 23-21. FOUR-CHANNEL AND TWO-CHANNEL MAGNETIC TAPES AND RECORD PLAYBACK HEADS

dirt. He also states that the reduction of tape width and speed causes a decrease of 6 db in the signal-to-noise ratio, which also reduces the quality of performance and increases the amount of tape hiss.[40]

Courtesy, Radio Corporation of America

FIG. 23-22. RCA VICTOR STEREOPHONIC TAPE CARTRIDGE

It is also argued that the tone quality from the 3.75-ips tape cartridge will not satisfy sound-conscious listeners who have become accustomed to the relative perfection of dual-head, higher-speed, reel-type tape. As the tape speed decreases, any unevenness in the rate of tape travel will produce more noticeable flutter and wow.[41]

According to a recent survey, the general opinion was that these tapes were obviously not equal in fidelity to the conventional, two-track, 7.5-ips

tape. Furthermore, they appeared to possess lower volume level and higher background noise. They were judged adequate for providing casual background or mood music but not for providing sound of high-fidelity quality.[42] In the words of one writer: "It is now felt that at the present state of the art and with the present materials, including tape, it is not a commercially practical proposition to have four-track, 3.75-ips stereo tapes genuinely competitive with today's stereo discs."[43]

A final major disadvantage is the fact that these new tapes cannot be played on conventional tape equipment.

In rebuttal to some of these arguments, proponents of the newer system claim that the frequency range can be extended to 15,000 cps through the use of an extremely narrow magnet gap in the playback head. One engineer reports that experiments have revealed that when a precisely engineered, quarter-track record-playback head is used, the frequency response obtained at 3.75 ips is comparable to that obtained with conventional single laminar half-track heads at 7.5 ips.[44]

Nevertheless, it is fairly obvious that many additional mechanical and electronic problems must be solved before this slow-speed, four-track system can gain wide acceptance among audiophiles.[45]

23.15 *MRIA four-track stereo tape*

In 1959, 19 firms, including the Ampex Corporation, acting under the leadership of the Magnetic Recording Industry Association, joined together to promote a new variety of stereo tape. This tape represents a compromise between the other types. It is a four-track or quarter-track tape, operating at the higher speed of 7.5 ips, and is of the open-reel type that must be threaded and rewound (Fig. 23-23). When it is first played, only two tracks, 1 and 3, are used to provide stereo reproduction, while the other tracks, 2 and 4, are silent. When the tape is reversed, tracks 2 and 4 produce sound while tracks 1 and 3 remain silent. This doubles the length of playing time of a tape.[46] It is designed to sell for approximately $6.95

for a 30-minute reel and $7.95 for a 45-minute reel. It is believed that this will provide a high-quality stereo medium at a reasonable price, while the slower magazine tapes will supply the mass market.[47] [48]

23.16 *The present stereo situation*

One expert has summed up the present situation concerning the rivalry between the convenience of stereo discs and the quality of two-channel stereo tape in the following words: "The mass stereo market will probably be in disc, whereas the high-fidelity field will probably prefer tape."[49]

In other words, it is very likely that stereo discs and tape will not be competitive but will augment each other.[50] Thus, the president of the Magnetic

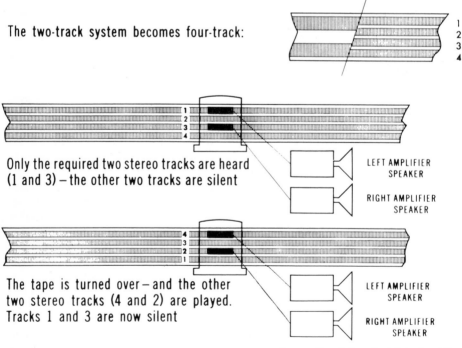

The two-track system becomes four-track:

```
                                              1
                                              2
                                              3
                                              4
```

Only the required two stereo tracks are heard (1 and 3) – the other two tracks are silent

LEFT AMPLIFIER
SPEAKER

RIGHT AMPLIFIER
SPEAKER

The tape is turned over – and the other two stereo tracks (4 and 2) are played. Tracks 1 and 3 are now silent

LEFT AMPLIFIER
SPEAKER

RIGHT AMPLIFIER
SPEAKER

Courtesy, Magnetic Recording Industry Association

FIG. 23-23. MRIA FOUR-TRACK STEREO TAPE

Recording Industry Association has agreed with the statement made by one writer that the stereo disc was probably the best thing that ever happened to magnetic tape. In support of this statement, he pointed out that as a result of the development of the stereo disc, within one year the potential audience of stereo tape has expanded from 5 million to 95 million Americans and that many of those introduced to stereo through discs will eventually adopt stereo tape.[51]

Passing over this controversy between these rival forms of stereo recording, it should be pointed out that these new techniques of stereo recording have aroused the interest and attention of both the laymen and the expert audiophile, and that they will provide valuable tools for achieving the goal of providing truer and more faithful reproduction of good music in the home. It is also likely that the development of stereo discs may have a considerable effect upon the type of music that will be recorded for commercial reproduction. This is due to the fact that stereo is ideal for symphony, opera, organ, and larger jazz combinations but offers little advantage to chamber music, and may actually be a hindrance, as far as realism is concerned, to solo voice, violin, and piano recordings.

23.17 *FM-AM simulcasting*

A development that must not be overlooked is the fact that a great many broadcasting stations are also converting to stereo. The most common method of accomplishing this is the simulcasting method. One channel is broadcast by an FM station and the other by an AM station. The listener requires both an FM and AM receiver or tuner in order to reproduce both channels (Figs. 23-24 and 23-25).

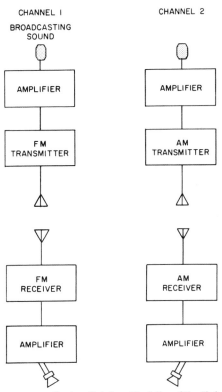

Courtesy, *Tech News*, City College of New York
FIG. 23-24. FM-AM SIMULCASTING

During the late 1950's, television stations began to experiment with a modified version of this technique known as the TV-AM method. In this method, one channel is broadcast over the television frequency-modulated audio carrier, and the second over an affiliated AM station. In October 1958, the NBC George Gobel show presented the first nationwide network experimental program of this type.

The various versions of this method have produced good results, but critics argue that this system is uneconomical, inefficient, and wasteful of spectrum space, since two complete stations are required. In addition, the quality of reception on the AM channel may not be satisfactory, since the signal-to-noise

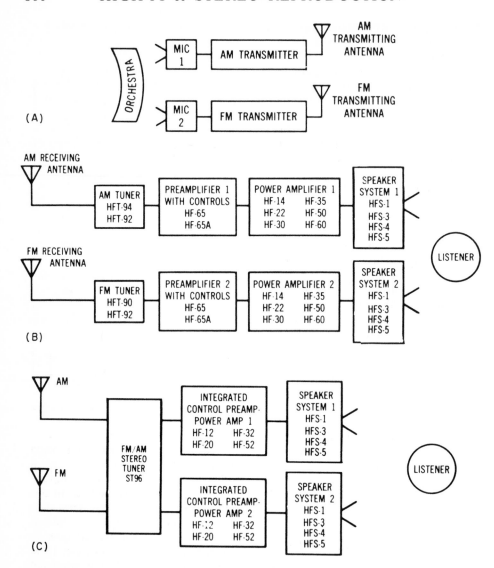

Courtesy, EICO

FIG. 23-25. SYSTEMS EMPLOYED FOR FM-AM STEREO TRANSMISSION AND RECEPTION
(A) AM-FM stereo transmission by radio; (B) stereo reception using two monophonic preamplifiers and two monophonic power amplifiers (examples of each, as manufactured by EICO in kit or wired form, are listed near each component; the ST96 stereo FM/AM tuner may be substituted for the tuners shown); (C) stereo reception using two monophonic integrated preamplifier power amplifier units (examples of each, as manufactured by EICO in kit or wired form, are listed near component; the tuners shown in (B) may be substituted for the ST96).

ratio and the frequency response of an AM signal are usually poorer than those of an FM signal. Nevertheless, by the middle of 1958, there were at least 50 FM stations engaged in simulcasting operations.

23.18 *FM-FM multicasting*

A second method is the FM-FM or multicasting method, in which the two channels are broadcast by two separate FM stations that are in the same locality and of about the same power. The listener requires two FM receivers or tuners. This system is also wasteful of spectrum space, since two FM channels are required.

23.19 *Single-sideband AM*

The third system, developed by RCA and still in the experimental stage, employs single-sideband AM transmission, the nature of which will be described in a later chapter. One stereo channel is broadcast on one sideband, and the second channel is broadcast on the other sideband.[52] A single special AM receiver is then used to detect the two signals and to feed each into a separate audio-amplifier system.[53]

23.20 *FM Multiplex*

A fourth system is FM Multiplex. One of the stereo channels is transmitted by the FM station over its main channel. The other stereo channel is stepped up to an ultrasonic frequency, and this ultrasonic signal or subcarrier is also used to modulate the same FM carrier. In technical terminology, this may be described by stating that the ultrasonic channel is a subchannel that has been multiplexed onto the carrier.

At the receiver, the regular signal is demodulated by conventional means, while the second multiplexed channel is applied to a special multiplex adapter which steps down the frequency of this signal to the audible range (Fig. 23-26).[54] A modified version of FM Multiplex is now in commercial use for non-stereo broadcasting of background music for stores and industry.[55]

NBC station WRCA-FM has conducted experimental broadcasts on

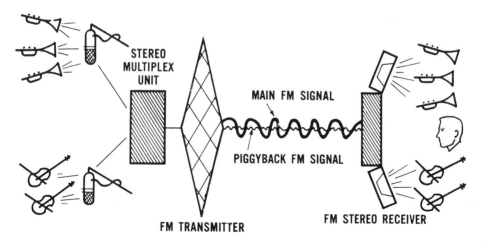

Courtesy, General Electric Co.

FIG. 23-26. PRINCIPLES OF FM STEREOCASTING

Sound from separate sources is picked up by studio microphones and fed into the broadcasting station's stereo multiplexing equipment. It is transmitted as two separate signals—a main signal and an ultrasonic sub-carrier. Both signals are broadcast over a single FM channel, but each modulates independently. The listener hears sound emanating from the same relative positions he would if he were actually present in the broadcasting studio or concert hall.

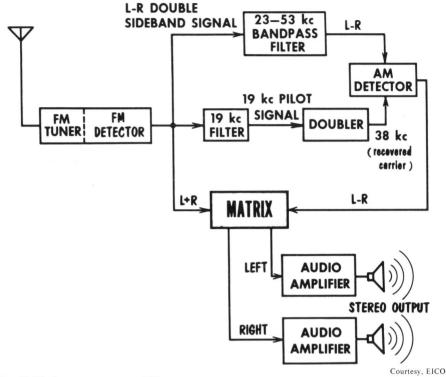

FIG. 23-27. BLOCK DIAGRAM OF FM MULTIPLEX RECEIVING SYSTEM

compatible FM stereo-multiplexing system developed by Murray G. Crosby of Crosby Laboratories. In this method, the main FM channel carries the complete program, which is the sum of the left and right signals. This can be received by an FM receiver. The multiplex subchannel carries a difference signal which is the difference between the left and right signals. An FM receiver that is equipped with a multiplex adapter can separate the left and right signals and distribute each one to its correct amplifier (Fig. 23-27).[56 57 58] In 1959, there were about 10 FM stations in the United States that were transmitting this type of compatible multiplexed stereophonic signal.

Stereo broadcasting is probably the fastest-moving branch of the entire stereo field. Several additional compatible multiplex systems have been developed besides the Crosby system. One of these is the Calbest system developed by the Calbest Electronics Company. This uses a sum-and-difference method and a narrow-band multiplex subcarrier which makes it possible to use two subcarriers besides the main carrier. The second subcarrier can be used for monophonic music transmitted to factories and stores.[59] Another compatible FM-Multiplex system was developed by Motorola. This system, which was demonstrated early in 1959 on station WGN-TV, Chicago, adds a multiplex sound subcarrier to a television signal.[60]

Since as late as 1960 the FM-Multiplex situation was still not very clear, many manufacturers of frequency-modulated equipment advised prospective purchasers not to buy any of the available multiplex adapters. They pointed out that when the Federal Communications Commission would finally give its approval to one of these many experimental multiplex systems, many of the other adapters currently on the market would not be usable.

23.21 *Philco compatible AM system*

In 1959, the Philco Corporation asked the FCC for permission to conduct field tests of its compatible stereophonic system on the AM broadcast band. In this system, the sum of left and right audio tracks is transmitted by the conventional AM method. A signal containing the difference is transmitted on the same carrier frequency by means of phase modulation. It is claimed that stereo receivers and converters can be produced economically, that stereo broadcasts can be received monophonically by conventional AM receivers without distortion, that broadcast stations can switch from monophonic to stereophonic at any time, and that no revision of existing radio-frequency assignments is required.[61][62]

23.22 *Westinghouse compatible AM system*

The Westinghouse system is based upon a 30-year-old patent issued to one of the pioneers of radio broadcasting, Frank Conrad. In this system, the sum of the two stereo channels is used to amplitude-modulate the carrier of an AM station. Simultaneously, the difference between the two channels is converted into a narrow band of frequencies and is used to frequency-modulate the same carrier.

Two ordinary AM receivers are used to recover the stereo information by means of a process called slope detection. In this process, one receiver is detuned slightly above the carrier frequency, and the other one is detuned slightly below the carrier frequency. This produces a complex mixing or matrixing effect that causes the left-channel signal to be applied to the left speaker and the right-channel signal to the right speaker.[63][64]

23.23 *Bell Laboratories compatible stereo*

The Bell stereo system, which was successfully demonstrated in 1959 on a Perry Como show, was developed by F. K. Becker of Bell Telephone Laboratories. It utilizes frequency-modulation-amplitude-modulation or television-amplitude-modulation transmission, and since it does not employ multiplex, it requires no FCC authorization. The operation of this system depends upon a psycho-acoustic principle known as the precedence effect, by which the ear distinguishes a sound source from its echoes and reverberations. When two identical sounds of the same intensity are played through dual channels, if one of them is delayed approximately 10 milliseconds by a delay line, the sound will apparently emanate only from the undelayed speaker, and the second speaker will seem to be silent.

In this stereo system, the signals from both microphones are fed to both channels. However, the signal from the left microphone is delayed about 10 milliseconds before being fed to the right channel, and the signal from the right microphone is delayed 10 milliseconds before being fed to the left channel. If two receiving channels are used, the undelayed signal in each channel will override the other signal, and a stereo effect will be produced. If only one receiving channel is used, the listener cannot detect the delay of one of the signals, and the two signals blend to produce perfect monophonic reception.[65] [66] [67]

23.24 *Current status of stereo broadcasting*

Space limitations prevent discussion of the many other stereo broadcasting systems, such as the Halstead, the Burden, and the Percival systems. Detailed descriptions of their operating principles may be found in the literature.[68]

It soon became obvious that before long, a decision would have to be made by responsible authorities concerning which one of these many competing systems should be adopted as the standard and accepted one. The FCC investigated the situation, and December 11th, 1959 was set as the deadline by which proponents of each system could file application for consideration for adoption. The FCC was assisted in this study by an advisory group from the industry, the National Stereophonic Radio Committee of the Electronics Industry Association.[69] [70]

The decision of the FCC was announced on April 19, 1961. The system selected was called the Zenith - General Electric Multiplex stereo system, and it closely resembles the previously described Crosby system (Fig. 23-28 and 23-29). Now that mandatory standards have been promulgated, this branch of the industry has been able to begin mass production of stereo radio receivers.

Courtesy, Zenith Radio Corp.
FIG. 23-28. ZENITH STEREO TRANSMITTER PANEL

Courtesy, Zenith Radio Corp.
FIG. 23-29. A STEREOPHONIC FM BROADCASTING STATION IN OPERATION
At midnight, June 1, 1961, WEFM, Chicago, transmitted the first stereophonic FM broadcast on the new FCC standards.

REFERENCES

1. H. A. Chinn and Philip Eisenberg, "Tonal Range and Sound Intensity Preferences of Broadcast Listeners," *Proc. IRE*, 33:571-581, Sept. 1945.
2. "High Fidelity?," *Radio-Electronics*, 24:132, Nov. 1953.
3. Norman H. Crowhurst, "Shopping for a Hi-Fi amplifier," *Electronics World*, 62:40-41, Aug. 1959.
4. Victor Robinson, "Power Output Ratings for Hi-Fi Amplifiers," *Electronics World*, 62:44-46, Oct. 1959.

5. W. A. Stocklin, "Standards and the Hi-Fi Industry," *Electronics World*, 62:8, Oct. 1959.
6. Joseph N. Benjamin, "The Hi-Fi Institute," *Electronics World*, 62:47, Oct. 1959.
7. "Direct Comparison," *Radio-Electronics*, 30:10, Feb. 1959.
8. "Performance Standards," *Radio-Electronics*, 30:18, 22, May 1959.
9. J. Donald Harris, "The Stereo Illusion," *Electronics World*, 62:37-40, Oct. 1959.

10. "Stereo, The New Hi-Fi Sound," *Motorola Service News*, 6:1-2, Sept. 1958.
11. Bud Tomer, *An Introduction to Stereophonic Sound*, Bull. E-305, CBS-Hytron, Danvers, Mass.
12. "Stereo Defined," *Radio and TV News*, 61:97, Feb. 1959.
13. "Stereo, The New Hi-Fi Sound," *Op. cit.*, p. 2.
14. Donald C. Hoefler, "Ready for Stereo?," *Radio-Electronics*, 29:36, Oct. 1958.
15. Robert O. Jordan and James Cunningham, *The Sound of High Fidelity*, Popular Mechanics Press, Chicago, Ill., p. 72.
16. P. L. Jensen, "Reminiscing about Stereo," *Radio and TV News*, 61:112, Feb. 1959.
17. Jack Thornton, "Experiments in Stereo for PA Systems," *Electronics World*, 61:128, May 1959.
18. Louis E. Garner, Jr., "Stereo Then and Now," *Radio-Electronics*, 30:53, Mar. 1959.
19. Sidney Frey, "The Stereo Disc Today," *Electronics World*, 62:54, Oct. 1959.
20. Harry Walton and Hubert Luckett, "Listening with Both Ears," *Popular Science*, 167:227-231, Oct. 1955.
21. Norman H. Crowhurst, "Single-Groove Stereo Discs," *Radio-Electronics*, 29:54, Jan. 1958.
22. Norman H. Crowhurst, "Compatibility and the Stereo Disc," *Radio-Electronics*, 29:35, Aug. 1958.
23. Jerry B. Minter, "Stereo Disc Recording Methods," *Radio and TV News*, 60:66, Oct. 1958.
24. L. E. Garner, Jr., *Op. cit.*, pp. 54-55.
25. J. B. Minter, *Op. cit.*, p. 66.
26. Norman H. Crowhurst, "Pickup Cartridges for Stereo," *Radio and TV News*, 60:35, Oct. 1958.
27. Published advertisement, *Radio-Electronics*, 30:24, Oct. 1959.
28. Norman H. Crowhurst, "Compatibility and the Stereo Disc," *Op. cit.*, p. 36.
29. *Stereo Simplified*, SAH-19, Sonotone Corp., Elmsford, N.Y., 1959, p. 8.
30. Bud Tomer, *Hints on Using the Columbia CD Stereo Cartridge*, Bull. E-306, CBS - Hytron, Danvers, Mass., p. 4.
31. Norman H. Crowhurst, "Compatibility and the Stereo Disc," *Op. cit.*, p. 38.
32. Milton S. Snitzer, "New Compatible Stereo Disc," *Radio and TV News*, 59:53, June 1958.
33. Herman Burstein, "News for the Audiophile," *Radio Electronics*, 29:38, Apr. 1958.
34. "All Lateral Stereo Disc Demonstrated," *Radio and TV News*, 59:125, Apr. 1958.
35. W. Stocklin, "Stereo Boom Ahead," *Radio and TV News*, 60:8, Aug. 1958.
36. P. L. Jensen, *Op. cit.*, p. 113.
37. John G. Dodgson, "Hi-Fi Corner," *National Radio Institute News*, 18:22, Oct. 1959.
38. "4-Track Stereo Tapes Coming," *Radio-Electronics*, 29:29, July 1958.
39. "RCA's 4-Track Stereo Cartridge," *Radio and TV News*, 60:80, Aug. 1958.
40. C. J. LeBel, "Stereo . . Tape or Disc?," *Radio and TV News*, 60:40, Oct. 1958.
41. Robert Gorman, "What's Coming in Stereo Tape?," *Popular Science*, 174:158, June 1959.
42. Norman Eisenberg, "All About Hi-Fi Tape Cartridges," *Electronics Illustrated*, 2:40, Mar. 1959.
43. Bert Whyte, "Sound On Tape," *Electronics World*, 61:112, June 1959.
44. John W. Hogan, "Slow-Speed Tape Recording," *Electronics World*, 61:58,119, June 1959.
45. W. Stocklin, "Stereo Tape or Disc?," *Radio and TV News*, 60:8,150, Oct. 1958.
46. "$\frac{1}{4}$ Track Tape," *Electronic Technician*, 71:81, Jan. 1960.
47. Ernest John, "Stereo Tape is Back—To Stay!," *Popular Electronics*, 11:80-81, Oct. 1959.
48. "Industry Launches Stereo Tape Drive," *Electronics World*, 62:80, Aug. 1959.
49. C. J. LeBel, "Stereo Discs," *Audio Record*, 13:7, Dec. 1957.
50. W. Stocklin, *Op. cit.*, p. 8.
51. Herbert L. Brown, "The Tape Recording Industry," *Electronics World*, 62:67, Oct. 1959.
52. "New Stereo System for AM Band," *Radio and TV News*, 61:143, Jan. 1959.
53. "Stereo Sound Adapted for AM Radio Sets," *Science Digest*, 45:90, Feb. 1959.
54. Paul F. Hille, Jr., "FM Multiplex—Its Present and Future, Part 1," *Radio and TV News*, 61:139-141, Jan. 1959.
55. Milton S. Snitzer, "Stereo Broadcasting—Now and in the Future," *Radio and TV News*, 60:65, Oct. 1959.
56. Leonard Feldman, "MX Means Multiplex," *Popular Electronics*, 10:43-45, Jan. 1959.
57. Norman H. Crowhurst, "What is Compatible Stereo FM Multiplex?," *Radio-Electronics*, 30:91, Mar. 1959.
58. Norman H. Crowhurst, "More About Multiplexing for Stereo," *Radio-Electronics*, 30:73-74, July 1959.
59. *Ibid*, p. 75.
60. "Two More Stereo Systems," *Radio-Electronics*, 30:96, Mar. 1959.
61. "AM Stereo Broadcasting," *Radio-Electronics*, 30:6, 10, Feb. 1959.
62. "New System of Broadcasting for Stereo," *Radio and TV News*, 61:32, Feb. 1959.
63. "Compatible Stereo for AM Stations," *Electronics World*, 61:86, May 1959.
64. "AM Stereophony," *Radio-Electronics*, 30:6, 8, May 1959.
65. *Ibid*, p. 8.
66. "Compatible Stereo Broadcasts," *Electronics World*, 61:125, May 1959.
67. "Bell Labs Stereo," *Popular Electronics*, 10:8, May 1959.
68. Norman H. Crowhurst, "More about Multiplexing for Stereo," *Radio-Electronics*, 30:73-75, July 1959.
69. *Ibid*, p. 75.
70. "Stereocasting Situation," *Radio-Electronics*, 30:8, 10, Oct. 1959.

24-HEARING AIDS & AUDIOMETERS

24.1 *Development of hearing aids*

A modern hearing aid is a device containing a microphone, amplifier, batteries, and receiver (Fig. 24-1). Used to augment the amount of sound energy reaching the ear of the user, it is fundamentally a miniature, personal public-address system. Hearing aids have largely replaced the trumpets and speaking tubes formerly used by the hard-of-hearing (Fig. 24-2). The first electrical hearing aid, developed in 1924,

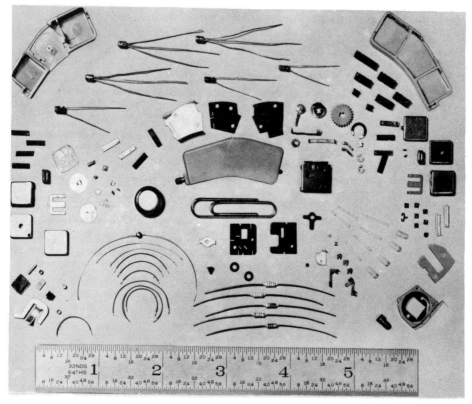

Courtesy, Sonotone Corp.

FIG. 24-1. HEARING AID COMPONENTS
The Sonotone Model 55 "Wisp", weighs $\frac{1}{4}$ oz, and contains 129 components. Assembled hearing aid is shown in center compared in size with a paper clip.

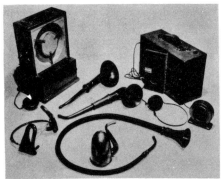

FIG. 24-2. EARLY TYPES OF HEARING AIDS: TRUMPETS, SPEAKING TUBES, AND CARBON-TYPE AMPLIFIERS

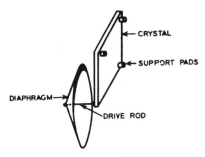

FIG. 24-4. ARRANGEMENT OF THE CRYSTAL MICROPHONE OF A HEARING AID

weighed 185 lb. It was powered by a 6-volt automobile storage battery and a 135-volt dry battery. By 1928, the weight had been reduced sufficiently so that the device could be carried in a satchel. Today, some of the hearing aids on the market weigh approximately 0.5 oz (Fig. 24-3).

24.2 *Hearing-aid components*

Hearing aids usually employ crystal microphones. These microphones are smaller than the microphones employed in broadcasting and public-address systems but serve the same function, namely the conversion of sound energy into electrical energy (Fig. 24-4).

There may possibly still be a few of the old carbon-amplifier hearing aids in use (Fig. 24-5). These carbon amplifiers required smaller batteries and cost less to operate than vacuum-tube amplifiers, but they did not give as good performance. Modern hearing aids usually employ transformer-coupled or resistance-coupled amplifier circuits. These circuits are usually conventional amplifier circuits, except that they involve transistors and frequently employ printed-circuit components to replace conventional capacitors, resistors, coils, and wire connections.

FIG. 24-3. EVOLUTION OF THE HEARING AID BETWEEN 1938 AND 1956

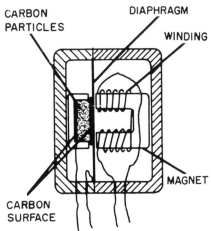

FIG. 24-5. CARBON TYPE AMPLIFIER

Some of the circuit components are so tiny that both a magnifying glass and a watchmaker's craftsmanship are required to handle them. Despite their small size, the amplifier circuits are capable of boosting the power of a signal over one billion times. The amount of amplification obtained by the amplifier is limited solely by the possibility of feedback from the receiver to the microphone. If the amount of amplification is too great, this feedback will produce oscillations and loud whistling sounds.

Types of receivers. Receivers are designed to convert electrical energy back into sound vibrations. They may be of the magnetic or crystal type and may utilize either air or bone conduction.

Air-conduction receivers are commonly used unless the middle ear or eardrum mechanism has been destroyed or badly affected. This type of receiver tends to keep the normal ear passage active and is usually fitted to the ear having the greatest hearing loss.

Bone-conduction receivers are used when the middle ear or eardrum has been destroyed or badly affected, but little or no auditory nerve loss is indicated. This type of receiver is usually fitted to the side of the head that has better bone conduction; it rests on the mastoid bone back of the ear.

Hearing-aid batteries. Hearing-aid batteries are essentially similar to the dry cells employed in flashlights. Recently, mercury batteries (Fig. 24-6) and small rechargeable storage batteries of the nickel-cadmium type have been used by some manufacturers. Weight for weight, the mercury batteries deliver more hours of service than the conventional zinc-carbon batteries. The initial voltage of the mercury battery, 1.25 volts, is maintained at a relatively high level during use until most of the available energy is exhausted. However, the mercury battery is considerably more expensive than the older zinc-carbon battery—a serious drawback.

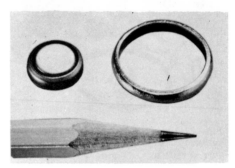

Courtesy, Sonotone Corp.
FIG. 24-6. SIZE OF A MERCURY HEARING AID BATTERY COMPARED WITH A PENCIL AND A RING

Volume and tone controls. Hearing aids usually contain volume controls to enable the user to regulate the amount of amplification. They also contain tone controls to adapt the hearing aid to the pitch characteristics of the individual's impairment and help suppress undesired sounds in noisy surroundings.[1]

24.3 *Recent developments in hearing aids*

The trend in hearing-aid design is toward miniaturization of the various components and concealment of the entire device.[2] Sonotone has produced a vacuum-tube model that is slightly larger than a box of safety matches and as thin as a package of chewing gum. Its battery is half the size of a thimble and its total weight, including that of the battery, is 3 oz. This aid can be concealed in a woman's hairdo or kept in a man's pocket without producing a noticeable bulge. It is capable of doing an even better job than the bulky aids produced only a few years ago.

The development of the transistor gave hearing-aid miniaturization an additional impetus. The Sonotone Model 100 is a four-transistor hearing aid that is the same size as a book of matches and weighs only 1 oz, including the battery. The Sonotone Model 79 also contains four transistors, and has a total weight of less than 0.75 oz (Fig. 24-7). Other recently developed models contain automatic volume-control circuits and a special telephone-pickup coil and amplifier to improve hearing of telephone conversations (Figs. 24-8, 24-9, and 24-10).

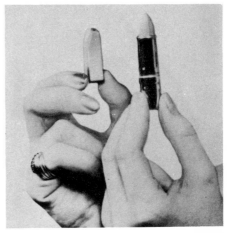

Courtesy, Sonotone Corp.

FIG. 24-9. SIZE OF A SONOTONE $\frac{1}{4}$ OZ WISP HEARING AID COMPARED WITH THAT OF A LIPSTICK

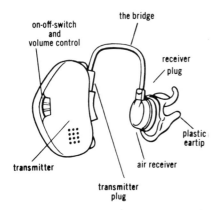

Courtesy, Sonotone Corp.

FIG. 24-7. SONOTONE MODEL 79 FOUR-TRANSISTOR HEARING AID

Courtesy, Otarion Listener Corp.

FIG. 24-10. OTARION NORMALIZER HEARING AID COMPARED IN SIZE WITH A DIME

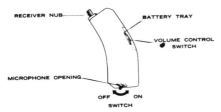

Courtesy, Sonotone Corp.

FIG. 24-8. SONOTONE MODEL 55 WISP HEARING AID

In 1957, the same company went one step further and produced a model without wires and small enough to fit into the ear. This Model 222 three-transistor hearing aid is approximately 0.75 in. in each dimension, weighs 0.5 oz, and is powered by a battery which,

though smaller than a dime, will supply the required energy for 50 hr at a cost of 32 cents (Fig. 24-11). As a result of the employment of transistors, operating costs have been cut by more than 90 per cent, and general efficiency has been increased by more than 300 per cent.

Another recent innovation is a transistor model invented by Rosemond and produced by Otarion Listener Corp. (Fig. 24-12) and Maico Electronics. All hearing-aid components are fitted in the bows of a horned-rim eyeglass frame of standard weight and width (Fig. 24-13). The unit contains a tiny dime-size battery which lasts 180 hr. The increase in weight produced by the hearing aid is 2.5 oz. The end of one

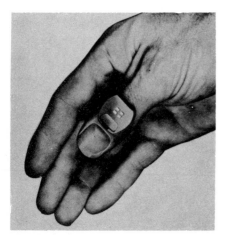

Courtesy, Otarion Listener Corp.

FIG. 24-12. OTARION EYEGLASS-TYPE HEARING AID

Courtesy, Sonotone Corp.

FIG. 24-11. SONOTONE MODEL 222 HEARING AID

sidepiece contains a thin, flexible, transparent tube that conducts sound directly to the ear. Incorporation of the microphone in the front frame makes it unnecessary for the listener to turn his head away from the person speaking in order to direct the sound toward the microphone, which is usually located on the side of the head.

Zenith has also brought out an eyeglass-type of hearing aid that is powered by solar batteries (see chapter 5). This model has its greatest market in the South, where there is more sunshine during the year.

Devices such as these tend to encourage the use of hearing aids by

people who are reluctant to wear conventional models containing conspicuous wires and ear buttons.[3] By 1959, eyeglass-type hearing aids had been brought out by most manufacturers, and their sales accounted for more than 75 per cent of the total market. By that year also, the hearing-aid industry in the United States had been completely converted to transistors, and it was estimated that the hearing-aid manufacturers were using over one million transistors a year. The typical unit that was being produced employed three or four transistors, although some contained as many as five.

Several manufacturers have brought out eyeglass-frame hearing-aid models incorporating binaural hearing principles (See Chap. 18). These contain a separate microphone for each ear and twin amplifier circuits. The sound reception is much more natural than is the case with

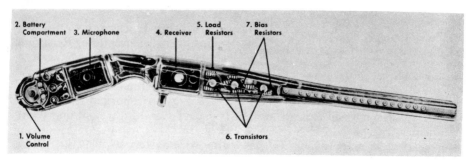

2. Battery Compartment   3. Microphone   4. Receiver   5. Load Resistors   7. Bias Resistors

1. Volume Control   6. Transistors

Courtesy, Maico Electronics Inc.

FIG. 24-13. INTERIOR VIEW OF THE MAICO EYEGLASS HEARING AID

monaural models, and the user is able to gauge the direction and distance of sources of sounds with a greater degree of accuracy.[4] [5]

It has also been suggested that the hearing-aid industry has been ignoring another field which possesses great possibilities—the manufacture of small portable amplifiers which could be used to amplify a very weak voice.[6]

24.4 Other electronic aids for the deaf

In 1957, Djourno, a professor of electrophysiology of the Faculty of Medicine in Paris, developed a revolutionary surgical technique which may eventually be used to restore hearing to thousands of deaf people. He prepared a tiny coil of silver wire and embedded it in plastic for placement behind the temporal bone of a patient whose eardrums had been damaged beyond any possibility of surgical repair. One of the wires of the coil was attached to the auditory nerve. After the patient had recovered, he was tested by means of a microphone connected to a primary coil. When words were spoken into the microphone, the patient reported hearing incomprehensible whistling noises. Within a short while, he was able to identify several simple words. According to the explanation given, the microphone current in the primary coil induced voltages and currents in the silver secondary coil. This coil, in turn, transmitted to the auditory nerve tiny currents corresponding to the audio-frequency currents.

However, as the signals that now reached the patient's brain were not in an intelligible "code", the patient had to relearn how to hear. After several months of practice and study with a tape recorder, he was able to understand 75 per cent of the words spoken

to him. The same operation has since been performed successfully upon several other patients.

An interesting by-product of this experiment was the discovery that the patient could detect sonic vibrations above and below the normal range of human hearing. While normal adults do not hear sounds whose frequencies are much above 15 kc, the patient was able to hear sounds as high as 40 kc. Thus, a deaf man became the first person capable of hearing ultrasonic vibrations.[7] [8]

24.5 Audiometers

Audiometers are electronic precision instruments designed to test hearing acuity. An audiometer produces sounds whose frequency and intensity may be independently controlled in a definite and known manner.[9] All audiometric test results show a comparison between the average normal threshold of hearing acuity and that of the person being tested.

Early methods of measuring hearing. The earliest methods of measuring hearing involved the employment of the conversational voice, whispers, coin clicks, or watch ticks. These methods were rapid and inexpensive but not well standardized. Later on, tuning forks based on octave frequencies of 64, 128, 256, 512, etc. cycles per second were employed. This method of measuring hearing was fairly simple and cheap, but it suffered from the difficulty of standardizing the "standard blow" given to the forks.

24.6 Group-testing audio-meters

In 1925, Western Electric developed the 4A Group Audiometer at the request of the American Society for the Hard of Hearing. The purpose of this device was to identify those children who had impaired hearing. The instrument was designed to be capable of making a dependable test of hearing on a large scale in a reasonably short period of time. Since then, it has been replaced by Models 4B and 4C, which are similar in principle. A spring-wound magnetic phonograph delivers an output to 40 headphones. A record is played which contains two-digit numbers recorded at successively lower intensities. The children being tested write the numbers that they hear on special blanks which are easily scored.

24.7 *Pure-tone audiometers*

The first widely used model of electrical audiometer was the unwieldy and expensive two-way audiometer produced in the middle 1920's by Western Electric. In a pure-tone audiometer, alternating current of the desired frequency is generated by an electronic oscillator, whose frequency is controlled by turning a dial (Fig. 24-14). Some models provide the fixed octaves of the old tuning forks; others allow the selection of any intermediate frequency or permit a continuous sweep through the entire frequency range. The intensity of the sound output is regulated by means of another dial, which is usually graduated in 5-decibel steps. The electric current produces sound

Courtesy, Sonotone Corp.
FIG. 24-14. SONOTONE MODEL 91D PURE-TONE AUDIOMETER

in a receiver that is held against the ear of the subject. As a wide range of intensities, up to 120 decibels, is available, any useful remnant of hearing can be detected.

An important convenience is a special switching circuit that causes the test tone to fade in or out without any extra audible click. Another useful accessory is a masking circuit that generates a buzz to be delivered to the ear opposite the one being tested. This may be necessary if the ear being tested is quite hard of hearing and the opposite ear hears well by bone conduction. Still another accessory is a bone-conduction receiver that delivers vibrations to the mastoid bone instead of generating sound waves in a headphone. The same electrical circuits are employed, with no changes except in the scale on which the amount of hearing loss is read.

The heart of the audiometer is neither the generator that determines the frequency nor the attenuator that controls the intensity, but the receiver which converts electrical energy into acoustical energy. The calibration of an audiometer is initially set up by adjusting the scale on which the number of decibels of hearing loss is read, so that when the dial is set to zero, an average ear will just be able to hear the tone.

24.8 *Audiograms*

The audiogram is a graphic summary of the measurements of hearing loss. The audiometer readings are plotted on prepared charts (Fig. 24-15). Normal hearing at all frequencies is represented by a straight horizontal line near the top, and hearing loss is plotted downward. The audiogram shows at a glance whether the hearing loss is equal at all frequencies, or whether the high tones or the low tones are particularly

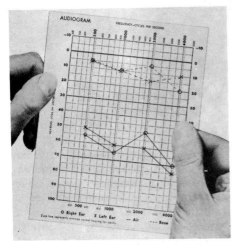

Courtesy, Sonotone Corp.

FIG. 24-15. TYPICAL AUDIOGRAM

affected. The audiogram is very useful to the otologist in making a diagnosis, and audiograms taken periodically form an accurate record of the improvement or deterioration of hearing.

Industrial audiometric testing. Many large industrial organizations have adopted a policy of administering preplacement audiometric tests to pros-

pective employees. The audiograms produced by these tests serve as a placement guide to ensure that an employee is not placed in a situation where a hearing handicap might endanger his safety due to his inability to hear warning signals or might cause him to alienate customers by his inability to understand their questions or requests.

In some instances, a slight hearing loss might be used advantageously by assigning the employee to work in a noisy area where he would not experience as much fatigue as would a person with normal hearing. Finally, the audiogram provides the company with legal protection in the event a claim is later made that the employee's hearing has been damaged due to his being exposed to high noise levels during working hours. One writer states that the question of noise in industry is "the biggest single problem we have facing us under the Workman's Compensation Law today."[10] The audiogram can be used to prove or disprove the existence of a work-induced loss of hearing and to establish the degree of loss if it actually does exist.[11]

REFERENCES

1. H. Davis and others, "The Selection of Hearing Aids," *The Laryngoscope,* 56:85, Mar. 1946.
2. "Miniaturization Shrinks Hearing Aids," *Popular Electronics,* 5:103, Aug. 1956.
3. "Hearing Aids of the Eyeglass and Contour Types," *Consumer Bulletin,* 42:16-20, Jan. 1959.
4. "Stereo Hi-Fi Hearing Aid," *Popular Electronics,* 7:38, Aug. 1957.
5. "Binaural Hearing," *Radio-Electronics,* 28:8, Aug. 1957.
6. H. E. Marrows, "Marketing and Production Trends in the Semiconductor Industry," *Semiconductor Products,* 1:39, July 1958.
7. Pierre de Latil, "Electronic Ears for the Deaf," *Science Digest,* 44:15-19, Nov. 1958.
8. "Electronic Ears," *Radio-Electronics,* 29:6, Dec. 1958.
9. *Hearing Measurement and Speech Interpretation,* Sonotone Corp., Elmsford, N.Y., 1947, p. 9.
10. Nelson Hartz, "Sound, Noise and Hearing," *Instruments and Control Systems,* 33:249, Feb. 1960.
11. *Ears and Industry,* Maico Co., Minneapolis, Minn., 1957, p. 4.

25 - RADIO TRANSMITTERS

25.1 *History of radio transmission and broadcasting*

As early as 1864, James Clerk Maxwell predicted mathematically the probable existence and speed of propagation of electromagnetic radio waves (Fig. 25-1). From his investigations of the nature of light, he concluded that light was an electromagnetic wave. The wave front consisted of electrical vibrations at right angles to the direction of propagation and a magnetic force at right angles to the electric displacement

FIG. 25-1. JAMES CLERK MAXWELL

(Fig. 25-2). He also stated that if his reasoning was correct, different sources of disturbances should produce other electrical waves at frequencies different from those of light. They would not be visible, but it would be possible to detect them with appropriate instruments. Unfortunately, Maxwell did not live to see their discovery.[1]

The magnitude of this tremendous achievement of the unaided human mind was stated in 1939 by the British scientist Ernest Rutherford: "We should fittingly honor Maxwell as the great pioneer of radio communication, for he not only had the genius to foresee that electric waves must be produced, but had given (in 1864) the complete theory of their generation and propagation long before their existence had been suspected by science."[2]

25.2 *Contributions of Heinrich Hertz*

Almost 20 years later, and 10 years after Maxwell's death, the German physicist Hermann von Helmholtz suggested to his student Heinrich Hertz that he should attempt to obtain experimental proof of Maxwell's theory (Fig. 25-3). Hertz set to work testing Maxwell's original assumptions and ultimate conclusions. In one of his lectures on Maxwell's theory, he stated: "I am here to support the assertion that light of every kind is itself an electrical phenomenon—the light of the sun, the light of a candle, the light of a glow-worm."[3]

814

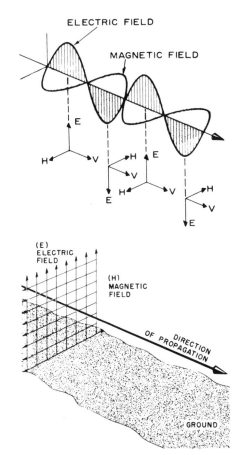

ELECTRIC FIELD

MAGNETIC FIELD

(E) ELECTRIC FIELD

(H) MAGNETIC FIELD

DIRECTION OF PROPAGATION

GROUND

FIG. 25-2. DIRECTION OF FIELDS AND PROPAGATION OF AN ELECTROMAGNETIC WAVE

FIG. 25-3. HEINRICH HERTZ

In 1887, Hertz demonstrated that rapid variations of electric energy could be projected into space in the form of electromagnetic radio waves similar to light and heat by connecting the terminals of an induction coil to two metal plates which acted as a capacitor (Fig. 25-4). The German physicist Feddersen had previously verified experimentally the oscillatory nature of the spark discharge of a charged capacitor, a phenomenon which had been predicted as early as 1847 by Helmholtz when he stated: "We assume that the discharge of a Leyden Jar is not a simple motion

of the electricity in one direction, but a backward and forward motion between the coatings..."[4] It might also be noted that a complete theoretical explanation of the oscillatory nature of the discharge of a Leyden Jar and

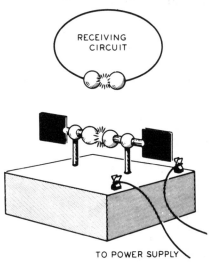

RECEIVING CIRCUIT

TO POWER SUPPLY

FIG. 25-4. APPARATUS USED BY HERTZ FOR PRODUCING ELECTROMAGNETIC WAVES

capacitor had been developed by Lord Kelvin by the year 1853.

By charging and discharging a capacitor at a very rapid rate, Hertz produced electromagnetic waves. These waves caused sparks to be produced in a nearby loop of wire that contained a small spark gap. Thus, Maxwell's electromagnetic theory of radiation was confirmed, and radio waves were produced for the first time by man.

Hertz discovered that these waves traveled with the speed of light. He measured their frequency and wavelength and discovered that their wavelength was considerably greater than that of visible light, being measurable in meters and yards rather than in fractions of an inch. They were also much more penetrating than light waves, passing easily through wood and stone. The waves that Hertz produced would today be classified as microwaves, since their frequencies were between 500 and 600 mc.

Hertz also demonstrated that the behavior of these waves greatly resembled that of light waves. He showed that they could be reflected by metal surfaces, and he used parabolic metallic mirrors to concentrate and project them. Hertz was also able to refract these waves with a prism made of pitch.[5]

Strangely enough, Hertz could see little practical use for his waves, and it was another scientist, Sir William Crookes, who first suggested in 1892 the possibility of using Hertz's waves or Hertzian waves for communication purposes. In talking about electromagnetic waves, Crookes stated: "Here is unfolded to us a new and astonishing world, one which it is hard to conceive should contain no possibilities of transmitting and receiving intelligence."[6]

25.3 Contributions of Guglielmo Marconi

The new waves were harnessed for commercial purposes by enlarging the plates of Hertz's capacitor. Guglielmo Marconi conceived the idea of substituting a system of wires called an antenna for one plate of the capacitor and using ground as the other plate (Fig. 25-5). A high-frequency induction coil was connected to this arrangement, and by placing a key between this coil and a battery, sparks could be produced between the antenna wires and ground. These sparks produced relatively powerful radio waves. In some of the early models of commercial receivers that were used in connection with these spark transmissions, the incoming radio waves operated a Branly coherer, which consisted of a primitive type of relay that rang a doorbell and produced dots and dashes.

FIG. 25-5. GUGLIELMO MARCONI

In 1896, Marconi transmitted radio signals that were picked up by receiving equipment located two miles away. Following his initial success, Marconi then began to study methods of increasing the distance over which radio waves could be detected. This undertaking met with adverse criticism from scientists who reasoned that since radio waves resembled light waves, the horizon must be the limit for radio waves as well as for light waves.

In 1899, Marconi extended the distance of radio transmission to 30 miles, and during the same year, regular radiotelegraph service was established across the English Channel. By 1901, Marconi had conducted successful trans-Atlantic tests, transmitting pulses of radio-frequency energy corresponding to the letter "S" from Cornwall in southwest England to St. John's, Newfoundland. In 1907, the first trans-oceanic radio service was established between Glace Bay, Nova Scotia, and Clifden, Ireland. As a result of this work, Marconi shared the 1909 Nobel Prize in physics with Karl Braun, one of the developers of the cathode-ray tube.

25.4 *Other pioneers of radio transmission*

Without discrediting Marconi's accomplishments, note may be made of the fact that as early as 1872, two years before the birth of Marconi, Mahlon Loomis, an American dentist, was granted a patent for a system of wireless telegraphy "employing an aerial used to radiate or to receive the pulsation caused by producing a disturbance in the electrical equilibrium of the atmosphere" (Fig. 25-6). Using kites as his aerials, and galvanometers as his detectors, by 1866 he was able to transmit signals over a distance of 14 miles (Fig. 25-7).

From his patent specifications, it is apparent that Loomis did not realize that his method of communication involved radio waves, and he considered his method to be similar to that used for wire telegraphy. Unfortunately, a simple detector such as the Branly coherer had not yet been invented, and Loomis' system was deemed impractical at that time. Congress refused to raise

Courtesy, *Radio Electronics*

FIG. 25-6. DR. MAHLON LOOMIS

money to assist him, and two companies organized by him were wiped out by stock-market crashes and fires. Loomis died soon afterwards without realizing his ambitions of developing a world-wide communication system employing his ideas.[7][8]

It has also been claimed that Amos E. Dolbear, an American physicist, developed an electrostatic wireless telephone system using an elevated aerial at least ten years before Marconi did (Fig. 25-8). This system was capable of operating over a distance of 12 miles.[9] In March 1882, he demonstrated his electrostatic telephone in London before the meeting of the Society of Telegraph Engineers and Electricians. This was probably the first time that the human voice had been transmitted by radio. He was issued two patents on this invention but made no attempt to commercialize it. According to one writer, Dolbear had a wireless transmitter in 1883 that was equal to and almost identical with the one that Marconi demonstrated in 1896.[10]

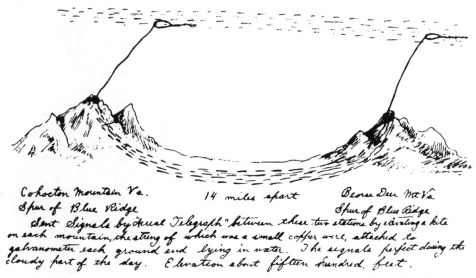

Cohocton Mountain Va.   *14 miles apart*   *Bears Den Mt Va*
Spur of Blue Ridge   *Spur of Blue Ridge*
   Sent Signals by "Aerial Telegraph" between these two stations by twirling a kite
on each mountain, the string of which was a small copper wire, attached to
galvanometer each ground end lying in water. The signals perfect during the
cloudy part of the day. Elevation about fifteen hundred feet.

Courtesy, *Radio-Electronics*

FIG. 25-7. THE FIRST ANTENNAS
Reproduction from Dr. Mahlon Loomis' sketch, 1865.

Another claim has been made by the Russians, who, at an exhibition held in New York City in 1959, labeled a bust of Alexander S. Popov or Popoff with the title "The Inventor of Radio". They claim that he established a radio station at Kronstadt in 1897, that in 1899 he established wireless communication between the battleship Admiral Aprasin and a coast-based station 45 miles away, and that in 1900 his equipment was used for the first radio rescue at sea when a group of fishermen who were marooned on an ice floe in the Gulf of Finland were rescued by a wireless message transmitted to the icebreaker Ermak. They also claim that in 1901, the Russian army used Popov's equipment, and that in 1903 a commercial wireless service was established that employed his equipment.[11] [12]

The claim has also been made that it was the British physicist, Sir Oliver Lodge, who first patented, in 1898, the idea of placing adjustable coils in the antenna circuits of transmitters and receivers to provide selectivity by enabling one circuit to be placed in tune

Courtesy, *Radio-Electronics*

FIG. 25-8. AMOS EMERSON DOLBEAR

with the other (Fig. 25-9). Marconi did not patent his four-circuit tuning system until 1900. Lodge's patent was purchased by the Marconi Company in 1912. In 1943, the United States Supreme Court concluded that an American scientist, John Stone, had actually patented a tuning circuit several months before Marconi had.

Despite these various claims of prior discovery, few will dispute the statement made in an opinion handed down in 1914 by Judge Veeder of the United States District Court, Eastern District of New York, that: "I find that the evidence establishes Marconi's claim that he was the first to discover and use any practical means for effective telegraphic transmission and intelligible reception of signals produced by artificially formed Hertz oscillations."[13]

25.5 *Other contributions of Marconi*

In 1924, Marconi opened the door to world-wide radio communication by discovering the effectiveness of shorter waves for long-distance communications. Prior to this time, the lower frequency and longer waves were believed to be the best. The builders of transoceanic transmitters put their faith in frequencies much lower than the ship-

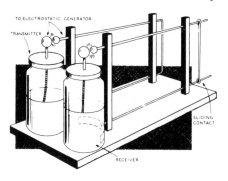

TO ELECTROSTATIC GENERATOR
TRANSMITTER
SLIDING CONTACT
RECEIVER

to-shore frequency of 500 kc. They generally employed frequencies between 50 and 150 kc, and the Germans even experimented with a 10-kc carrier wave. Marconi found that a 50-watt station on the 3 to 30-mc band could deliver a stronger signal over a distance of several thousand miles with greater ease than a 100-kilowatt, low-frequency station could.[14] Unlike the longer waves then in use, which were propagated as ground waves parallel with the earth, these waves were transmitted over much greater distances by means of reflections from the ionosphere in accordance with the theory postulated back in 1902 by Heaviside and Kennelly.[15]

25.6 *Radio broadcasting*

The first practical application of radio was in safeguarding life and property at sea. In 1900, Reginald Fessenden became the first person to transmit speech by wireless, voice-modulating a spark transmitter to produce a signal that was detected one mile away. In 1906, he broadcast a program of speech and music from Brant Rock, Mass., to amazed listeners on ships at sea. In 1907, Eugenia Farrar probably became the first important singer to broadcast a program via radio. She sang several songs which were broadcast by de Forest's transmitter which was located in his experimental laboratory in New York City.

Radio broadcasting as we know it today was made possible largely by the development of the vacuum tube by Fleming in 1904 and its improvement by de Forest in 1906. The first transmitter tube was developed by White of General Electric in 1915. It was used to modulate a 50-kilowatt Alexanderson high-frequency alternator located in New Brunswick (Fig. 25-10). During the

Courtesy, Radio Corporation of America

FIG. 25-10. LONG-WAVE ALEXANDERSON ALTERNATORS

same year, Western Electric, employing de Forest's audion tubes as both amplifiers and generators of radio waves, succeeded in transmitting the human voice from Arlington, Va., to Paris and to Honolulu (Fig. 25-11). This introduction of the vacuum-tube oscillator led to the eventual abandonment of high-frequency alternators and spark-gap transmitters.

The idea of broadcasting programs to the public probably originated in 1916, when David Sarnoff, who was later to become chairman of the board of RCA, sent a memorandum to the vice-president of the Marconi Wireless Telegraph Company of America. At that time, Sarnoff was assistant traffic manager of the Marconi Company. In his memorandum, Sarnoff stated: "I have in mind a plan of development

Courtesy, Western Electric Co., Inc.

FIG. 25-11. NAVY RADIO TOWERS AT ARLINGTON WHICH TRANSMITTED THE FIRST TRANSOCEANIC RADIOTELEPHONE MESSAGES TO HONOLULU AND PARIS

which would make radio a household utility in the same sense as the piano or phonograph. The idea is to bring music into the home by wireless...A radio-telephone transmitter having a range of, say, 25 to 50 miles can be installed at a fixed point where instrumental or vocal music or both are produced... The receiver can be designed in the form of a simple radio music box and arranged for seven different wave-lengths which would be changeable with the throwing of a single switch or the pressing of a single button...The same principle can be extended to numerous other fields, as for example, receiving lectures at home, which can be made perfectly audible; also events of national importance can be simul-taneously announced and received. Baseball scores can be transmitted in the air.... This proposition would be especially interesting to farmers and others in outlying districts removed from cities. By the purchase of a radio music box they could enjoy concerts, lectures, music recitals, etc., which may be going on in the nearest city within their radius."[16]

However, four years were to elapse before commercial broadcasting be-came a reality. In 1919, Frank Conrad, an engineer working for Westinghouse, built a transmitter and played recor-dings every Wednesday and Saturday evening, thus becoming radio's first disc jockey. He acquired a considerable audience. The rapid growth of this audience created quite a large market for electrical parts. Recognizing the commercial possibilities of this, Wes-tinghouse built station KDKA, Pitts-burgh, in 1920. According to records, this station was the first commercially licensed broadcast station, although radio historians have pointed out that in 1915, station WGI of Medford Hill-side, Mass., began broadcasting inter-mittent programs that were heard hundreds of miles away by ship radio operators at sea. Station KDKA began operations in November 1920 by broad-casting for the first time the results of a presidential election—the triumph of Harding over Cox.

25.7 The electromagnetic spectrum

The electromagnetic spectrum, ranging from the lowest frequency to the highest frequency, is as follows: ra-dio, infrared, visible light, ultraviolet, X-rays, gamma rays, and cosmic rays. The radio spectrum contains those fre-quencies which can be used for com-munication and similar purposes. Radio frequencies are usually measured in kilocycles and megacycles. As has been previously mentioned, a kilocycle is 1,000 cycles per second, whereas a megacycle is 1 million cycles per se-cond. The usable portion of the radio spectrum now covers the range from 10 kc to 300,000 mc. That portion of the spectrum from 550 kc to 1,600 kc has been set aside for commercial radio broadcasting and is therefore known as the broadcast band.

25.8 The Transmitter

A radio transmitter is a device for producing radio-frequency energy con-trolled or modulated by the intelligence to be transmitted. This modulation may be obtained by mechanical means such as the key of a continuous-wave trans-mitter, by means of sound energy as in the a-f modulator of a radiotelephone transmitter, or by means of visual im-ages such as those produced in the cam-era tubes of television broadcasting stations. Consequently, the essential components of a modern transmitter are an oscillator, one or more power amplifiers, a frequency multiplier if needed, a modulating device or keying system, and a power supply (Fig. 25-12).

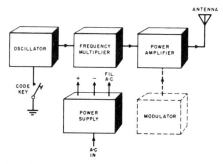

FIG. 25-12. BLOCK DIAGRAM OF A TRANSMITTER

25.9 *The oscillator*

The oscillator generates the carrier wave and determines the frequency of the transmitted signal. It may be a self-excited oscillator such as the Hartley, Colpitts, or electron-coupled oscillator, or it may be a crystal-controlled oscillator. In the early days of radio, the broadcasting of the harmonics produced by the oscillator and the following stages of certain broadcast transmitters caused considerable trouble and interference with other stations. However, in more recent times, the FCC has become so strict about insisting upon attenuation of these harmonics at the transmitter site that this trouble is seldom encountered unless one is unfortunate enough to be located very close to a powerful radio transmitter. In that instance, the only satisfactory procedure is to install a tuned circuit within the receiver that will act as a wave trap and absorb the energy of the undesired harmonic signal.[17]

25.10 *The buffer amplifier*

If an oscillator is followed immediately by a Class C power amplifier that is keyed, a varying load is placed upon the oscillator. This usually produces frequency instability. Consequently, the oscillator is often followed by a buffer amplifier (Fig. 25-13). The primary purpose of this amplifier is not amplification but the isolation of the oscillator from its load. Ideally, the buffer amplifier is a Class A amplifier.

25.11 *Frequency multipliers*

There is a limit to the highest frequency that can be produced by a crystal-controlled oscillator. Very thin crystals are required for the production of high-frequency signals. These crystals are therefore extremely fragile and liable to damage. A frequency-multiplier stage is usually employed in order to obtain a high-frequency output from a crystal oscillator (Fig. 25-14). The frequency multiplier is essentially a Class C amplifier which is biased considerably beyond cutoff (Fig. 25-15). This high bias results in distortion and the production of strong harmonics. If the tuned circuit or tank cir-

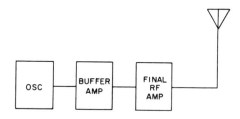

FIG. 25-13. BLOCK DIAGRAM OF TRANSMITTER WITH BUFFER AMPLIFIER

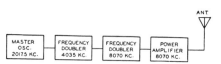

FIG. 25-14. BLOCK DIAGRAM OF A TRANSMITTER CONTAINING FREQUENCY DOUBLER STAGES

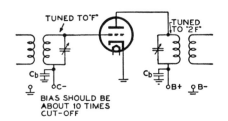

FIG. 25-15. AN R-F FREQUENCY-DOUBLER STAGE

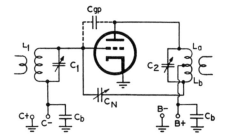

FIG. 25-16. SCHEMATIC DIAGRAM OF A PLATE-NEUTRALIZED AMPLIFIER

cuit of the plate is made to resonate with the frequency of the harmonic desired, the flywheel effect of this circuit will supply the remaining portion of the signal at the higher desired frequency. Since the plate and grid circuits are not tuned to the same frequency, the process of neutralization, which will be described in the following section, does not have to be employed with this type of amplifier.

25.12 *The power amplifier*

The power-amplifier stage of the transmitter is usually a Class B or C triode amplifier that is capable of dissipating large amounts of power. Since a triode radio-frequency amplifier has a tendency to oscillate, it is necessary to neutralize the amplifier. This is accomplished by feeding back to the grid a voltage which is equal to, and 180 deg out-of-phase with, the voltage that is fed back through the grid-to-plate capacitance of the tube. The out-of-phase feedback is accomplished by adjusting a variable neutralizing capacitor that is connected between the grid of the tube and a source of out-of-phase voltage (Fig. 25-16).

25.13 *The antenna*

The transmitting antenna is designed for the purpose of radiating into space the radio-frequency signal produced by the power-amplifier stage of the transmitter (Figs. 25-17 and 25-18).

One of the criteria used in selecting a transmitting antenna is efficiency. A good antenna should radiate a high percentage of the power supplied to it

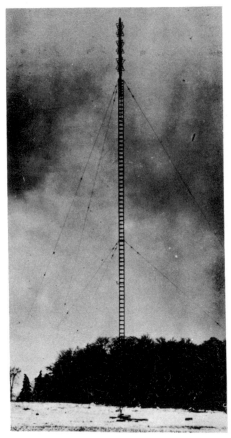

FIG. 25-17. BROADCAST TRANSMITTING ANTENNA ARRAY

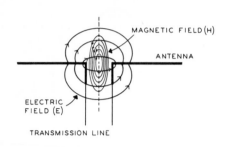

FIG. 25-18. ELECTRIC AND MAGNETIC FIELDS ABOUT AN ANTENNA

by the transmitter. In some instances, possession of directional character-istics may also be considered desirable.

Information concerning the directivity of an antenna is often conveyed by means of a graph on polar-coordinate paper. This graph resembles the one used to indicate the directional pattern of a microphone (Fig. 25-19). The antenna is at the center of the chart, and the graph shows the intensity of the electromagnetic radiation field at various angles to, but at a constant distance from, the antenna. The rounded projections representing maximum radiation are called lobes, whereas the points on the graph corresponding to low or no radiation are called nulls.

It must also be kept in mind that the radiation pattern is actually three-dimensional. In order to obtain a true picture of the entire radiation pattern, it may be necessary to employ three polar graphs depicting the radiation patterns in each of three mutually perpendicular planes.

Credit is usually given to Nikola Tesla for the invention of the antenna for the transmission and reception of radio-frequency signals. In 1893, he delivered a lecture at the Franklin Institute in which he employed the first modern radio diagrams showing a transmitter coupled to a transmitting

antenna and a receiving antenna coupled to a receiver.[18]

Many types of antennas are now in use. They vary as to size, shape, methods of feed, and electrical charac-teristics, but they all operate on the same basic principle—that a wire which is freely suspended in space will reson-ate electrically at one or more fre-quencies. The lowest frequency at which the wire will resonate is called its fundamental frequency. At this frequency, the wire is approximately one-half the length of the radio wave. The other frequencies at which the wire will resonate are harmonics or integral multiples of this fundamental fre-quency.

The constructional requirements of a transmitting antenna system are very critical. If the antenna is not properly constructed, or if the dimen-sions are not exact, the result will be low efficiency of radiation. Consequent-ly, the selection, design, and construc-tion of the transmitting antenna are of the utmost importance in insuring maximum reliability of a radio circuit. The transmitting antenna has a pro-nounced effect upon the strength of the signal picked up by the receiver. Satisfactory communication exists only when the strength of this receiver signal is sufficiently greater than the strength of the accompanying undesired signals, thereby making intelligible reception possible. This signal-to-noise ratio can be improved by increasing the power output of the transmitter. It is, however, more economical to increase this ratio by improving the design and construction of the transmitting antenna. A typical transmitting antenna system consists of three parts—a coupling device, feeders, and the antenna proper.

Antenna coupling. There are many methods employed to couple the final power amplifier to the transmission

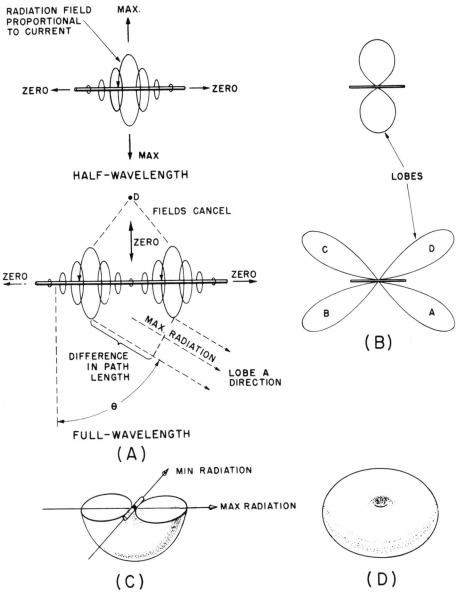

FIG. 25-19. NATURE AND EVOLUTION OF ANTENNA DIRECTIVITY AND DIRECTIVITY PATTERNS
(A) Half-wavelength antenna—one current loop—and full-wavelength antenna—two current loops; (B) radiation patterns for these two antennas; (C) three-dimensional view of the radiation patterns of a dipole mounted horizontally in space; (D) complete view of this pattern.

line or feeder. In direct coupling, the transmission line is connected through a small capacitor to the plate tank coil (Fig. 25-20). A second method of coupling is accomplished by means of a tuned transformer-secondary coil which

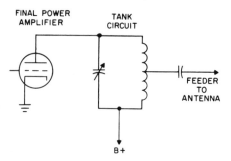

FIG. 25-20. DIRECT COUPLING OF FINAL POWER AMPLIFIER TO TRANSMISSION LINE

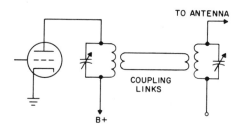

FIG. 25-22. LINK COUPLING

is inductively coupled to the plate tank coil (Fig. 25-21). This method is probably the one most widely used. When the antenna unit is located at some distance from the transmitter, link coupling is employed (Fig. 25-22). The plate tank is coupled to the transmission line by means of a few turns of wire placed around the low r-f voltage end of the tank coil.

25.14 Feeders and transmission lines

The purpose of a feeder or transmission line is to transfer the radio-frequency energy from the transmitter to the antenna with a minimum amount of loss (Fig. 25-23). There are two general types of feeders, resonant feeders and nonresonant feeders (Fig. 25-24).

Resonant or tuned feeders are the easiest kind to construct and to adjust. The electrical length of the wire bears a simple relationship to the wavelength

of the signal to be transmitted (Figs. 25-25 and 25-26). These feeders are characterized by some tendency to radiate energy.

Nonresonant feeders solve the problem of radiation by connecting the transmitter to a point on the antenna where the impedance of the antenna matches the impedance of the wire (Fig. 25-27). If there is a mismatch of impedances, some of the radio-frequency energy sent from the transmitter to the antenna is reflected back to the transmitter. The interaction of the original electrical wave with the reflected wave produces the phenomenon known as a standing wave. The formation of standing waves on the feeder is accompanied by the production of points of maximum and minimum voltage and current along the length of the feeder (Fig. 25-28). These maximum and minimum points, known as voltage and current loops and nodes respectively, are generally assosiated with the undesired radiation of some of the radio-frequency energy from the feeder instead of from the antenna. When these impedances are

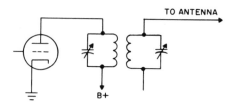

FIG. 25-21. INDUCTIVE COUPLING

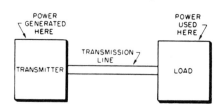

FIG. 25-23. USE OF A TRANSMISSION LINE

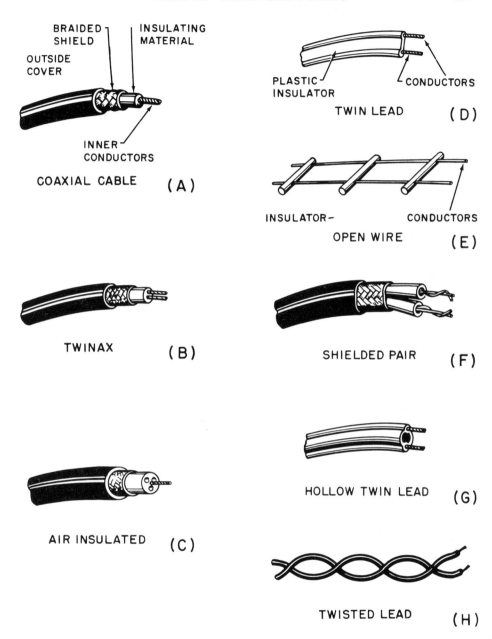

BRAIDED SHIELD
INSULATING MATERIAL
OUTSIDE COVER
INNER CONDUCTORS
COAXIAL CABLE (A)

TWINAX (B)

AIR INSULATED (C)

COAXIAL CABLE

PLASTIC INSULATOR
CONDUCTORS
TWIN LEAD (D)

INSULATOR
CONDUCTORS
OPEN WIRE (E)

SHIELDED PAIR (F)

HOLLOW TWIN LEAD (G)

TWISTED LEAD (H)

PARALLEL CONDUCTOR

FIG. 25-24. SOME COMMON EXAMPLES OF R-F TRANSMISSION LINES

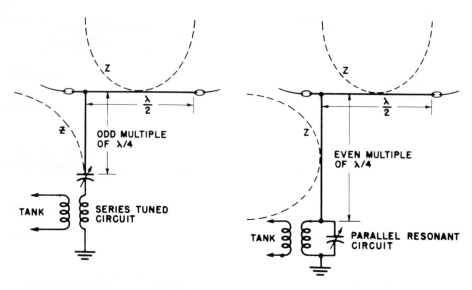

FIG. 25-25. SINGLE-WIRE RESONANT FEEDER SYSTEMS

properly matched, no standing waves will exist on the feeder line and there will be no radiation from the feeder (Fig. 25-29). Twisted-pair wires and coaxial cables are frequently employed as nonresonant feeders.

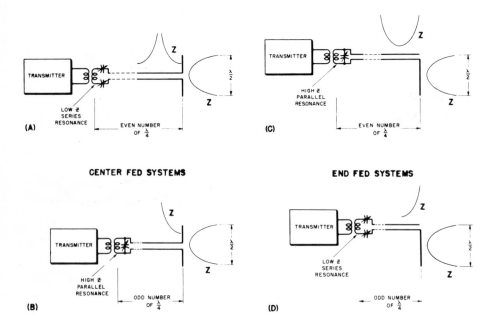

FIG. 25-26. TWO-WIRE RESONANT FEEDER SYSTEMS

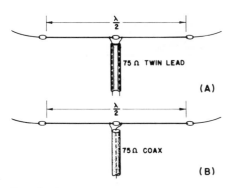

FIG. 25-27. NON-RESONANT TRANSMISSION LINES MATCHED TO A HALF-WAVE DIPOLE ANTENNA

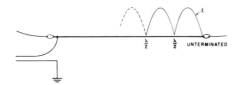

FIG. 25-28. PRODUCTION OF STANDING WAVES ON AN UNTERMINATED OR AN IMPROPERLY TERMINATED LINE

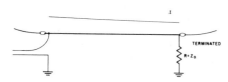

FIG. 25-29. ELIMINATION OF STANDING WAVES ON A LINE BY TERMINATING IT IN ITS CORRECT OR CHARACTERISTIC IMPEDANCE

25.15 *Types of antennas*

The two types of resonant antennas most frequently used are the Hertz half-wave antenna and the Marconi quarter-wave antenna. The flow of radio-frequency current through the conductors of either of these antennas sets up a rapidly expanding and contracting magnetic field. If the frequency of the current is sufficiently high, only a portion of the energy supplied to the field returns to the antenna when the field collapses. The remaining energy is radiated in waves with a frequency the same as that of the r-f current passing through the antenna (Fig. 25-30).

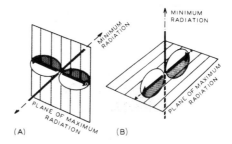

FIG. 25-30. RADIATION PATTERN ABOUT (A) HERTZIAN AND (B) MARCONI ANTENNAS

The Hertz antenna. The Hertz antenna is one-half wavelength in size and is insulated from ground. Usually mounted in a horizontal position, it is also known as a half-wave dipole or doublet antenna. The electrical length of such an antenna may be varied by placing an inductance or a capacitance in series with it. Additional inductance tends to increase the effective electrical length of the antenna, whereas additional capacitance produces the effect of shortening the antenna. The radio-frequency voltage is at a maximum at the two ends of the antenna and at a minimum in the center, whereas the opposite is true of the current.

Since the ends of the antenna have high voltages and low currents, they are characterized by high impedance. At the center, there exists low voltage and high current; consequently, the center usually possesses a relatively low impedance of about 72 to 73 ohms (Fig. 25-31).

The ungrounded half-wave antenna is often used for high-frequency transmission when directivity is not very important (Fig. 25-32). Moderate directivity can be achieved by employing an array of antennas. When operating at frequencies above 7 mc, the wave

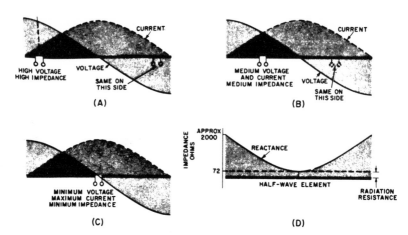

FIG. 25-31. VARIATION OF IMPEDANCE WITH LOCATION ALONG A HALF-WAVE ELEMENT

that is radiated by the dipole antenna is usually horizontally polarized (Fig. 25-33). This type of antenna is usually employed for the transmission and re-

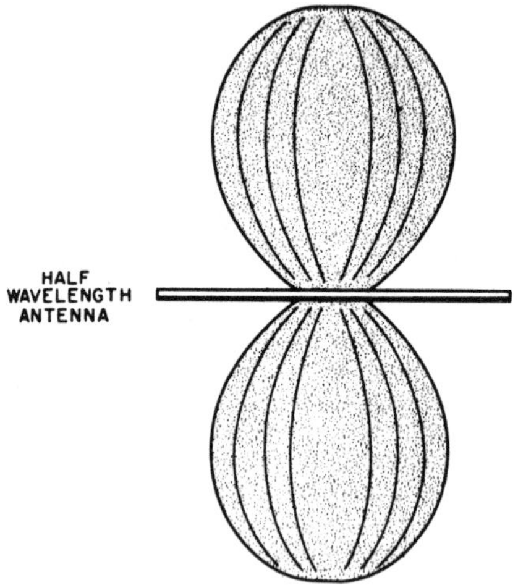

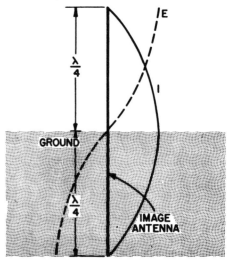

FIG. 25-32. RADIATION PATTERN OF A HALF-WAVE HORIZONTAL ANTENNA

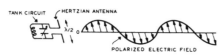

FIG. 25-33. HORIZONTALLY POLARIZED ELECTRIC WAVES EMITTED FROM A HERTZ HALF-WAVE DIPOLE

ception of signals within the range of 1.6 to 30 mc.

The Marconi antenna. The Marconi antenna is a vertical antenna one-quarter wavelength long that operates as a half-wave antenna (Fig. 25-34). It is able to operate in this manner because the bottom part of the antenna is connected to ground. The earth then supplies the additional quarter wavelength. The point which is grounded is effectively the center of a half-wave

FIG. 25-34. THE GROUNDED MARCONI ANTENNA

antenna and is therefore a point of low impedance, whereas the other ungrounded end is a point of high impedance. This type of antenna requires either a good ground connection or a substitute for ground which is known as a counterpoise.

The counterpoise is used to reduce energy loss produced by the passage of current through a ground system of low conductivity. It usually consists of a network of 15 or more wires, either buried or above ground, extending radially from the base of the antenna, like the spokes of a wheel. When transmitters are installed in vehicles, the chassis of the vehicle is usually employed as a counterpoise.

As the Marconi antenna has the advantage of being much shorter than the Hertz antenna, it is frequently used with military and vehicular transmitters for medium- and low-frequency transmission and reception where vertical polarization is desirable (Fig. 25-35). Grounded antennas are generally used at low frequencies where vertical polarization and a low angle of radiation are desired for aircraft, vehicular, and commercial broadcasting purposes (Fig. 25-36). Where directional characteristics are required, simple arrays of these antennas may be employed.

Terminated antennas. Antennas known as terminated antennas possess very high directional characteristics, being capable of radiating a relatively

narrow beam of radio waves in a desired direction. These terminated antennas are usually several wavelengths long and are terminated at one end by a power-dissipating resistor (Fig. 25-37). The antenna wires may be strung up in any one of several geometric shapes, such as a straight line, a V, a diamond, or a rhombus (Figs. 25-38 and 25-39).

As a result of the directional characteristics of a terminated antenna, a greater amount of energy is propagated in certain directions than in others. The ratio between the amount of energy propagated in these directions to the amount of energy that would be transmitted if the antenna were not directional is known as the antenna gain. Because of the property known as reciprocity, when a terminated transmitting antenna with a certain gain is used as a receiving antenna, its gain remains the same.

Beam antennas. A high degree of directivity may also be obtained by the use of a beam antenna. This variation of the Hertz antenna operates on the

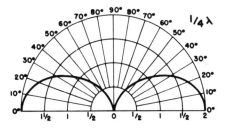

FIG. 25-36. CROSS-SECTION RADIATION PATTERN OF A GROUNDED MARCONI ANTENNA

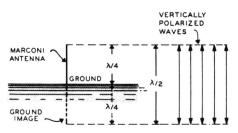

FIG. 25-35. VERTICALLY POLARIZED ELECTRIC WAVES EMITTED FROM A MARCONI ANTENNA

FIG. 25-37. TERMINATED LONG-WIRE ANTENNA AND ITS RADIATION PATTERN

FIG. 25-38. UNTERMINATED V ANTENNA AND ITS RADIATION PATTERN

principle that if a piece of wire approximately one-half wavelength long is brought near and parallel to a transmitting antenna, it will absorb some of the radiated energy and will then reradiate it. This reradiated energy may combine with the energy that is directly radiated by the antenna in such a manner as to modify the directional pattern of the antenna. The originally excited antenna wire is called the driven element, whereas the wire that reradiates some of this energy is known as the parasitic element (Fig. 25-40).

If the parasitic element is placed in front of the driven element, it is called a director, while if it is placed in back, it is called a reflector (Figs. 25-41 and 25-42). A director is slightly shorter than the driven element and is placed approximately 0.1 wavelengths away. A reflector is slightly longer than the driven element and is placed approximately 0.15 wavelengths away.

It is possible to employ complex combination antennas containing several directors and several reflectors (Fig. 25-43). The addition of more elements usually increases the directivity of the beam (Fig. 25-44). These beam antennas are frequently employed for television systems and for VHF point-to-point communication systems. The relatively small size of the elements required for these high-frequency signals makes it quite practical to design beam-antenna systems capable of being rotated in any desired direction.

25.16 *Energy radiation*

It is important to note that considerable amounts of energy may be radiated by the antenna of a transmitter and that this energy may sometimes produce surprising results. In a report issued in 1959 by the U.S. Air Force, the statement was made that the accidental destruction of both a Thor and a Polaris missile was caused by the triggering by commercial television signals of radio-controlled safety detonators located within the missiles.

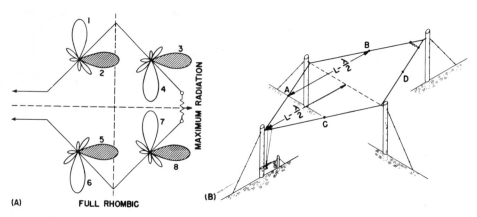

FIG. 25-39. THE FULL RHOMBIC ANTENNA, SHOWING LOBES AND THE DIRECTION OF MAXIMUM RADIATION

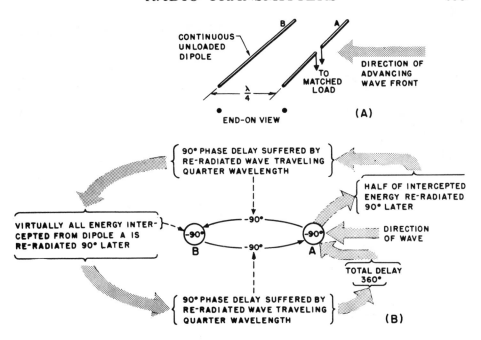

FIG. 25-40. HOW A PARASITIC ANTENNA WORKS

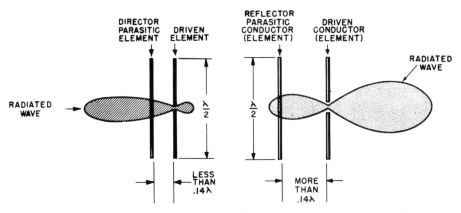

FIG. 25-41. A DIRECTOR AND THE RESULTING RADIATION PATTERN

FIG. 25-42. A REFLECTOR AND THE RESULTING RADIATION PATTERN

At approximately the same time, the Secretary of the Army complained that signals from station KSAY in San Francisco were interfering with the handling of ship cargoes at the Oakland Army Terminal. These signals were being absorbed by the giant steel cranes used in unloading ships, and the resulting electrical currents produced painful burns among the crew members. The Army Secretary has recommended to the FCC that the radio station change either its power or its transmitter location.

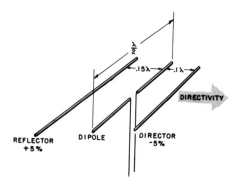

REFLECTOR
+5%

DIPOLE

DIRECTOR
-5%

DIRECTIVITY

FIG. 25-43. A THREE-ELEMENT PARASITIC ARRAY

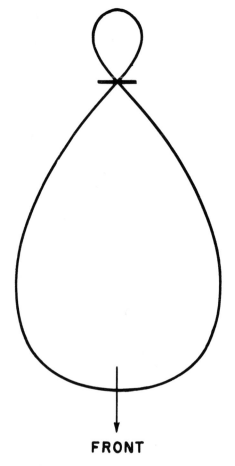

FRONT

FIG. 25-44. HORIZONTAL RESPONSE PATTERN OF A THREE-ELEMENT PARASITIC ARRAY

25.17 *Transmitter keying*

Keying a transmitter causes a signal to be radiated only during the time that the key is closed (Figs. 25-45 and 25-46). This type of radio transmission is usually referred to as continuous-wave or c-w transmission, and the entire process is called radiotelegraphy.

One method of keying is known as plate keying (Fig. 25-47). The key is placed between the negative side of the B or plate supply and ground. When the key is opened, no plate current will flow. The second method of keying places the key in the cathode circuit (Fig. 25-48). This method opens up both plate and grid circuits when the key is open. A third commonly employed method is known as grid-block keying (Fig. 25-49). In this method, a large resistor is placed in the cathode circuit, and the key is connected in parallel with this resistor. The value of resistance is large enough so that the flow of plate current through this resistor will develop sufficient cathode bias to produce practical cutoff. When the key is closed, the resistor is shorted out, and plate current will flow.

Except in very small transmitters, the oscillator is usually not keyed, since doing so tends to produce undesirable variations in the frequency of the radiated signal. Keying is usually accomplished in the power-amplifier circuit. As considerable danger is involved in keying such high-powered circuits directly, the keying is often accomplished by means of a keying relay which is operated by the key and powered by a low-voltage power supply (Fig. 25-50).

The sudden application and removal of power while keying causes high-frequency transient surges of current which tend to produce clicking or thumping noises in nearby receivers. In

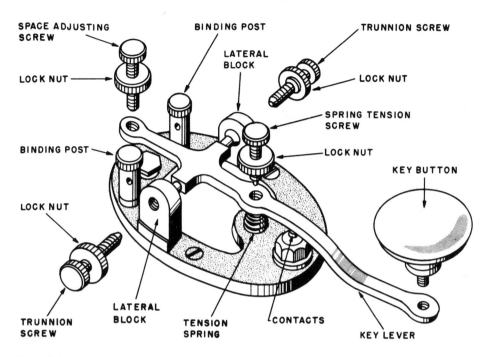

SPACE ADJUSTING SCREW

BINDING POST

TRUNNION SCREW

LATERAL BLOCK

LOCK NUT

LOCK NUT

BINDING POST

SPRING TENSION SCREW

LOCK NUT

KEY BUTTON

LOCK NUT

LOCK NUT

TRUNNION SCREW

LATERAL BLOCK

TENSION SPRING

CONTACTS

KEY LEVER

FIG. 25-45. DETAILS OF A TYPICAL HAND CODE KEY

order to prevent this type of interference, key-click filters, consisting of series chokes and shunt capacitors, are connected to the keying circuit (Fig. 25-51).[19]

25.18 Frequency-shift keying

Frequency-shift keying is another type of keying technique. In this system, which is closely related to frequency modulation, the transmitter operates at one frequency during the on, or marking intervals, and at a second frequency during the off, or spacing intervals. The difference between the two frequencies is generally in the range of 500 to 2,000 cps. This system of keying is employed in radioteletype transmission. It possesses the advantageous characteristic of frequency modulation in that it discriminates against all noise voltages that are weaker than the received signal. This characteristic is extremely useful in reducing errors in the teletype receiving system.

25.19 Radiotelegraphy compared with radiotelephony

It is obvious that continuous-wave radiotelegraphy suffers from the disadvantages of being rather slow and requiring the services of operators skilled in Morse code. On the other hand, radiotelegraphy possesses several compensating advantages which frequently make its employment extremely desirable for amateur, military, and general communications purposes. Among these advantages are the following:

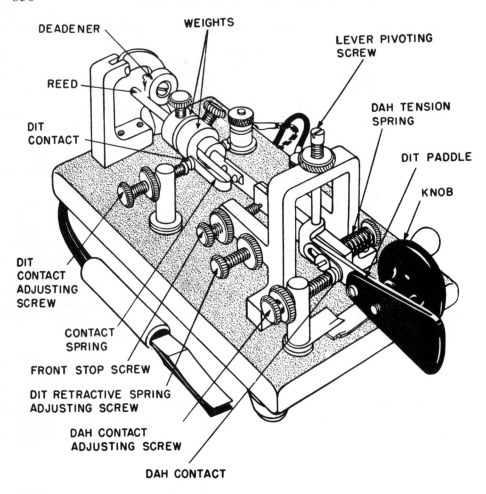

FIG. 25-46. TYPICAL SEMI-AUTOMATIC KEY OR BUG

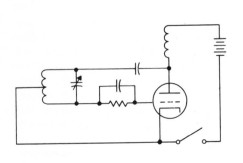

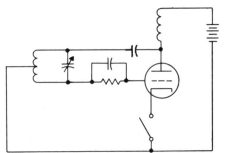

FIG. 25-47. PLATE KEYING OF AN OSCILLATOR

FIG. 25-48. CATHODE KEYING OF AN OSCILLATOR

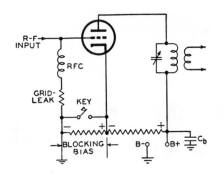

FIG. 25-49. GRID-BLOCK METHOD OF TRANS-
MITTER KEYING

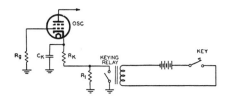

FIG. 25-50. KEYING A TRANSMITTER OSCILLA-
TOR BY USE OF A KEYING RELAY

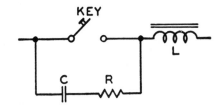

FIG 25-51. A KEY-CLICK FILTER

1. A radiotelegraph transmitter is smaller and simpler than a radiotelephone transmitter of the same power rating.

2. A radiotelegraph transmission covers a very narrow frequency range. Consequently, within a given frequency band, it is possible to operate many more radiotelegraph transmitters than radiotelephone transmitters, thus providing more channels of communication.

3. The transmission range of a radiotelegraph transmitter is much greater than that of a radiotelephone transmitter. When code signals from a distant location are audible, they are usually intelligible. On the other hand, speech transmitted from the same location may be audible but unintelligible.

4. Equipment designed to receive code signals may be made extremely selective with the aid of crystal filter circuits. These enable the receiver to reject a great deal of the static and interference frequently associated with the reception of a radiotelephone signal. This use of the crystal filter dates back to the middle 1930's. The man associated with this development is James Lamb. In 1959, his contributions received recognition when the American Radio Relay League awarded him its annual Merit Award.[20]

25.20 Improved radiotelegraph-receiving equipment

In recent years, special equipment has been developed to insure greater communication reliability and to minimize time-wasting repeating of messages. An example of this type of equipment is the Trak Static Rejector (Fig. 25-52), which performs the following functions:

1. An amplitude-limiter circuit clips high-amplitude noise pulses.

2. A spectrum-suppression circuit operates on the audio output of the c-w receiver on the principle that the desired code signal will appear on only one frequency whereas impulse noise will occupy a wider spectrum. It employs filters to analyze the audio spectrum of the receiver and then uses noise sideband energy to generate a cancel-

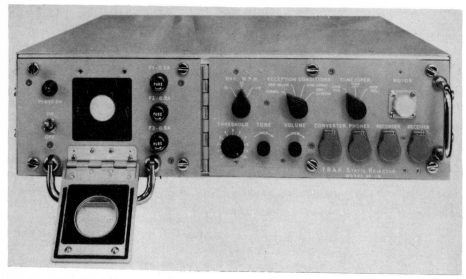

FIG. 25-52. TRAK STATIC REJECTOR

lation signal whenever noise impulses occur (Figs. 25-53 and 25-54).

3. When the device is set to the approximate word-per-minute rate of the received signal, it blocks much of the impulse noise by rejecting all impulses whose duration is less than half the length of a dot.

4. Whenever the receiver drifts from its correct frequency, an error signal is sent to a magnetic servo amplifier. This operates a reversible motor that applies correction to the tuning shaft of the receiver. This automatic-frequency-control circuit maintains a tuning accuracy of plus or minus 15 cps.[21]

25.21 *Radiotelephone transmitters*

A radiotelephone transmitter is designed to convey intelligence by impressing an audio signal upon a radio-frequency carrier wave. This type of transmitter requires all of the components found in a c-w transmitter except for the key, and requires in addition microphones, a-f amplifiers, and a modulator (Fig. 25-55).

25.22 *Principles of radio broadcasting*

A microphone in the broadcasting station converts sound waves into electrical impulses that possess the same characteristics as the originating sounds (Fig. 25-56). These impulses are sent over wires to the transmitting station (Fig. 25-57) where they are amplified millions of times before being impressed upon the carrier wave. The intensity and frequency of the carrier wave are constant (Fig. 25-58). As this wave, by itself, does not transmit music or speech, it is varied to correspond with the fluctuations of the speech or music received at the microphone in a process called modulation. In a standard amplitude-modulated (AM) broad-

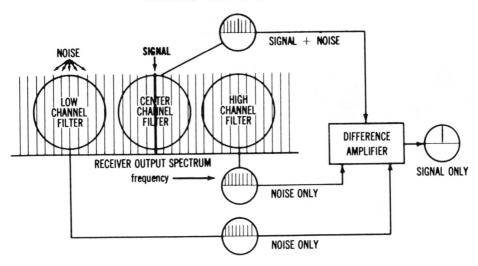

Courtesy, Trak Electronics Co., Inc.

FIG. 25-53. HOW THE STATIC REJECTOR WORKS

The static rejector is a demodulator. Its two level d-c output is so polarized that it is more positive when there is an output tone from the receiver. Audio tones are also reconstructed for aural monitoring. Noise is minimized by three processes; (a) Filters analyze the audio spectrum at the signal frequency and on both sides of it. Since the desired code signal appears at only one frequency, while impulse noise will occupy a wider spectrum, the rejector uses noise "sideband" energy to generate a cancellation signal whenever noise impulses occur at one or both sides of the desired frequency; (b) signals are limited and clipped; (c) short duration pulses are eliminated from the output by an adjustable low-pass filter.

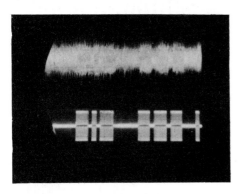

Courtesy, Trak Electronics Co., Inc.

FIG. 25-54. UNRETOUCHED OSCILLOGRAMS SHOWING CW SIGNAL BEFORE GOING THROUGH THE TRAK STATIC REJECTOR (ABOVE) AND AFTER GOING THROUGH (BOTTOM)

cast, the audio waves are impressed upon the carrier wave in such a manner as to cause the amplitude or power of the carrier wave to vary in accordance with the audio waves. This is known as

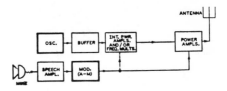

FIG. 25-55. BLOCK DIAGRAM OF AN AM RADIO-TELEPHONE TRANSMITTER

amplitude modulation. In frequency modulation (FM), the amplitude of the carrier remains unchanged, but the frequency is varied.

25.23 *Amplitude modulation*

In amplitude modulation, the amplitude of the radio-frequency carrier wave is varied at an audio rate by a modulator (Fig. 25-59). A modulator is really a special type of audio frequency power amplifier that is capable of supplying sufficient undistorted

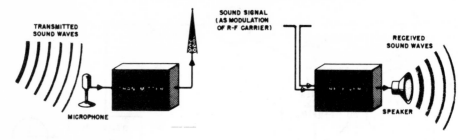

FIG. 25-56. SIMPLE RADIO BROADCASTING AND RECEIVING SYSTEM

audio power to produce effective modulation. The effect of amplitude modulation is to produce a modulated carrier wave whose variations in amplitude are proportional to the variations in amplitude of the modulating audio waves.

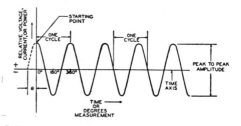

FIG. 25-58. REPRESENTATION OF AN UNMODULATED CARRIER WAVE

FIG. 25-57. A BROADCAST TRANSMITTER

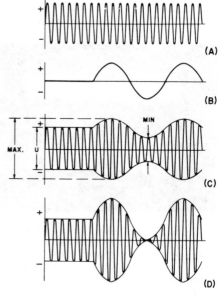

FIG. 25-59. NATURE OF AMPLITUDE MODULATION

(A) unmodulated carrier; (B) modulating signal; (C) modulated carrier, low modulation percentage; (D) modulated carrier, high modulation percentage.

This was the first method of modulation devised; it is still widely used for broadcast and communication purposes.

It may be noted that in the process of modulation, signal frequencies are produced which were not present in the input. Thus, modulation is actually a type of nonlinear distortion that is produced by impressing signal voltages upon nonlinear circuit elements such as vacuum tubes, saturated iron-core inductances, galena crystals, and special copper-oxide rectifiers known as Varistors (Fig. 25-60). The stage that is generally called the modulator is actually an a-f amplifier that is used to drive the

non-linear element in which the distortion and modulation are to be produced.

The modulator tube is usually connected to the plate circuit of the r-f amplifier stage to be modulated; this method is known as Heising constant-current plate modulation (Fig. 25-61). The audio-frequency modulating voltage is usually applied to the plate of the final radio-frequency amplifier stage. However, modulation may also be accomplished by injecting the audio-frequency voltage on the cathode, the control grid, the screen grid, or the suppressor grid of the radio-frequency amplifier (Figs. 25-62 to 25-65).[22][23] If the modulator is connected to the plate circuit of the final radio-frequency amplifier stage, this is known as high-level modulation.

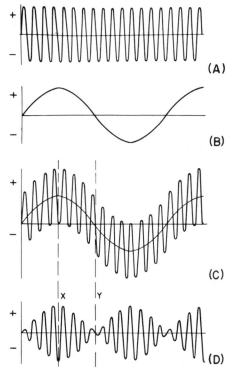

(A)

(B)

(C)

(D)

FIG. 25-60. EFFECTS PRODUCED BY LINEAR AND NON-LINEAR ELEMENTS

(A) Unmodulated carrier wave; (B) audio modulating signal; (C) effect of impressing both simultaneously upon a linear resistor; (D) effect of impressing both simultaneously upon a non-linear load.

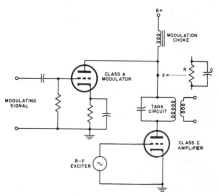

FIG. 25-61. BASIC HEISING MODULATION SYSTEM

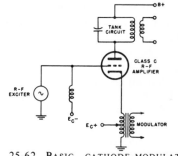

FIG. 25-62. BASIC CATHODE-MODULATION SYSTEM

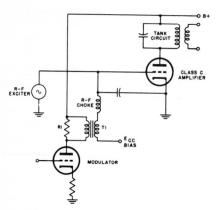

FIG. 25-63. TYPICAL CONTROL-GRID MODULA-
TED POWER-AMPLIFIER CIRCUIT

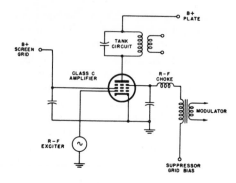

FIG. 25-65. SUPPRESSOR-GRID MODULATION OF
AN RF PENTODE

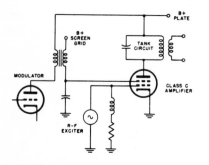

FIG. 25-64. SCREEN-GRID MODULATION OF A
TETRODE

Low-level modulation is produced
when the modulator is connected to any
other circuit of the final r-f amplifier,
such as the control-grid circuit, or when
the modulator is connected to any circuit of any stage preceding the final r-f
amplifier. Low-level modulation possesses the advantage of requiring relatively
little audio modulating power. Its disadvantages are low operating efficiency
and relatively low power output.

The maximum permissible percentage of modulation is 100 per cent. At
100 per cent modulation, the amplitude
of the r-f carrier rises to double its unmodulated value one moment and sinks
to zero the next (Fig. 25-66). Increasing

the percentage of modulation beyond
this point will produce distortion. The
percentage of modulation may be defined as the ratio, expressed in a percentage, of half of the difference between
the maximum and minimum amplitudes
of modulated wave to the average amplitude of that wave.

An overmodulated transmitter will
radiate harmonics which will cause
interference over a wide band of frequencies. Many transmitters therefore
contain either automatic-modulation-
control or speech-clipping circuits.

The automatic-modulation-control
or volume-compression circuit permits
constant gain in the audio-frequency
amplifier circuit until the input signal
voltage reaches a certain level. When
the signal strength exceeds this level,
the gain of the audio-frequency amplifier decreases rapidly.

The speech-clipping or speech-
limiting circuit clips off the peaks of
very-high-amplitude signals, reducing
their amplitudes to those of the average
peaks of audio-frequency signal voltages. Both circuits are effective in reducing the probability of overmodula-
ting the carrier wave. However, by
reducing the amplitudes of the peak
audio voltages, they reduce the dynamic
range of the signal being transmitted,

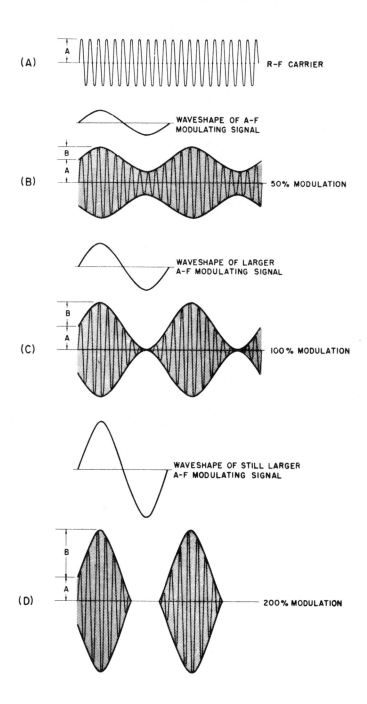

FIG. 25-66. MODULATION ENVELOPE WAVEFORMS

thus affecting adversely the fidelity of the signal that is reproduced at the receiver.

When a carrier wave is amplitude-modulated by a group of audio signals, such as those which correspond to voice or music, a group of additional signal frequencies called sidebands will be produced (Fig. 25-67). These sidebands are frequency bands on either side of the carrier frequency, within which fall the frequencies of the new waves produced by the process of modulation. The intelligence or signal is carried entirely by these sidebands. The carrier wave of an amplitude-modulated signal conveys no intelligence and produces no sound in the receiver. The existence of these sidebands was first demonstrated by H. D. Arnold in 1915.

When the carrier wave is modulated 100 per cent, 50 per cent additional power is added to the signal, and the antenna current is increased by 22.5 per cent. This additional power is the result of the production of new sideband frequencies, which are generally 5 kc above and 5 kc below the carrier frequency when the maximum frequency of the audio modulating signal is 5,000 cps. Thus, in order to prevent interference, each station requires a channel that is 10 kc wide.

25.24 *Single-sideband transmission*

It did not take long for the early radio engineers to discover that amplitude modulation is inherently a wasteful and inefficient method of radio communication. They soon learned that all of the necessary intelligence is contained in one of the sidebands. Yet, the radiated AM signal contains a duplicate of this sideband carrying the same information, as well as a carrier wave that carries no intelligence. The AM carrier is needed only for modulation and demodulation as a reference frequency; it is not required otherwise, since, as has been previously mentioned, it carries no intelligence. The entire AM signal transmitted power is six times greater than that of the single sideband, and it occupies twice as much of the spectrum bandwidth as the single sideband does.

Since the carrier itself, which accounts for at least two-thirds of the power of a fully modulated signal, carries no intelligence, and since one sideband contains the same amount of intelligence as the other, considerable power and spectrum space can be saved by suppressing the carrier and one of the sidebands at the transmitter. This method of transmission, called single-sideband or SSB transmission, saves approximately 70 per cent of the transmitted power and reduces by over 50 per cent the width of the channel required for broadcasting, thus improving the signal-to-noise ratio at the receiver.

In addition, since the selectivity of the receiver can be made very high, there is a corresponding reduction in the strength of the interfering signals that would normally be picked up by a less selective receiver with wider-bandpass characteristics. The SSB system

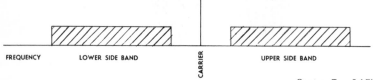

FREQUENCY   LOWER SIDE BAND   CARRIER   UPPER SIDE BAND

Courtesy, Tung-Sol Electric, Inc.

Fɪɢ. 25-67. Lᴏᴡᴇʀ ᴀɴᴅ Uᴘᴘᴇʀ Sɪᴅᴇʙᴀɴᴅs

has a signal-to-noise ratio that is eight times as great as that of a fully modulated conventional system for the same amount of peak power. As a result, this SSB system may produce a received signal that is from 6 to 16 db stronger than the one produced by a comparable conventional double-sideband system, and a 50 watt SSB transmitter can provide the same coverage as that of a standard AM transmitter that is rated at several hundred watts.[24][25][26] Thus, in 1957, when three B-52 bombers circled the globe, their SSB transmitters enabled them to maintain almost constant communication with SAC Headquarters near Omaha, Neb. Even at times when conventional AM transmission was not usable because of interference, SSB reception was loud and clear.[27]

Since SSB transmission is accompanied by a reduction in the average power of the final r-f stage, a high-power modulator stage is not required, and substantial reductions in power input, weight, and cost are effected. In addition, there is a greater amount of freedom from the distortion frequently encountered with conventional AM signals that results from the selective fading of the various sidebands of the carrier.[28]

At the transmitter, the carrier is eliminated or suppressed by a type of circuit called a balanced push-pull modulator circuit (Fig. 25-68). This is essentially just a push-pull amplifier in which the carrier signals fed to the two grids are in phase with each other, rather than being 180 deg out of phase as in a conventional push-pull amplifier. The tubes are biased on a nonlinear portion of their characteristic curves so that modulation of the carrier occurs. The audio signal develops practically no output voltage, the carrier is cancelled out in the resonant load circuit, and only the upper and lower sideband signals are developed across the load-circuit. The undesired sideband is eliminated by means of a filter circuit. Depending upon the frequency of the SSB signal, this filter may be either of the conventional L-C (inductor-capacitor) type, crystal type, or mechanical (magnetostriction) type (Fig. 25-69).

If desired, the resulting SSB signal may then be transposed to a higher operating frequency by using mixer circuits to heterodyne or beat this signal against higher frequency carriers. It may also be noted that there is a newer method of producing a SSB signal that is called the phasing method, which eliminates the need for mixer stages. However, this method involves two balanced-modulator stages and several

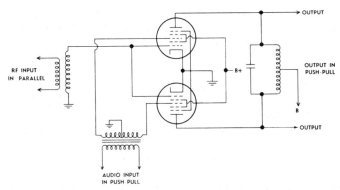

Courtesy, Tung-Sol Electric Inc.

FIG. 25-68. TWO-TUBE BALANCED MODULATOR CIRCUIT

FIG. 25-69. EMPLOYING A FILTER TO ELIMINATE THE UNDESIRED SIDEBAND

In the "filter" method, the RF signal is generated at low frequencies and after the carrier has been eliminated, a sharp filter is used to eliminate one of the sidebands. If ordinary LC circuits are used, this must be done at very low frequencies and the required circuit Q's are difficult to attain. Mechanical filters are employed very satisfactorily in the frequency range from 250 to 500 kc and crystal filters in the frequency range from 100 kc to several megacycles. The signal is then heterodyned up to the desired frequency.

complicated phase-splitting circuits which will not be described here.[29]

At the receiver, the carrier frequency is restored by means of a local oscillator. This carrier can be inserted at any point between the antenna and the second detector, but it is generally injected either at the receiving-antenna input terminals or at one of the i-f amplifier stages.[30] In order to avoid distortion and to obtain intelligible reproduction of speech, this oscillator must generate a signal whose frequency is within 30 cps of the original carrier frequency. If telephone-like quality is to be obtained, this error must be reduced to 20 cps, while if excellent fidelity is required, this frequency error must not exceed 10 cps. The voltage delivered by this oscillator must be 5 to 10 times greater than that delivered by a beat-frequency oscillator that is used for c-w detection.[31]

The main disadvantage of SSB transmission is the complexity of the equipment needed to maintain the high degree of frequency stability required and that is also needed to remove the sideband at the transmitter and to restore the carrier wave at the receiver. Consequently, in the past, SSB transmission has usually been employed by military and commercial communication agencies in long-distance carrier-current telephone systems and in transoceanic radiotelephone circuits, where the saving in channel space and the economy of power justified the use of such relatively complex equipment.

25.25 Historical background of single-sideband transmission

The employment of SSB radiotelephone transmission dates back to 1915, when J. R. Carson of the American Telephone and Telegraph Company, who is known as the father of single sideband, obtained a patent on a SSB system. Within the next few years, he demonstrated that the two sidebands were mirror images of each other and contained identical information. He also showed that although most of the power radiated by the antenna was contained in the carrier, this wave carried no useful information.

In 1923, Carson received a patent for a SSB balanced-modulator system that eliminated the carrier and one sideband. During that same year, experiments with single sideband succeeded in bringing about voice communication between New York and London and several ships at sea, and a reliable system of SSB communication was established between Amsterdam and Java.

In the United States, the first commercial application was in connection with carrier-current land-line telephone circuits. During the year 1927, RCA and the American Telephone and Telegraph Co. developed a SSB system that spanned the Atlantic from New York to London. In 1928, the first commercial short-wave trans-Atlantic SSB radio-telephone circuit was placed in operation.

Very little additional progress was made until the entry of the United States into World War II. The various military services required more radio channels than were available. In order to help meet this need, American Telephone and Telegraph cooperated with the military forces in developing equipment furnishing SSB circuits for radiotelephone and radioteletype applications. This activity resulted in the development of a system of single-sideband generation that was more practical and less expensive than the method previously used. In addition, at the receiving end, the equipment was stabilized to a degree never before realized. This encouraged amateurs to experiment with single sideband, and as a result of their experiences, considerable progress in SSB technique was achieved.

25.26 Recent developments and trends in single-sideband transmission

Today, the bulk of military point-to-point communication is handled by single sideband. A single SSB transmitter may provide as many as 14 communication circuits consisting of 2 radiotelephone channels and 12 teletype channels. Because of this economy, the military services have continued their expansion of the use of SSB circuits.[32]

For example, the Air Force is using single sideband for its global bombers and their jet refueling tankers all over the world. Within a relatively short time, the communication systems of all the Strategic Air Command's B-52 and B-47 bombers and KC-135 and KC-97 tankers were converted to SSB operation. The Air Force has also programmed construction of SSB ground stations in Louisiana, California, and Massachusetts.[33]

In 1957, the United States Department of the Army announced the installation in the Pentagon of a powerful SSB shortwave transmitter called the World Spanner. One model covers the range from 4 to 30 mc, while a second model covers the range from 20 to 65 mc. It is capable of transmitting 64 teletype or 4 radiotelephone channels at the same time. With ordinary design, this transmitter would have a power of 300 kilowatts. With the addition of SSB refinements plus a beam antenna, its effective power reaches 24,000 kilowatts. This transmitter is capable of beaming messages to any spot on earth, even through severe interference.[34]

In 1959, the United States Navy also moved into SSB communications. In August of that year, it announced that the first of 180 500-watt Navy-designed SSB transmitters, built by Collins Radio Company, had been installed aboard one of its ships. At that time it was stated that the remainder of the transmitters would be installed on other ships within the next two months.

Thus, by 1959 so much progress had been made in the development of SSB techniques, that it was estimated that by 1964 virtually all government services would be using this type of transmission instead of conventional AM transmission.[35]

25.27 Broadcast applications of single-sideband

During 1957, an AM station, WMGM of New York City, conducted broadcasting experiments with a modified compatible SSB system developed by L. Kahn of Kahn Research Laboratories, Inc., that required no modification of the receiver in order to receive the signals. In this compatible system, the carrier is transmitted along with the single sideband. This signal can be picked up merely by tuning the receiver in a normal manner for best signal response. A conventional AM receiver has a bandpass width of 10 kc. This limits the width of the conventional upper and lower sideband components to 5 kc each. With compatible SSB transmission, this limit is raised to 10 kc. Consequently, the frequency range of the audio components of the modulated signal is raised from a maximum of 5 kc to a maximum of 10 kc, and improved fidelity becomes possible with ordinary AM broadcast receivers.[36]

This compatible-single-sideband or CSSB system has also been used by the Voice of America station in Munich, Germany, to penetrate through Russian jamming. It has been found that the use of CSSB reduces interference and almost doubles the strength of the signal without increasing the size of the transmitter.[37] It is also possible that this CSSB system may be employed by AM broadcasting stations for stereo transmission. One sideband could be used for one of these stereo channels, the second sideband for the other. Of course, it would be necessary to use special circuits at the receiver to separate the two sidebands.[38] It may be noted that in January 1960, the Kahn Research Laboratories filed a petition with the FCC to permit AM radio stations to operate with CSSB.

Furthermore, as a result of recent technical developments which make it possible to produce a SSB signal with simpler equipment than was heretofore possible, there has been rapid growth in SSB activity among the radio amateurs of the United States. It is also apparent that single sideband is destined for increased use in the commercial services. It is quite possible that in order to conserve channels on the radio spectrum, the FCC may make the use of SSB transmission mandatory for all commercial services below 25 mc.[39] At any rate, present trends seem to indicate that, before many more years have passed, most commercial services will have adopted SSB operation.

25.28 Citizens band radio

In 1947, the FCC allocated a band of frequencies from 460 to 470 mc for communications applications by the general public. These applications, referred to as the Citizens Radio Service, provided for the first time a means by which citizens could engage in radio communication without the necessity of passing a license examination. This band of frequencies has consequently become known as the Citizens Band.

In 1958, this band was enlarged to include the 11-meter band, ranging from 27.23 mc to 29.96 mc.[40] Several companies have become engaged in manufacturing special transmitting and receiving equipment for use in this band.[41] [42]

There are four classes of service, A, B, C, and D. Class A employs frequencies between 462.55 mc and 466.45 mc, has a maximum power limit of 60 watts, and is for FM and AM personal radiotelephone communication only. There is no limit to the height of the antenna employed. In contrast, Class B, C, and D services are limited to 5 watts and the antennas may not extend more than 20 ft above the surface upon which they are mounted. Class B service operates in the frequency range between 462.525 and 475 kc and employs either AM or FM transmission for remote-control purposes. Class C service uses AM transmission for remote control only and operates on the frequency range between 26.965 and 27.255 kc. Class D service is used for AM radiotelephone only and employs frequencies ranging from 26.965 to 27.255 kc.

All transmitters used for Class A, B, or C services must be obtained from a manufacturer who has received FCC approval. Class D stations may use home-built transmitters, provided that they are crystal controlled, with an input power of 5 watts or less, and that the crystal frequency tolerance is 0.005 percent or less.[43] Class A and D services are now being widely used by workers in industrial plants, construction-project personnel, boating enthusiasts, farmers, ranchers, department-store employees, dairy and laundry-truck dispatchers, and for the purpose of paging doctors, nurses and other professional personnel.

The higher-frequency portion of the Citizens Band possesses several interesting propagation characteristics. Rain, snow, and fog have less effect upon transmission in this band than upon higher frequencies. Absorption by buildings and natural growths is also much less than exists with higher frequencies. This band is also less subject to fading and interference produced by signal reflections. The effects of atmospheric and man-made static are very low. Transmission is quite directional, and yet the beam width is great enough so that there is a fair degree of latitude in mounting an antenna system.

Transmission is limited to line of sight, which reduces interference between transmitters broadcasting on the same frequency. On this frequency band waveguides are not required, and relatively inexpensive transmission lines may be employed.

It is important to note that although a license is not required to purchase, install, or operate approved equipment for the Citizens Band, a station license is required for operation. Adjustments of the transmitter portion of the equipment that might result in improper operation when the unit is connected to an antenna must be made only by a person holding a First-Class or Second-Class Radiotelephone license.[44]

According to reports, the booming interest in Citizens Band Radio is breaking all records for operating grants. As of October 1959, over 300 applications were being processed daily and over 50,000 authorizations had been issued.[45] By August 1960, the number of authorizations had exceeded the 127,000 mark.

Unfortunately, in August 1958 the FCC gave in to pressure exerted by users of industrial, taxicab, and telephone radio services and allocated 6.550 mc of the 10-mc band to these services. A total of 2.450 mc was retained for use by the Citizens Service. The FCC also warned that 1.900 mc of this remaining allotment might be reallocated at a later time. Consequently, it appears that the future of Citizens Radio may be somewhat uncertain.[46] Furthermore, late in 1959, the FCC called attention to the fact that many users of the Citizens Radio Service were violating Part 19 of the FCC regulations which prohibits the use of Class D Citizens Band equipment for amateur type communications, calling unknown stations, attempting long-distance contacts, or contacting stations in amateur or other classes of services, except in emergencies. The FCC warned that a crackdown with widespread licence revocations would be in order if this abuse continued.[47] [48]

25.29 Frequency modulation

One of the great disadvantages of amplitude modulation is that static noises, which possess the characteristics of AM signals, combine with the incoming signal at the receiving antenna. Both the signal and the static will therefore be heard in the loudspeaker. To eliminate this fault, the necessity arose for developing some method of modulation in which the character of the desired modulation was different from the amplitude variations produced by static. Frequency modulation answers that need.

The first patent on frequency modulation was issued to Cornelius D. Ehret in 1905, but it attracted little attention. In fact, during the 1920's, there were several articles written by eminent radio engineers such as John Carson, which seemed to prove mathematically that frequency modulation was a completely impractical system.[49]

However, in 1934 a workable FM system was perfected by Edwin H. Armstrong. This system was successfully demonstrated in 1935.

In 1938, in order to introduce frequency modulation, Armstrong spent more than 2 million dollars in building and operating the first experimental FM broadcasting station, W2XMN, in Alpine, New Jersey. The FCC authorized FM radio broadcasting in 1940, and during the following year it approved the use of frequency modulation for television broadcasting.

Commercial broadcasting of frequency modulation was halted by World War II. Armstrong then donated his invention to the government for military application and worked for the government for a dollar a year. He issued licenses to a number of radio manufacturers and collected substantial royalties for a period of time. Eventually, some of the major manufacturers refused to pay, and lawsuits ensued. The patent litigation in which Armstrong argued his rights to frequency modulation sapped his resources and broke up his marriage. Penniless and alone, he took his own life in 1954. In December 1954, RCA settled one of these lawsuits for approximately one million dollars. Five years later, in 1959, the United States District Courts upheld the validity of Armstrong's FM patents in a suit filed against the Emerson Radio and Phonograph Corporation. In the opinion that was rendered by Federal Judge Palmieri, elimination of broadcasting static was regarded as impossible prior to Armstrong's inventions, and his inventions were scoffed at and did not win acceptance until they were demonstrated before a group of RCA engineers and executives. Judge Palmieri found the Emerson Radio and Phonograph Company guilty of having infringed upon patents issued in 1933 and reissued in 1940 concerning "important discoveries in the radio art."[50]

By 1963, 19 out of 21 manufacturers of FM radio equipment who had not taken licenses under Armstrong's FM patents had paid damages to his estate amounting to several million dollars. Among those who had settled were the Admiral Corp. and the Allen B. DuMont Laboratories, while suits were pending against the two remaining holdouts, Motorola, Inc. and the Philco Corp.

In frequency modulation, the modulating signal varies the frequency of the carrier (Fig. 25-70). The rate at which the frequency of the carrier is varied depends upon the frequency of the modulating signal (Fig. 25-71). The extent to which the frequency of the carrier is varied depends upon the strength or amplitude of the modulating signal (Fig. 25-72). On the standard 88 to 108-mc FM broadcast band, the maximum permissible deviation from the carrier frequency is 75 kc.

An analogy with signaling by means of a beam of light may help clarify the differences between AM and FM transmission. When one is signaling with a beam of light, information may be conveyed by changing

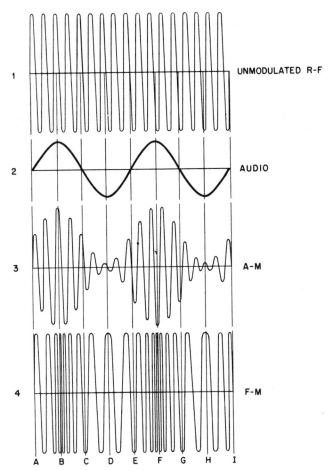

1 — UNMODULATED R-F

2 — AUDIO

3 — A-M

4 — F-M

A   B   C   D   E   F   G   H   I

FIG. 25-70. COMPARISON BETWEEN WAVEFORMS OF AN AM SIGNAL (3) AND FM SIGNAL (4), EACH DERIVED FROM A SINGLE-FREQUENCY CARRIER (1) AND MODULATING SIGNAL (2).

either the intensity of the light or its color. Amplitude modulation corresponds to varying the intensity or amplitude of the light, while frequency modulation corresponds to changing the color or frequency of the light.

The advantage of FM transmission is that any amplitude variations produced by static can be removed in the receiver before detection, without affecting the desired signal in any way. In addition, FM broadcasting produces a much higher signal-to-noise ratio. This effect is obtained by taking

advantage of the fact that the noise that is picked up by a receiver is concentrated principally in the high-frequency end of the audio spectrum. At the transmitter, the higher-frequency components of the audio signal are preemphasized or boosted before modulation (Figs. 25-73 and 25-74). When these high-frequency components are deemphasized or attenuated in the receiver in order to restore the flat-frequency characteristic, the noise is also attenuated to the same extent (Fig. 25-75). This is accomplished by means

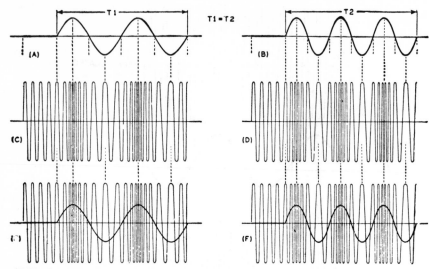

FIG. 25-71. COMPARISON BETWEEN TWO FM SIGNALS (C AND D) PRODUCED BY TWO AUDIO SIGNALS (A AND B) OF EQUAL AMPLITUDES BUT DIFFERENT FREQUENCIES (MODULATING WAVES SUPERIMPOSED ON THEIR RESPECTIVE MODULATED CARRIERS IN E AND F).

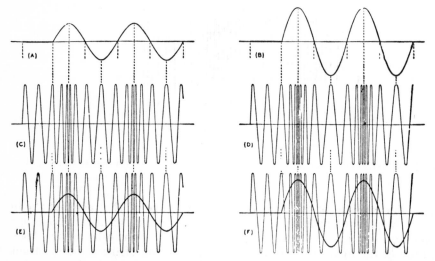

FIG. 25-72. COMPARISON BETWEEN TWO FM SIGNALS (C AND D) PRODUCED BY TWO AUDIO SIGNALS (A AND B) OF EQUAL FREQUENCIES BUT DIFFERENT AMPLITUDES (MODULATING WAVES SUPERIMPOSED ON THEIR RESPECTIVE MODULATED CARRIERS IN E AND F).

of a restorer circuit that follows the second detector in the receiver. While satisfactory reception with an AM receiver is not assured until the signal-to-noise ratio at the receiver-antenna input is at least 100 to 1, FM receivers can operate satisfactorily with signal-to-noise ratios as low as 2 to 1. As a result, with a good receiver, FM reception is as quiet as the performance of a modern vinylite phonograph record.

The use of broad-band frequency

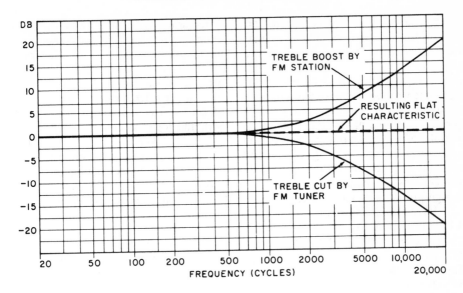

FIG. 25-73. STANDARD FCC PRE-EMPHASIS AND DE-EMPHASIS EQUALIZATION CURVES FOR FM BROAD-
CASTING AND RECEPTION

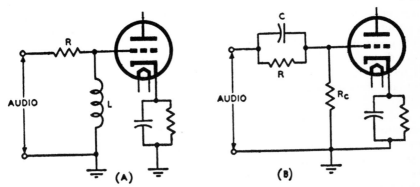

FIG. 25-74. IN THESE TWO PRE-EMPHASIS NETWORKS, AS THE FREQUENCY OF THE AUDIO SIGNAL
INCREASES, THE VOLTAGES APPLIED TO THE GRIDS OF THE TUBE ALSO INCREASE

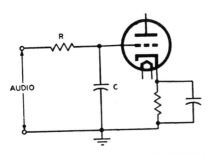

FIG. 25-75. A TYPICAL DE-EMPHASIS NETWORK

modulation in reducing noise was first
demonstrated by Armstrong in 1936.
This demonstration astounded radio
engineers who had previously concluded that since noise increases with
bandwidth, the best way to reduce noise
was to limit the bandwidth. Since this
demonstration revealed that in an FM
system noise could be reduced by increasing the bandwidth, it became apparent that in an over-all transmission

system the relation between noise and bandwidth was not as simple as had been previously assumed by all of the experts.

The power output of an FM signal does not vary, since the signal is of constant amplitude. The tubes may therefore be operated at constant maximum output. Since the modulator does not change the amplitude of the carrier wave, it does not have to supply much power. This eliminates the necessity for a high-power modulator tube.

It is also possible for two nearby FM transmitters to be broadcasting on the same frequency without producing serious interference. The stronger of the two signals will be the only one which will get through the receiver. This "capture effect" prevents interference within the service area of one station by transmissions from another station outside this area. In AM reception, there is no way of rejecting interfering signals of the same frequency as the desired signal. The problem of AM interference at night has become more and more acute to all except city dwellers.

A decided advantage of frequency modulation over amplitude modulation is the ability of frequency modulation to avoid cross-talk interference from stations transmitting on adjacent channels. An FM system provides good reception of a signal that is only slightly stronger than an undesired signal, while an AM system requires a much higher ratio between the strength of the desired and the undesired signals. In an AM system, this ratio is about 25 times greater than in an FM system. On a watt-for-watt basis, an FM transmitter will outperform the coverage of an AM transmitter with respect to interference-free, fade-free, and static-free service.

In AM broadcasting, if interference is being caused, an FCC ruling makes

it necessary to limit to 7.5 kc the maximum frequency of the audio signal that modulates the carrier wave. Generally, all audio-frequency signals higher than 5 kc are discarded. Unless this is done, the upper-sideband-frequency signals of one station are likely to interfere with the lower-sideband-frequency signals of another station transmitting on an adjacent frequency channel. Another reason for restricting the bandwidth of AM transmission is to decrease the amount of noise picked up by the receiver. Since noise consists of AM signals of various frequencies, decreasing the bandwidth of the transmitter and receiver helps to reduce the amount of noise entering the receiver.[51]

There are a few AM stations that broadcast signals containing audio modulating frequencies as high as 8 kc, but in general, it can safely be stated that conventional AM broadcasting is unsuitable for the transmission of high-quality sound.

These limitations do not apply to FM transmission. It is a relatively simple matter to modulate an FM carrier with a 15 kc audio signal. Consequently, from its very beginning in 1934, FM broadcasting has been on a wide-range, high-fidelity basis.

Another advantage of FM transmission is the great dynamic range possible. The dynamic range or difference in power between the loudest and weakest sounds of a large orchestra is about 75 decibels. Because of noise limitations and the danger of overmodulation, there is a difference of only 50 db between the weakest and strongest modulating signal of an AM transmission. Consequently, an AM system cannot handle the dynamic range of an orchestra. In contrast, the noise level of an FM transmission is low, permitting transmission of very soft musical passages, while loud passages need not be attenuated to prevent overmodulation and distortion. The result is that the entire dynamic range of the orchestra can easily be handled when FM transmission is employed.

However, frequency modulation possesses certain disadvantages. A single channel requires a very wide frequency band. Transmission by means of frequency modulation is therefore confined to the higher frequencies where sufficient space is available. Commercial broadcasters of FM signals are assigned channels in the very-high-frequency band ranging from 88 to 108 mc. The sky wave is not very dependable at these higher frequencies, and the range of reception of FM signals is consequently rather limited.

Another disadvantage is the relative cost of an FM receiver. An FM receiver necessarily contains more tubes and circuits than an AM receiver. The cheapest FM receiver costs approximately three times as much as a cheap AM receiver and provides poor results. A good FM receiver contains a minimum of 8 to 10 tubes plus a rectifier unit and is consequently a relatively expensive piece of equipment.

Frequency modulation has been employed principally in high-quality radio broadcasting, in police, military and aircraft communication equipment, and for conveying the audio portion of television transmissions.

25.30 *Production of frequency-modulated signals*

The simplest method of producing a frequency-modulated signal is to connect a condenser microphone across the tank circuit of a Hartley or Armstrong oscillator (Fig. 25-76). The variations in sound energy produce corresponding changes in the capacitance of

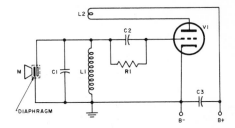

FIG. 25-76. FREQUENCY MODULATION PRODUCED BY MEANS OF A CONDENSER MICROPHONE

the condenser microphone (Fig. 25-77). These changes, in turn, vary the capacitance of the tank circuit, thus producing a radio-frequency signal which varies in frequency at an audio rate. This deviation from the normal carrier frequency is proportional to the amplitude of the modulating signal. The term carrier swing is used to denote the total deviation on either side of the carrier frequency. Military practice limits the maximum deviation to 40 kc, while in commercial broadcasting the maximum permissible deviation is 75 kc.

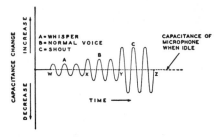

FIG. 25-77. RELATION BETWEEN THE INTENSITY OF THE IMPINGING SOUND AND THE CHANGE IN OUTPUT CAPACITANCE OF A CONDENSER MICROPHONE

However, this condenser-microphone method of modulating is not a very practical one, since the resulting changes in capacity are too small. This method also restricts FM transmission to the employment of only one type of microphone.

25.31 *The Crosby or reactance-tube modulator*

A modification of the previously described method employs a reactance tube modulator. This circuit generally contains a Hartley oscillator. An audio signal is fed to the grid of a second tube. This second tube is connected across the tank circuit of the oscillator and acts as a variable capacitor, whose capacitance changes in accordance with the signal that appears on the grid of the tube (Fig. 25-78). This variation in capacitance across the oscillator tank circuit produces a frequency-modulated signal. The modulator stage is usually followed by a combination of Class C amplifier and frequency-multiplier stages.

This system possesses the advantage of being compact and dependable. It can be used with self-excited oscillators. However, it cannot produce sufficient frequency deviation when it is used with crystal-controlled oscillators. In addition, some system of crystal-controlled frequency stabilization is necessary in order to insure that the oscillator will return to its

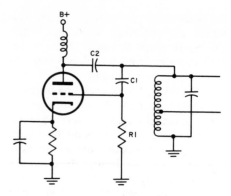

FIG. 25-78. A REACTANCE TUBE MODULATOR CIRCUIT
This tube simulates a variable capacitor.

original or resting frequency at the end of each audio-frequency signal cycle (Fig. 25-79).

25.32 *The Armstrong balanced-modulator system*

Another method of producing a frequency-modulated signal was designed by Armstrong and is known as the balanced-modulator system. In this system, the output of a crystal oscillator

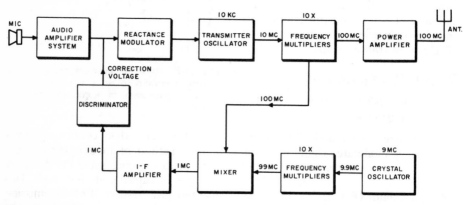

FIG. 25-79. BLOCK DIAGRAM OF AN FM TRANSMITTER CONTAINING A CRYSTAL CONTROLLED AFC SYSTEM

is fed to a balanced modulator (Fig. 25-80). The balanced modulator separates the carrier and sideband frequencies of the amplitude-modulated signal that is produced. The sideband and carrier frequencies are then fed through a network so that they are phased 90 deg apart from each other and are then recombined (Fig. 25-81). The result is an approximation of a phase-modulated wave, in which the deviation of the carrier wave from its normal or resting frequency is proportional to the frequency, as well as to the amplitude, of the modulating signal. This technique of causing the frequency deviation produced by a given modulating voltage to be greater for a high-frequency modulating signal than for a low-frequency signal is called pre-emphasis. Pre-emphasis tends to reduce the background noise of the received signal and is therefore employed by most FM transmitters.

The phase-modulated signal may then be converted to an FM signal by inserting a filter in series with the source of modulating voltage. The output of this filter should be inversely proportional to the impressed frequency. Finally, in order to improve the signal-to-noise ratio, about twelve frequency-doubler stages are employed (Fig. 25-82) This method requires a good many tubes. However, the power requirements are small, and low-priced, receiver-type tubes may therefore be used. As a result, neither the initial cost nor the power consumption is unduly excessive.[52]

25.33 The saturable-reactor modulator

The saturable-reactor method of producing an FM signal depends upon the principle that the permeability of a ferrite core varies when the

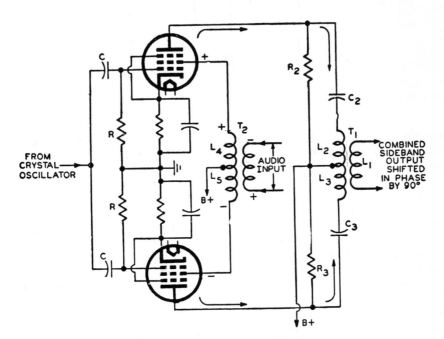

FIG. 25-80. SCHEMATIC OF THE ARMSTRONG BALANCED-MODULATOR CIRCUIT

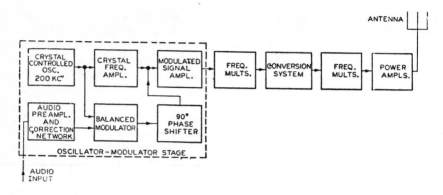

FIG. 25-81. BLOCK DIAGRAM OF AN ARMSTRONG FM TRANSMITTER

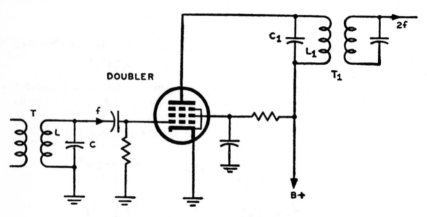

FIG. 25-82. A FREQUENCY-DOUBLER STAGE
The plate circuit, T_1, is tuned to the second harmonic of the grid circuit, T.

strength of a nearby external magnetic field varies. If the ferrite is used as the core of a coil, the inductance of the coil can be varied by varying the strength of the external magnetic field.

In operation, this external magnetic field is provided by the modulating signal passing through a coil containing a nickel-iron core. This nickel-iron modulating core has a gap in which the ferrite coil is placed. As the modulating signal passes through the modulating coil, a proportional variation in the magnetic field is produced. This causes corresponding changes in the inductance of the ferrite-cored coil. Since this latter coil is part of the resonant circuit of an oscillator, the frequency of the oscillator will vary in accordance with the modulating signal through the nickel-iron coil.

The chief advantages of the saturable-reactor modulator are its simplicity and the fact that the required deviation in frequency can be obtained directly from the oscillator without having to use stages of frequency multiplication. This system is employed in many types of FM signal generators and test oscillators.

25.34 Recent developments in frequency modulation

Shortly before his tragic and untimely death in 1954, Armstrong had perfected a system of radio transmission, called multiplexing, that permitted FM broadcasting stations to transmit simultaneously three different programs. In this system the FM station transmits its regular 50 to 15,000-cps audio program which can be picked up by means of an ordinary FM receiver. At the same time, the station transmits two other programs in the ultrasonic range, generally around 41 kc and 67 kc. This is accomplished by using 41-kc and 67-kc subcarriers to modulate the high-frequency carrier. Each subcarrier is in turn modulated by the additional program material.[53] In order to receive these additional channels, a modified FM receiver is required.

In March 1955, the FCC authorized multiplexing on commercial FM stations. According to this ruling, all FM stations distributing commercial music were obliged to employ multiplexing by the end of 1958. However, this was nullified in 1959 when the United States Supreme Court backed up the Court of Appeals which voided this FCC order.[54] Despite this nullification, the original FCC order resulted in the creation of a new industry called Musicasting, in which continuous background music without vocals or commercials is made available on these additional channels. Special receivers capable of receiving these channels are rented to owners of restaurants and other establishments where uninterrupted background music is considered desirable. By 1957, this young industry was grossing over 15 million dollars per year.[55]

The multiplexing system also lends itself well to broadcasting of stereo programs, as has been previously described. In 1957, station WGHF went on the air at Brookfield, Conn. This FM station was designed to transmit stereo by multiplex. It broadcasts a standard high-fidelity program on its own channel. One of the two subchannels provides station income by carrying background music. The other is combined with the main channel for stereocasting.[56] In New York City, WBAI-FM started using multiplexing for stereophony in September 1958. By early 1959, there were 10 FM stations that were transmitting authorized multiplexed broadcasts of this type.

25.35 The past and the future of frequency modulation

Following World War II, frequency modulation almost faded out of the entertainment picture. It was overshadowed by television, and only three radio-receiver manufacturers produced FM sets in quantity between 1949 and 1957. Sales of FM receivers tumbled from 1.5 million in 1950 to less than 200,000 in 1954, and by that year only 50 licensed FM stations remained on the air.

After 1957, partially as a result of the boom in high-fidelity equipment, more and more people began purchasing FM receivers. In 1957, the sale of AM-FM combinations amounted to 2.2 per cent of the radio receivers sold. This increased to 3.1 per cent in 1958, and 5.1 per cent in 1959. These figures do not include the sales of tuners and construction kits designed to be used for FM reception. At the end of 1958, there were 578 FM stations operating. By the end of 1959, the number had increased to 646, and 157 additional stations were under construction. In 1959, manufacturers also began making automobile radio receivers that could receive FM broadcasts.[57]

While those in the radio industry believe that frequency modulation has a long way to go before it overcomes the present lead of amplitude modulation, they point out that the gap is steadily closing. One of the most enthusiastic supporters of the future of frequency modulation is Henry Fogel, president of Granco Products, a medium-sized company that is turning out 1,500 FM radio receivers each day. According to Fogel: "The days of AM radio are numbered. Not too long after the FCC approves multiplexing, we'll be reading about the demise of AM just as the monaural record player is biting the dust right now under the impact of stereophonic records."

These samples are picked off and transmitted at periodic intervals and are sufficient in number-per-second to define the pattern. Each sample is transmitted as a pulse of voltage. As few as 8,000 samplings per second are sufficient to obtain near perfect reproduction of speech, but high-quality music requires much more frequent sampling. Since the duration of each pulse is very brief, about 1 microsecond, there is a long waiting interval between pulses. During this interval, the pulses of many other conversations may be sent over the same system.[59] The term multiplexing, which has been used previously, can also be applied to a system of this type. The composite signal to be transmitted thus consists of a series of pulses, each of which represents the magnitude of a single signal at that particular instant of time.

25.36 *Time-division pulse modulation*

As was previously indicated in an earlier chapter, we do not need to know every point of a curve in order to plot it. A very few points are sufficient to define a simple shape. Even a complex waveform can be reproduced by taking samples of this wave at regular intervals and using these samples to produce pulses, which modulate the carrier wave.[58] This fact provides the basis for time-division pulse modulation in which various different signals can be transmitted on a single frequency channel by using a mechanical or electronic switching device to sample the various signals in succession (Figs. 22-38, 22-39, and 22-40).

In time-division pulse modulation, only samples of the pattern are sent.

25.37 *Time assignment speech interpolation*

A type of time-division multiplexing was developed in 1959 by the American Telephone and Telegraph Company for its trans-Atlantic phone cables between the United States and France. This system is called TASI, for Time Assignment Speech Interpolation. It is based upon the discovery that each of the 36 speech channels produced by a frequency-division carrier system is actually in use only 25 per cent of the time during a telephone conversation. In this system, the efficiency of operation is increased by assigning each circuit to other speakers when the first party is not talking, and during the time between words, phrases, and sentences. In this manner, the 36 original channels handle 72 to 90 conversations.[60] [61]

25.38 *Types of pulse-modulation systems*

There are several different systems of coding pulses so that they can convey the desired information. Some of these have been described in the chapter dealing with magnetic recording. The most commonly used systems of pulse modulation are the following:

1. Pulse-amplitude modulation, in which the various pulses have essentially constant width and position, but vary in amplitude (Fig. 25-83). These amplitude variations of the pulses are proportional to the magnitude of the signal. This system is the least complex and requires the simplest circuit techniques. However, it is not used in microwave pulse-communication systems because most microwave oscillators, such as the magnetron, are not well-suited for amplitude modulation.

2. Pulse-time modulation, in which all the pulses except for the synchronizing or reference pulse have constant amplitude but vary in their relative time positions (Fig. 25-84). The time position of each pulse relative to the preceding pulse or to a fixed time-reference pulse is proportional to the magnitude of the desired signal. This system is also known as pulse-position modulation and is employed in many microwave-relay pulse-communication systems.

UNIDIRECTIONAL PAM

BIDIRECTIONAL PAM

FIG. 25-83. TWO FORMS OF PULSE-AMPLITUDE MODULATION (PAM)

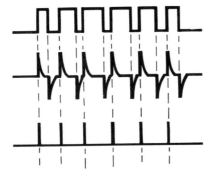

PULSE WIDTH MODULATED SIGNAL

DIFFERENTIATED WIDTH MODULATED SIGNAL

WITH NEGATIVE PEAKS SUPPRESSED. A PTM SIGNAL IS PRODUCED.

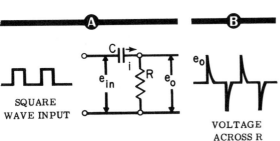

SQUARE WAVE INPUT

VOLTAGE ACROSS R

Voltage across R is the rate of change or differentiation of the input across C and R, while C will accumulate charges from the pulses and give their integration over a period of time.

FIG. 25-84. PRODUCTION OF A PULSE-TIME MODULATED (PTM) SIGNAL

3. Pulse-width or pulse-duration modulation, in which the duration of the pulse varies, while the amplitude and relative time position of the pulse remains constant (Figs. 22-37, 22-41, 22-42, 25-85, and 25-86). The duration of the pulse is related to the magnitude of the signal.

4. Pulse-frequency modulation, in which the frequency of repetition of the pulses is varied in accordance with the information that is to be transmitted. It resembles somewhat the

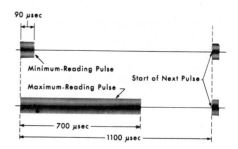

FIG. 25-85. IN THE PDM SYSTEM, RELATIVE PULSE DURATION IS USED TO REPRESENT THE MAGNITUDE OF THE READING OF THE INFORMATION.

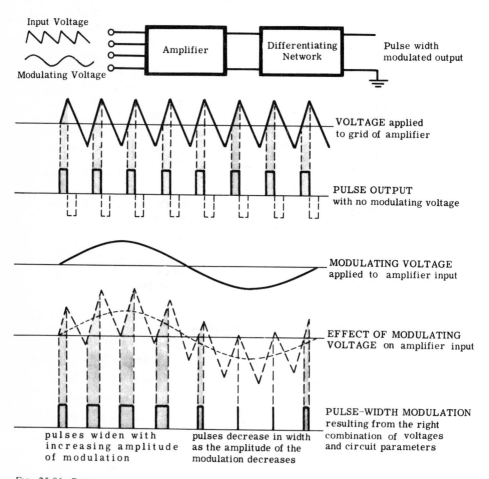

FIG. 25-86. PULSE-WIDTH MODULATION

frequency modulation of a continuous wave.

5. Pulse-code modulation, which is a specialized and sophisticated form of any of the preceding types of pulse-modulation systems. The instantaneous magnitude of the signal is converted into a sequential group of pulses representing a binary code (Figs. 22-43, 22-44, and 25-87).[62][63] By means of pulse-code modulation, it is possible to transmit more than 2,000 messages simultaneously over a single circuit with a high degree of accuracy, despite a considerable amount of noise. The principal application of pulse-code modulation is in multichannel telephone communications over wire circuits.

25.39 Applications of pulse modulation in telemetry

Pulse modulation can also be employed in telemetric systems designed to transmit different types of data on one frequency channel. Telemetry, which means to measure from a distance, is the relatively new technique of determining, from a radio signal transmitted from a remote point, information concerning what is happening at the source of the signal. This is accomplished by means of a transducer that translates information about temperature, acceleration, pressure, etc., into electrical signals which are then used to modulate a radio wave (Fig. 25-88).

These systems are used for recording experimental test data from missiles, satellites, and aircraft, where hazard, space limitations and the volume of data to be gathered make the use of a human observer impossible (Fig. 25-89).[64] Measurements of such quantities as acceleration, strain, pressure, temperature, altitude, position, and rate of flow are made at rates that are thousands of times faster and far more accurate than measurements obtained

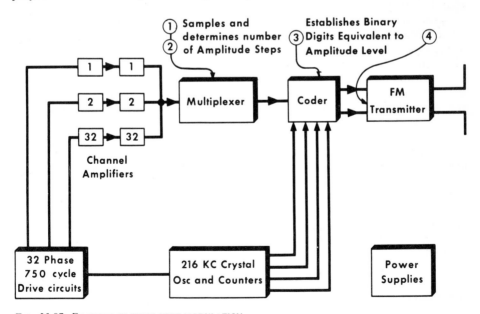

Fig. 25-87. Example of pulse-code modulation

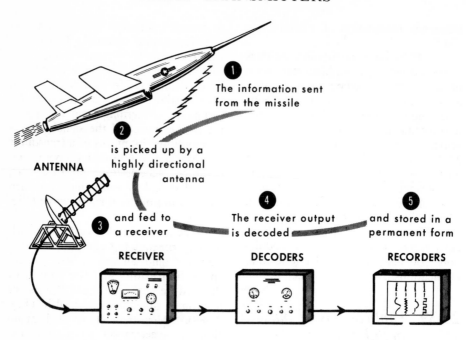

FIG. 25-88. BASIC RADIO-TELEMETRY SYSTEM

by visual observation and manual recording.[65] [66]

The Minitrack system for tracking United States earth satellites employs a network of radio-receiving stations scattered over the Western hemisphere and Australia. These stations are capable of receiving the telemetered beacon or tracking signals transmitted by a satellite.

The tracking signals are transmitted at a frequency of 108 mc, with a power of 10 to 50 milliwatts. The information is relayed from the receiving stations to the Naval Research Laboratory in Washington, D.C., where it is fed into an electronic computer, which calculates the velocity, direction, and orbit of the satellite.[67] [68]

The information related to temperature, pressure, meteorite erosion, and radiation is fed into a telemetry converter contained in the satellite.

This device combines the various signals and produces a single digital or encoded signal that is used to modulate the transmitter of the satellite. The major systems of telemetry used for this type of application are pulse-position modulation of an AM signal, pulse-width modulation of an FM signal, and frequency multiplexing of an FM signal.

Another recent development in telemetry is known as DOVAP (Doppler, Velocity, and Position), produced by the International Telephone and Telegraph Corporation. It consists of a 10-lb radio transmitter that delivers information to scientists concerning the performance of missiles and high-altitude research rockets. The transmitted signals convey information concerning velocity, trajectory, fuel consumption, and atmospheric conditions.[69] [70]

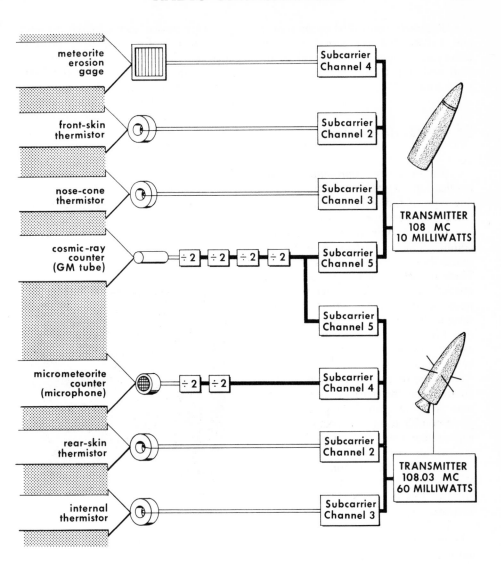

FIG. 25-89. EXPLORER 1 SATELLITE TELEMETRY SYSTEM

Less well known are the methods of applying telemetry in the process industries, such as in the petroleum industry, for transmitting both information and control signals over various types of communication facilities, including low-grade telegraph circuits. Thus, one system called the Telepulse system, recently installed for the Aurora Gasoline Company, reports remote readings of liquid level and temperature in petroleum storage tanks. An alarm system immediately reports any abnormal conditions, such as excessive tank level, high temperature, high or low pressure, incorrect flow rate, and fire. Remotely controlled pump motors and valves that are actuated by the pulse signals open and close valves and start and stop motors at stations many miles away.[71][72]

25.40 *Radioteletype*

Radioteletype represents another application of pulse transmission. In one type of radioteletype transmission, when the operator presses a teletype key corresponding to a given letter, a combination of marks (pulses) and spaces (absence of pulses) is produced. These marks and spaces are used to frequency-modulate the carrier wave, the mark shifting the carrier frequency several hundred cycles-per-second in one direction, while the space shifts the carrier frequency by an equal amount in the opposite direction.

At the receiver, the signal is demodulated and the marks and spaces are sent to a teleprinter (Fig. 25-90). A given combination of marks and spaces will actuate a series of relays that cause the printer to type the same letter that was struck by the transmitting operator (Fig. 25-91). The average rate of operation of this device is between 60 and 75 words per minute.

In 1958, the Smith-Corona Kleinschmidt Laboratories developed a new automatic printer for the U.S. Signal Corps. Unlike the conventional teleprinter, it does not use ordinary typing keys. Instead, a wheel rimmed with letters spins at 3,750 rpm, hesitating momentarily when the correct letters come into position. At that instant, a small hammer presses the paper against the wheel. This device can type at the rate of 750 words per minute and can type an entire newspaper page in less than 8 minutes.[73]

This device seems merely to have set the stage for high-speed printing devices. IBM has developed a teleprinter that is capable of typing 3,600 words per minute, while Remington-Rand has developed a UNIVAC printer that types a 200-word paragraph in only 1 second.[74]

In 1959, the Burroughs Corporation announced the development of a 3,000 words-per-minute electronic teleprinter for the United States Signal Corps. Even at this speed, the device is operating in low gear, since it has a theoretical top speed of 50,000 words per minute.[75]

Courtesy, Teletype Corp.
FIG. 25-90. TELETYPE MODEL 28 SEND-RECEIVE SET

25.41 *Transmitters for radio-control applications*

Radio transmitters are now being used for other purposes besides the major one of communication. They are being employed to control all types of

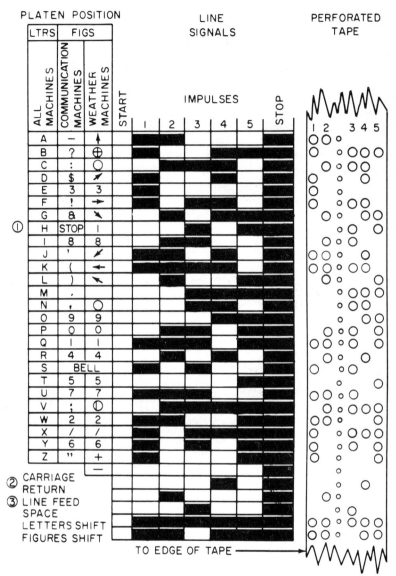

SIGNAL, LENGTHS IN MILLISECONDS, STANDARD SPEED 60 WORDS PER MIN.

|←22→|←22→|←22→|←22→|←22→|←22→|← 31 →|

☐ SPACING IMPULSES
■ MARKING IMPULSES

① MOTOR STOP OPTIONAL ON WEATHER MACHINES
② < IS PRINTED ON TYPING REPERFORATORS
③ ≡ IS PRINTED ON TYPING REPERFORATORS

Courtesy, United States Army Signal Corps

FIG. 25-91. FIVE-UNIT. START-STOP TELETYPEWRITER CODE

equipment, from model boats and air-planes, through remotely located pipe-line pumps, to military weapons such as drone airplanes and guided missiles (Fig. 25-92).

Probably the first United States patent for a radio-controlled device was the one issued in 1898 to Tesla. It was for a radio-controlled vessel that was basically a guided torpedo. Tesla conducted a demonstration at Madison Square Garden in New York City, in which he demonstrated that he could light, start, and steer the vessel by radio.[76][77]

During the same year, Tesla wrote an article for the New York *Sun* in which he anticipated the use of guided missiles in warfare. In this article, he stated: "We shall be able ... to send a projectile at a much greater distance .... we shall be able to submerge it at command, to arrest it in its flight and call it back, and to send it out again, and explode it again; and more than this it will never make a miss ...."

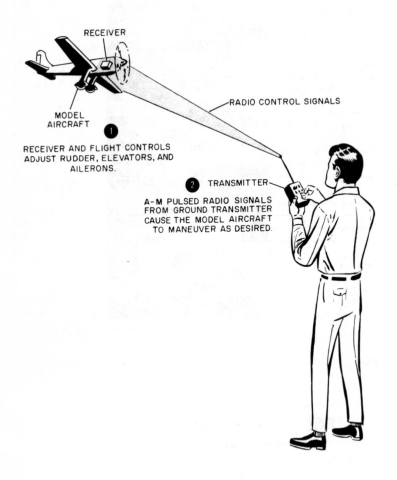

FIG. 25-92. REMOTE CONTROL ACCOMPLISHED BY RADIO CONTROL SIGNALS

In 1900, in a published article in *Century Magazine,* he further predicted: "....an automaton may be contrived which will have its 'own mind'.... It will be able to follow a course laid out or to obey orders given far in advance; it will be capable of distinguishing between what it ought and what it ought not to do."

Typical of the reaction of conservative technical men to Tesla's prediction of radio-controlled guided missiles was Brackett's article in the *Electrical Engineer* in which he stated: "What Tesla has done is merely to make theoretical application of inventions which had already been discovered.... the theory is perfect, but the application absurd."[78]

Work in this field was carried further by John Hays Hammond, Jr., who is also noted for the development of electric organs and pianos. Hammond developed boats and torpedoes that were successfully controlled by radio impulses.[79]

Since the end of World War II, tens of thousands of individuals have become interested in the hobby of building radio-controlled or R/C model airplanes and boats. Catering to this hobby are several dozen manufacturers of transmitters, receivers, servos, and accessories. This rapid growth of a hobby previously restricted to a relatively small number of individuals is primarily due to the creation of the previously described Citizens Radio Service by the FCC. As has been mentioned, this Citizens Radio Service was created to permit the public to operate radio equipment for public and business short-distance radio communication, signaling, and radio control of objects and devices such as garage doors and model airplanes.

Hobbyists are permitted to operate with a maximum power input of 5 watts on two examination-free frequencies of 27.255 mc and 465 mc. In addition, in 1958 the FCC removed the 11-meter band ranging from 27.255 to 29.965 mc from amateur use and allocated 28 channels in this band for R/C, voice communication, and other Citizens Radio Band uses.[80]

The R/C model transmitters are usually one- or two-tube affairs employing c-w transmission (Fig. 25-93). About 10 per cent are more elaborate,

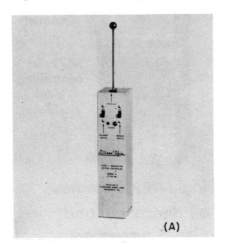
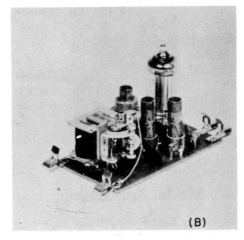

(A)   (B)

FIG. 25-93. MODEL AIRPLANE TRANSMITTER (A) AND RECEIVER (B)

using audio, and imposing as many as 8 modulating tones to operate the various controls of the model (Fig. 25-94).

The receiver, which is usually transistorized, detects the signals sent by the transmitter to the model plane or boat. The various control signals are filtered and separated, and each signal is routed to its proper relay. The relay then completes a circuit which causes either an escapement or a servo to actuate or move the control.[81]

The same principles can be used to design transmitters and receivers for the remote control of larger objects.

Drone airplanes used as aerial-gunnery targets can be controlled at distances as great as 100 miles from the operator (Fig. 25-95).[82]

The United States Army Research Laboratory has recently announced the development of an R/C tractor equipped with a television camera. It can be controlled from distances up to 15 miles and is intended for use in applications such as construction work in radioactive and combat zones and also for fighting fuel-storage fires.[83] An application that is not quite as grim is revealed by the announcement of the Western Tool and Stamping Co. that it is working on a

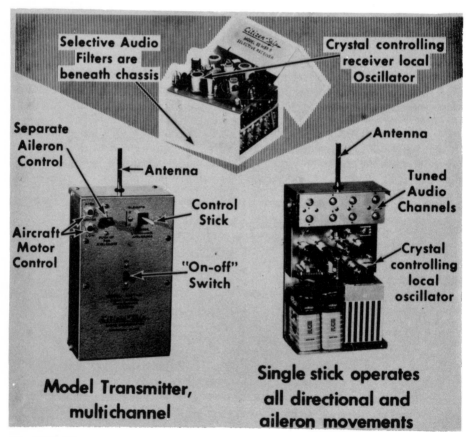

Selective Audio Filters are beneath chassis

Crystal controlling receiver local Oscillator

Separate Aileron Control

Antenna

Control Stick

Aircraft Motor Control

"On-off" Switch

Model Transmitter, multichannel

Antenna

Tuned Audio Channels

Crystal controlling local oscillator

Single stick operates all directional and aileron movements

FIG. 25-94. MULTI-SIMULTANEOUS EIGHT-CHANNEL R/C TRANSMITTER AND RECEIVER

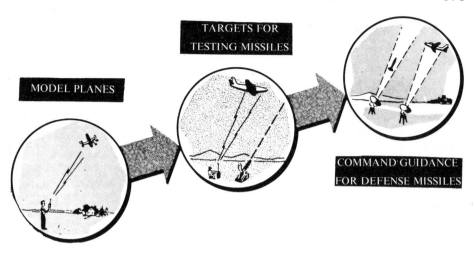

MODEL PLANES

TARGETS FOR TESTING MISSILES

COMMAND GUIDANCE FOR DEFENSE MISSILES

FIG. 25-95. TRANSITION TO WEAPON CONTROL BY COMMAND GUIDANCE

R/C wireless lawn mower that can be operated from one's porch or hammock. Systems have also been developed for the remote control of unmanned locomotives (Fig. 25-96).

The city of Baltimore has now installed a system of emergency vehicle-traffic radio controls known as EL-TEC. This system permits police cars, fire trucks, and ambulances to control traffic lights by means of radio signals that are produced by operating a control on the dashboard of the vehicle.[84]

In 1959, the city of New York awarded the first contracts for an electronic traffic-control system that will eventually enable the Traffic Department to control by radio from a single control point the timing of each one of its 50,000 traffic lights. This will enable a single operator, working at department headquarters in downtown Manhattan, to change light sequences to favor inbound traffic in the morning and outbound traffic in the afternoon.[85]

Another interesting R/C device is the Standard Camera Corporation's

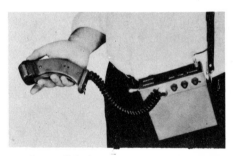

Courtesy, Union Switch and Signal Division of west-house Air Brake Co.

FIG. 25-96. RADIO REMOTE CONTROL SYSTEM FOR UNMANNED LOCOMOTIVES

Praktina FX radio unit which is designed to control a 35-mm camera. A radio receiver is connected to a battery-operated electric motor that is attached to the camera. When a photographer, who may be as far away as 1 mile, presses a transmitter button, a relay circuit in the receiver is closed. This releases the camera shutter and takes a picture. The film is then transported to the next frame, and the shutter is wound for the next exposure.

25.42 *Modulation of a beam of light*

The idea of conveying intelligence by modulating a light beam is not a new one. In 1880, Alexander Graham Bell described a method of modulating a beam of light by means of voice frequencies. In order to transmit speech by light, it is necessary to modulate a beam of light so that it varies in intensity or in frequency in accordance with the voice vibrations. These variations in light are then picked up at a distant station, and converted back into sound.

In 1877, Bell and his assistant Tainter constructed a device which they called a Photophone. Sunlight was reflected from a mirror attached to the small end of a megaphone. Sound waves that entered the megaphone caused the mirror to vibrate and to vary the light that was reflected from the mirror. At the receiving end, a selenium photoconductive cell was connected to a battery and a telephone receiver. The received variations in light were converted into electrical variations which were in turn, converted into sound waves that corresponded to the words originally spoken into the microphone (Fig. 25-97).[86]

In a later experiment, Bell assembled a telephone transmitter, a light source, a parabolic reflector, and a selenium cell connected to earphones, and transmitted voice over a distance of several hundred yards by the modulation of visible light.

During the North African campaign, the German army used a portable infrared communication unit. Words that were spoken into the microphone were converted into audio-frequency signals, amplified, and passed into a mirror galvanometer. This caused a small mirror to vibrate and to modulate a beam of light that was emitted by a tungsten lamp. The receiver used a lead sulphide photoconductive cell.

Infrared Industries, Inc., manufactures an infrared communication device called the Astro-Phone (Figs. 25-98 and 25-99).

Cesium lamps were also developed during the war for use in convoy duty and troop-landing operations. They are now used for private wireless-telephone service between ships and shore stations in crowded harbors, since they require no license for operation. They can be used by airplanes flying in formation through a radio blackout, or under conditions where the atmosphere is favorable for light transmission and unfavorable for radio. They may also be used in extremely noisy locations where the high level of noise makes it impractical to use the direct reception of sound from the centrally located speaker of a public address system.[87]

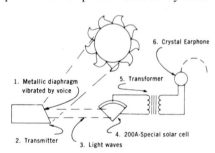

6. Crystal Earphone
1. Metallic diaphragm vibrated by voice
5. Transformer
2. Transmitter
3. Light waves
4. 200A-Special solar cell

Courtesy, Hoffman Electronics Corp. & Hearever Co., Inc.

FIG. 25-97. OPERATING PRINCIPLES OF THE SOLAR SPACE PHONE

The rays of the sun are reflected from the mirror-like portion of the transmitter contained in the receiver. The transmitter mirror, in the form of a thin metal diaphragm, is vibrated by the voice of the speaker. This modulates the reflected light and in turn modulates the output of the solar cell.

These systems produce highly directional transmissions, which is an advantage in military applications, although this characteristic can at

FIG. 25-99. A DISASSEMBLED ASTRO-PHONE

Courtesy, Infrared Industries, Inc.

FIG. 25-98. THE ASTRO-PHONE, AN INFRARED COMMUNICATION DEVICE

times be disadvantageous. An additional disadvantage is the fact that smoke and fog may seriously interfere with transmission over a light beam if the droplets and particles are relatively large. The most recent development in the transmission of voice over a light beam includes the transmission of television pictures as well. In 1947, DuMont engineers demonstrated that such a device could work over a range of several miles.[88] [89]

REFERENCES

1. James R. Newman, "James Clerk Maxwell," *Scientific American*, 192:68-69, June 1955.
2. Orrin E. Dunlap, Jr., *Radio and Television Almanac*, Harper and Bros., N.Y., 1951, p. 119.
3. Philip and Emily Morrison, "Heinrich Hertz," *Scientific American*, 197:100, Dec. 1957.
4. Orrin E. Dunlap, Jr., *Radio's 100 Men of Science*, Harper and Bros., N.Y., 1944, p. 54.
5. W. G. Lipsett, "Heinrich Hertz—Discoverer of Radio Waves," *Science Digest*, Oct. 1957.
6. O. E. Dunlap, Jr., *Radio and Television Almanac, Op. cit.*, p. 25.
7. Darrell L. Geiger, "Radio Telegraphy in 1866," *Radio-Electronics*, 30:48, Apr. 1959.
8. O. E. Dunlap, Jr., *Radio's 100 Men of Science, Op. cit.*, pp. 58-59.
9. *Ibid*, pp. 74-75.
10. Eric Leslie, "Inventors of Radio—Prof. A. E. Dolbear," *Radio-Electronics*, 30:38, Nov. 1959.
11. "A. S. Popov," *Radio-Electronics*, Sept. 1959.
12. O. E. Dunlap, Jr., *Radio's 100 Men of Science, Op. cit.*, pp. 127-128.
13. *Ibid*, pp. 175-176.
14. Monroe Upton, "Meet the Radio Wave Family," *Science Digest*, 40:25, Aug. 1956.
15. Edwin H. Armstrong, "Marconi," *Science Digest*, 29:81-86, June 1951.
16. *RCA—What It Is—What It Does*, Radio Corporation of America, New York, 1956, pp. 12-13.
17. J. Richard Johnson, "Problems in AM Reception," *Electronics World*, 62:90, Aug. 1959.
18. "Nikola Tesla's 100th Birthday," *Radio-Electronics*, 27:29, July 1956.
19. Ruben Lee, "Radio Telegraph Keying Transients," *Proc. IRE*, 22:213, Feb. 1934
20. "ARRL Merit Award," *Radio-Electronics*, 30:10, Nov. 1959.
21. *Trak Static Rejector*, CGS Labs, Inc., Stamford, Conn., 1956, pp. 2-3.
22. H. A. Robinson, "An Experimental Study of the Tetrode as a Modulated Radio-Frequency Amplifier," *Proc. IRE*, 20:131, Jan. 1932.
23. C. B. Green, "Suppressor-grid Modulation," *Bell Lab. Record*, 17:41, Oct. 1938.

24. Jack N. Brown, "Commercial Aspects of Single-Sideband—Part I," *Radio and Television News*, 55:61, May 1956.
25. Don Stoner, *New Sideband Handbook*, Cowan Publishing Corp., New York, 1958, p. 18.
26. Edward M. Noll, "The Single-Sideband Story—Part I," *Radio-Electronics*, 30:37, May 1959.
27. Alan Andrews, "Single-Sideband Transmission—Part I," *Electronics World*, 62:68, Sept. 1959.
28. "Single-Sideband Spectra," *Panoramic Analyzer*, 1:1-2, No. 3.
29. *Electronics Reference Data*, Howard W. Sams and Co., Indianapolis, Ind., 1957, p. 110.
30. Alan Andrews, "Single-Sideband Transmission—Part 2," *Electronics World*, 62:78, Oct. 1959.
31. Fritz Franke, "Single-Sideband Systems," *Radio and Television News*, 54:114, Dec. 1955.
32. J. N. Brown, *Op. cit.*, p. 59.
33. "Birdcall," *Collins Signal*, 7:3, Fall 1958.
34. "Super-Power SSB Army Transmitter," *Radio and TV News*, 58:117, July 1957.
35. Alan Andrews, "Single-Sideband Transmission—Part I," *Op. cit.*, p. 68.
36. "SSB Broadcasts Promise Hi-Fi," *Radio and TV News*, 58:127, Aug. 1957.
37. Philip James, "Spreading the Stations with CSSB," *Popular Electronics*, 7:52, Nov. 1957.
38. Milton S. Snitzer, "Stereo Broadcasting—Now and in the future," *Radio and TV News*, 60:65, Oct. 1958.
39. J. N. Brown, *Op. cit.*, p. 59.
40. "FCC Information on the Citizens Radio Service," *Electronics World*, 61:130, June 1959.
41. "Private Two-Way Radios for Private Citizens," *Science Digest*, 46:92-93, Aug. 1959.
42. Robert F. Scott, "Citizen's Band Radios . . . How They Work," *Radio Electronics*, 30:42, Sept. 1959.
43. Andrew Mandala, "Citizens Band Radio," *Popular Electronics*, 10:60-61, Mar. 1959.
44. Leo G. Sands, "Two-Way Radio for All," *Electronics Illustrated*, 1:56-58, 110, Sept. 1958.
45. "Citizens Radio Authorizations Pass 50,000 Mark," *Electronics World*, 62:29, Oct. 1959.
46. Harold B. McKay, "Citizens Radio Faces the Future," *Radio and TV News*, 60:30, Nov. 1958.
47. "Citizens Talking Too Much," *Radio-Electronics*, 30:6, Nov. 1959.
48. "Violations of Citizens Radio Regulation," *Electronics World*, 62:106, Nov. 1959.
49. "FM: Theoretical and Practical Analysis," *Panoramic Analyzer*, 1:1, No. 4.
50. "FM's Major Armstrong," *Radio-Electronics*, 30:6, Nov. 1959.
51. John R. Pierce, *Electrons, Waves, and Messages*, Hanover House, New York, 1956, p. 233.
52. Edwin H. Armstrong, "A Method of Reducing Disturbances in Radio Signaling by a System of Frequency Modulation," *Proc. IRE*, 24-689, May 1936.
53. Louis E. Garner, Jr., "Stereo Tuner Features Multiplex Outlet," *Radio-Electronics*, 29:53, Oct. 1958.
54. "FM Multiplex," *Radio-Electronics*, 30:6, Dec. 1959.
55. Walton N. Hershfield, "FM Musicasting—A New Industry," *Radio and TV News*, 57:128, June 1957.
56. Don Lewis, "Multiplexing and You," *Radio-Electronics*, 28:89, Oct. 1957.
57. "FM is Growing Again," *Radio-Electronics*, 30:8, Oct. 1959.
58. E. M. Deloraine, "Pulse Modulation," *Proc. IRE*, 37:702, June 1949.
59. Kenneth A. Kaufmann, "Soap Opera or Nothing?—No More," *R.P.I. Engineer*, 2:14, Oct. 1948.
60. "This Month in Science," *Popular Science*, 175:19-20, July 1959.
61. "System Doubles Capacity of Undersea Phone Cable," *Science Digest*, 45:90, May 1959.
62. Robert Endall, "Magnetic Tape Data Recording Systems," *Radio and Television News* (Engineering Edition), 47:4A, Mar. 1952.
63. B. M. Oliver and others, "The Philosophy of PCM," *Proc. IRE*, 36:1324, Nov. 1948.
64. Frank Henry, "Messages from Outer Space," *Science Digest*, 45:16-20, Apr. 1959.
65. Thomas S. Mederos, Jr., "Pulse Width Data Systems," *Amphenol Engineering News*, 9:336, Feb. 1956.
66. Earl Ubell, "How Rocket Radios Talk Back," *Science Digest*, 45:58, Jan. 1959.
67. "Tracking the Satellite—Part 1," *Skylights*, 4:1, Oct. 1957.
68. Jordan McQuay, "Electronics in Outer Space—Part 1," *Electronics World*, 62:38, 124, Aug. 1959.
69. Jordan McQuay, "Electronics in Outer Space—Part 2," *Electronics World*, 62:73, 120, Sept. 1959.
70. "Rocket-Rider Radio," *Radio and TV News*, 60:130, Sept. 1958.
71. "Industrial Telemetry Gaining Ground," *Control Engineering*, 5:31, July 1958.
72. Marvin Tepper, "Industrial Telemetry for Technicians," *Electronics World*, 62:46, Sept. 1959.
73. "Printer Types Faster Than Woman Can Talk," *Science Digest*, 44:91, Sept. 1958.
74. David O. Woodbury, *Let ERMA Do It*, Harcourt, Brace and Co., New York, 1956, p. 257.
75. "World's Fastest Typist," *Science Digest*, 45:89, Feb. 1959.
76. "Nikola Tesla's 100th Birthday," *Op. cit.*, p. 29.
77. Gardner Soule, "Mr. Tesla, Who Made Work Easier," *Popular Science*, 169:85, July 1956.
78. Kenneth M. Swezey, "Nikola Tesla," *Science*, 127:1156, May 16, 1958.
79. O. E. Dunlap, Jr., *Radio's 100 Men of Science*, *Op. cit.*, pp. 229-230.
80. Donald L. Stoner, "Build This Citizens Band Transceiver," *Radio and TV News*, Mar. 1959.
81. William Winter, "Radio Control of Models," *Popular Electronics*, 1:43-44, Oct. 1954.
82. E. D. Morgan, "Drones Put R/C into War Games," *Popular Electronics*, 4:108, Apr. 1956.
83. "Tractor Operated by Remote Radio Control," *Design News*, 12:11, June 15, 1957.
84. "Electronic Cop," *Electronic Design*, 5:11, June 15, 1957.
85. David Lachenbruch, "Electronics on the Highway," *Radio-Electronics*, 30:40-43, May 1959.
86. Alfred Morgan, *The Boys' Second Book of Radio and Electronics*, Charles Scribner's Sons, New York, 1957, pp. 146-147.
87. Eric Leslie, "Experimental Communication with Light Beams," *Radio-Electronics*, 24:46, Oct. 1953.
88. "Television Over a Light Beam," *Radio-Craft*, 18:22, July 1947.
89. "Light Beams Replace Radio Waves in TV," *Industrial Laboratories*, 8:103, Apr. 1957.

26 - RADIO RECEIVERS

26.1 *The detector*

The simplest possible radio receiver, such as a crystal or a one-tube receiver, consists of an antenna, a detector, and a pair of headphones (Fig. 26-1). The receiving antenna extracts energy from the passing radio waves, causing signal currents to flow within the antenna circuit. Fortunately, the design and selection of the correct antenna and transmission line are not as critical for good performance in a receiver as they are in a transmitter.

The detector stage demodulates the signal, or separates the audio-frequency component from the radio-frequency signal, by rectifying the incoming signal and then filtering or separating the audio-frequency component from the radio-frequency component.

The earliest detector was the Hertz loop. This was followed by the coherer, a device invented in 1890 by Edouard Branly, a French scientist. The primitive coherer-detector circuit consisted of a glass tube filled with fine iron filings or nickel dust. In series with the tube were a voltaic cell and a galvanometer. The presence of electromagnetic waves caused the small metallic particles to cohere. The resulting change in the electrical conductivity produced a deflection of the galvanometer. Later, a vibrating tapper, resembling the clapper of a doorbell, was added to cause the cohered particles to separate again.[1]

It was Sir Oliver Lodge, however, who gave the coherer its name, and first conceived of using the coherer as a detector in place of the Hertz loop. Marconi improved the design of the coherer and made it a far-more dependable detector of radio waves. The coherer was used for many years by early pioneers in wireless transmission and reception.

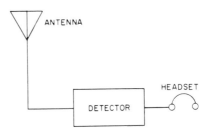

FIG. 26-1. THE SIMPLEST RADIO RECEIVER

In 1906, H. C. Dunwoody discovered the rectifying properties of carborundum crystals. During that same year, Greenleaf W. Pickard discovered that silicon crystals behaved in a similar manner.[2] This led to the development of crystal detectors, and early receivers employed these crystals and galena crystals as detectors. Crystals of carborundum proved to be the most satisfactory for shipboard use, since they were not easily upset by vibration, while the more sensitive galena crystals were widely employed for use in home receivers.

Modern receivers employ diode tubes to perform the same function. This application is based upon the principle of the two-element thermionic-valve detector patented by Fleming in 1904. Occasionally, receivers are encountered that make use of triodes or pentodes as detectors. These detectors are then called either grid-leak detectors, plate detectors, or regenerative detectors, according to how their components are connected. They possess the advantage over diode detectors of producing considerable amplification, but in doing so they generally introduce a great deal of distortion. The characteristics of these various types of electronic detectors have been discussed in Chapter 10.

26.2 *The tuned radio frequency or TRF receiver*

In order to enable a diode detector to operate a loudspeaker, a considerable amount of amplification is required. Stages that are designed to amplify this signal before it is detected generally possess tuned circuits and are called r-f amplifiers. Amplifiers that follow the detector stage are generally untuned and are called a-f amplifiers. The final a-f amplifier is usually a power amplifier that is designed to drive the loudspeaker. In addition, for sets operating from the power line, there is generally a selenium, copper oxide, or diode rectifier stage to convert the alternating current from the power line to the d-c voltages equivalent to those

supplied by a B-battery. Consequently, the minimum essentials for a TRF receiver are: an antenna, r-f amplifier, detector, a-f amplifier, loudspeaker, and power-supply rectifier (Figs. 26-2 and 26-3). This receiver will generally employ a manual volume control and possibly automatic volume control (AVC).

26.3 *The superheterodyne receiver*

The TRF receiver suffers from the following disadvantages:

1. The selectivity or ability to discriminate between signals of different frequencies decreases at the high-frequency end of the dial.

2. The sensitivity or amount of amplification also tends to decrease at the high-frequency end of the dial.

In order to overcome these difficulties, Armstrong designed the superheterodyne receiver, for which he was granted a patent in 1920. No matter what the frequency is of the signal that is received by this superheterodyne receiver, the signal is converted into a new signal of constant lower-frequency value, generally 455 or 456 kc. This new frequency is usually called the intermediate frequency or i-f signal. The i-f signal is then amplified by an i-f amplifier stage. Thus the amplification of all signals in this stage is accomplished at the same constant frequency (Fig. 26-4).

The formation of the new signal frequency results from the action of an oscillator stage and a mixer stage (Fig. 26-5). This mixer is sometimes known

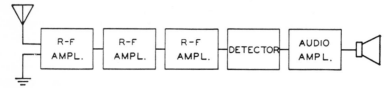

FIG. 26-2. BLOCK DIAGRAM OF A TRF RECEIVER

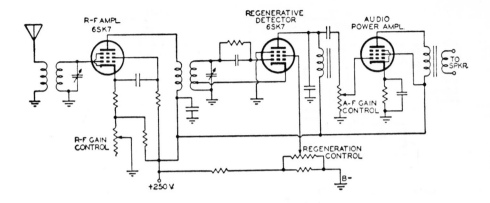

FIG. 26-3. CIRCUIT DIAGRAM OF A TRF RECEIVER

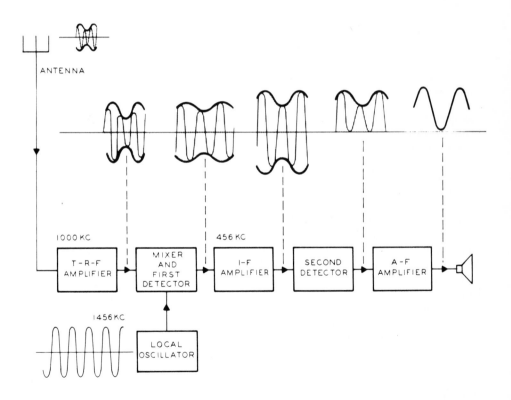

FIG. 26-4. BLOCK DIAGRAM OF A SUPERHETERODYNE RECEIVER AND ITS ASSOCIATED WAVEFORMS

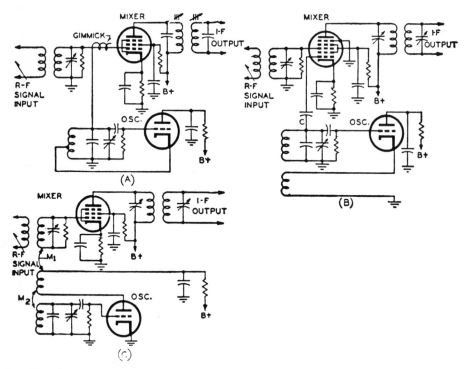

FIG. 26-5. THREE TYPES OF OSCILLATOR-MIXER CIRCUITS WHICH EMPLOY DIFFERENT METHODS OF COUPLING THE OSCILLATOR SIGNAL TO THE MIXER TUBE

as the first detector. The oscillator section is adjusted to produce a signal whose frequency is 456 kc higher than that of the station that is being tuned in. When these two signals are mixed in the mixer or converter stage, the process of beating or heterodyning takes place (Figs. 26-6, 26-7 and 26-8). A new signal is formed which carries all the intelligence of the old signal. The only difference is that its frequency is lower than that of the incoming signal. The new frequency or intermediate frequency is equal to the difference between the other two frequencies. This new signal is transferred to the following stage by means of a tuned i-f transformer (Fig. 26-9).

Thus, if one is tuned to a station broadcasting on 1,000 kc, the local oscillator of the receiver is producing a signal of 1,456 kc. When these two signals mix, an i-f signal of 456 kc is produced. If one then tunes to a station broadcasting on 880 kc, the oscillator is automatically retuned to 1,336 kc. Again the i-f signal is 456 kc. This i-f signal is then amplified by one or more i-f amplifiers, detected, amplified by a-f amplifiers, and converted into sound by the loudspeaker. The high selectivity and sensitivity of the superheterodyne receiver are primarily due to the characteristics of the i-f amplifier circuits (Fig. 26-10). Virtually all AM and FM receivers in use today are of the superheterodyne type.

Because of transit time and noise effects to be described in Chapter 31, vacuum-tube mixers do not work effectively at frequencies above 1,000 mc. They are then usually replaced by a

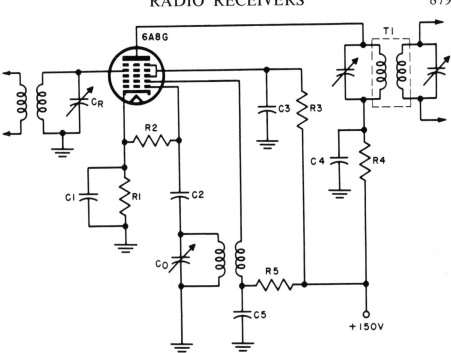

FIG. 26-6. CONVERTER CIRCUIT EMPLOYING A TYPE 6A8G TUBE

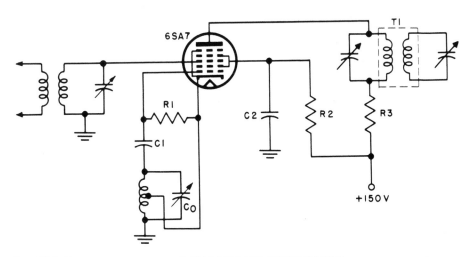

FIG. 26-7. CIRCUIT EMPLOYING A TYPE 6SA7 PENTAGRID CONVERTER TUBE

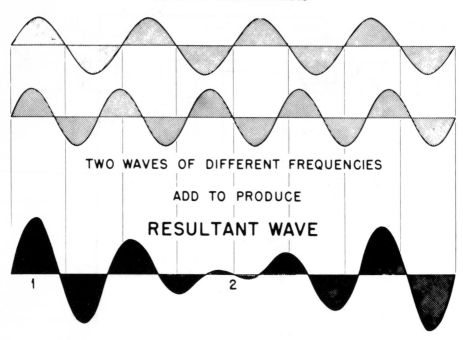

TWO WAVES OF DIFFERENT FREQUENCIES

ADD TO PRODUCE

RESULTANT WAVE

FIG. 26-8. HETERODYNING OR THE FORMATION OF BEATS

FIG. 26-9. TYPICAL I-F TRANSFORMER

mixer consisting of a silicon or a germanium crystal diode.[3] Mixers of this type can be designed to operate satisfactorily at frequencies even higher than 25,000 mc.

26.4 *Automatic volume control or AVC systems*

Superheterodyne receivers usually employ a system of automatic gain control or automatic volume control in addition to the manual volume control. The need for automatic volume control becomes apparent when it is realized that the signal from a strong local station may be 1 million times stronger than the signal received from a distant station. If the gain of the receiver is kept high enough to bring in the weaker station, the stronger station will produce an annoying blasting effect when one is tuning across the band. Furthermore, after a desired station has been tuned in, there are likely to be variations in loudness produced as a result of fading of the signal.

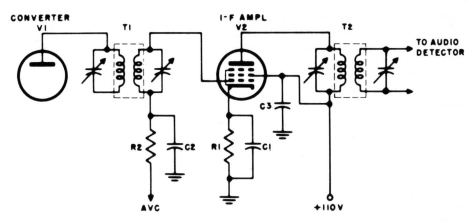

FIG. 26-10. CIRCUIT DIAGRAM OF AN I-F AMPLIFIER

In an AVC system, a negative d-c voltage is obtained from the output of the detector stage (Fig. 26-11). This negative voltage is fed back to the grid of a variable-mu amplifier tube in one or more of the preceding amplifier stages. The magnitude of this negative-feedback voltage depends upon the strength of the signal. When a strong signal is received, it produces a high, negative, AVC voltage which increases the bias of the variable-mu tube, thus decreasing the gain of the strong signal. When a weak signal is detected, the AVC voltage is reduced, and there is a greater amount of gain for the weak signal. This system possesses one disadvantageous characteristic, namely the fact that the AVC action does tend to reduce somewhat the strength of a weak

signal. This disadvantage can be eliminated by the use of a DAVC or delayed automatic volume control circuit, in which the AVC system is inoperative until the signal reaches a desired minimum level of strength (Fig. 26-12).[4]

26.5 *Image frequencies*

One of the disadvantages of the superheterodyne receiver is its tendency ιo receive certain unwanted signals called images. When a radio receiver is tuned to a station broadcasting on 550 kc, the local oscillator is tuned to 1,006 kc in order to produce an i-f signal of 456 kc. If another station

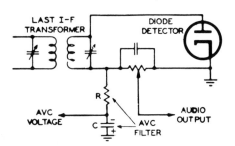

FIG. 26-11. AUTOMATIC VOLUME CONTROL (AVC) CIRCUIT

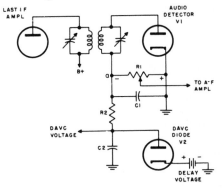

FIG. 26-12. CIRCUIT OF A DELAYED AVC (DAVC) SYSTEM

nearby is broadcasting on a frequency of 1,462 kc, this signal will also beat against the 1,006-kc oscillator signal to produce an i-f signal of 456 kc. This second broadcast signal, called the image-frequency signal, will naturally produce interference with the original signal.

The image-frequency effect can be reduced by using a higher value of intermediate frequency. This places the image-frequency station in a different frequency band which is less likely to be picked up by the receiver. A second method of reducing image-frequency interference is to have additional tuned preselector stages before the mixer or converter stage. This is accomplished by adding one or two stages of r-f amplification before the converter stage.

26.6 Radio-frequency amplifier stage

The addition of an r-f amplifier stage also improves the signal-to-noise ratio. The mixer stage usually produces more noise than an r-f amplifier stage, and this noise is amplified together with the signal. When the signal is amplified by an r-f stage, less amplification is required in the following stages, and the noises that are introduced by the mixer stage receive less amplification. Consequently, the r-f stage is one of the more important elements of a high-quality radio receiver, since it determines how weak a signal the receiver can respond to satisfactorily (Fig. 26-13).[5]

Another useful function of the r-f amplifier is to serve as a buffer between the local oscillator and the antenna. Without the presence of this buffer stage, there is a tendency for the oscillator to produce radiation of energy from the antenna, thus interfering with reception of nearby receivers.

26.7 Multiband receivers

Some receivers are designed to receive signals on several different operating bands of frequencies. Since a given combination of a coil and capacitor will usually tune only to one frequency band, some arrangement is employed to substitute coils when it is desired to switch from one band to another.

Some receivers use plug-in coils that are removed and replaced manually. Others have the coils permanently connected in the receiver circuit to a multicontact rotary ganged switch that is used to connect and disconnect the various coils. This switch is usually called the selector or band switch.

The coils that are involved are usually those associated with the r-f amplifier, the mixer, and the local-oscillator stages (Fig. 26-14). Occasionally, where an extremely-wide range of frequencies is to be covered, two sets of i-f transformers are provided. These transformers correspond to two different intermediate frequencies employed by the receiver, one for the low-frequency ranges and the other for the higher-frequency ranges.

26.8 Diversity systems

Changes in the conditions of the ionosphere can produce fading of the received signal. One method of overcoming this is to employ a space-diversity receiving system (Fig. 26-15). It has been found that signals received in antennas that are separated by a distance of from 3 to 10 wavelengths usually fade at different times and seldom fade simultaneously. In this space-diversity antenna system, two or three antennas are separated by 5 to 10 wavelengths. The signal appearing at

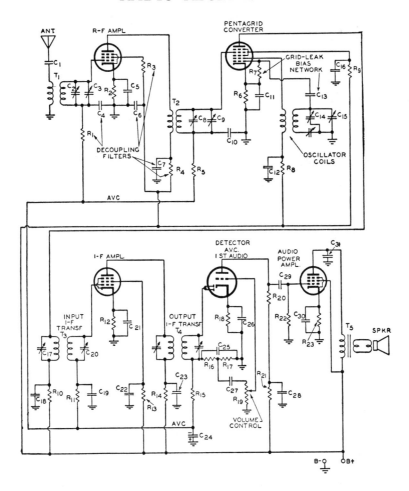

FIG. 26-13. CIRCUIT DIAGRAM OF A TYPICAL SUPERHETERODYNE RECEIVER

each antenna is fed into a separate receiver. The outputs of these two or
three receivers are fed into a circuit
that selects the output from the channel
that has the strongest signal. It then
sends that signal to the loudspeaker.
Since there will always be at least one
channel that has a strong signal output,
the effects of ionospheric fading are
minimized.

A second type of diversity system
is called frequency diversity. In this
system, advantage is taken of the fact
that signals of slightly different fre-

quencies do not fade in synchronization.
The diversity receiver possesses two or
more input circuits which are tuned to
the different frequencies being transmitted. The signal that has the greatest
amplitude at a given instant is the one
that is fed into the remaining circuits
of the receiver to produce a useful
output.

Mention may also be made of a
polarization diversity system, which is
used where space limitations or other
factors do not permit using the other
types of diversity systems. It is based

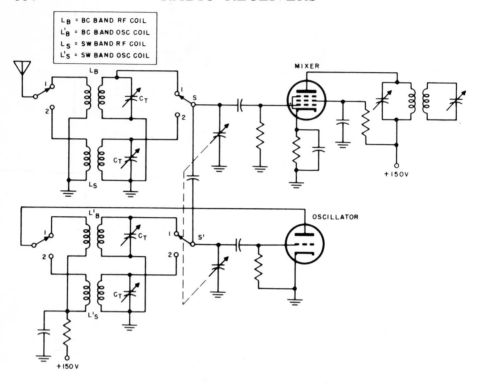

FIG. 26-14. MULTIBAND RECEIVER CONVERTER SECTION

upon the fact that the vertically and horizontally polarized components of the electromagnetic wave do not usually fade simultaneously. Diversity reception may therefore be obtained by using two antennas, one designed to respond to horizontally polarized waves and the other to vertically polarized waves.

26.9 The single-sideband selector

The General Electric single-sideband selector is a device that is designed to improve the selectivity and fidelity of a communications receiver. It can be used for the single-sideband detection of conventional amplitude-modulated, single-sideband, or unmodulated c-w transmissions.

During the process of selective fading of a signal, the phase and amplitude of the upper and lower sideband pairs are altered. This condition leads to high distortion in conventional detection systems. By pushing a selector button, it is possible to eliminate one sideband and to select the sideband that has minimum interference. Since the audio signal is now dependent on one sideband only, any distortion effects produced by unequal propagation of the two sidebands are eliminated.

Another interesting feature of this device is known as *reinforced carrier*. When selective fading causes the level of the carrier to fall below twice the level of the sideband, a type of distortion similar to overmodulation is produced. By pressing a button on this device, it is possible to lock a

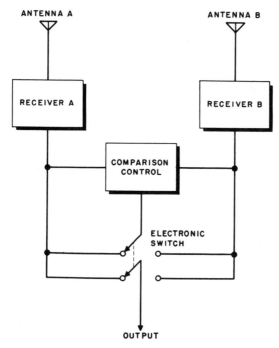

FIG. 26-15. PRINCIPLE OF DIVERSITY RECEPTION

local oscillator to the frequency of the carrier wave and exalt or reinforce the level of the carrier by a factor of twenty. This exalted-carrier action helps reduce any distortion that is produced by selective fading of the carrier.

26.10 *Antennas for small receivers*

In the past, it was customary to employ flat air-core loop antennas in small broadcast-band receivers. During the last few years there has been a tendency to replace these loop antennas by ferrite-rod antennas. This has been particularly noticeable in portable and table-model sets, and to a lesser extent in console receivers.

One advantage of a ferrite-rod antenna is its higher "Q" or figure of merit. This produces greater operating efficiency. The smaller size of the ferrite-rod is an advantage in portable receivers. A third advantage is the fact that, unlike the loop antenna, the ferrite-rod is non-directional and does not have to be oriented in any particular manner for best signal reception. A fourth advantage is the fact that the inductance of the antenna may easily be adjusted by varying the position of the coil along the ferrite rod. Finally, it has been found that the replacement of an air-core loop by a ferrite-rod antenna will usually improve both the sensitivity and the signal-to-noise ratio.[6]

26.11 *Continuous-wave reception*

In order to receive c-w signals with a superheterodyne receiver, a second oscillator is required (Fig. 26-16). This oscillator is known as a beat-frequency

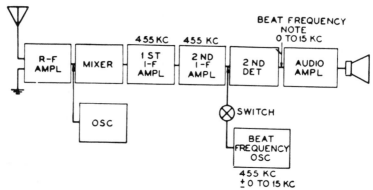

FIG. 26-16. BLOCK DIAGRAM OF A SUPERHETERODYNE RECEIVER CAPABLE OF RECEIVING C-W SIGNALS

oscillator or BFO. The BFO is tuned to a frequency, such as 457 kc, that is slightly different from that of the intermediate frequency. The BFO is then coupled to the second-detector stage. Heterodyning action between this signal and the i-f signal of 456 kc produces a 1-kc or 1,000-cps audio-frequency signal of constant pitch. The frequency of this audio-frequency signal may be varied by adjusting the frequency of the BFO.

26.12 *The frequency-modulation receiver*

The main difference between an FM receiver and an AM super-heterodyne receiver that is designed for VHF reception is that the detector of the latter has been replaced by two other stages called respectively the limiter and the discriminator (Fig. 26-17).

The limiter cuts out any AM signal variations, such as those produced by noise, static, and fading. The output of the limiter is a signal of constant amplitude. The peaks or variations in amplitudes have been clipped off (Fig. 26-18).

The typical limiter circuit is that of a tuned r-f amplifier operating at very-low screen and plate voltages.

Saturation is easily reached during the positive half of the signal cycle, and cutoff is easily produced during the negative half (Fig. 26-19). These clipping actions remove any spurious amplitude variations of the signal (Fig. 26-20).

It is obvious that if the signal reaching the antenna of the receiver is very weak, the signal appearing in the limiter will not possess sufficient amplitude to enable this stage to clip the amplitude variations that are produced by noise (Fig. 26-21). Consequently, the sensitivity of an FM receiver is rated in terms of the lowest signal that can be received at the antenna that will produce full limiting by the limiter.

The quieting figure of an FM receiver indicates how far down the noise level is below the signal level after the limiter and discriminator have done their jobs. Thus, a quieting figure of 20 db of quieting at 3 microvolts means that when a 3-microvolt signal reaches the antenna, the level of the noise output of the receiver will be 20 db below that of the signal. A figure of 30 db of quieting at 5 microvolts means that when the strength of the received signal is increased to 5 microvolts, the improved limiting action reduces the noise output to a level 30 db below that of the signal.[7]

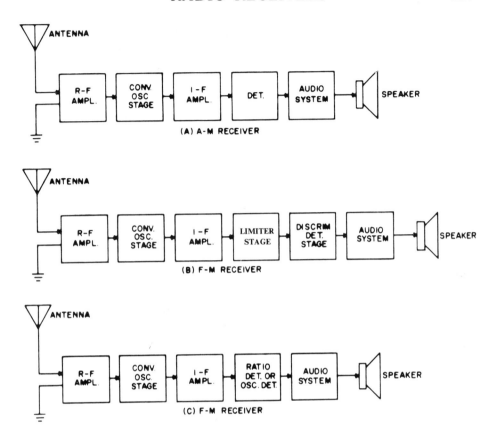

FIG. 26-17. BLOCK DIAGRAMS SHOWING DIFFERENCES BETWEEN AM AND FM RECEIVERS

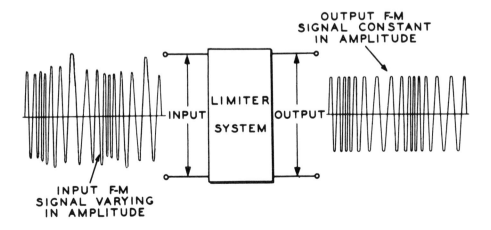

FIG. 26-18. THE FUNCTION OF THE LIMITER

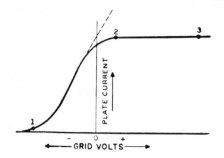

FIG. 26-19. IP-EG CURVE OF A LIMITER TUBE
Note the sudden flattening in the positive region beyond point 2.

The discriminator corresponds to the detector of an AM receiver. In an AM receiver the detector converts the amplitude variations of the received AM signal into an audio-frequency signal. In an FM receiver, the discriminator converts the frequency variations of the FM signal into an audio-frequency signal. The audio-frequency signal is then amplified by ordinary a-f amplifiers and is sent through the loudspeakers.[8]

The conventional discriminator is designed to respond to the differences between the voltages developed across two diodes (Fig. 26-22). There is a second type of FM detector, called a ratio detector, which is based upon the changes in the ratios of the voltages produced across the two diodes (Fig. 26-23). This ratio detector is relatively insensitive to variations in amplitude

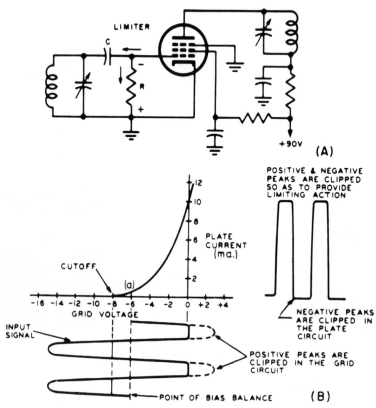

FIG. 26-20. TYPICAL LIMITER CIRCUIT (A): CLIPPING ACTION ON THE INPUT SIGNAL (B).

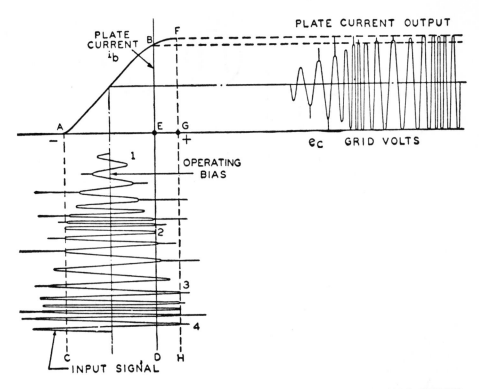

FIG. 26-21. IF THE F-M INPUT SIGNAL TO THE LIMITER STAGE DOES NOT HAVE SUFFICIENT AMPLITUDE TO PRODUCE LIMITER ACTION, ANY NOISE SUPERIMPOSED ON THE SIGNAL WILL APPEAR IN THE PLATE-CURRENT OUTPUT

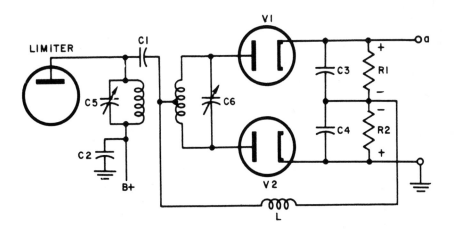

FIG. 26-22. FOSTER-SEELEY DISCRIMINATOR CIRCUIT

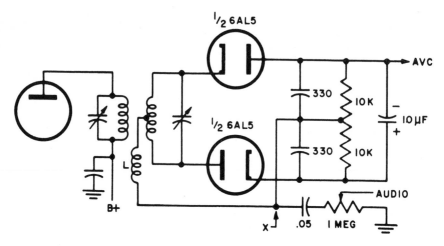

FIG. 26-23. MODERN RATIO DETECTOR

of the signal and does not require a preceding limiter stage.[9] Both the discriminator and the ratio detector are specialized forms of a type of detector called the slope detector, and they are the most popular types of FM detector circuits employed today.

A third type of FM detector, the gated-beam detector, performs both the limiting and detecting functions in one stage and also acts as the first stage of audio amplification (Fig. 26-24). It contains a specially designed tube called a gated-beam tube, in which a narrow, vertical, sheet-like beam of electrons travels from the cathode to the plate. The 6BN6 is a good example of a tube that is frequently employed in this type of circuit (Fig. 26-25).[10]

26.13 *The squelch circuit*

An interesting circuit that is found in some FM receivers is known as a squelch circuit. It is also known as a muting or quieting circuit, and is designed to reduce background noise when no signal is present. When no signal voltage is developed by the discriminator, a squelch-tube circuit prevents

the audio-frequency amplifier circuit from operating by cutting off the flow of plate current of the first a-f amplifier. When a signal comes in, a negative voltage that is produced in the discriminator circuit cuts off the squelch tube and permits a signal to pass through the first a-f amplifier.

26.14 *Automatic frequency control*

Another circuit that is frequently found in good FM receivers and tuners is an automatic frequency control or AFC circuit. This circuit locks the tuned circuits of the receiver to the frequency of the FM broadcasting station that has been tuned in and reduces the tendency of the receiver to drift away from the frequency of the station to which it is tuned.

FM receivers are more susceptible to drift than their AM counterparts because the values of inductance and capacitance used in FM tuning circuits are much lower than those used in AM tuning circuits. The values of these reactances approach those of the tube and stray-circuit capacitances. Since

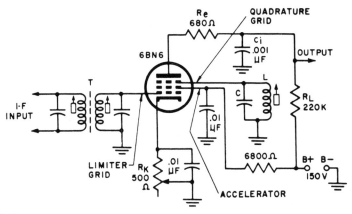

Fig. 26-24. Basic gated-beam circuit

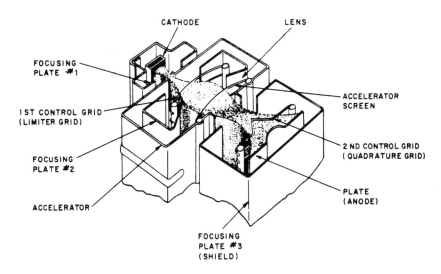

Fig. 26-25. Internal construction of Type 6BN6 gated-beam tube

the value of the latter may vary considerably as the temperature changes during the warm-up period, an undesirable change in the resonant frequencies of the tuned circuits of the oscillator may be produced. Since these changes tend to make the frequency drift downward, some FM receivers employ capacitors that possess a negative temperature coefficient. A capacitor of this type decreases in capacitance as the temperature increases, thus tending to raise the resonant frequency during the warm-up period and compensating for the downward tendency.[11]

Automatic frequency control can also be achieved by using the voltage obtained from the FM detector or discriminator to key an AFC tube (Figs. 26-26 and 26-27). This tube, which is a reactance tube, is connected to the tank circuit of the oscillator of the

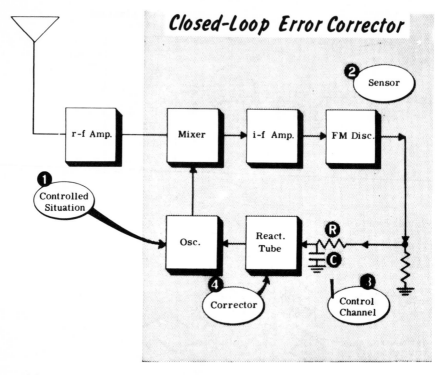

FIG. 26-26. BLOCK DIAGRAM OF AN AFC OSCILLATOR CIRCUIT
The circuit is an example of a closed-loop system.

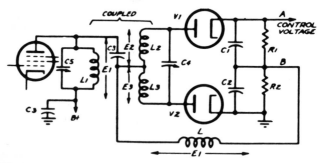

FIG. 26-27. AFC VOLTAGE OBTAINED FROM A DISCRIMINATOR

receiver (Fig. 26-28.) The voltage obtained from point A of the FM detector is used to bias this tube. When the station is tuned in perfectly, this voltage is equal to zero. The bias becomes negative when the receiver is detuned one way, and positive when it is detuned the other way. If the oscillator tube begins to drift away from the correct frequency, a corrective bias voltage is thus applied to the reactance tube. This changes the capacitance of the tube and of the oscillator tank circuit in such a manner that it restores the oscillator to the correct original frequency. Since this circuit makes it very difficult to tune

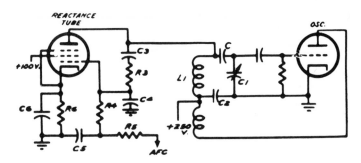

FIG. 26-28. AFC REACTANCE TUBE CIRCUIT

in a weak station which is close to a powerful station, an AFC-defeat switch is usually provided to disable the AFC circuit when AFC operation is not desired.

Some manufacturers of FM receivers and tuners have abandoned the use of AFC circuits entirely and are using extremely-wide-band i-f amplifiers and detector stages. Consequently, even when the oscillator drifts, this great bandwidth still permits the passage of the i-f signal without distortion.[12][13]

It may be recalled that mention has previously been made of the fact that most FM transmitters preemphasize the higher audio modulating frequencies in order to reduce noise effects (Figs. 25-73 and 25-74). Consequently, the audio-frequency and amplifier circuits of the FM receiver must be designed to deemphasize or reduce the higher audio frequencies in the same proportions (Figs. 25-75, 26-29, and 26-30).

26.15 Radio receiver and transmitter statistics

As of 1959, the number of broadcast receivers had increased from the 18.5 million of 1935 to 200 million. Of these, 150 million were AM or FM receivers, while 50 million were television receivers. Thus the nation had more broadcast receivers than people, and three times as many sets as automobiles.

Radio stations of all kinds increased from 51,000 in 1934 to more than 507,000. From 600 stations in 1934, the number of broadcast authorizations increased to over 10,000, of which 930 were for FM transmission. Amateur radio authorizations have grown from 36,000 to more than 204,000 during that period, while the number of commercial radio-operator's permits has increased from 21,000 to more than 1.7 million. The personalized use of radio is reflected by the fact that there are over 127,000 Citizens Radio Band authorizations outstanding. It is obvious from these facts that the business of manufacturing radio receivers and transmitters is in a very healthy state.[14]

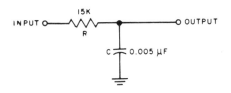

FIG. 26-29. DE-EMPHASIS CIRCUIT IN A RECEIVER

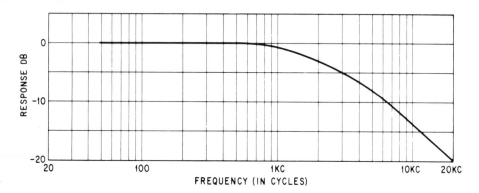

FIG. 26-30. DE-EMPHASIS CURVE FOR AN FM RECEIVER OR TUNER

REFERENCES

1. O. E. Dunlap, Jr., *Radio's 100 Men of Science,* Harper & Bros., N.Y., 1944, pp. 76-77.
2. *Ibid,* p. 188.
3. C. F. Edwards, "Microwave Mixers," *Proc. IRE,* 35:1181, Nov. 1944.
4. Art Widman, "AGC Systems," *National Radio Institute News,* 19:1-2, 16, Feb. 1960.
5. Joseph Marshall, "Inside the Hi-Fi Tuner," *Popular Electronics,* 11:84, Sept. 1959.
6. M. S. Kay, "Latest Trends in AM Receivers," *Radio and Television News,* 51:50-51, Mar. 1954.
7. "What is Quieting in an FM Radio Tuner?," *Better Listening,* 2:4, Apr. 1956.

8. J. G. Chaffee, "The Detection of Frequency Modulated Waves," *Proc. IRE.* 23:517, May 1935.
9. S. W. Seeley and J. Avins, "The Ratio Detector," *RCA Review,* 8:201, June 1947.
10. J. S. Allen, "Gated Beam Discriminator-Type 6BN6," *Sylvania News,* 23:5, Apr. 1956.
11. J. Richard Johnson, "Drift and AFC in FM," *Radio and TV News,* 61:111, Apr. 1959.
12. *Ibid,* p. 111.
13 J. Marshall, *Op. cit.,* pp. 84-86.
14. "Record Number of Sets in Use During '58," *Radio and TV News,* 61:136, Mar. 1959.

27 - TELEVISION TRANSMISSION AND RECEPTION

27.1 *History of television*

Television is not a new invention; its basic principles were outlined between 1875 and 1880 by Lebano and Carey. One proposed "closed-circuit" television system consisted of a mosaic containing a large bank of selenium photocells upon which the light from the image was focused. Each selenium cell was connnected through an amplifier to an electromagnet that controlled the shutter to a similarly positioned light at the receiving end. An experimental system based upon this principle was actually constructed. It was capable of transmitting blurred figures and letters with a rather considerable lack of detail.

In 1884, Paul Nipkow invented the mechanical scanning disc—the predecessor of all present-day scanning devices. Another early pioneer was Boris Rosing, of the Russian St. Petersburg Technological Institute, under whom Zworykin studied. In 1907, Rosing used a light cell and mechanical scanning mirrors to produce a television picture, and a Braun cathode-ray tube to reproduce this picture.

Until 1933, almost all scanning systems utilized Nipkow's idea involving a flying spot of light which was controlled by a rotating disc (Fig. 27-1).[1] However, as early as 1923, Vladimir Zworykin had demonstrated the successful operation of a television system employing an iconoscope that produced a rough pattern on the face of a kinescope tube.

Television transmission of half-tone pictures by means of a mechanical scanning system was demonstrated in England by John L. Baird early in 1926. A few months later, Bell Telephone Laboratories constructed a television system employing a mechanical scanning disc. With this system, a picture of poor definition was successfully transmitted from New York City to Whippany, New Jersey, where it was reproduced by a receiver containing 2,000 neon glow tubes (Fig. 27-2).[2]

During the same year, 1927, Bell Telephone Laboratories demonstrated television transmission over wire circuits between New York City and Washington, D.C. (Fig. 27-3). In 1928, the first television dramatic program

Courtesy, Radio Corporation of America
FIG. 27-1. MECHANICAL SCANNING EQUIPMENT USED IN RCA-NBC EXPERIMENTAL TELEVISION STATION (1928)

Courtesy, Bell Telephone Laboratories

Fig. 27-2. BACK OF EARLY TELEVISION RECEIVER *Hundreds of wires are connected to the different segments of the neon-filled tubes. Current flowing from the transmitter through these wires created a pattern of light and dark areas on the tubes to form a picture.*

Atlantic. Television programs were actually broadcast on a fairly regular schedule in England during the years 1929 to 1931.

The electronic method of scanning that is now in use was developed in 1933 with the perfecting by Zworykin (Fig. 27-5) of a type of vacuum tube known as the iconoscope, and the invention by Philo T. Farnsworth of a scanning tube which he called the image dissector. Regular transmission of television programs was inaugurated in 1936; three years later, the first commercial television sets were put on the market for sale to the public (Fig. 27-6). In July 1941 the first television program was sold to a commercial sponsor by a station in New York City.

Courtesy, General Electric Co.

Fig. 27-4. Dr. ALEXANDERSON'S "TV PROJECTOR"

Courtesy, Bell Telephone Laboratories

Fig. 27-3. BELL SYSTEM DEMONSTRATION OF TRANSMISSION OF TELEVISION OVER WIRE CIRCUITS (1927).

was telecast by station WGY, Schenectady, New York (Fig. 27-4). During that same year, Baird also succeeded in transmitting a televised image from London to Hartsdale, New York, the first image to be telecast across the

In the United States, by 1960, of the 670 commercial television broadcasting stations that had been authorized, there were 568 television stations on the air, and it was estimated that there were over 50 million television receivers in operation in American homes. Approximately 85 per cent of all homes possessed one or more television receivers. Over 90 per cent of the population was within range of at least one operating television station, and 75

Courtesy, Radio Corporation of America

FIG. 27-5. DR. V. K. ZWORYKIN DEMONSTRAT-
ING HIS ELECTRONIC TELEVISION RECEIVER (1929)

per cent were in the service areas of two or more television stations.[3]

In 1959, over 6.3 million black-and-white television receivers, with a value of over 870 million dollars, were produced. This represented an increase of 30 per cent in value and 29 per cent in the number of units over 1958.

27.2 The iconoscope

In television broadcasting, since a picture must be transformed into a varying voltage, some means must be used to convert the picture areas into successive time intervals. The method employed for doing this is called scanning. One of the devices that was used in the 1930's to scan the picture and to convert it into successive electrical impulses was called the iconoscope, from the Greek words *eikon*, meaning a

figure or image, and *skopein*, meaning to see.

Other devices that perform the same scanning function are the image orthicon and the image dissector tubes. The operation of all these scanning tubes has been described in Chapter 15. Consequently, in the following discussion, only the operation of the iconoscope will be reviewed. The operation of each of the other types of camera tubes is very similar in principle to that of the iconoscope.

The iconoscope is a specialized type of cathode-ray tube (Fig. 27-7). It contains an electron gun which generates and directs an electron beam at a photosensitive plate called a mosaic. The picture that is to be transmitted is focused on the mosaic by an optical lens. In effect, the mosaic and lens act as a camera, with the mosaic corresponding to the film.

The lens focuses the image onto the mosaic. The nature of the mosaic is such that it will record the amount of light striking it and stores up the information in the form of minute electrical charges distributed over its surface. In this manner, the picture information is collected where it can later be removed by an electron beam and passed on to the following circuits of the television system. It should be noted that the iconoscope is today regarded as obsolescent. It is being replaced rapidly by the image orthicon and other orthicon camera tubes.

27.3 Scanning

In scanning, the electron beam of the iconoscope is moved in a fixed, repeated path over the area of the mosaic. As the electron beam strikes each of the charged cells of the mosaic, the electron balance of each cell is returned to neutral. The voltage variations which

Fig. 27-6. RCA's experimental television set (1939)

are produced by the scanning process thus become the electrical equivalent of the picture.

The technique of scanning employs two separate sweep circuits to deflect the electron beam along a horizontal and a vertical path. The EIA standard scanning pattern consists of 525 horizontal sweeps of the electron beam while it is moving from the top to the bottom of the image area in one-thirtieth of a second, resulting in the producing of one frame (Fig. 27-8). In actual practice, so-called interlaced scanning, which was developed in 1928 by U. A. Sanabria, is usually employed (Fig. 27-9). In the interlaced method, one field, consisting of the odd-numbered lines, is swept from top to bottom in one-sixtieth of a second, and then the other half of the line is swept during the next sixtieth of a second (Fig. 27-10). These two fields make up one frame (Fig. 27-11).

This type of interlaced scanning tends to reduce picture flicker. The same scanning pattern is followed in the cathode-ray tube of the receiver. Separate sweep circuits, in synchronization with the iconoscope sweep circuits, drive the beam of the cathode-ray tube in the receiver.[4]

Since there are 60 fields each second, the vertical sweep frequency is 60 cps (Fig. 27-12). The horizontal sweep frequency of 15,750 cps is based upon the fact that there are 525 lines per frame and 30 frames per second. The required sweep voltages should possess a sawtooth shape and may be

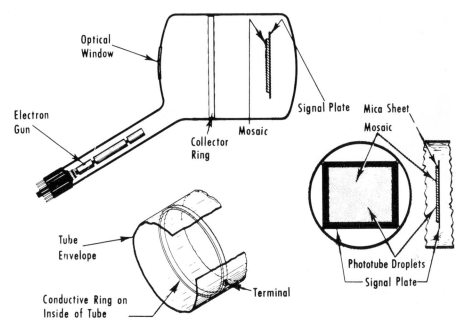

Fig. 27-7. Parts of the iconoscope

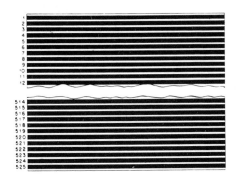

Fig. 27-8. EIA standard scanning pattern
Imagine the image on the target divided into 525 horizontal rows of picture content.

generated either by a multivibrator, or by a blocking oscillator or similar type of sine-wave oscillator that is then followed by special wave-shaping circuits.

27.4 Wobbled scanning

Many attempts have been made to eliminate the dark horizontal lines that are clearly visible between the successive traces of a display on a television picture tube. Some viewers deliberately misadjust the focus control. This blends the scanning lines together and makes them indistinguishable. However, this also blurs the beam in a horizontal direction and gives the picture a smeared quality. For a long time, the only alternative was for the viewer to sit far enough back so that the individual lines could not be distinguished.

In 1953, the British developed a wobbler circuit. This contained an oscillator whose output deflected the scanning lines and caused them to wobble up and down, producing a thicker white line and reducing the width of the black line. However, this system was expensive and required the use of coils around the neck of the picture tube. These coils radiated interfering signals.

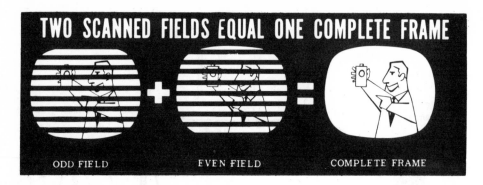

FIG. 27-9. NATURE OF INTERLACED SCANNING

Each Field Is Made Up Of 262.5 Scanning Lines

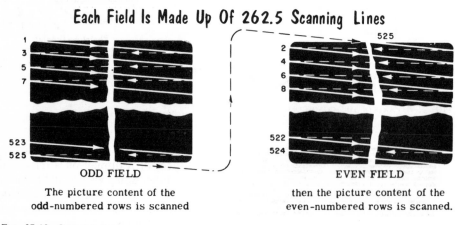

ODD FIELD

The picture content of the
odd-numbered rows is scanned

EVEN FIELD

then the picture content of the
even-numbered rows is scanned.

FIG. 27-10. ODD AND EVEN FIELDS

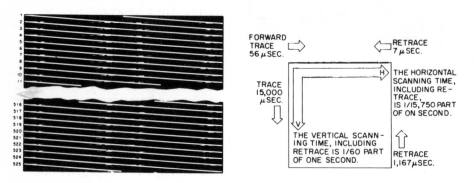

FIG. 27-11. INTERLACED SCANNING PATTERN
Instantaneous return from bottom to top of mosaic is assumed.

FORWARD
TRACE ⇨
56 μSEC.

RETRACE
7 μSEC. ⇦

TRACE
15,000
μSEC.

THE HORIZONTAL
SCANNING TIME,
INCLUDING RE-
TRACE,
IS 1/15,750 PART
OF ON SECOND.

THE VERTICAL SCANN-
ING TIME, INCLUDING
RETRACE IS 1/60 PART
OF ONE SECOND.

RETRACE
1,167 μSEC.

FIG. 27-12. HORIZONTAL AND VERTICAL SCAN-
NING FREQUENCIES

In 1957, Atti and Hall of Westinghouse announced another solution to this problem. Following a suggestion made by Thompson of the Westinghouse Research Laboratories, they developed a simple method of producing wobbling. This was accomplished by modifying the electron-gun structure of the picture tube by splitting the focusing grid in half. This focusing grid still serves its regular function of concentrating the electron beam on the screen. At the same time, a fluctuating voltage is applied to this grid from a tube near the base of the picture tube. This fluctuating voltage causes the beam to wobble up and down at a frequency of 15 mc. The wobble is sufficient to fill in the blank areas between the sweeps without blurring the image.[5][6]

The wobbling technique also helps to prolong the life of the camera tube. Prior to its development, the cameraman was required to keep moving his camera in order to prevent an undesirable effect known as burn-in or stickiness, which made frequent replacement of camera tubes necessary. Image-wobbler circuits eliminate the danger of burn-in and improve camera techniques by enabling the cameraman to spend more time on one scene.[7]

27.5 *Television broadcasting*

It should be noted that in television broadcasting, both the sound and the picture are transmitted simultaneously (Fig. 27-13). The sounds of television are transmitted by means of a standard FM sound-transmission system (Fig. 27-14). The only difference between this FM transmission and the conventional FM transmission that is found on the 88 to 108-mc band is that the maximum frequency deviation produced by the sound of television is 25 kc instead of 75 kc.

The waveforms from the output circuit of the iconoscope or other camera tube are amplified and used to amplitude-modulate the picture-signal carrier (Fig. 27-15). In order to obtain optimum modulation with the smallest amount of video modulating power, grid modulation is usually employed. Any lack of linearity present in this modulator stage can be compensated for by deliberately introducing distortion in the preceding video-amplifier stages.

It is interesting to note that the maximum amplitude is produced by a black signal. As the brightness of the area being scanned increases from

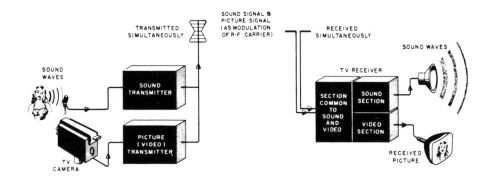

FIG. 27-13. TV BROADCASTING AND RECEIVING

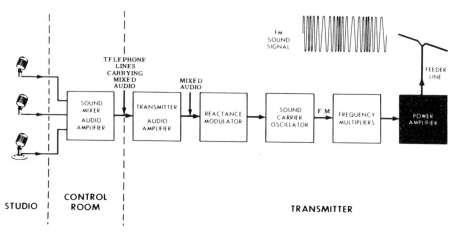

FIG. 27-14. BLOCK DIAGRAM OF THE SOUND PORTION OF A TV TRANSMITTER

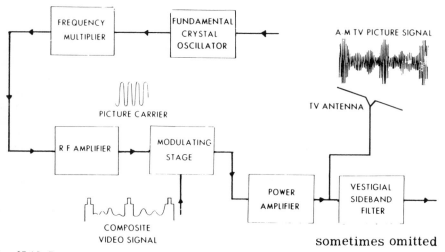

FIG. 27-15. BLOCK DIAGRAM OF THE PICTURE PORTION OF A TV TRANSMITTER

black to white, the amplitude of the video signal decreases from the black reference level (Fig. 27-16). This type of video signal transmission is called negative picture transmission and is the standard system employed in the United States. It was selected by a group representing the radio industry. This group was called the NTSC or National Television Standards Committee. The NTSC functioned as an advisory group for the FCC in determining television standards.

In Great Britain, the reverse type or positive picture transmission is preferred, in which the brightest portions of the picture being scanned produce video signals of the greatest amplitude. Each method has its own advantages. Adherents of the negative system claim that it produces better reception under adverse conditions. Static and man-made noises from electric razors and automobiles tend to produce high-amplitude pulses that result in black spots on the picture instead of bright

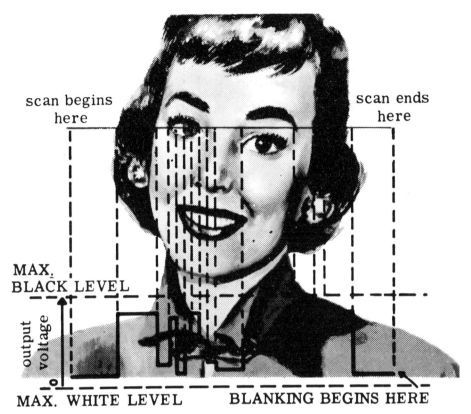

scan begins
here

scan ends
here

MAX.
BLACK LEVEL

output voltage

MAX. WHITE LEVEL   BLANKING BEGINS HERE

FIG. 27-16. VIDEO SIGNAL PRODUCED BY SCANNING ONE LINE

flashes of light. Another advantage of negative transmission is the fact that the synchronizing pulses are produced at maximum carrier amplitude. This provides for better synchronization of the receiver with the transmitter in fringe areas where the signal is weak. If a receiver that is designed to be used with one system is employed to receive the signals sent out by the other system, the picture that will appear on the screen will have reversed light values and will resemble a photographic negative.

Another interesting characteristic of the radiated television signals emitted by the television broadcasting stations of the United States is the fact that

the waves are horizontally polarized. This means that the electrostatic component of the radiated wave is parallel to the earth's surface. Consequently, horizontal antennas are required at both the transmitter and the receiver. In Great Britain, vertical polarization is accepted as standard. Among the advantages claimed for horizontal polarization of the radiated waves are the following:

1. Most man-made interference is vertically polarized. Consequently, a horizontally polarized antenna at the receiver tends to reduce the amount of interference that is picked up.

2. There is less attenuation of a

horizontally polarized wave while it is passing through the atmosphere and is being reflected from the earth.

A synchronizing generator creates two series of synchronizing or sync pulses—one for horizontal-path timing and one for vertical-path timing (Fig. 27-17). These pulses are added to the picture signals so that the sweep generators in the television receiver can be synchronized to the pattern of the iconoscope.

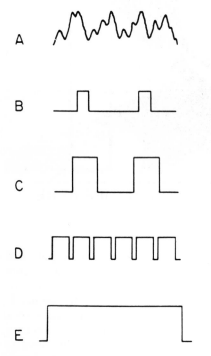

FIG. 27-17. PRINCIPAL PARTS OF THE PICTURE SIGNAL
(A) Picture information derived from the camera tube; (B) horizontal synchronizing pulses from the transmitter used to control horizontal scanning; (C) horizontal blanking pulses from the transmitter that extinguish the scanning beam at the end of its horizontal travel and during retrace; (D) vertical synchronizing pulse to control the vertical movement of the scanning beam; (E) vertical blanking pulse that extinguishes the scanning beam while it is returning from the bottom of the screen to the top.

The voltages of these synchronizing pulses are greater than that of the black reference level. As a consequence, the picture-tube screen is darkened for the duration of each pulse. This blanks out the objectionable trace that would otherwise be formed on the screen of the picture tube by the return of the beam to its starting position. The two signals, the picture and the synchronizing pulses, are transmitted together and compose what is called the video signal (Fig. 27-18).

27.6 *Band width*

In order to transmit pictures with fine detail, it is necessary that the picture or video signal contain modulating frequencies as high as 4 mc (Figs. 27-19 and 27-20). The lower-frequency video signals provide information concerning large objects in the picture and the background of the picture. Tl e higher video frequencies supply fine detail to the received picture. This is the chief reason why the twelve major television channels have been assigned to the very-high-frequency or VHF band between 54 mc and 216 mc where there is more room (Fig. 27-21).

Originally, there were 13 channels on this band. However, the FCC found it necessary to delete Channel 1 in order to eliminate sharing of television frequencies with other services. The sound

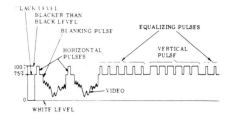

Courtesy, Radio-Electronics-Television Manufacturers Assoc.
FIG. 27-18. SIMPLIFIED WAVEFORM FOR A TELEVISION SIGNAL

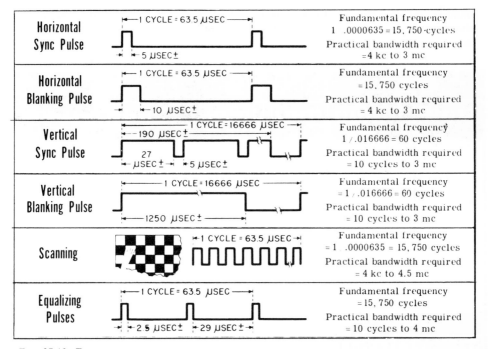

Horizontal Sync Pulse	⊢—1 CYCLE = 63.5 μSEC —⊣ ⊢—5 μSEC±	Fundamental frequency 1 .0000635 = 15,750 cycles Practical bandwidth required =4 kc to 3 mc
Horizontal Blanking Pulse	⊢—1 CYCLE = 63.5 μSEC —⊣ ⊢—10 μSEC±	Fundamental frequency = 15,750 cycles Practical bandwidth required = 4 kc to 3 mc
Vertical Sync Pulse	⊢——1 CYCLE = 16666 μSEC —⊣ ⊢—190 μSEC±—— 27 μSEC± ⊢—5 μSEC±	Fundamental frequency 1 /.016666 = 60 cycles Practical bandwidth required = 10 cycles to 3 mc
Vertical Blanking Pulse	⊢——1 CYCLE = 16666 μSEC ——⊣ ⊢——1250 μSEC±——⊣	Fundamental frequency = 1 /.016666 = 60 cycles Practical bandwidth required = 10 cycles to 3 mc
Scanning	⊢1 CYCLE = 63.5 μSEC→	Fundamental frequency = 1 .0000635 = 15,750 cycles Practical bandwidth required = 4 kc to 4.5 mc
Equalizing Pulses	⊢——1 CYCLE = 63.5 μSEC —⊣ ⊢2.5 μSEC± ⊢29 μSEC±→	Fundamental frequency = 15,750 cycles Practical bandwidth required = 10 cycles to 4 mc

FIG. 27-19. FREQUENCIES AND PRACTICAL RECEIVER BAND WIDTHS

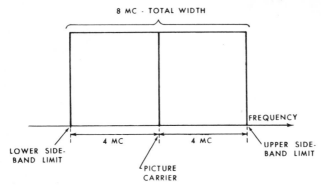

FIG. 27-20. BAND WIDTH OF THE TELEVISION PICTURE SIGNAL BEFORE CORRECTION

carrier and the necessary clearance between the sound and picture carriers and between the carriers and edges of the bands require another two megacycles. Therefore, a six-megacycle band is allocated to each television-transmitting channel so that both sound and picture signals may be broadcast simultaneously.

This six-megacycle channel is not wide enough to accommodate both sidebands of the video signal. For this reason partial suppression of the lower sideband of the video signal is necessary (Fig. 27-22). The upper sideband and frequencies in the lower sideband that are within 0.75 mc of the video carrier are transmitted completely. Lower sideband frequencies that are further away than 0.75 mc from the carrier are rapidly attenuated, and frequencies that are more than 1.25 mc below the carrier are completely removed. This special type of single-sideband transmission is called

VHF		UHF		'UHF	
Channel	Frequency limits	Channel	Frequency limits	Channel	Frequency limits
2	54-60	35	596-602	73	824-830
3	60-66	36	602-608	74	830-836
4	66-72	37	608-614	75	836-842
5	76-82	38	614-620	76	842-848
6	82-88	39	620-626	77	848-854
7	174-180	40	626-632	78	854-860
8	180-186	41	632-638	79	860-866
9	186-192	42	638-644	80	866-872
10	192-198	43	644-650	81	872-878
11	198-204	44	650-656	82	878-884
12	204-210	45	656-662	83	884-890
13	210-216	46	662-668		

UHF			
Channel	Frequency limits		
14	470-476	47	668-674
15	476-482	48	674-680
16	482-488	49	680-686
17	488-494	50	686-692
18	494-500	51	692-698
19	500-506	52	698-704
20	506-512	53	704-710
21	512-518	54	710-716
22	518-524	55	716-722
23	524-530	56	722-728
24	530-536	57	728-734
25	536-542	58	734-740
26	542-548	59	740-746
27	548-554	60	746-752
28	554-560	61	752-758
29	560-566	62	758-764
30	566-572	63	764-770
31	572-578	64	770-776
32	578-584	65	776-782
33	584-590	66	782-788
34	590-596	67	788-794
		68	794-800
		69	800-806
		70	806-812
		71	812-818
		72	818-824

List of Television Channel Frequencies

FIG. 27-21. LIST OF TELEVISION CHANNEL FREQUENCIES

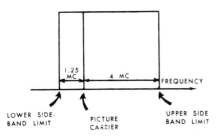

FIG. 27-22. AUTHORIZED BAND WIDTH OF THE TRANSMITTED PICTURE SIGNAL

vestigial-sideband transmission (Fig. 27-23). The most common method of obtaining this type of signal is to generate both sidebands and then remove the undesired portion of the lower sideband by means of a filter network that is inserted in the transmission line that connects the transmitter with the antenna.

These filters contain segments of coaxial line instead of ordinary capacitors and inductors. For the high-frequency signals being transmitted,

lengths of coaxial line that are longer or shorter than a quarter of a wavelength function as inductors or capacitors, whereas sections exactly one-quarter wavelength long act as series-resonant circuits.

Since single-sideband transmission permits greater utilization of channel space, the question may be raised why vestigial-sideband rather than single-sideband transmisson is used. In answer to this, it may be pointed out that in order to obtain single-sideband transmission, a type of filter must be inserted which distorts the low-frequency components of the video signal, producing a blurred picture. A second reason is the fact that single-sideband transmission requires very careful tuning of the receiver and requires the use of an oscillator with extremely low frequency drift. It is therefore not difficult to see why this vestigial-sideband transmission was selected as standard for television broadcasting.

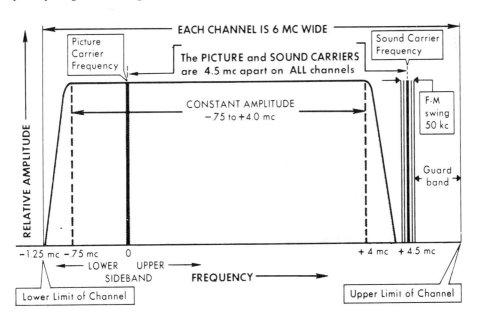

FIG. 27-23. VESTIGIAL SIDEBAND RESPONSE CURVE OF A TELEVISION CHANNEL

It may be of some interest to note that this system in which the picture, synchronizing information, and the sound are transmitted simultaneously over a television channel with a width of 6 megacycles was not always the accepted standard. In the early days of television broadcasting, both the audio and video intelligence were used to amplitude-modulate separate carriers that differed in frequency by 4.5 mc. Demonstration of the fidelity and noise-reducing properties of frequency modulation led to suggestions that the audio character of the television receiver could be improved by the use of frequency modulation. Consequently, in 1942, the FCC established the current standards which include the use of amplitude modulation for the video carrier and frequency modulation for the sound carrier (Fig. 27-24).

27.7 *Television receivers*

The television receiver generally contains seven major sections: the r-f section; the sound channel; the picture

or video channel; the vertical-sweep generator; the horizontal-sweep generator; the cathode-ray tube; and the power supply (Fig. 27-25).

The r-f or tuner section tunes to the desired frequency and picks up the two modulated carriers from the antenna (Fig. 27-26). The television receiving antenna is far more important and critical than the antennas employed for ordinary AM and FM sound reception. The simple dipole antenna that produces satisfactory results with a standard FM receiver generally produces unsatisfactory television reception except in areas very close to a television transmitter. For better results, more complex receiving antennas are used such as the following:

1. Dipole antennas. The folded dipole type of antenna is made up of two parallel half-wave dipoles (Fig. 27-27). They are placed close to each other and their ends are connected to each other. Like the conventional dipole, the folded dipole is bidirectional, the two major lobes being at right angles to the elements, but it possesses the advan-

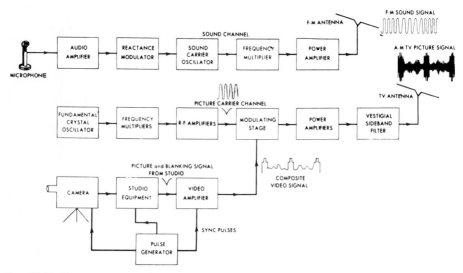

FIG. 27-24. BLOCK DIAGRAM OF A TELEVISION TRANSMITTER

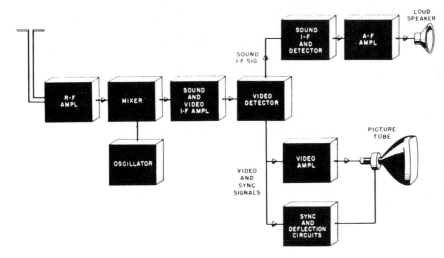

FIG. 27-25. GENERALIZED BLOCK DIAGRAM OF A TELEVISION RECEIVER

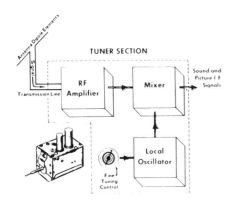

FIG.27-26. BLOCK DIAGRAM OF THE FRONT END CONTAINING THE R-F OR TUNER SECTION

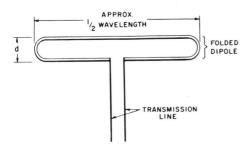

FIG. 27-27. BASIC FOLDED DIPOLE

tages of broader tuning and higher impedance. No appreciable amount of energy is radiated from or received at the ends. Dipoles may be stacked vertically to increase gain, a gain of 3 db being produced each time that the number of antennas is doubled. Thus, two vertically stacked dipoles produce a gain of 3 db over a single half-wave dipole, a four-unit or four-bay antenna produces a gain of 6 db, and an eight-bay antenna produces a gain of 9 db. Stacking also tends to increase the directivity of the antenna.[8]

2. Multiple-element or Yagi arrays. These antennas are named in honor of the Japanese scientist who first designed them. They contain a parasitic dipole antenna called a reflector, which is placed parallel to the main dipole, usually a folded dipole and approximately a quarter-wavelength behind it (Fig. 27-28). Another parasitic dipole, which is called the director, is placed a quarter-wavelength in front of the main or driven dipole. The reflector is slightly longer than, and the director is slightly shorter than, the driven dipole. An

array of this type is exceptionally directional, but does not respond to a very wide band of frequencies. Certain types of Yagi antenna arrays may be very complex, some of them containing as many as ten elements.

The r-f amplifier stage, which is sometimes omitted in less expensive receivers, increases the gain, the selectivity, and the signal-to-noise ratio of the receiver, and provides better suppression of image frequencies. The r-f amplifier also reduces interfering radiation from the receiver's oscillator. This stage must be capable of passing the entire 6-mc band of frequencies. In order to achieve these wide-bandpass characteristics, the antenna is coupled to the grid circuit of the r-f amplifier through two closely coupled tuned circuits that produce a double-humped selectivity curve. Resistors are also placed in parallel with these tuned circuits to load the circuits and produce a broad selectivity curve with a flat top that possesses the desired wide-bandpass characteristics (Fig. 27-29).

The r-f section also contains an oscillator whose output is mixed with the incoming signals in the same manner as is done in conventional superheterodyne receivers (Figs. 27-30 and 27-31). This action produces two intermediate frequencies, one from the picture carrier, and one from the sound carrier. The sound i-f carrier has a frequency that is 4.5 mc lower than that of the video i-f carrier. Tuned circuits placed at this point pass the picture signal through the video i-f channel and the sound signal through the sound i-f channel.

Folded Dipole connected element

Directors

FIG. 27-28. THE YAGI ANTENNA

The oscillator circuits that are usually employed are either the Hartley, a modified Colpitts, or an Armstrong tickler-coil type. The main problem associated with this circuit is that of the frequency drift produced by fluctuating voltages, humidity, and heat. Drift produced by the first two causes can be reduced by using regulated power supplies and by impregnating the tank circuit so that moisture cannot get at it. Drift produced by temperature changes can be reduced by using permeability-tuned coils and fixed capacitors in the tank circuit. The fixed capacitors have negative temperature coefficients which tend to counteract the increases produced by the other components when the temperature rises. Some receivers employ an automatic frequency-control or AFC system to keep the oscillator signal at the proper frequency. In this system, a frequency-regulating voltage is obtained from the output of the discriminator stage of the sound channel. This voltage is then applied to a correcting control tube that is connected to the local oscillator.

The sound section amplifies the FM sound signal, passes it through a limiter and then to a discriminator where it is detected or converted into an a-f signal (Fig. 27-32). This sound channel resembles an ordinary FM receiver except for the fact that the frequency of the i-f signal is different from the 10.7-mc i-f signal usually found in conventional FM receivers.

The task of demodulating the FM signal is usually performed by a ratio detector (Fig. 27-33). This circuit is generally employed in television receivers because it does not require multiple limiters to keep the input level constant; it is unaffected by periodic reduction of signal level; it requires little drive; and finally, it is extremely stable. The detected signal is then amplified by an

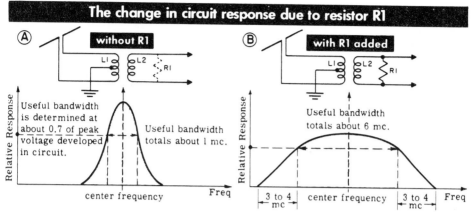

FIG. 27-29. RESPONSE CURVE OF THE R-F AMPLIFIER

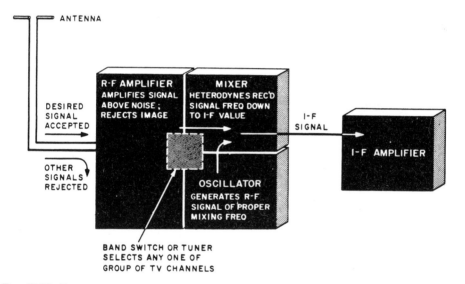

FIG. 27-30. FUNCTIONS OF THE FRONT END OF THE TV RECEIVER

audio amplifier and is fed into the loud-speaker where it is converted into sound energy.

The picture section amplifies the amplitude-modulated video i-f signal, detects it, and feeds the resulting video signal to the video amplifier. The video detector is generally a diode detector similar to the one found in AM broadcast receivers. The only signifi-cant circuit differences are based upon the fact that the polarity of the output voltage must be considered, and that compensating elements must be added to prevent loss of the higher video frequencies.

Some television receivers now employ germanium crystal diodes for video detection. It is claimed that in addition to lower power consumption resulting

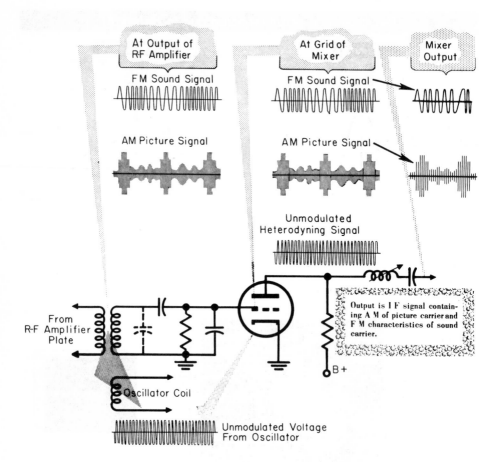

FIG. 27-31. SIGNALS IN THE MIXER SYSTEM

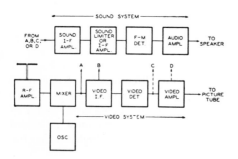

FIG. 27-32. BLOCK DIAGRAM OF THE FM SOUND AND VIDEO SECTION OF A TV RECEIVER, INDICATING POSSIBLE POINTS OF SOUND I-F TAKE-OFF

from the absence of the heater circuit, the crystal possesses the additional advantages of smaller size, reduced internal capacitance, increased linearity, and greater ease of mounting, since a tube socket is not required.

The detected signal is then fed to the video amplifier. This amplifier must be capable of reproducing without distortion all frequencies between 30 cps and 4 mc. The video amplifier then applies the signal to the grid of the cathode-ray tube. The signal thus controls the intensity of the beam in accordance with the picture pattern originally produced on the mosaic of the transmitter camera tube.

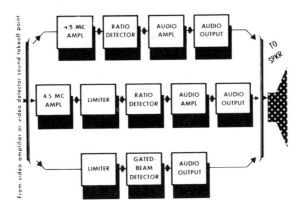

FIG. 27-33. TRENDS IN TV SOUND SYSTEMS

Most television receivers contain an automatic-gain-control or AGC circuit in the video section (Fig. 27-34). This circuit, which resembles the automatic volume-control circuit of a conventional superheterodyne receiver, automatically controls the overall amplification, thus maintaining a constant video level at the picture tube. The AGC circuit makes it possible to switch from one station to another with little change in picture contrast. It also reduces the effect of fluctuations resulting from reflections by airplanes and from signal fading and helps to stabilize the synchronizing circuits in fringe areas.

There is an important difference between the AGC system of a television receiver and the AVC system of an AM sound receiver. The AVC system produces a biasing voltage that is

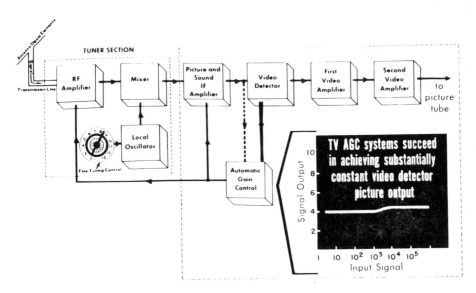

FIG. 27-34. AUTOMATIC GAIN CONTROL IN THE INTERCARRIER RECEIVER

proportional to the average strength of the carrier wave. On the other hand, the AGC system produces a bias that is proportional to the maximum strength of the carrier. Since these maxima correspond to the synchronizing pulses, the AGC system tends to keep these peak voltages constant, thus improving the synchronization of the receiver with the transmitter. Consequently, nearly all AGC systems in use today develop bias voltages from the sync-pulse level of the incoming signal.

There is one slight disadvantage accompanying the use of the AGC circuit in a television receiver. When the receiver is shifted from one station to another, the bias levels vary in accordance with the strength of the received signal. An effect known as the Miller effect results in which there is a change in input capacitance of a tuned stage, such as an i-f amplifier, whenever the operating gain and bias of that stage are changed. This effect causes the input capacitance to decrease and the resonant frequency to increase as the bias increases. It is possible to compensate for this effect by using an unbypassed cathode-bias resistor. This causes the input capacitance to increase and the resonant frequency to decrease as the bias increases.

Another important circuit in a television receiver is one which is called variously a d-c restorer, reinserter, or a clamper (Fig. 27-35). The d-c component of a video signal provides information concerning the average brightness of a scene. Since the output of the video detector is coupled to the video amplifier by means of a resistance-capacitance network, the d-c component of the signal is blocked and lost, with consequent damage to the tonal values of the picture. It is the function of the clamper circuit to restore this d-c component.

One method of doing this is to connect a diode across a portion of the load circuit of the video amplifier. This diode conducts during signal pulses and produces a varying d-c component whose magnitude is proportional to the amplitude of each pulse. The addition of this d-c component to the varying signal restores it to the proper d-c level.

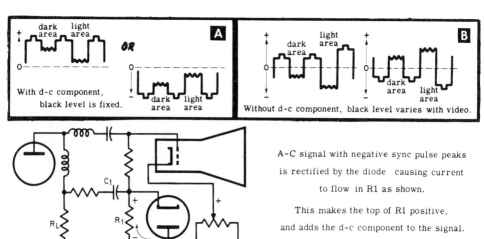

FIG. 27-35. THE D-C RESTORER

A-C signal with negative sync pulse peaks is rectified by the diode causing current to flow in R1 as shown.

This makes the top of R1 positive, and adds the d-c component to the signal.

At some point in the video-amplifier stage, generally at the plate of the first video-amplifier tube, the synchronizing pulses are separated from the video signal and are fed to the respective vertical and horizontal sweep-generator sections (Fig. 27-36). The synchronizing pulses serve to synchronize these two circuits which sweep the beam vertically and horizontally across the screen of the tube (Figs. 27-37 and 27-38). As the beam moves across the screen and varies in intensity, the phenomenon of persistence of vision

produces the illusion of a continuously moving picture corresponding to the original scene televised at the studio.

27.8 Intercarrier method of television sound reception

The old-fashioned split-sound method of television reception that has just been described involves the use of separate sound and video i-f sections (Fig. 27-39). These split-sound receivers are obsolete, and are no longer being

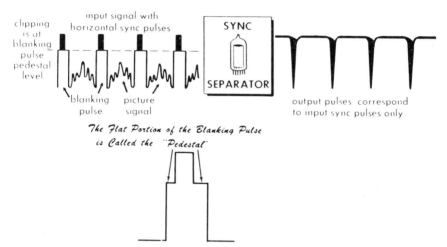

FIG. 27-36. FUNCTION OF THE SYNC SEPARATOR
The separator removes the blanking and picture signals from the composite video signal.

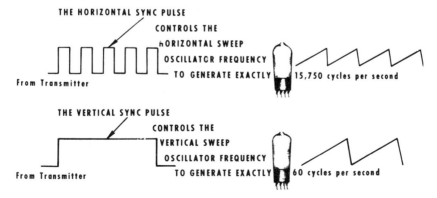

FIG. 27-37. HORIZONTAL AND VERTICAL SYNC PULSES

THE PICTURE TUBE IS FED FROM MANY SOURCES

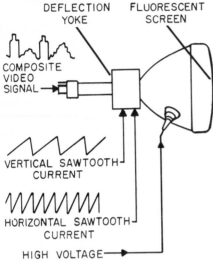

FIG. 27-38. SOURCES FEEDING THE PICTURE TUBE

manufactured. In 1947, L. W. Parker and R. B. Dome announced the development of a new type of circuit called the intercarrier circuit.[9] It is also known as interchannel sound or carrier-difference reception. In this circuit, both the video and sound signals pass through common i-f amplifier, video-detector, and video-amplifier stages, thus reducing the number of tubes and components required for the i-f amplifier stages (Figs. 27-40 and 27-41).[10]

In a standard television broadcast there is a spacing of 4.5 mc between the frequency of the sound carrier wave and the frequency of the picture carrier wave. In a typical receiver, when the output of the local oscillator is heterodyned with or beaten against these two carrier frequencies, an AM picture i-f carrier wave of 25.75 mc and an FM sound i-f carrier wave of 21.25 mc are produced. In more recent models of television receivers, these frequencies may be 45.75 mc and 41.25 mc respectively. The interaction of the two carriers upon each other produces an AM and FM beat signal whose carrier frequency is 4.5 mc (Fig. 27-42). This 4.5-mc signal contains the sound information.

In an intercarrier receiver, the same i-f amplifier is used to amplify the 25.75-mc picture i-f carrier and the 4.5-mc sound i-f carrier. The frequency response of the i-f amplifier is controlled in such a manner that the gain of the

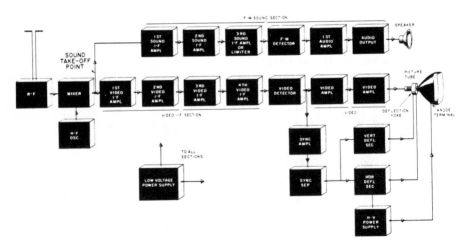

FIG. 27-39. BLOCK DIAGRAM OF THE SPLIT-SOUND TV RECEIVER SYSTEM

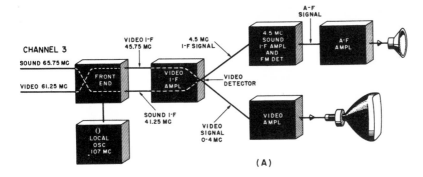

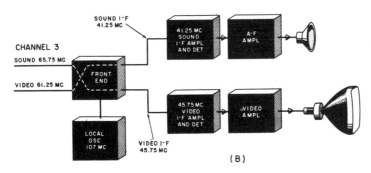

FIG. 27-40. COMPARISON BETWEEN FREQUENCY ARRANGEMENTS
(A) Modern intercarrier system; (B) older split-sound systems.

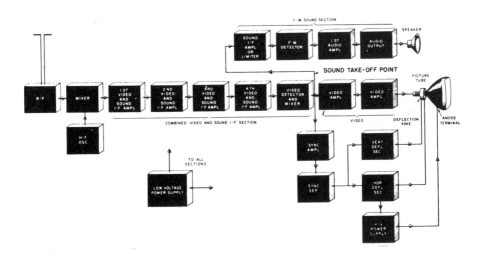

FIG. 27-41. BLOCK DIAGRAM OF AN INTERCARRIER-TYPE TV RECEIVER SYSTEM

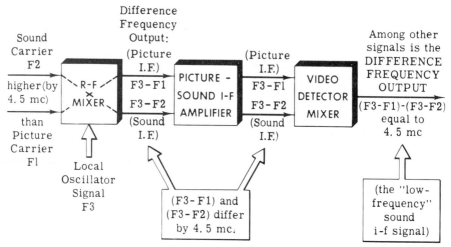

FIG. 27-42. MIXING IN THE INTERCARRIER RECEIVER

sound i-f carrier is between 30 and 40 db below that of the picture i-f carrier. As a result, the amplitude of the sound i-f carrier is only between 5 and 7.5 per cent that of the picture i-f carrier.

Both carriers are then sent through the video-detector stage. The useful output of this stage consists of two signals (Fig. 27-43). One is a strong video signal containing frequencies from 30 cps to 4 mc. The other is the low-level AM and FM beat signal of 4.5 mc. Both signals are amplified by a video-amplifier stage. At the output of this stage,

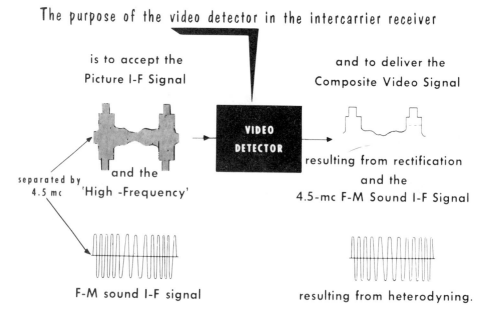

FIG. 27-43. THE VIDEO DETECTOR'S FUNCTION IN THE INTERCARRIER RECEIVER

the video signal is sent along the proper channels to the picture tube, while the low-level 4.5-mc signal is passed through a selective coupling circuit to a 4.5-mc amplifier. A 4.5-mc trap circuit is used to prevent the signal from modulating the signal reaching the picture tube. The output of this amplifier then passes into a very sensitive FM detector such as a ratio detector. The audio output of the detector is then amplified by an a-f amplifier and fed to the loudspeaker.

An advantage of this circuit, in addition to simplifying the circuitry and tuning and reducing the number of tubes and components required, is the fact that this type of receiver does not require as high a degree of frequency stability on the part of the local oscillator. Any frequency shift of the local oscillator changes the frequency of both the sound and picture i-f carriers by the same amount, leaving the difference frequency of 4.5 mc unchanged. For the same reason, effects produced by hum modulation of the local oscillator tend to be cancelled out.

It should be noted that in order for the sound to be received, the transmitter must radiate some carrier power at all times. The disappearance of the picture carrier causes a disappearance of the 4.5-mc beat note, and there will be no sound output obtained from the receiver, except for a 60-cps note corresponding to the field-repetition rate, and a 15,750-cps whistle corresponding to the horizontal-scanning rate.

Thus. when a television station has trouble and the picture carrier is lost, the sound is also lost and the viewer cannot hear the announcement of trouble which is sent over the sound carrier. Consequently, the listener often believes that the trouble is in his own receiver. A similar effect is produced when the video signal is overmodulated by a bright object in the picture. Since this loss of the video carrier due to overmodulation is repeated for each scanning of the field, and this scanning rate is 60 per second, it usually results in an audible 60-cps buzz.

In order to obtain a satisfactory sound output, the minimum power of the picture carrier for a white signal should not be permitted to drop below 1 per cent of the peak power produced during the interval when synchronizing pulses are sent.[11] In terms of voltage, this means that the voltage of the white signal must be at least 10 per cent of the maximum voltage of the carrier. Since FCC regulations state that this white level may not exceed 15 per cent of the maximum amplitude of the carrier, the introduction of the intercarrier circuit in receivers means that broadcasting stations must keep the level of the white signal within very narrow limits.

Some intercarrier receivers have produced an annoying high-level intercarrier buzz in their sound-output circuits. This noise results from the modulation of the sound by the picture information, and its level is affected by the tuning alignment and contrast setting of the receiver. While it cannot always be eliminated, this noise may be minimized by correct alignment, and by the use of an excellent limiter circuit or by the use of a gated-beam limiter-discriminator circuit.[12]

27.9 Television-receiver power supplies

Most television receivers contain two power supplies. One is a conventional low-voltage, high-current power supply with a capacitor-input filter (Fig. 27-44). It is designed to supply the positive voltages for all tubes except

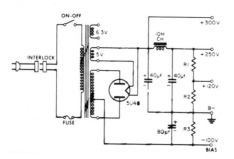

FIG. 27-44. COMPLETE LOW-VOLTAGE POWER SUPPLY FOR TV RECEIVER

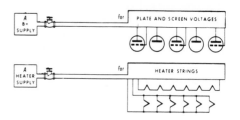

FIG. 27-45. FUNCTIONS OF THE LOW-VOLTAGE POWER SUPPLY

the picture tube (Fig. 27-45). The other power supply is a high-voltage, low-current power supply designed to provide positive voltages as high as 30,000 volts, and currents of less than 1 ma to the anode of the picture tube. When this power supply is of conventional design, it employs a bulky power transformer and a half-wave rectifier with a high inverse-peak-voltage rating. A capacitor-input filter usually follows this. Since large electrolytic capacitors with high voltage ratings are expensive, it is customary to use small capacitors and to depend upon very large filter chokes or filter resistors for most of the filtering action.

Because the conventional high-voltage power supply requires bulky and expensive components, new types of power supplies have been developed: power supply is a high-voltage, low-

the flyback or kickback power supply, the r-f power supply, and the pulse-type power supply.

The flyback or kickback power supply, which is based on the inductive kickback action produced by a rapid change in current through a coil, was first developed in 1930 by Farnsworth (Fig. 27-46). The retrace or decay portion of the sawtooth wave used for the sweep voltage requires a time interval of less than 7 microseconds. During this time, the current in the deflecting coil or yoke associated with the cathode-ray tube decreases from maximum value to zero. The rapid collapse of the magnetic field produces high-frequency oscillations in the yoke. The circuit oscillates for a half-cycle only. During the second half-cycle, a damping or damper tube conducts, preventing any furthur oscillations. This damper tube is usually a diode, which, by conducting, absorbs energy from the oscillating circuit.

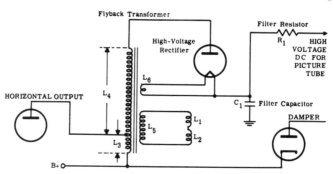

FIG. 27-46. FLYBACK HIGH-VOLTAGE POWER SUPPLY

The output voltage generated by the high-frequency pulse produced by the first half-cycle is applied through a step-up r-f transformer to the plate of a high-voltage, half-wave rectifier (Fig. 27-47). The filament circuit of this high-voltage rectifier is also heated by induced r-f energy. The d-c output can be smoothed out by using a filter circuit consisting of a small capacitor and a resistor of high value.

Courtesy, Radio Corporation of America

FIG. 27-47. TYPES OF HIGH-VOLTAGE RECTIFIER TUBES FOR TV RECEIVERS

This type of power supply is the one that is most widely used in television receivers employing magnetic-deflection systems. It requires the least number of additional components. Since it functions during the retrace period when the electron beam is blanked out, any interference that may be produced in adjacent circuits is not visible. In addition, it is efficient in that it utilizes energy from transient voltages in the horizontal-sweep circuit that would otherwise be wasted.[13][14]

In the r-f power supply, which was first designed in 1943 by Schade of RCA, a conventional, low-voltage, full-wave power supply provides voltage to an Armstrong oscillator, which produces a voltage whose frequency is between 100 and 300 kc (Fig. 27-48). These r-f voltages can be stepped up

by a small, light weight, r-f transformer. The output from the secondary of this r-f transformer is then rectified by a half-wave, high-voltage rectifier. Since the frequency of the pulsating direct current that is produced is quite high, a very small (0.0005-μfd), high-voltage capacitor plus a resistor of high ohmic value and low wattage provide all of the filtering required.

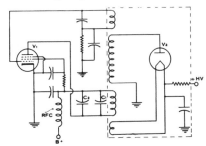

Courtesy, Sylvania Electric Products, Inc.

FIG. 27-48. TYPICAL R-F TYPE HIGH VOLTAGE SUPPLY

It should also be noted that the filament of the high-voltage rectifier is also heated by r-f energy picked up from the output of the oscillator. The ripple frequency produced by the r-f variations of the filament current are much easier to filter than are the 60-cycle ripple frequencies produced when 60-cps current is used. This arrangement also eliminates the need for a heavy iron-core filament transformer with high voltage insulation.

An additional advantage of this and other types of r-f power supplies is that the small filter capacitors employed reduce some of the hazards of electrical shock, since these small capacitors cannot store much energy. In addition, making accidental contact with the circuit loads the rectifier circuit and detunes the oscillator, reducing the output voltage substantially. Its principal disadvantage lies in the fact that it sometimes produces sufficient harmonic radiation to cause interference with other circuits. In order to prevent this, complete filtering and shielding of the supply leads are necessary.[15]

A third type of high-voltage power supply is called the pulse type (Fig. 27-49). Its operation is very similar to that of the flyback power supply previously described, and it contains a similar type of transformer and rectifier. A blocking oscillator is triggered by the decay of the horizontal-deflection voltage. This stage produces oscillations which are amplified and fed through an auto-transformer to the plate of a high-voltage rectifier.

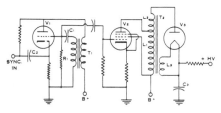

Courtesy, Sylvania Electric Products Inc.

FIG. 27-49. TYPICAL PULSE TYPE HIGH VOLTAGE SUPPLY

Like the r-f power supply, this system has the disadvantage of requiring additional components and power sources. However, it possesses the advantage of the flyback power supply in that the synchronizing pulse occurs during the blanking period, so that minimum radiation interference is observed. This system also protects the picture tube against damage to the screen by holding the high-voltage supply inactive when the sweep circuit fails. A final advantage is the fact that this type of power supply can be used for picture tubes employing electrostatic deflection.

Because of the hazards produced by the high-voltage generator, these high-voltage power supplies are usually placed in a protective "doghouse" in the receiver chassis. Another precaution is the use of an interlocking safety switch which automatically disables the high-voltage power-supply circuit when the back cover of the receiver is opened.

It is dangerous to measure the voltage of the output of this power supply, and it is recommended that resistance measurements rather than voltage measurements be used when one is troubleshooting a defective high-voltage power-supply unit. In general, these high-voltage power-supply systems are less hazardous to life than are the conventional 60-cps systems. This is due to their low total-power capacity and the fact that the very small filter capacitors cannot store much energy. However, it must still be kept in mind that although a high-frequency power supply is not as dangerous as a 60-cps power supply, direct contact with the output of one of these power supplies may be extremely painful and can sometimes be fatal.

27.10 *Television interference*

There are many possible sources of TVI or television-signal interference. The nearby amateur radio operator, who is usually the first person blamed for causing television interference, is often quite innocent. If he has reduced the radiation of harmonics and spurious signals from his transmitter to the extent that they do not cause interference on the same frequency as that of the local television station, he has met his obligations. In many instances, the fault lies with the manufacturer of the set, who in order to reduce costs, sometimes errs in producing a receiver that does not possess sufficient selectivity to reject image interference and other interfering signals that are not on the same frequency as the desired station.

Some interference may be attributed to spurious radiation from the transmitters of other services, such as second-harmonic radiation by FM stations, second and higher harmonic radiation by amateur transmitters, and radiation from the local oscillators of nearby FM receivers and television receivers. A great deal of interference is caused by man-made devices, such as ignition-system spark plugs, motor commutators, neon signs, ultraviolet lamps, and diathermy and industrial radio-frequency heating equipment operating on the 26.96 to 27.28-mc band and on 33.5 mc. In one rare instance, the cause of interference was found to be a defective insulator on a power-line pole, while in another instance, it turned out to be an old-fashioned incandescent lamp bulb.

While it is obviously impossible to eliminate all sources of interference, recent improvements in the design of television receivers, in antennas, and in equipment tending to produce interference (for example, the development of the resistor spark plug) have done much to alleviate the problem of television interference. Another factor has been the development of efficient frequency-selective filters for use either at the source of interference or associated with the television receiver.[16]

Mention may also be made of a cyclic type of television interference that is correlated with great sunspot activity. Under ordinary conditions, the ionosphere neither reflects nor refracts VHF signals used in television transmission. However, during the peak of a sunspot cycle, ionospheric disturbances occur which result in the reflection or refraction of television signals, particularly the lower-frequency signals in Channels 2 to 6. This may cause the signal from a distant station, thousands of miles away, to arrive strong enough to interfere with reception of a local transmission, and produce waving lines,

loss of synchronization, and buzzing sounds. Occasionally, the reflected signal will be strong enough to force its way over the local transmission on the same channel, taking over the screen completely and producing a different picture.

Unfortunately, a universal cure for this type of interference does not exist. Sometimes it may be alleviated by reorienting the antenna or replacing the antenna with a more efficient and more directional one. Other suggestions are to reduce the gain of the r-f and i-f stages, to set the AGC control to a less sensitive position, to replace some of the older tubes, and to realign the set. If these adjustments do not clear up the difficulty, there is little that the serviceman and viewer can do except to wait for ionospheric conditions to improve.[17][18]

27.11 UHF television

The transmission of television on the VHF band suffers from the limitation that the total number of channels available is limited to 12 (Fig. 27-50). Of these channels, no more than 7 may be allocated to any one area. This limitation of channel assignments is necessary in order to prevent interference between stations on certain adjacent channels.

In April 1952, 70 new television channels were made available in the UHF band. These channels, covering the band of frequencies between 470 and 890 mc, are numbered 14 through 83 (Fig. 27-51). They were generally assigned to new stations in cities and towns that did not previously possess local television facilities. By the spring of 1963, 91 stations were broadcasting in the UHF band, 153 had been authorized, and 29 channel applications were pending.

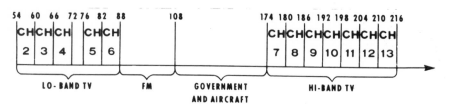

FIG. 27-50. THE R-F RANGE FOR VHF TV CHANNELS IN MEGACYCLES

470 476 482 488
mc mc mc mc

CH 14 CH 15 CH 16

872 878 884 890
mc mc mc mc

CH 81 CH 82 CH 83

←TV CHANNELS 14 TO 83 IN THE UHF BAND DIVIDED INTO 70 CHANNELS →

FIG. 27-51. THE UHF TV BAND

Extensive tests conducted in 1949 at Bridgeport, Connecticut, by RCA and NBC with television transmitters operating on Channels 24 and 72 proved that when the receiving equipment is properly installed, television reception on the UHF band can be as clear and stable as on the VHF band. In some instances it can be even better, since UHF signals are not affected by nearby X-ray equipment, neon signs, home appliances, or automobile ignition circuits, which have a pronounced effect upon VHF signals. In addition, color television can be broadcast as easily on UHF as on VHF.[19]

However, other tests have also indicated that UHF transmissions are usually limited to line-of-sight reception equivalent to an effective range of approximately 40 to 50 miles over flat terrain. Within the radius of the station, there may be shadow effects and dead spots requiring special attention if satisfactory reception is to be obtained. Another fact discovered by tests is that a UHF signal must be over three times as strong as a VHF signal to produce a comparable picture. Because of this, the FCC now permits radiation of greater power on UHF channels than on VHF channels.

In addition, great care must frequently be exercised in selecting a receiving antenna of the correct design. These designs range from the economical bow-tie antenna, through the stacked-V and rhombic types, to the extremely sensitive corner-reflector and parabolic-antenna systems (Fig. 27-52).

Courtesy, Channel Master Co.

FIG. 27-52. BOW-TIE ANTENNA FOR UHF RECEPTION

Owners of VHF receivers desiring to receive UHF telecasts must install a special small UHF antenna and also a special converter (Figs. 27-53 and 27-54).

It is also necessary to pay great attention to placing the antenna in a good location. Movement of the antenna by as little as 2 ft in one direction, or a slight difference in its vertical or horizontal position, may be the cause of the difference between a good picture and a snowy picture. Slight vibration of the UHF antenna will produce flashes in the receiver screen, and seasonal changes in the local foliage can produce marked changes in UHF reception. Since UHF signals are more readily reflected than VHF signals are, the problem of ghosts produced by reflections becomes a more serious one in UHF receivers (Fig. 27-55).

In 1956, the FCC announced that it was considering whether or not to adopt a policy which would eventually force all television stations to broadcast on channels in the UHF band. This proposal was strongly opposed by the major television stations and networks on the VHF band as well as by organizations representing certain groups of

Courtesy, Blonder-Tongue Laboratories, Inc.
FIG. 27-54. UHF TV CONVERTER

manufacturers and consumers. On the other hand, advocates of educational television pointed out that an all-UHF system would substantially promote the development of educational television, since two-thirds of the channels reserved for educational television are in the UHF band.

A second solution proposed by the FCC was known as de-intermixture. This would create certain zones in which all television transmission would be VHF and other zones in which all would be UHF. This would require a shuffling of channel assignments in many cities. This solution was opposed by those who claimed it would remove

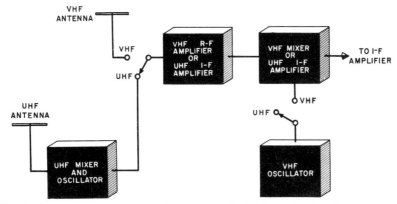

FIG. 27-53. METHOD OF CONVERTING A VHF TUNER TO UHF USE WITH A SEPARATE CONVERTER SECTION OR UNIT
The VHF r-f amplifier and mixer become i-f amplifiers during UHF operation.

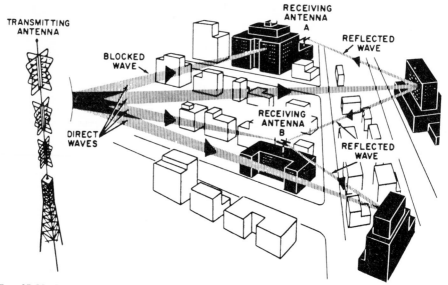

FIG. 27-55. REFLECTION OF TV SIGNALS
At location A, direct reception is almost impossible, due to the intervening portion of a building, but a reflected wave from another building is received. At B, both the direct and the reflected waves are received strongly, and ghosts will probably be produced.

the incentive for manufacturers to build all-channel sets or to contribute to the promotion of increased use of the UHF band. It would also deprive many viewers, who are now located in the fringe areas of VHF reception, of all television service, since the lower bands provide greater coverage than the higher-frequency bands do. In addition, it would mean that many persons would have to purchase new television receivers or obtain converters for their old television receivers.

A third proposal attempted to solve the problem by encouraging the production of receivers equipped to cover Channels 2 through 83. Naturally, the production of such sets would involve a higher manufacturing cost than the production of conventional VHF sets. It was proposed to equalize the retail cost of the VHF receiver and the all-channel receiver by setting aside the 10 per cent Federal excise tax on all-channel receivers. There would then be no competitive advantage for a manufacturer in not making an all-channel receiver.

This proposal was opposed by the Treasury Department, which maintained that if only all-channel sets were made, there would be no excise revenue from any television sets. It also objected on the ground that the proposal would involve modification of the tax laws for an ulterior purpose, namely, promoting a particular form of industrial development.

In 1959, J. C. Doerfer, who was then chairman of the FCC, presented a progress report to the Senate Interstate Commerce Committee in which he recommended the establishment of a 50-channel VHF television system as the only practical solution of the television-allocation problem. This would permit the assignment of at least 5 television stations, 4 commercial and 1 educational, to each major receiving area. This proposal threw cold water on deintermixture and apparently sounded the death knell for the idea of moving all television transmission to the UHF band.

According to this suggestion, the television channels would be divided into three non-contiguous segments as follows: Channels 2 to 4, 54-72 mc; Channels 5 and 6, 76-88 mc; and Channels 7 to 51, 173-444 mc. This would require an additional block of 228 megacycles above Channel 13. The UHF allocations extending from 470 to 890 mc could then be released for non-broadcast services. Under this system, 26 of the 50 channels would be located in the VHF band below 300 mc, and the remaining 24 channels would be in the UHF band. This would necessitate all-channel sets at additional cost to the public. Doerfer recommended that Congress enact legislation requiring that all television receivers moving in interstate commerce be capable of receiving all channels and noted that if the requirement for all-channel sets were coupled with removal of the excise tax, this would partially offset the added cost.

A similar type of 50-channel compromise allocation was also advocated by other members of the FCC and by certain people in the industry. This would extend the present VHF band to 474 mc and would require the surrender and exchange of a block of government channels between 216 and 300 mc. The economic magnitude of such a frequency shift has been pointed out by Commissioner J. S. Cross who stated: "Swapping some existing UHF and VHF space with the military ... involves replacing hundreds of millions of dollars worth of current military and allied electronic equipment ... and, in addition, has receiver incompatibility disadvantages."[20] Needless to say, it did not take long for the military authorities to express their emphatic disapproval of this exchange.

In April 1960, the FCC asked Congress for a special appropriation of 2.25 million dollars. When this request was granted, the FCC announced that it planned to use this money to build two experimental UHF television stations, one on top of the Empire State Building in New York City, and the other across the Hudson River in Alpine, New Jersey, where an antenna tower is standing that was used by Armstrong for his FM station. It was planned to conduct this experiment for two years in an attempt to determine whether or not UHF channels are capable of providing nationwide television service. The New York City area was selected for this experiment because, as a result of its high buildings, it is the worst area in this country as far as reception of UHF television is concerned. The results of this experiment were used to determine the future of UHF television broadcasting.

All controversy was finally settled in July 1962 when Congress passed an all-channel law requiring TV makers to switch their output to sets that can receive both the 12 VHF channels and the 70 UHF channels. The changeover was to be made by April 30, 1964. To promote this development of UHF broadcasting, a government-industry joint committee was formed in Washington in March 1963.

27.12 Community-antenna television systems and related systems

Because of the propagation characteristics of VHF television signals, certain locations in fringe areas suffer from poor reception, while excellent reception is enjoyed at other nearby locations within the same general area. In the United States, hundreds of medium-sized cities and communities are cut off from outside television signals by excessive distances or by mountains and other natural barriers. They cannot set up their own local stations because, at present, it is economically impractical to construct a television station unless a community has a minimum population of 50,000, with 150,000 additional people in the station's normal coverage area.

A CATV or community-antenna television system offers one solution to the problem of providing television reception to these communities (Fig. 27-56). Most of the present CATV systems were developed as a result of attempts to employ the principles used in apartment-house master-antenna systems to pick up a good signal and distribute it via coaxial cable to homes in areas where these signals were usually blacked out. The difficulties encountered were numerous, since proper electronic equipment for these applications had not yet been designed, and unheard of cable problems were encountered.[21] Most of these obstacles were eventually surmounted, and this

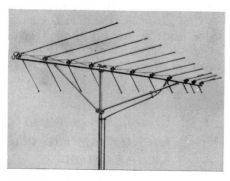

Courtesy, JFD Electronics Corp.
FIG. 27-56. COMMUNITY ANTENNA

relatively new and unpublicized industry has been responsible for bringing television to more than 700 communities containing over one million people.

In engineering this type of closed-circuit television system, the first step is to locate a site where television signals of the desired magnitude and consistency may be obtained. This site is frequently located on a mountain top amidst rugged terrain. A tower is then erected at this point, and receiving antennas are mounted on the tower. The signals from these antennas are fed to banks of amplifiers at the tower base, where they are amplified up to 10,000 times. The signals are then sent down the mountainside by means of coaxial cables.

The signals received at the antenna site are usually converted to the lower television channels, numbers 2 to 6, in order to take advantage of lower cable losses at these frequencies. Relay amplifiers are used when necessary to compensate for attenuation of the signal. The signal is then distributed via cable to the subscribers in the area to be served. Arrangements are made to isolate each receiver in order to prevent radiation produced by the local oscillator of one receiver from affecting the operation of another receiver.

The typical CATV system accommodates five channels and is adaptable to closed-circuit programming and to toll-television systems. It is also capable of handling color-television signals. The average subscriber installation charge is 125 dollars, which is comparable to the cost of installation of a good fringe-area antenna that probably could not deliver as good or consistent a picture to the customer. The monthly service charge is in the neighborhood of 4 dollars.

This type of community-television system does not require a license or permission from the FCC. The only prerequisites are obtaining the cooperation of municipal authorities and local power and telephone companies. However, in the spring of 1959, the FCC requested Congress to give it authority over the 700 CATV systems in existence, and it is quite possible that sometime within the near future these systems will come under FCC control.

Use of microwave relay. Other variations of this system involve the use of microwave relay. An example is the system connecting Houston to Lufkin, Tex. This 110-mile distance is covered in 4 hops. An FCC license is required in order to operate this type of system.[22]

A similar type of system is used in Reno, Nev. (Fig. 27-57). An array of Yagi antennas, located on Slide Mountain picks up signals on Channels 3 and 10 from Sacramento, Calif., Channel 5 from San Francisco, and Channel 13 from Stockton. Another antenna array on Mt. Rose picks up Channels 5 and 7 from San Francisco and Channel 10 from Sacramento. These signals are demodulated, used to modulate a microwave carrier, and are thus relayed via microwave into the city, which is 16 miles away. When the microwave signals are picked up in Reno, the engineers are able to make a choice of three of these channels for distribution to the subscribers. The selection made depends upon the nature of the programs and the quality of the signals. The three selected signals are demodulated and used to modulate carriers operating on Channels 2, 4, and 6, respectively. These outputs are then sent to the subscribers via coaxial cable, and the subscriber can select the desired program by tuning to Channels 2, 4 or 6.[23]

Use of passive relay antennas. Some early types of systems employed passive relay antennas. The high-gain receiving antenna was located at a favorable spot for receiving signals from the television transmitter. The signal was then fed via a transmission line to a high-gain transmitting antenna that re-radiated the signal to the subscribers. In this manner, the television signals were lifted over mountains and beamed into valleys. This system required no source of electrical power and no FCC approval.

Booster-station systems. A booster-station system is very similar in nature, except that it incorporates an amplifier to increase the strength of the signal before it is re-radiated. Consequently, it requires a source of electric power and (theoretically) also requires approval of the FCC and of the stations whose programs are being relayed.[24]

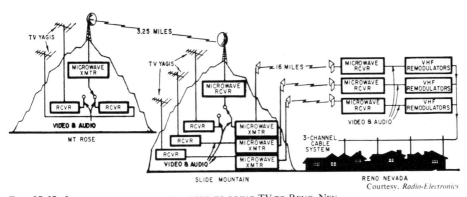

Fig. 27-57. Involved antenna system used to bring TV to Reno, Nev.

These devices have often produced considerable interference with direct reception of signals from television stations, and in 1956 the FCC issued an order that they either be shut down or be converted to UHF-translator operation. However, despite the efforts of the FCC to keep these booster stations off the air, it was estimated in 1959 that at least 1,000 of them were still in operation, bringing their communities bootleg television.[25] In Montana alone, there were over 150 of these illegal boosters, which were described as low-powered projects that received a television signal on one VHF channel and re-transmitted it on another channel.[26]

In the spring of 1959, recognizing its lack of success in removing these many hundreds of booster stations, the FCC asked Congress to pass legislation that would enable it to authorize the operation of VHF booster stations. It was hoped that once these stations obtained legal sanction, they would be encouraged to improve their engineering standards and that they would cease operation on Channels 4 and 5, which are perilously close to the aircraft bands upon which aviation safety depends.[27]

In July 1960, President Eisenhower signed a bill that authorized the FCC to legalize existing booster stations and to regulate operation of all boosters. One month later, the FCC set up rules for operation of VHF translator stations that became effective in September 1960. These rules granted temporary authorization to these stations and gave them until October 1961 to comply with new translator requirements, which included a maximum power of 1 watt, and meeting minimum technical requirements to assure orderly operations and protection of regular television-broadcasting stations from unwarranted interference.

Satellite stations. In recent years, other types of authorized devices called satellite stations have been developed. One of these is the previously mentioned television translator, produced by Adler Electronics Co. It solves the interference problem by picking up the standard VHF telecasts, converting or translating them to a high UHF channel, and without demodulation, retransmitting them from a satellite station for the benefit of the viewers in a given area.[28][29] The power of an average translator is low, ranging between 0.5 and 1 watt, but it is usually adequate for the intended purpose. In 1959, there were approximately 175 of these licensed translators in operation.

However, unlike closed-circuit CATV systems, translators require permission of the originating station for "rebroadcasting" the signal, and plans for constructing many translators have been abandoned because some of these television stations withheld rebroadcast rights. In some instances, the refusal was due to friendly relations with a CATV system in the area; in others, it was caused by the demands of television-film program distributors or broadcast unions for additional payment for "rebroadcasts".[30]

Future of CATV. Community-antenna systems vary considerably in size, from small systems with 25 subscribers to large systems with 10,000 subscribers and an investment of over 100,000 dollars. The favorable reaction of the public is shown by the fact that the mortality rate of CATV systems is less than 1 per cent. It seems likely that they will continue to flourish until electronic research finds some way of using scatter-propagation techniques to bring television signals directly to isolated communities. However, as CATV becomes big business, it can expect attacks from organizations such as ASCAP and BMI, who feel that their material is being used free of charge. It will also encounter the opposition of the operators of small local television stations who resent the competition of the large-city network programs provided by the CATV systems.

27.13 *Color television*

History. The idea of transmitting television pictures in color dates back to the early days of mechanical television. As early as 1928, Baird demonstrated a crude system employing a whirling disc with two color filters. In 1929, Ives of Bell Telephone Laboratories used a perforated disc to demonstrate a similar type of color-television system. At this demonstration, a group of newspaper reporters gathered at the Bell Telephone Laboratories in New York City observed a color telecast of an American flag rippling in the breeze. In 1930, a patent was issued to Kell of General Electric for a color-television system containing a double-spiral scanning disc with two color filters.

Principles. Transmission of color television is based upon the optical principle that any visible color may be reproduced by using the proper combinations of the three primary or chromatic colors, red, blue, and green (Figs. 27-58 and 27-59). Conversely, it is possible to use colored filters or color-selective mirrors to analyze any color in terms of these three component colors.

Consequently, all systems of transmitting color-television signals use some method of analyzing the colors of the scene being scanned in terms of these three colors and of converting this information into electrical signals (Fig. 27-60). At the receiver, these electrical signals are used to reproduce the three primary colors in the correct proportions so as to duplicate the color of the

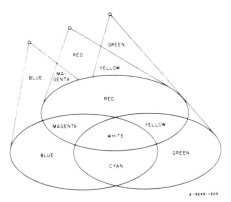

Courtesy, Stanford Research Institute

FIG. 27-58. ADDITIVE COLOR FROM THREE PROJECTORS

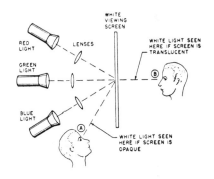

FIG. 27-59. RECOMBINING OF COLORS BY THE ADDITIVE PROCESS

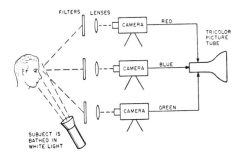

FIG. 27-60. BASIC PRINCIPLE OF COLOR PICTURE TRANSMISSION AND RECEPTION
The light from the camera image is divided into three parts, each representing a primary color. At the receiver, the three colors are recombined.

original scene being scanned at the studio.

Major systems. Until a few years ago, there were two major competitive systems of color television, the CBS field-sequential additive system and the RCA simultaneous system. Although the CBS system was the one first adopted officially in 1950 by the FCC, it was not generally accepted by the industry. In 1953, the FCC reversed itself and gave its approval to the RCA system. Since then, the RCA system seems to have won out and is now the only system used for commercial telecasting. The system has been modified slightly and is now called the NTSC system. The CBS system is not used for commercial telecasting and has only a relatively minor application in the field of industrial closed-circuit color television.

27.14 *The CBS sequential system*

In the CBS sequential system for color television, a mechanical scanning disc containing colored filters is used to scan the scene. The first field is scanned with a red filter, the second with a blue filter, the third with a green filter (Fig. 27-61). Since a field consists of half the lines of a frame or image, it requires six scannings to scan a scene completely in all three colors. Electrical pulses are then produced corresponding to the color information provided by

the one-color scanning of each field. These pulses, containing single-color information, are then transmitted in sequence.

The color information arrives in the same sequence at the receiver, and produces variations in intensity of the beam of the color tube. The tube is viewed through a synchronized rotating disc or drum containing color filters corresponding to those at the transmitter. The trichromatic color images blend to produce a complete colored picture (Fig. 27-62).

This system possesses many disadvantages. Since it scans 144 fields per second instead of 60, it is incompatible with ordinary black-and-white receivers. It requires a noisy and cumbersome scanning disc at the receiver, which

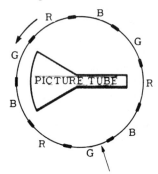

REVOLVING FILTER DRUM

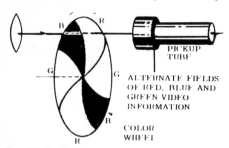

FIG. 27-61. SEQUENTIAL COLOR CAMERA

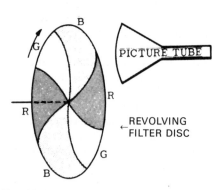

FIG. 27-62. TWO TYPES OF FIELD-SEQUENTIAL DISPLAYS

must be synchronized with the disc at the transmitter. The color filter discs have low transmission efficiencies, which reduce the brightness of the picture. This process requires only 405 lines per frame in place of the customary 525, resulting in a lower definition of the fine picture detail. Finally, it requires a channel 16 megacycles in width, in contrast with the 6-megacycle channel required for black-and-white television.

27.15 *The NTSC simultaneous system*

The NTSC system is a modified version of the dot-sequential system developed by RCA during the 1940's. It is the outgrowth of the work of the National Television Standards Committee, which was formed by a group of television manufacturers to develop an acceptable compatible color-television system after the incompatible CBS system had won FCC approval. The result of this committee's work was the development of a high-efficiency system in which the equivalent of a 12-megacycle system, 4 megacycles for each channel, is transmitted within a conventional 6-megacycle television channel.

In this system, there are three independent modulators of the complete color signal. The basis of the system is the fact that a color may be specified by the three fundamental characteristics of brightness, hue, and saturation. The brightness, or luminance, component is the same signal that is produced by a monochrome or black-and-white transmitter. The hue and saturation information is contained in the color signal that is conveyed by a 3.8-mc color subcarrier. The color signal that is transmitted is actually a color signal from which the brightness or luminance component has been subtracted. Consequently, it is called the color-difference

signal. At the receiver, an adding-network unit, called a matrix, adds the brightness or luminance component, restoring it to the signal.

A modern version of this system uses a single camera lens. The light is then split into its three chromatic components, red, green, and blue, by a system of dichroic mirrors. A dichroic mirror reflects light of only one color and transmits all other colors. The three colored images are transmitted to three separate image orthicon or vidicon camera tubes (Fig. 27-63).

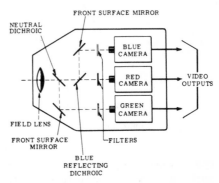

FIG. 27-63. THREE-VIDICON COLOR-TV CAMERA SYSTEM

Each camera tube is fitted with a primary color filter. The scene is scanned approximately 60 times each second to produce 60 fields. The output of each camera is fed into a gamma unit (Fig. 27-64). This unit contains non-linear amplifiers designed to compensate for the non-linearity of the screen-brightness versus signal-voltage characteristic curve of receiver picture tubes. This characteristic tends to stretch the brightness range in the high-light regions and to compress it in the shadows. In monochrome transmission, adequate compensation is made by operating the camera tube on the straighter portion of the curve above the knee. Since this type of correction is impractical in color cameras and since it would be wasteful

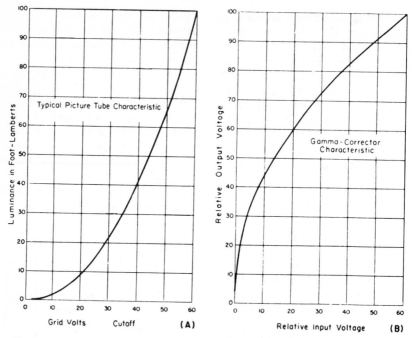

FIG. 27-64. CHARACTERISTICS OF TYPICAL PICTURE TUBE AND CORRESPONDING GAMMA-CORRECTOR CHARACTERISTIC

and expensive to put correcting gamma units in each television receiver, the units are incorporated in the transmitter. An additional advantage of placing the gamma units at the transmitter is the improvement that is produced in the signal-to-noise ratio.

The outputs of the three gamma units are then fed into an analog-computer type of network called the matrix unit. This matrix unit produces three outputs. One is a luminance or brightness signal similar to the signal produced by a monochrome or black-and-white television transmitter. This signal is sometimes called the Y signal. It is this signal that makes this system compatible with monochrome receivers and enables a monochrome receiver to reproduce color programs in black-and-white (Fig. 27-65).

The other two outputs of the matrix unit contain color information

and are called the I and Q signals. The I signal corresponds to the color response of the eye to medium-fine detail and covers the band of frequencies between 0.5 and 1.5 mc. The Q signal corresponds to the color response of the eye to coarse detail, which is a three-color response. It covers the band of frequencies that lie between zero and 0.5 mc.

The I and Q signals are then passed through filter circuits and applied to their respective balanced modulators, where each signal modulates a 3.58-mc subcarrier, which is called the color subcarrier (Fig. 27-66). Both color subcarriers possess the same frequency but differ in phase by 90 deg. The subcarrier signal for the Q modulator lags the subcarrier for the I modulator by 90 deg. The type of modulation that has just been described is sometimes called quadrature modulation.

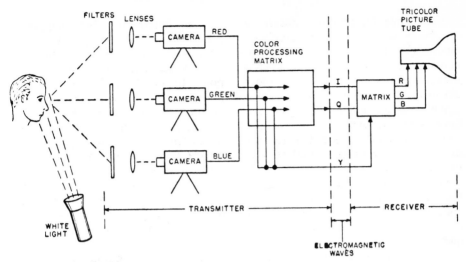

FIG. 27-65. HOW COLOR VIDEO INFORMATION IS DIVIDED INTO A MONOCHROME (Y SIGNAL) PORTION AND A COLOR (I AND Q SIGNALS) PORTION FOR TRANSMISSION

Since balanced modulators are employed, the subcarriers are suppressed and the output consists of the sideband frequencies only. These sideband frequencies are then combined to form a color-information signal called the chrominance signal. The suppression of the 3.58-mc subcarrier is designed to eliminate or reduce the constant interfering beat between the subcarrier and the picture carrier. Provision is made in the color-television

receiver for reinserting the carrier in a stage where it is not likely to produce interference.

The chrominance signal, which provides information concerning both hue or color and degree of saturation, supplies the information required by the receiver to reproduce the large areas of the picture in their proper colors. In this chrominance signal, information concerning hue or color is transmitted by phase modulating the

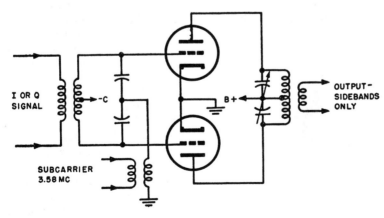

FIG. 27-66. BALANCED MODULATOR

carrier, while information concerning saturation is conveyed by amplitude modulating the same carrier. The chrominance signal is equal to zero when a white or gray area is scanned. An adder circuit then combines this chrominance signal with the luminance signal, the burst signal (a synchronizing signal), and the synchronizing pulses to produce the color video signal that is to be transmitted. Since balanced-modulator circuits are used, neither the carrier nor the modulating video appear at the output but are cancelled out, leaving only the sideband frequencies.

The basic differences between a color and a monochrome television signal are the addition of sidebands of a suppressed color or chrominance subcarrier, whose frequency is 3.58 mc above that of the picture carrier, and the addition of a burst synchronizing signal to the horizontal-synchronizing pulse (Fig. 27-67). This signal consists of 8 or 9 cycles of the subcarrier frequency and is used to lock-in the receiver color circuits for proper color demodulation. It functions as a frequency and phase reference for a local 3.58-mc subcarrier oscillator in the receiver in a manner similar to that in which horizontal synchronizing pulses are used in monochrome receivers.

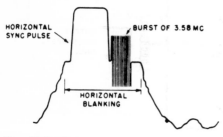

FIG. 27-67. HOW THE COLOR BURST REFERENCE SIGNAL IS INSERTED ON THE BACK PORCH OF THE HORIZONTAL BLANKING PULSE

An interesting fact, mentioned previously, is that people are color-blind with respect to small objects or small areas. These small areas correspond to the higher frequency components of the video signal. Consequently, for the rather large areas of the picture, corresponding to video frequencies below 0.5 mc, it is necessary to transmit complete three-color information. In areas of intermediate size, whose video frequencies correspond to between 0.5 and 1.5 mc, the eye is color-blind to blue, and only green and red information need be transmitted. In the very small areas of the picture, corresponding to video frequencies above 1.5 mc, the eye is completely color-blind, and no color information at all need be transmitted. This reduces the bandwidth of the signal to be televised.

Another interesting detail is related to the problem of interference between the sidebands of the video carrier and those of the color subcarrier. A phenomenon known as interleaving or frequency multiplexing comes to the rescue. This phenomenon is based upon a discovery made in 1934 by Mertz and Gray, which was developed further by Dome of General Electric. From the work of these scientists, it was concluded that most of the energy of the video signal is bunched at harmonics of the 15,750-cps horizontal-scanning-frequency signal (Fig. 27-68). If the frequency of the color subcarrier is an odd multiple of half this scanning frequency, the energy in the color signal will fall in between the harmonics of the scanning frequency.

In this manner, it is possible to cause the color and video signals to be interleaved, producing minimum interference (Fig. 27-69). When the exact frequency of the subcarrier is 3.579545 mc, the color information can be inter-

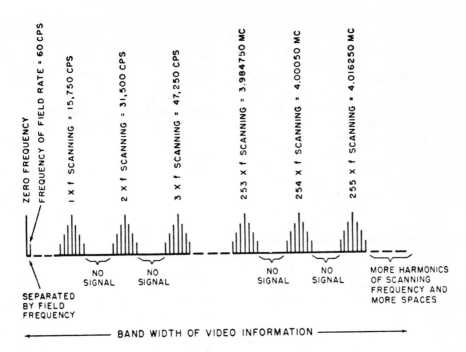

FIG. 27-68. SPECTRUM OF TYPICAL MONOCHROME VIDEO SIGNAL

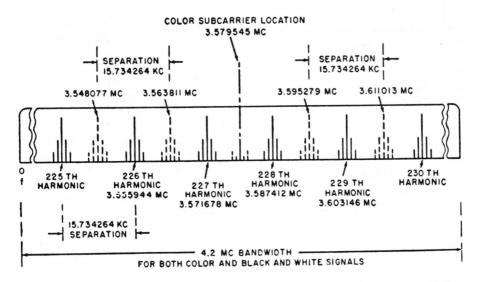

FIG. 27-69. ILLUSTRATION OF FREQUENCY INTERLEAVING OF BLACK AND WHITE (Y) AND COLOR (I AND Q) SIDEBAND FREQUENCIES
Solid lines are black and white, whereas dotted lines are color-sideband frequencies.

leaved so as to fit into the gaps in the video signals, thus reducing the required bandwidth of the channel (Fig. 27-70). The value of this subcarrier frequency was obtained by taking half of the horizontal-scanning frequency (which is approximately 15,734 cps for color television) and multiplying this value by 455. It may perhaps be noted that the horizontal line frequency of a color signal is slightly lower than that of a monochrome signal. The same is true of the vertical field-frequency signal, which is 59.94 cps instead of 60 cps. These changes in standards were adopted to prevent the production of interference signals. The changes in frequency are too slight to affect the operation of a monochrome receiver that is receiving these color signals.

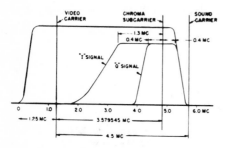

Courtesy, General Electric Co.

FIG. 27-70. SIX-MEGACYCLE COLOR TV CHANNEL SHOWING POSITION AND BANDWIDTH OF CHROMA SIGNALS

27.16 Color-television receivers

The color receiver usually contains a picture tube with three electron guns. The picture screen contains phosphor dots, each one of which is capable of producing either a blue, green, or red glow when struck by an electron beam. A masking plate with many tiny holes covers the screen. This plate and the electron guns are positioned in such a manner that the beam from one electron gun can strike the red dots only, whereas the second gun can strike the blue dots only, and the third gun can strike green dots only. Any color can then be produced on the screen by using beams of the correct intensities.

When the color video signal arrives at the receiver, it is fed into the luminance channel, where it is used to produce voltages that control the brightness of the spot appearing on the face of the picture tube (Fig. 27-71). The color video signal is also passed to the chrominance-signal channel where a filter removes the luminance signal. The chrominance signal is demodulated and fed into a matrix or color-decoder unit which performs in reverse the function of the matrix unit employed at the transmitter.

In reality, the matrix is a high-speed electronic analog-computer. It accepts the encoded color data and processes these data into three color-difference signals. A luminance signal is then added to each color-difference signal and each combined color signal is fed to its proper electron gun, thus controlling the brightness, hue, and saturation of the color tube.

When a monochrome picture is received, all of the color information goes through the luminance channel to the electron guns. No signal passes through the chrominance channel, and a monochrome picture is produced. Since this system allows a color receiver to receive a monochrome picture and also allows a monochrome receiver to receive a color picture in black-and-white, it obviously possesses the advantage of being a very compatible system.

It is interesting to note that the earliest color-television receivers had 15-in. screens and were priced at approximately 1,000 dollars. They were extremely difficult to tune, containing

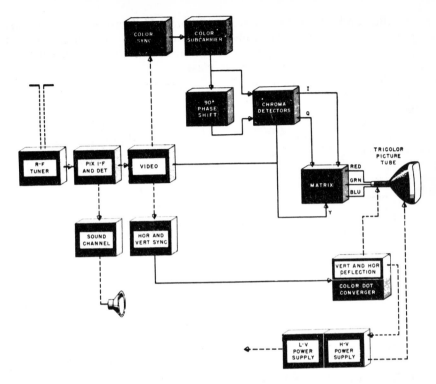

FIG. 27-71. SIMPLIFIED BLOCK DIAGRAM OF A COLOR TV RECEIVER

four different sensitive controls, each of which had to be adjusted to precisely the correct position.

In contrast, by 1960, a 21-in. color receiver cost only 495 dollars and contained only two controls. In one of these sets, if one control is misadjusted, it is frequently possible to compensate by adjusting either the other control or the fine-tuning control. One color control, usually labeled COLOR, adjusts the intensity of the color, somewhat in the manner of a volume control. The other, labeled TINT, controls the extent of color balance.[31]

At this point, it would be appropriate to present a more detailed description of some of the more-important tri-color picture tubes employed in color-television receivers. Each of the various tube types described has its own particular advantages and disadvantages. At present, it is impossible to predict which one will win out, or whether perhaps a new type will be developed that will make all of the other types obsolete.[32]

27.17 Tri-color picture tubes

Three-gun picture tube. In a previous section of this chapter, a brief description was given of one type of color tube, the Flat Shadow Mask-Three-Gun type with phosphor dots, known as the RCA Tri-Color tube (Fig. 27-72). This tube was invented by Alfred N. Goldsmith in 1940. It contains three separately controllable electron guns spaced 120 deg apart with respect to each other and whose beams are electrostatically or electromagnetically converged at an aperture plate or shadow mask (Fig. 27-73). Perhaps this tube may best be regarded as three separate tubes contained within a single envelope.

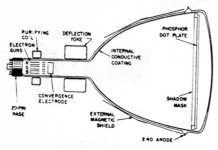

Courtesy, Radio Corporation of America

FIG. 27-72. CROSS-SECTION OF THE RCA THREE-GUN, SHADOW-MASK TRI-COLOR KINESCOPE TUBE

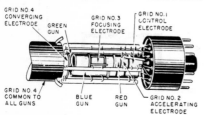

Courtesy, Radio Corporation of America

FIG. 27-73. ELECTRON-GUN ASSEMBLY IN THE THREE-GUN COLOR TUBE

The shadow mask of a 15-in. tube contains approximately 200,000 tiny holes, and the screen contains 600,000 phosphor dots that are deposited by means of a silk-screen process. Thus each hole corresponds to three dots, one red, one blue, and one green (Fig. 27-74). This triad grouping of dots was invented by Allen B. DuMont. Larger tubes contain more aperture holes and dots, the 21-in. tube containing about 357,000 holes and over a million triad phosphor dots. Although the conventional masks are made of metal, Corning Glass has recently developed a glass mask in which holes are produced by

a photoetching process. A special coating must be placed on the mask to eliminate the charging effect of the glass.

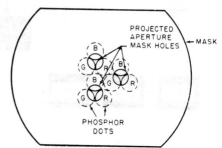

FIG. 27-74. ARRANGEMENT OF GROUPS OF PHOSPHOR DOTS, VIEWED FROM THE GUN END OF THE TUBE

Unlike the phosphors of picture tubes employed for monochrome reception, the phosphors of this type of color tube are placed on a straight screen that is separate from the curved face plate, and the phosphor screen is viewed through this faceplate. The holes in the mask are placed in such a manner that electrons from one particular beam can excite only one color over the entire face of the tube (Fig. 27-75). Thus each of the three electron guns produces only one color, red, blue, or green (Figs. 27-76 and 27-77). Any desired color may be produced by superimposing the proper amounts of colors produced by the three electron guns. Black is produced when all three guns are cut off, while shades of gray are produced by using the luminance signal to excite the electron guns.

A large coil, called the color-purity coil, is mounted on the neck of the tube. The field produced when direct current is sent through this coil is used to adjust the axes of the electron beams so that each beam strikes the correct color dot. This adjustment is made by varying the amount of current flowing through the coil and by varying

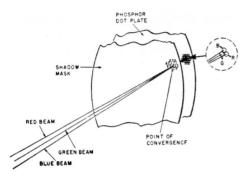

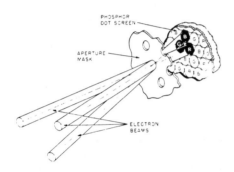

FIG. 27-76. CONVERGENCE OF THE THREE BEAMS AT A SINGLE HOLE IN THE APERTURE MASK
Note that the converged beams pass through the hole and strike their respective phosphor dots.

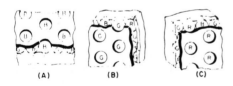

FIG. 27-77. MASK-AND-SCREEN ASSEMBLY AS SEEN FROM THE DEFLECTION POINTS OF THE THREE BEAMS
(A) Blue gun; (B) green gun; (C) red gun.

the positions of three small permanent magnets that are mounted on the purity coil spaced 120 deg apart to correspond with the positions of the electron guns.

The manufacturing tolerances required for making such a tube are staggering. A blocked hole or a phosphor dot that is the wrong color will show up readily. Precise registration between aperture mask and phosphor-dot screen must be maintained over a wide variation in temperatures as the set warms up. The tube is so sensitive that moving it in the earth's magnetic field can throw it out of adjustment. An entire complement of compensating permanent magnets is required, and it may take an experienced man many hours of adjusting to align one of these tubes.

The three-gun tube is generally considered to be unsatisfactory because of the expense of production and the complicated adjustments that are required. Despite these limitations, most color-television manufacturers regard it as the best interim tube available until something better comes along.[33] Consequently, all commercial color-television receivers currently being manufactured and all receivers now being planned for future production employ this type of tube, although DuMont has indicated that it may use the Chromatron tube sometime within the future.[34]

Colortron tube. The second type of color tube is the Curved Shadow Mask type, usually called the CBS Colortron (Fig. 27-78). This tube, which was developed in 1953, resembles the tri-color type of tube except for the fact that it has a curved mask and the phosphor dots are laid directly on the surface of the curved faceplate by means of automatic photographic techniques. In this process, each shadow mask is used as a negative to print its own individual screen, thus bringing mask and screen into perfect registration. The use of a curved mask and screen eliminates many problems of beam convergence that are present in the flat-shadow-mask type.

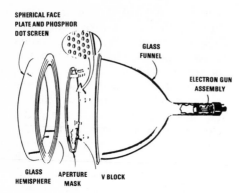

SPHERICAL FACE PLATE AND PHOSPHOR DOT SCREEN

GLASS FUNNEL

ELECTRON GUN ASSEMBLY

GLASS HEMISPHERE   APERTURE MASK   V BLOCK

Courtesy, CBS-Hytron

FIG. 27-78. INTERNAL COMPONENTS OF THE CBS-COLORTRON

It is claimed that this type of tube weighs less than the corresponding RCA type, that its design simplifies the problem of exhausting the air, thus substantially reducing its cost, and that it is designed for manufacture by mass-production techniques. It is further claimed that the curved surface of the Colortron tube enables it to avoid the size limitations inherent in the RCA type with its two flat parallel plates.[35] Both types of shadow-mask tubes suffer from the common disadvantages of requiring precision-machine parts, special circuitry to provide for beam convergence and focusing, and very well regulated high-voltage power supplies.

Chromatron tube. A third type of tube is the Color Grid-Single Gun, Post-Deflection type with phosphor strips. Usually called the Chromatron or Field Deflector color tube (Fig. 27-79), it was developed by Ernest O. Lawrence in the early 1950's. Lawrence is perhaps better known as a Nobel laureate and the inventor of the cyclotron. The Chromatron contains a single electron gun, no shadow mask, and no provision for converging the electron beam. The deflection components used for this tube are essentially the same as those used in a monochrome picture

tube. Consequently, it does not require the purity coil, the complex deflection yokes, and the convergence and centering adjustments characteristic of shadow-mask color tubes.

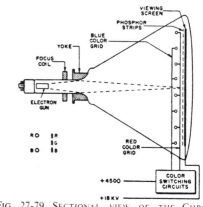

VIEWING SCREEN

PHOSPHOR STRIPS

BLUE COLOR GRID

YOKE

FOCUS COIL

ELECTRON GUN

RO   IR
      IG
BO   IB

RED COLOR GRID

+4500

COLOR SWITCHING CIRCUITS

+18 KV

FIG. 27-79. SECTIONAL VIEW OF THE CHROMATRON TUBE

The colored phosphors are laid down in strips instead of dots on an aluminum-backed screen, and horizontal wire grids are placed adjacent to the red and blue phosphor strips, between these strips and the electron gun. The green phosphor strips have no adjacent wire grids. All of the red grids are connected together, and the blue grids are all similarly interconnected.

When there is no potential applied to these grids, the beam of electrons will strike the green phosphor strips. When the red grid wires are given a positive potential with respect to the blue wires, the beam is deflected toward the red phosphor strip and strikes the red phosphor (Figs. 27-80 and 27-81). Similarly, when the blue grid is made positive, the beam is deflected in such a manner as to strike the blue phosphor. In contrast with the two types of tubes previously described, colors in this type of tube are displayed sequentially instead of simultaneously as in a three-gun tube. Consequently, the color-output circuits of the receiver must be

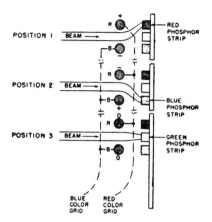

FIG. 27-80. HOW THE BEAM OF THE CHRO-MATRON IS DEFLECTED TO DIFFERENT PHOSPHORS

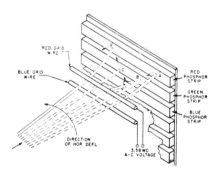

FIG. 27-81. HOW THE CHROMATRON SINGLE-GUN BEAM IS DEFLECTED SINUSOIDALLY IN THE VERTICAL DIRECTION AS IT SWEEPS ACROSS THE SCREEN

capable of converting the simultaneous information provided by the incoming signal into sequential information.[36] This is accomplished by a keying section that switches the output of the three different color-video amplifiers so that each delivers its signal in turn to the picture tube.

It is claimed that one of the advantages of the Chromatron lies in the simplicity of the color-decoding circuit associated with the use of a single-gun tube, and with the fact that some of the

color decoding is performed by the tube itself. It is also claimed that this reduces the number of tubes required by 20 per cent and that a complete color-television receiver can be constructed with only 22 tubes.[37]

Other advantages are the ease of tube construction and the somewhat higher light-transfer efficiency obtainable from the glass face of this tube. Among its disadvantages are the noticeable horizontal-line structure and the radiation of r-f energy from a rather-complex switching system associated with the grid wires.[38] [39]

Another problem is the difficulty of making a tube whose color strips are small enough to provide good detail without having the little grid wires vibrate into each other. However, reports emanating from Paramount Pictures, owner of the patents, and DuMont, which has been working on perfecting this tube, indicate that the Lawrence Chromatron may soon be ready for commercial use in home receivers.[40]

Post-acceleration tube. A fourth type of color tube is the General Electric Post-Acceleration tube, which is not yet commercially available. It contains three electron guns which all lie on the same horizontal plane. The screen consists of groups of vertical color-phosphor stripes deposited on the faceplate. The direction mechanism which causes each beam to strike the correctly colored phosphor consists of an array or grill of parallel wires called the color-selection electrode. These wires are located close to, and in front of, the phosphor screen. This grill, which is at a potential approximately 200 volts lower than that of the electron gun, functions as an electron-optical lens, and focuses a fine beam of electrons upon the correct phosphor stripe.

It is claimed that this grill has a transparency greater than 90 per cent, meaning that more than 90 per cent of the electrons emitted from the guns reach the phosphor screen. In contrast, the transparency of an aperture-masked tube is only between 12 and 14 per cent.

This means that theoretically a Post-Acceleration tube can produce a picture over six times brighter than the one produced by an aperture-masked tube when both are operating under equal high-voltage input conditions. Another claimed advantage is based upon the fact that this tube employs a 6,500-volt beam in place of the 27,000-volt beam used in other types of color tubes. This lower-voltage beam is easier to deflect, resulting in a considerable saving in deflection power.[41]

Apple tube. Philco has recently come out with a single-gun color picture tube called the Apple tube (Fig. 27-82). The face of this tube contains a repeated pattern of narrow red, blue, and green vertical phosphor stripes. The desired colors may be produced by causing an electron beam to strike the correct stripes. An interesting innovation is the use of a second beam produced by the same electron gun. This beam, called a marker beam, is aligned so that it always strikes the same color stripe as the picture-writing beam. On the gun side of each green stripe is a marker or index stripe. When the modulated, low-energy marker beam strikes the marker stripe, it produces a signal by means of secondary emission. This signal enables the circuits that process the incoming broadcast-signal information to "know" the exact position of the picture-writing beam. Consequently, the circuits are able to produce any desired color by turning the writing beam on as it crosses the correct phosphor stripes.[42]

Andromeda tube. In 1959, the president of Andromeda, Inc., announced the development of a color tube whose claimed advantages include compatibility with present transmitted color signals, improved quality of reception, increased reliability, reduced servicing requirements, and a reduction of 30 per cent in the cost of a color-television receiver. It was anticipated that a demonstration color receiver incorporating this tube would be in operation sometime during 1960.[43][44]

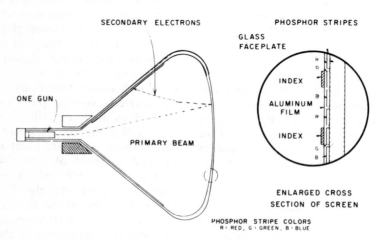

FIG. 27-82. SECTIONAL VIEW OF PHILCO APPLE TUBE

Courtesy, Stanford Research Institute

The tube employs a single electron gun that simultaneously emits three closely spaced electron beams. The color phosphors are deposited on the screen of the tube in the form of 1,500 horizontal stripes, alternately red, blue, and green. The beams are not controlled by an internal physical element such as a wire, grid element, or shadow mask. Instead, the beams are coordinated and positioned electronically by means of special circuits.

27.18 *Land color theory*

In the spring of 1959, Edwin H. Land, founder and president of the Polaroid Corporation, described an extremely simple way of producing pictures in full colors by mixing light of only two different colors. This may upset current thinking based upon the classic Newtonian tristimulus or three-color theory, and may have important bearings upon the reduction of cost of color television and color photography.

Land's discovery is not an entirely original one, since he has called attention to the fact that in 1914 W. F. Fox and W. F. Hickey patented a two-color, red-and-white, color-motion-picture process, and in 1929, A. Bernardi obtained a British patent for a similar type of system. However, these innovations were ignored and forgotten.

Land discovered that he could produce a colored image by taking simultaneous pictures through any two color filters, such as green and red, and developing this to form black-and-white transparencies. When the "green" picture was projected directly on a screen, while the "red" image was superimposed through a red filter, a very satisfactory, full-range colored picture was observed.

Land also discovered that this system was not limited to two particular colors, but that any two filters operating in the spectrum between 425 and 615 millimicrons and separated by 15 millimicrons would work. He concluded that the color message relayed by the eye to the brain depends only upon the ratio between the short-wavelength stimulus and the long-wavelength stimulus.

If his discoveries are applied in color-television systems, they should reduce the number of image orthicon tubes required at the transmitter from three to two. In the receiving tube, the three guns could be reduced to two, and the number of different types of phosphors required on the face of the tube could also be reduced from three to two, with resultant decreases in manufacturing costs.[45][46][47]

27.19 *Iowa State College system*

Another simplified color-television system was exhibited at the 1959 convention of the Institute of Radio Engineers in New York City. This system uses only two color cameras. One camera produces a luminance signal, while the other picks up a red and blue field alternately. A memory device holds each field during the time the next one is taken. Green is obtained by subtracting the red and blue from the total luminance field.

It is claimed that this system, which is in the experimental and developmental condition at Iowa State College, can simplify the problems of color-television recording, reduces the cost of color-television equipment for a television station, and might make it possible to convert existing monochrome television cameras to color.[48]

27.20 *Color-television projection systems*

In the United States, the most common system employed in large-theatre television projection systems is the Schmidt system (Fig. 27-83). In this system, the image is merely picked up from a very-high-intensity cathode-ray picture tube and is then magnified and projected by conventional optical means (Fig. 27-84).

A second system, known as the Eidophor system, was invented in 1939 by F. Fischer of Zurich. In this system, the video signal is projected by an electron gun upon an oil-covered concave mirror. The impact of the electrons distorts the oil layer. This in turn modulates an external light source that is first reflected off the mirror and then projected by means of a lens upon the viewing screen.

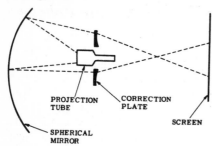

FIG. 27-83. SIMPLIFIED DIAGRAM OF A SCHMIDT OPTICAL SYSTEM

Color can be introduced if the signal employed is of the CBS field-sequential type. This, of course, involves the use of large synchronized color wheels in front of both the camera and the projector in order to produce three color impressions of an image which form a full-color picture.

The claimed advantage of the Eidophor is that it uses the controlled modulation of an external light source. This means that the brightness of the projected image is not dependent upon the brightness of the picture on the screen of a cathode-ray tube, and consequently, a projected image of high brilliance and resolution can be obtained.[49]

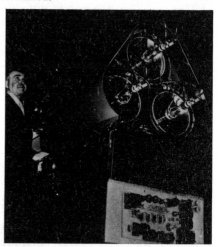

Courtesy, Radio Corporation of America
FIG. 27-84. EXPERIMENTAL TELEVISION RECEIVER-PROJECTOR

27.21 *Present and future status of color television*

RCA and its NBC affiliate have taken on the major share of the task of selling color television to the American public. It is estimated that they have invested over 130 million dollars in this effort. According to General Sarnoff of RCA, it was not until 1959 that the sale of color-television receivers reached the break-even point. Out of a total estimated number of 50 million television sets in use in 1959, 5 years after the introduction of commercial color television, less than 500,000, or approximately 1 per cent, were color sets. In 1960, only two major manufacturers were making color-television receivers. Over 90 per cent of these color sets were manufactured by RCA. Only one television network, that of the National Broadcasting Corporation, was pushing color, and over 90 per cent of the color programs transmitted were over the facilities of NBC.

There are many factors that have helped to impede the rapid growth of color television. Many of these are due to misconceptions that are based upon the faults that existed in early models of color-television receivers. Among them are the following:

1. The quality of the color is poor. According to surveys, the majority of color-television set owners classified the quality of the color as ranging from good to excellent to superb. Most of them agree, however, that the reception of a monochrome program is not quite as sharp as that observed over an ordinary set, and that a slight bluish-green tint is sometimes observable.

It has also been observed that the quality of the color depends to a large extent upon the ability of the studio technicians. Live color shows originating under studio conditions provide the best color. Filmed color is almost as good. However, at the present time, taped color programs are least satisfactory, frequently producing weak and unsaturated colors.

2. The sets are too expensive. As has been previously mentioned, the cost has dropped from 1,000 dollars per set to 495 dollars. While color sets are still rather expensive, most set owners who have been surveyed feel that they have received full value from their sets. Undoubtedly, however, the gap of several hundred dollars between comparable color and black-and-white sets is a formidable marketing hurdle, and color-television sets will not make any spectacular progress until their prices drop to within 100 dollars of comparable black-and-white television receivers.

3. They are too difficult to tune. This criticism was true of early sets. However, as has been previously explained, the present-day color receiver contains only two simple controls for adjusting the color.

4. Color sets break down too often. A survey of color-television repairmen reveal that the service problems associated with color-television sets are not significantly more important than those associated with black-and-white sets, with the exception of the picture tube. If this tube fails, it may cost 150 dollars to replace it. According to this survey, color-television sets require slightly more frequent repair than black-and-white sets, and the average repair bill for a color set was 30 dollars compared with a bill of 25 dollars for a black-and-white set. However, as an indication of the increased reliability of color sets, the price of an RCA one-year service contract has recently been reduced from approximately 150 dollars to approximately 70 dollars.

5. There are not enough color-television programs. This is a type of problem resembling that of the chicken and the egg. Sponsors are hardly likely to be enthusiastic about spending large sums of money on color-television programs unless they are assured of a large audience possessing color-television receivers. On the other hand, more color-television sets would be sold if there were a greater number and variety of color-television programs. However, it is possible that this log jam may soon be broken. The NBC color-television program of the 1959 season was almost one-third heavier than the previous year's, with at least one color program each night. Furthermore, other companies are beginning to produce color-television receivers. The Admiral Corporation, which is starting to produce a complete line of color sets,

believes that a mass color-television receiver market will soon open up. Another optimist, Sarnoff of RCA, predicts that color-television sets will be in most homes by 1970 and also envisages by that time global television in full color, relayed by orbiting artificial satellites.[50][51]

27.22 *Subscription or toll television*

The question of subscription television, or "tollevision," is one which has produced some of the most bitter controversy in the broadcast industry since its birth in the early 1920's. Since 1922, the public has received free broadcast-radio programs, and the expenses have been met by the advertiser who has something to sell. Occasionally, as in 1924, there were attempts to legalize coin-box radio systems that would collect money from the listeners, but these efforts seemed always doomed to failure. The attitudes of both legislators and the public seemed in accordance with the views expressed by Sarnoff of RCA when he made the following statement at a Congressional hearing in 1924:

"I cannot help feeling that not only should the public be left free from the payment of any license fee to the Government or others for the privilege of listening on a broadcast receiver, but that it should also be free from fees or tolls of any kind in the field of broadcasting through space.... The air belongs to the people."[52]

Since the development of television broadcasting, this question of charging the consumer for watching and listening has again been raised. Lined up on one side are the proponents of toll television, the manufacturers of subscription-television equipment, and the producers of sports, drama, and motion pictures. In the opposite corner are the large television networks and the theatre owners. Somewhere in the middle is the public—the ultimate consumer.

The controversy has become a heated one, and spokesmen for both sides have lifted their voices in anger and have thrown recriminations at each other. The stakes are high; the total estimated receipts if toll television were permitted would probably exceed 3.5 billion dollars a year. Before analyzing the pros and cons, it might be well to look into the technical aspects of tollevision.

27.23 *Systems of toll television*

The major systems of toll television employ similar fundamental principles. They cause a jumbled picture to be transmitted by changing the time relationships between the video signals and the synchronizing pulses (Fig. 27-85). This scrambling may be accomplished by either of two methods. In one method, groups of lines are shifted in relation to each other, and the voltage polarities may also be inverted. In the second method, the two fields of the picture are shifted in relation to each

Courtesy, Zenith Radio Corp.
FIG. 27-85. THE PHONEVISION CODED OR "SCRAMBLED" PICTURE

other.[53][54] With either method of scrambling, it is necessary to purchase the services of the tollevision system in order to receive a clear picture free from blur (Fig. 27-86).

Courtesy, Zenith Radio Corp.

FIG. 27-86. THE PHONEVISION DECODED OR CLEAR PICTURE

Zenith Phonevision. One of the leading subscription systems is the Zenith Phonevision. In this system, the consumer is charged separately for each program he watches. In order to unscramble the program, the subscriber must call a local telephone operator. A key signal is then sent via the telephone line to a decoder unit installed in the television receiver (Fig. 27-87). This unit unscrambles the picture when it receives the key signal. The subscriber is then billed at the end of the month. In newer versions of this system, it is possible for the subscriber to purchase a card or to insert a coin into a mechanism which will cause the decoder to begin unscrambling the signal. This renders the system independent of the telephone company.

The Phonevision system was tested in 1951 on a group of 300 television-set owners in Chicago. They were offered three recent motion pictures each day at a cost of one dollar per picture. The average family paid for 1.73 films per week, approximately four times the average American weekly movie attendance.[55]

The Zenith Radio Corporation and the Hartford Phonevision Corporation, a subsidiary of RKO General, Inc., is now operating an experimental subscription-television program over station WHCT, Hartford, Conn. It is showing first-run movies, Broadway plays, operas, ballets, symphony concerts, and sports events; and most programs cost between 75 cents and $1.50. This system uses an improved version of the Phonevision plan in which both the coding and decoding information is sent out over the air, and no telephone wires are involved (Fig. 27-88).

Courtesy, Zenith Radio Corp.

FIG. 27-87. ORIGINAL PHONEVISION DECODER UNIT

After dialing the program identification number, viewer closes decoder door. If an incorrect number has been selected, a buzzer tells subscriber to check for a dialing error and readjust the program number setting to correct index. Buzzer also indicates malfunctioning of the decoder or incorrect setting of the television receiver channel. When decoder is properly indexed and operating, a correlator light, seen on the front panel of the decoder, will begin to glow, after which the unscrambled program will appear on the screen within a few seconds. At the end of subscription broadcast, buzzer alerts subscriber to place lever in "TV" position before an advertising sponsored program can be viewed.

FIG. 27-88. CURRENT PHONEVISION OPERATION *(A) To receive clear subscription telecast, viewer first tunes TV set to proper channel and opens decoder door; (B) subscriber then turns a single dial until the program code (which is the same for all sets) appears in a window on the front of the unit; closing decoder door and turning knob at left activates decoding; (C) to pay for subscription events, subscriber is asked to dial special billing number periodically to unlock compartment where tape has accumulated. Opening compartment shears off tape and subscriber mails it with payment.*

Skiatron Subscriber Vision. A second proposed toll-television is the Skiatron Subscriber Vision system. This system also requires the attachment of a decoder unit to the receiver (Figs. 27-89 and 27-90). In order to unscramble the picture, it is necessary for the subscriber to obtain a special card which is good for a limited period of time. This card is a special IBM card on which a printed circuit has been

FIG. 27-89. SKIATRON CODER
The coder scrambles the image broadcast over the air.

superimposed. When the card is inserted into the decoder, it automatically sets the decoder into operation and a normal picture is produced. At the same time, a hole is punched on the card, providing information that is used for billing the subscriber.[56]

Telemeter system. A third system is the Telemeter system, developed by the International Telemeter Corporation,

FIG. 27-90. SKIATRON DECODER UNIT
Used to unscramble the image, the decoder is attached to the subscriber's television receiver.

an organization in which Paramount Pictures Corporation holds 50 per cent ownership. This system employs a process called multiplexing or frequency interleaving to send two pictures on the same channel or over a single wired closed circuit. The first picture, of somewhat inferior quality, is an advertising commercial or trailer describing the jumbled picture that is also being sent on that channel (Fig. 27-91). A dial indicates the cost of the program. When the correct amount of money is dropped into a coin-box, the other picture becomes visible (Figs. 27-92).

Another interesting feature is the incorporation of a tape recorder which

Courtesy, International Telemeter Co.

FIG. 27-92. TELEMETER CHASSIS REMOVED FROM ITS PLASTIC COVER

makes a record of what programs have been watched by the subscriber. This record could be extremely useful in

FIG. 27-91. TELEMETER CABLE SYSTEM

Three pay TV programs can be transmitted simultaneously. Shown here are the transmitter racks for channels A, B and C. The "barker" panel at the right serves as an information service for Telemeter subscribers.

surveying the viewing and listening habits of various groups of subscribers.

In 1953, a version of this system was tried out in Palm Springs, Calif. Despite the fact that at that time the free television stations did not possess the store of feature-length pictures that they now have, the test was a failure and was quietly dropped. In 1960, another experimental version of this system was placed in operation in Etobicok, a suburb of Toronto. First reactions seemed generally favorable. Within two months, 4,600 individuals had signed up, and the number was expected to reach 6,500 within a very short time. It was estimated that 10,000 subscribers would put the investment on a paying basis. One popular feature—in contrast to the unsuccessful Bartlesville, Okla., Telemovie experiment (to be described) that charged a minimum of $9.50 monthly—is that there is no minimum fee and the only charge is a 5-dollar installation fee.

The Bi-Tran system. The Blonder-Tongue Laboratories have developed a multiplexing system called Bi-Tran that enables two television programs to be transmitted simultaneously on the same channel. This doubles the available transmitting facilities and enables a station to transmit two programs at the same time, one free and the other one pay television. The alternate pay program can only be made visible and audible by the addition of coded signals carried via telephone wires into the home.[57][58]

The Boxoffice system. The Boxoffice system was developed by the Boxoffice Television Co. It is specifically designed for closed-circuit use in community antenna systems and in master-antenna systems for hotels and apartments. This enables it to be used for toll television without FCC approval. However, it can also be adapted for use with broadcast programs.

A standard video signal, produced by any normal source and transmitted by coaxial cable or microwave relay, is fed into a coding unit located in the hotel or apartment house. The output, a scrambled picture, is fed into the master antenna, the community antenna, or the closed-circuit system. In order to unscramble the picture, the user must obtain or rent a key which operates a decoder unit located in the television receiver.[59]

The Teleglobe system. A sixth system, called Teleglobe, claims to be the simplest and most economical, since it contains neither scrambling nor coding devices. In this system, only the picture signal is transmitted by the station. The audio portion is brought to the subscribers by means of inexpensive wire lines. The silent picture may be viewed free by the public. If the subscriber is sufficiently interested to desire to hear the sound portion of the program, he operates an automatic switch which then turns on the audio signal. A central switchboard then takes over the billing, eliminating the necessity for coin-boxes or cards.

The Jerrold Telemovie system. A proposal has been advanced by the Jerrold Electronics Co. to establish a toll-television system operating entirely on a closed-circuit basis. This company claims that the scrambling codes employed on the other systems can be broken. If this can be done without too much difficulty, it would mean that the other systems would eventually fail because they would find it difficult or impossible to collect tolls.

Jerrold proposes a system resembling a community-antenna system, in which a coaxial cable brings an unscrambled picture into the home. A simple switching and metering system would enable the subscriber to use this service whenever he desired. It is claimed that this system of toll television would offer a medium for those who desired to present sports, motion pictures, plays, and opera programs for a price, and would still leave the public in full possession of the present free-television channels.[60]

In September 1957, an experimental version of this system, called Telemovie, was tried out in Bartlesville, Okla. It was used to bring the latest motion pictures into the homes of subscribers via closed-circuit lines. At first, each subscriber was charged a flat monthly fee of $9.50. It was estimated that it would require at least 2,000 subscribers before the system could begin to make a profit. After six months of operation, when only 650 persons had subscribed, the fee was reduced to $4.95. The number of subscribers then rose to 800. In June 1958, the system closed down for lack of financial support. The failure of this experiment seemed to indicate that after years of receiving free entertainment, the public was not eager to pay for it.

The proponents of closed-circuit toll-television systems of this type have long maintained that the FCC has no control over the operation of these systems. However, in September 1955, J. C. Doerfer, chairman of the FCC, warned that if wired toll-television systems were successfully established, they would eventually be classified as a public service and would be placed under government regulation. He pointed out the telephone, power, gas, pipeline and motor-carrier companies as illustrations of the fact that few business enterprises that use public highways for a substantial portion of their plant investment and who charge the public for the service have escaped regulation.

27.24 *Advantages and disadvantages of toll TV*

Those who support tollevision maintain that it will result in better programs, sports events, shows, and first-run motion pictures that are at present beyond a sponsor's reach. It is claimed that it will provide quality and cultural programs appealing to small minorities and that the competition will improve the quality of free television programs. In addition, the absence of commercials alone is claimed to be worth the toll paid. Free television will not be harried, since the advocates of toll television have asked the FCC to rule that no station may use more than 15 per cent of its program time for pay television.

In sharp rebuttal, the opponents of toll television point out that the cost of a show is no gauge of its quality, and the most expensive show is not always the best show. In addition, many outstanding sports events are now available on free television, and the quality of the motion pictures shown on free television has been increasing steadily. Toll television is also being unfair to the millions of people who purchased television receivers under the assumption that they would not have to pay anything more to see television. They also claim that toll television would try to appeal to the largest possible audience rather than to minority groups interested in cultural programs and emphasize that the additional income provided by pay television does not guarantee high-quality programs. In addition, no promises have been made by the advocates of toll television not to carry commercials.[61]

It is pointed out that none of the promoters of pay television plan to invest any money in building new television stations. They plan to use the facilities that have been created by free television. Toll television and free television cannot live side by side. If more money is available from toll television than from free television, the best producers, writers, and actors will gravitate to tollevision. The resulting inferior programs on free television will be watched by a steadily dwindling audience. As the sponsor's messages reach fewer people, the sponsor will spend less money, and free television will eventually die. In the words of Frank Stanton. president of CBS: "Television could not long remain half pay and half free."

In areas served by one or two television stations, the listener would have little choice. For example, there are over 8 million people who receive all of their television service from a single free television station.[62] Although pay television would be limited to 15 per cent of a station's program time, the toll programs would be broadcast at choice times to insure the largest possible cash audience. During these choice hours, the viewer would have only two choices, that of paying for entertainment or turning off his set.

In conclusion, they state that pay television cannot in good faith promise the public anything that has not already been presented or that will not soon be presented on free television.

Action of the FCC and the Federal Government. No decisive action on the question of tollevision has as yet been taken by the FCC. In 1956, it shelved a request made by the Zenith Radio Corporation for immediate authorization of the Phonevision system. It stated that the basis for this decision was the fact that it did not know whether it was empowered legally to authorize tollevision. If it did not have that power, it would be necessary for Congress to enact new legislation giving the FCC

the proper authority to take action.

In the summer of 1957, the FCC decided that it had statutory authority to authorize the use of television-broadcasting frequencies for subscription-television operations and agreed to authorize trial runs of toll television after March 1958 for a period of 3 years. This statement encountered considerable criticism and opposition from members of both the House and the Senate. Chairman Emanuel Celler of the House Judiciary Committee stated that the FCC did not possess the authority to issue permits for subscription television. Celler and several other congressmen have indicated their sentiments by introducing bills which would prohibit the FCC from authorizing any system of toll television.

Early in 1958, the House Committee on Interstate and Foreign Commerce notified the FCC that the toll-television problem should be settled by Congress. After considering letters from the general public, which averaged 1,000 to 1 against pay television, the committee sent a resolution to the FCC stating that the public interest would not be served by granting authorization for subscription television: "It has not been established to the complete satisfaction of the committee that authority to license such an operation comes within the power of the Commission." As a result, the FCC decided that it would do nothing further about toll-television applications until September 1959.

In March 1959, the FCC stated that it would consider and act upon applications by television stations for toll-television tests. It lay down many restrictive limitations, including one stating that the public was not to be called upon to purchase any special receiving equipment required for subscription-television operations but not needed for reception of free television broadcasts. In addition, the applicants were required to develop safeguards against interference and against any degradation of signal quality in either subscription or non-subscription programs.[63] As of January 1960, the FCC reported that it had received no applications for test subscription television with the exception of the previously mentioned Hartford Phonevision system. The FCC is also conducting a detailed study of the entire pay-television problem and what type of a trial demonstration of toll television would be most feasible.

There are many questions that must be resolved. The leading question, of course, is whether the Commission has the power to authorize toll television. A second question is whether it is in the public interest to broadcast to one section of the public that is willing to pay and to exclude the remainder who are either unwilling or unable to pay.

The third question is whether pay television constitutes broadcasting or whether it is a common-carrier type of operation. Associated with this question is one concerning control of the toll charges and how the tolls would be calculated. Would Federal taxes on such tolls be similar to present communication taxes on telephone and telegraph services?

Another question that would have to be settled is whether pay television would mean the screening of motion pictures, plays, and major sporting events that would not otherwise be available to televiewers, or whether toll television would result in the withdrawal of the better free-television programs from the air and their transfer to the toll systems.

Additional problems are the possibility of interference of pay television with regular television service, the matter of patent and licensing arrange-ments, and the role of the motion-picture industry in tollevision. Another very real problem is the following. If the FCC does accept the principle of tolle-vision, should it approve of all the leading systems or give its approval to only one? If the latter, what shall be the criteria used in giving such a fabulous and valuable monopoly to one cor-poration?

Additional complications were introduced in the spring of 1959, when two anti-tollevision bills were intro-duced in the Senate and the House. One, offered by Representative Oren Harris, was an interim resolution designed to prohibit pay television, both broadcast and wire, until the passage of appropriate legislation detailing the regulation of subscription television. A second measure, intro-duced by Senators Dirksen and Langer, also forbade any FCC approval of pay television without congressional appro-val, but it granted to the FCC authority to determine which pay system would meet government standards.[64] [65]

It is obvious that the battle over toll television is one which will not be settled for many years to come. The FCC may conduct oral hearings, experiment with toll television, ask Congress for direc-tions, and will eventually come to some decision. Whatever the decision is, there will undoubtedly be legal challen-ges, and the final decision concerning pay television may eventually be made by the United States Supreme Court.

27.25 *ITV, or industrial television, and related applications*

While public attention has been focused upon the glamorous applica-tions of television in the fields of enter-tainment and communication, com-paratively little attention has been paid to the growth of industrial television—a growth which has been proceeding at an almost unbelievable rate. The term industrial television, or ITV, as used here includes all of the non-entertainment and non-educational uses of this medium.

Nature of ITV systems. ITV systems are almost invariably CCTV or closed-circuit television systems. This means that the signals are not radiated through space in the conventional manner but are carried via cable from the camera to the receiver (Fig. 27-93). This system does not require the type of high-powered transmitter needed by television-broadcasting systems. The low-powered transmitter can be made small enough to be built into the camera.

While some of the large CCTV cameras use image orthicon or image dissector tubes, most of these smaller cameras use the vidicon tube, which combines small size with good resolution (Fig. 27-94). Some of the cameras have been made small enough to fit into the drilling shaft of an oil well.

RCA has developed a Telemite transistorized ultra-miniature camera with a photoelectric sensitivity control.

Courtesy, Radio Corporation of America
FIG. 27-94. MINIATURE TYPE TK-202 VIDICON CAMERA FOR CLOSED-CIRCUIT USE

It weighs 1 lb, fits into one hand, and can be carried in a pocket. Other cameras are available that contain explosion-proof, weather-proof, or underwater housings for special applications (Fig. 27-95).[66]

Most of the CCTV cameras employ the conventional broadcast scanning standards of 525 lines per frame. This standardization makes the CCTV system compatible with broadcast-television

FIG. 27-93. COMPARISON BETWEEN CONVENTIONAL AND CLOSED CIRCUIT TELEVISION

Courtesy, Pye Canada, Ltd.
FIG. 27-95. PYE'S 12-INCH HAND-HELD UNDERWATER CAMERA

systems. It facilitates tying in CCTV systems with broadcast-television systems when desired and also makes it possible to employ conventional television receivers.[67]

Types of ITV systems. There are two methods of distributing the picture information (Fig. 27-96). One employs a video system in which the transmitted signal employs a video band of frequencies between zero and 6 mc and is received by a video monitor. Since no radio-frequency tuner is required by the monitor, a 600-line picture with a high degree of resolution of fine detail can be transmitted. However, the cost of a video monitor is usually higher than that of a conventional television receiver.

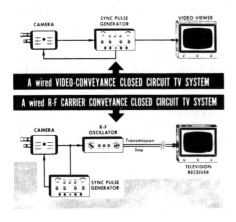

FIG. 27-96. TWO TYPES OF CLOSED-CIRCUIT TV SYSTEMS

The second method is a radio-frequency method. The signal is transmitted via a video-modulated VHF channel and can be received by a conventional low-cost television receiver. This system produces pictures of 350 to 400 lines and is used where reception of maximum detail is not of utmost importance.[68]

Growth of ITV. At present, only a negligible fraction of the potential of ITV has been tapped. According to *Electronics* magazine, the total sales volume of ITV in 1957 was only around 7 million dollars. This rose to 8.2 million dollars in 1958 and 13 million dollars in 1959. However, even this modest volume of sales indicates a tremendous rate of growth when one considers that as recently as 1950, the total annual volume of sales did not amount to more than a few thousand dollars.[69]

One factor that has retarded the advance of ITV is the fact that many businessmen have not grasped its advantages and still regard it as a toy or plaything. A second major obstacle has been the high cost of the equipment. This obstacle is being overcome by the development of low-cost lightweight equipment.

The prediction has been made that between 1960 and 1963, the number of closed-circuit ITV systems in operation will exceed the number of home television receivers.[70] Gen. Sarnoff, chairman of the board of RCA, has publicly expressed his belief that the dimensions of ITV will surpass the growth of broadcast television.[71] In addition, the widening scope of applications in business and industry during the past few years suggests that ITV is already working a revolution in the field of business comparable to that wrought by broadcast television in the field of mass communications and entertainment.

Wherever discomfort, inconvenience, danger, cost, or remoteness preclude the presence of a human observer, the ITV camera can take his place. This principle was succinctly expressed by Zworykin in his book entitled *Television in Science and Industry,* in which he stated: "Whenever it is too dangerous; too difficult; too expensive; too inconvenient; too inaccessible; too far; too hot; too cold; too high; too low; too dark; too small to observe directly, use television."[72]

Among the examples of such industrial applications are the observing of furnaces and remote stations, pouring of castings, and the handling of explosives and radioactive materials (Fig. 27-97). In general, CCTV can be used to perform the following basic functions in industry:

1. Provide greater safety
2. Reduce operating costs
3. Reduce capital investment
4. Provide greater intelligence than can be gained by direct observation
5. Save time
6. Transmit data rapidly
7. Provide continuous surveillance and scanning of wide areas.[73]

27.26 *Principles of ITV systems*

In order to avoid FCC regulation and permission, most of the ITV systems employ closed-circuit operation in which one or more television cameras are linked by means of cables or telephone wires to remotely located monitors and receivers. In situations such as supervising chemical reactions or heating metals, where observation or identification of color are important factors, field-sequential color-television systems are available.

Because of differences in purposes and operating conditions, the design and construction of ITV equipment differs from that of conventional television equipment. In general, the points to be considered in designing and selecting an ITV system are the following:

1. Simplicity of design—(approximately one-third as many tubes as a studio-television system)
2. Simplicity of operation
3. Dependability

Courtesy, American Iron and Steel Institute
FIG. 27-97. TELEVISION ASSISTS OPERATOR IN CONTROLLING LONG CONTINUOUS STRIP MILL

4. Freedom from excessive service requirements
5. Long life
6. Satisfactory performance
7. Reasonable cost
8. Portability.[74]

Diamond Utiliscope system. One of the oldest systems in use is the Diamond Utiliscope system (Fig. 27-98). An early model employed a cold-cathode image dissector tube with excellent long-life characteristics. The camera contained two lenses, each of which could be positioned and focused by motors that were capable of being activated from a remote monitor position.

One disadvantage of the image dissector tube is the fact that it requires an illumination of 300 foot-candles on the object to be televised. A newer model of the Utiliscope employs a vidicon camera tube, called the Utilicon 600, which is only slightly less sensitive than a studio-type image orthicon,

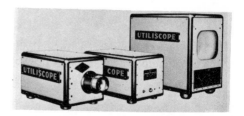

Courtesy, Diamond Power Specialty Corp.
FIG. 27-98. UNITS COMPRISING THE UTILISCOPE SYSTEM
Left to right, camera, power supply, monitor.

and whose light requirements are between 10 and 100 foot-candles.

General Electric Intra-Tel system. The General Electric Intra-Tel system also employs a vidicon camera tube. The monochrome picture may be transmitted to remote locations by means of either coaxial cable or microwave systems. The company has also developed a closed-circuit field-sequential color-television system with a video bandwidth of 15 mc. It has a horizontal scanning frequency of 39,690 cps and an interlaced vertical scanning frequency of 180 cps. At the receiving end, the colored picture may be viewed in a conventional monitor, it may be projected onto a 4.5-foot by 6-foot screen, or else, by employing the previously described Eidophor system, it may be projected onto large theatre-type screens.

Kin Tel system. The Kin Tel system used a vidicon camera tube and an amplifying system which can produce pictures with only 1 foot-candle of incident light (Fig. 27-99). The video output covers a bandwidth of 8 mc. A remotely controlled system aims the camera vertically and horizontally, controls the lens iris and focus adjustments, and provides selection of any one lens in a three-lens turret.

RCA TV-Eye system. The RCA TV-Eye system also employs a vidicon camera tube. It contains all of the remote-control features described in connection with preceding ITV systems and possesses in addition a split-screen viewing arrangement which permits several different scenes to be viewed simultaneously on a single monitor. This saves space and affords better control. Another feature is an arrangement by which the output of the camera may be connected to any channel between Channels 2 and 6 of an unaltered standard television receiver.

Courtesy, Kin-Tel Div., Cohu Electronics, Inc.
FIG. 27-99. KIN-TEL VIDICON TV CAMERA WITH REMOTE CONTROL OF PAN, TILT, IRIS, AND FOCUS

The preceding descriptions provide a good cross-sectional view of the outstanding features of modern ITV systems. There are many other ITV systems that are equally good, but space limitations make it impossible to describe their features and characteristics (Fig. 27-100).

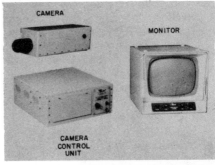

Courtesy, Friez Instrument Div., The Bendix Corp.
FIG. 27-100. BENDIX-FRIEZ BX-7 IMAGE ORTHICON CLOSED CIRCUIT TELEVISION SYSTEM

27.27 Applications of ITV

It is almost impossible to enumerate and describe all of the potentialities and applications of ITV. The descriptions which follow represent but a fraction of the number of applications of television in today's world of industry and commerce.

Banking, business, and financial applications. ITV can be used to enable bank clerks to make almost instant-aneous checks of signatures, bank balances, and documents by comparing them with the original records that are kept in a central depository to conserve valuable floor space. In another recent-ly-developed application, CCTV moni-tors are used by brokerage firms to dis-play the latest American and New York Stock Exchange tapes continuously to the executives, employees, and custom-ers without the distracting noise asso-ciated with conventional stock tickers (Fig. 27-101).[75]

Many large industrial organiza-tions have employed closed-circuit television, projected on large screens in theatres located in many different cities, for the purposes of direct sell-ing and holding sales conferences. Thus, IBM has on occasion hooked up their sales offices in 102 cities by closed-circuit television to introduce a new line. Other large organizations, such as General Electric and Johnson

Outboard Motors, have reported that such CCTV sales meetings have pro-duced tremendous spurts in sales. One expert has estimated that during 1959, corporations spent approximately 10 million dollars for such closed-circuit television conferences.

Industrial applications. Industry is employing CCTV for monitoring opera-tions that normally require standby personnel. Television cameras are also used to watch operations and events that are tedious, dangerous, difficult, or even impossible for human beings to watch.[76] Among a few of these applica-tions are the following:

1. Monitoring of conveyor line and warehousing operations

2. Distant reading of water levels, meters, and gauges

3. Observation of smokestacks for the most efficient combustion of fuels in boilers (Fig. 27-102)

4. Providing observation needed for accurate shearing of steel slabs

5. Observation of burner flames in furnaces

6. Checking interiors of open-hearth furnaces to produce uniform heating of steel slabs

7. Observing nuclear-power reac-tor tests.[77]

Courtesy, GPL Div., General Precision, Inc.

FIG. 27-101. TICKER TAPE TV

GPL TV camera with special accessories flashes stock exchange information to all TV monitors in an office. Standby camera insures service cannot be interrupted.

Courtesy, Consolidated Edison Co. of New York, Inc.

FIG. 27-102. SMOKE CONTROL BY TELEVISION

Attention is also called to the previously mentioned fact that the Hughes Aircraft Company has recently developed mobile robot devices called Mobots. They carry two television cameras as "eyes" and are operated by radio signals produced by an operator who is located in a remote shielded position. They are designed to be used under conditions of vacuum, high-pressure, high temperature, poisonous atmosphere, and nuclear radiation. It is also envisaged that they might be used in the future for space exploration.

Medical applications. Closed-circuit color-television has been installed in many hospitals to make surgical operations visible to large groups of internes and visiting doctors. A second application in medicine and biology is the use of CCTV for the projection of microscope color-slide specimens in the form of enlarged colored images on a color monitor. In visible-light microscopy, the structure of cells is made visible by means of staining. This process alters and sometimes kills the cells. In the UCTM or Ultraviolet Color-Translating Television Microscope—developed by Zworykin, Hatke, and Berkley of the Rockefeller Institute Medical Electronics Center—the differences in the amount of selective absorption of short pulses of ultraviolet energy by various parts of the cells are translated into visible colors and displayed by television methods. By use of this electronic staining method, it is possible to trace the distribution and metabolism of specific materials within the cells, and to determine the location of various absorbing chemical constituents without disturbing the cell.[78] [79]

A third recent development, which will be described in detail later, is the combining of X-ray with television techniques to transmit and display an X-ray image. This picture can be made 10,000 times brighter than the image produced on the conventional fluorescent screen and can be enlarged to permit close inspection. It can thus be used by medical centers in large cities to bring quick expert diagnosis to patients in remote areas or to permit medical specialists in one part of the country to participate in the diagnosis of a patient being X-rayed in another part of the country.

Another interesting application is the Sanguinometer, developed by Hellman of the Sloan-Kettering Institute. It combines a closed-circuit television system with an optical microscope and a computer to produce a device that is capable of counting the number of small particles, such as blood cells, that are within a given field. In operation, the camera tube of this device scans the specimen that is under the microscope and sends out video pulses as the scanning beam strikes the images of the particles to be counted. These pulses actuate an electronic counter. An ingenious diameter-compensation circuit compensates for the fact that large particles interrupt more scanning lines and produce more pulses than small particles do.

An additional medical application is the use of closed-circuit television in hospitals to enable the floor nurse to monitor every room on her floor, thus reducing the number of unnecessary trips made to the rooms of patients.[80]

Another important application is its use in hospitals, such as the Albert Einstein Memorial Hospital in Philadelphia, where a camera is set up in a cobalt chamber in which cancer patients are exposed to radiation. The camera enables the radiation technician outside of the chamber to observe the patient and prevents the technician from being subjected to needless exposure to this radiation.

Mention may also be made of the development of a 16-oz transistorized television camera in 1958 by Berci, Kont, and Davids of Melbourne University. It measures 2 by 3 by 5 in. and with its assistance, surgeons will be able to peer into cavities of the body previously hidden to medical science.

Another television type of optical probe was developed in 1959 for the U.S. Navy by the Avco Corporation. It enables dentists to view any part of a patient's mouth, and surgeons to explore within the human body (Fig. 27-103). The device consists of a bundle of several thousand optical fibers bound together in a fine cable, with a lens arrangement at the probing end. The light that is picked up by each fiber is transmitted to the other end and is combined to form a picture on a television screen. This image may be magnified up to 35 times its true size. The probe will not only give the dentist a better view, but will enable other dentists and dental students to watch the work of a skilled dentist. It will also enable the surgeon to view areas within the human body that are now inaccessible.

Military applications. The following are some of the outstanding military applications of television:

1. Aiding observation and inspection of guided missiles before and during flight.

2. Aiding testing of new models of airplanes by providing instrument-panel readings of remotely-operated planes.

3. Providing realistic instruction in military tactics through televised field exercises.

4. Providing reconnaissance and surveillance from piloted and pilotless airplanes, tanks, jeeps, satellites and other vehicles.

With respect to this last-mentioned military application of television, it

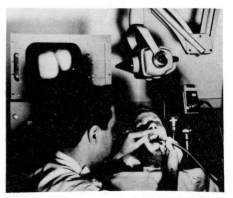

Courtesy, Avco Research and Development Div.
Fig. 27-103. TV OPTICAL DENTAL PROBE
The probe consists of a fingertip-size lens system, held in the dentist's hand, and a small bundle of 3-ft-long glass fibers leading to a closed-circuit TV camera.

might be fitting to mention that it was predicted as far back as 1927 by Sarnoff. Speaking before the Army War College, he said: "It is conceivable that a radio-television transmitter installed in an airplane might be useful in transmitting a direct image of the enemy's terrain, thus enabling greater accuracy in gun fire."[81]

It might also be mentioned that army tactical television has grown rapidly from the cumbersome studio-type equipment of only a few years ago to the man-pack television pick-up and transmitting stations of today.

In some aerial reconnaissance applications of television in airplanes and satellites, ordinary television is not satisfactory because of the low resolution of standard television compared with that of camera photography. This means that only small areas can be covered by television. In order to cover a reasonable amount of area, many more television frames must be taken within a given interval, thus requiring short exposure times and rapid movement of the camera. Furthermore, when the reconnaissance is made at a low altitude, conditions are not advantageous for line-of-sight television transmission. It would be far better if the signal could be stored and transmitted when the plane reached a higher altitude.

In order to surmount these difficulties, a system has been developed in which photography has been combined with television. An aerial camera is used to record in a few milliseconds the detailed information concerning a large area. The film is processed within a few seconds. When desired, a flying-spot scanner is then used to convert this information into a video signal that is then transmitted to its destination.[82]

Police and surveillance applications. Among the applications of television in aiding police and surveillance work are the following:

1. Control of vehicular traffic in tunnels, on bridges, and on congested highways.[83] As an example, Detroit has installed an experimental system of 14 CCTV cameras that scan a 3.2-mile segment of the John Lodge Expressway for accidents and areas of congestion. These television pictures are used in conjunction with other electronic sensors to supply information to a computer. On the basis of the information derived from this computer, operators control traffic through overhead-lane and ramp-control signals, so that if the expressway becomes unduly congested, traffic can be directed through bypass routes.

2. Aiding surveillance of plants, banks, stores, and penal institutions, thus preventing or discouraging bank holdups, pilfering, shoplifting, and unauthorized activities.[84] [85]

3. Remote observation of entrance gates to permit identification of people desiring entry.

4. Protecting tenants in automatic elevators of apartment houses. In this system, which was designed by Dage Television, a full view of the interior of the car is flashed to the lobby where it can be observed by the doorman. In the lobby, there is also an elevator-control button which the doorman can push to bring the elevator directly back to the lobby.

Applications in scientific research. Television cameras are now being used to enable engineers and scientists to observe tests and reactions which are likely to be hazardous. These would include observing radioactive reactors; the particle-beam patterns produced in cyclotrons, cosmotrons, and other particle accelerators; wind-tunnel tests; and tests of the performance of jet and rocket engines.

It is also expected that in the future, television will play a major role in aiding weather forecasting. During 1960, the National Aeronautics and Space Administration began a program known as Project Tiros, which involved the launching of weather satellites carrying television cameras. The information gathered by the cameras was stored on magnetic tape. When the satellites passed over weather stations in Hawaii and Ft. Monmouth, N.J., radio signals caused the images to be transmitted to earth, where they were analyzed by meteorologists.

The first of these, Tiros I, transmitted more than 20,000 pictures of the earth's cloud cover. These pictures provided meteorologists with much valuable data. Some of these "star's-eye" views of the planet Earth revealed the birth of a tornado. From others, scientists learn that there is a large degree of organization in cloud systems over much of the earth's surface.[86] David S. Johnson, head of the U.S. Weather Bureau's Satellite Section stated with regard to this type of information provided by the satellites: ".... in the future, detection of unusual cloud masses .... may well enhance the meteorologist's ability to recognize and pinpoint impending small-scale severe weather disturbances."

Transportation applications. The transportation applications of television include the following:

1. Providing long-range checking of numbers of freight cars in railroad yards

2. Aiding observation and identification of vessels in busy port areas

3. Reducing by as much as 90 per cent the length of time required to make a train reservation or to buy a ticket at busy railroad terminals such as Pennsylvania Station in New York City. The CCTV system installed there has reduced ticket-sale time from an average of 8 minutes per passenger to 2 minutes per passenger[87] [88]

4. Displaying information concerning arrivals and departures at airline, bus and railroad terminals

5. Observing aircraft landings on that portion of a runway that is not visible to the control tower of an airport.

Underwater applications. On at least two occasions, the British have employed underwater television to locate wrecks. In 1951, when the submarine Affray was lost in the English Channel, television cameras located the wreckage in 280 feet of water.[89]

A few years later when a Comet jet airplane was downed in the Mediterranean off the coast of Elba, underwater television cameras made it possible to recover thousands of small pieces of wreckage. When these were pieced together, engineers were able to determine that the cause of the disaster was metal fatigue.[90]

Another application of underwater television is on the ocean floor off the coast of California, where underwater cameras help oil companies to inch giant drills into position—an operation as delicate as threading a needle.

Underwater television has also been utilized in the construction and evaluation of the conditions of pier and dock pilings and underwater moorings for buoys, for evaluating damage and observing the repair of ship hulks, for aiding diver training, and for studying the best techniques of trawling (Fig. 27-104).[91]

Finally, mention may be made of the fact that the atomic submarine Nautilus used a supersensitive closed-circuit television system to enable it to "see" in the dark during its trip under the polar ice cap. The camera was mounted in a pressurized steel capsule in the conning tower. It was connected by cable to a 21-in. monitor that showed a clear picture of the ice overhead without the necessity of using any artificial illumination.

A similar type of system was also used by the atomic submarine Skate during its historic cruise to the Arctic. It is claimed that this device enabled the submarine to surface without damage in the polar ice pack, although the average thickness of the ice was 12 ft. It accomplished this by helping to locate "ice lakes"—regions where the ice

Courtesy, Scripps Institution of Oceanography, University of California

FIG. 27-104. REMOTE UNDERWATER MANIPULATOR (RUM) EMPLOYING CLOSED-CIRCUIT TV *This underwater vehicle is designed to crawl about the ocean floor in depths divers cannot penetrate. The powerful electro-mechanical manipulater mounted at its rear synthesizes the motions of the human arm. Five miles of cable are carried on the great drum. Four television cameras are mounted on the vehicle, which is still in experimental stages.*

was sufficiently thin so that the Skate could surface without damage.

TVX applications. In 1956, Jacobs of General Electric developed an industrial inspection system called TVX, which combines the principles of X-ray inspection with those of ITV. The X-ray beam passes through the object being examined and strikes a photoconductive layer of lead oxide inside a television camera tube (Fig. 27-105). The latent image formed is scanned, amplified, and displayed on a television picture tube to produce an image 10,000 times brighter than that appearing on the conventional fluorescent screen. This system makes it safe to generate high-voltage X-rays for remote visual inspection of dense materials such as steel. If desired, the amplified signal may be recorded on magnetic tape.

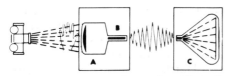

Courtesy, General Electric Co.

FIG. 27-105. HOW X-RAY TV WORKS
The X-ray beam passes through the object being examined—in this case, a patient's hand—and strikes a special television pickup tube (A). There, an X-ray image is imprinted on a layer of lead oxide painted on the tube. An electron gun (B) then "scans" the image and transmits it to a TV viewing tube (C).

27.28 *ETV or educational television*

It is difficult to define and classify educational television. It is obviously a non-entertainment application; yet it cannot be denied that many programs that are broadcast for entertainment purposes possess considerable educational value. It is obviously not industrial television; yet the type of closed-circuit equipment that is designed for

ITV is frequently found to be ideal for use in educational-television systems in schools and universities. Since the field is so vast and the applications are so important, the topic of educational television will be considered and discussed as an independent and separate unit.

The general concept of ETV involves the use of both local television broadcasting facilities directed either to the school or home and closed-circuit system facilities designed for use by a given school or group of schools. It assumes that in addition to the required equipment and money, there are available effective television teachers. A television teacher must possess all of the characteristics of any other good teacher, and should, in addition, possess a telegenic appearance and personality, be capable of making extensive use of stage props for demonstration purposes, and be a good showman.[92]

Under these conditions, ETV is capable of performing the following three distinct types of services:

1. Be a public-relations medium to develop a greater public awareness of and interest in the job that the schools are doing.

2. Be a supplement to classroom theory and discussion enabling students to witness programs and events which stimulate a better appreciation of curricular subjects.

3. Be an integrated part of the regular school curriculum.[93]

Laboratory courses, such as physics, chemistry, and biology, offer exceptional opportunities for the application of closed-circuit ETV. Such a system permits several large classes to witness simultaneously elaborate or dangerous experiments, or magnified images of experiments taking place under a television-microscope system. In areas such as these, where there are shortages of skilled teachers, a few highly qualified teachers can be used to teach large groups effectively.

History of ETV. In this country, ETV had its origin in the Midwest. In 1931, Kansas State College of Agriculture and Applied Science began experimenting with television. It became the first educational institution to obtain a construction permit for a non-commercial television station, KSAC-TV. Another early experimenter in ETV was the University of Iowa. Between 1932 and 1939, this institution transmitted over 400 programs over its experimental television station, W9XK.

According to the available records, the first known formal application of ETV in this country occurred in May 1938. C. C. Clark, a science professor at New York University, delivered a lecture on the principles of photoelectricity in a television studio in the RCA Building. His class of 200 students was assembled in front of 15 television receivers, 60 floors above him. A special talk-back radio circuit was used to link Clark with his students.

The first ETV network began operation in January 1949, when the Navy began telecasting a weekly schedule of ordnance and gunnery lectures from Sands Point, Long Island, to the Merchant Marine Academy at Kings Point, a distance of nearly five miles. The next important landmark in ETV occurred in 1952 when the FCC reserved 258 television channels for educational applications.[94]

By 1960, it was reported that more than 500,000 American students, from the first grade through college, were receiving part of their classroom instruction by television.[95] At that time, 569 school districts of the nation's 45,000 school districts were making regular use of televised instruction, 117 colleges and universities were offering courses for credit on television, and 241 colleges and universities were offering college credit for the modern physics course nationally televised via Continental Classroom.[96] There were 144 closed-circuit television systems in educational institutions, another 21 systems being used for military instruction, and 44 non-commercial ETV broadcasting stations in operation.[97]

The Hagerstown experiment. A five-year pilot-project television study, sponsored by the Fund for the Advancement of Education and the Electronics Industries Association, was begun in 1956 in Hagerstown, Md. Twenty-three schools were linked in a closed-circuit television system. On a typical day during the first year, a highly skilled science teacher performed basic science experiments for an audience of 554 students, while simultaneously a skilled specialist in mathematics explained elementary arithmetic to 400 second-grade students. Two additional channels were available for other instructional programs.[98]

During that first year, 5,300 students received ETV lessons each day. By 1960, six separate channels were available, and the experiment had included all of Washington County, Md., with a total of 16,500 pupils in 37 schools. By the end of 1960, twelve additional schools were also included within this group, involving a total of 19,000 pupils.

A progress report made in 1959, at the mid-point of the study, revealed that the great majority of the students, parents, and teachers favored the experiment, and the use of ETV was found to be highly satisfactory. Among some of the other findings were the following:

1. Superior teaching over television produces better learning than ordinary teaching in the classroom. Thus one investigation of the achievement in mathematics revealed that

groups having television instruction in areas such as arithmetic concepts and problem solving scored higher than the non-television groups at every level, grades 3 to 8. In a plane geometry study involving matched groups, those obtaining instruction by television scored significantly higher in the Cooperative Geometry test than the pupils who had had no television instruction.[99]

2. Televised instruction requires students to accept greater responsibility for their own learning.

3. Students in television classes tend to make more extensive use of the school library.

4. Televised instruction makes possible more effective use of teaching time and classroom space.

5. The use of superior teachers on television has helped improve the teaching techniques of other teachers, particularly beginning teachers.[100]

The report also revealed certain limitations of ETV, such as the fact that it provides only a one-way channel; the pupil cannot talk back. This had a tendency to affect the pacing of the lesson, and there was sometimes a tendency to cover too much territory too quickly. There were also problems associated with mechanical equipment failures. Finally, there were fears that television might be used in the wrong way to emphasize uniformity and submission and to "bring on the age of Big Brother is watching you".

In an article written at about the same time by the superintendent of schools of Washington County, the following observations were listed concerning ETV:

"1. Teachers appreciate having learning experiences presented through television which they could not have provided for their pupils because of limited equipment, time, or resources.

"2. Activities too dangerous to be handled in a classroom situation may be presented by television. These would include experiments involving poisonous gases, high voltage electricity, and demonstrations of building and extinguishing fires.

"3. The camera gives everyone in the classroom a front-row seat.

"4. When pupils in the classroom view community events or world happenings as they are taking place, a 'you are there' feeling is created.

"5. In every community there are people who are able to make valuable contributions to the educational program . . . . It usually is possible for these community members to visit only one or two schools. However, through television, such resource people are brought to all the pupils of a system regardless of the location of the school.

"6. The camera takes pupils to many places that are inaccessible to them, such as the site of the launching of a satellite. The camera peers into a blazing furnace to observe iron smelting. Readings from weather instruments located on the top of high buildings or in remote areas are transmitted to the classroom.

"7. Teaching equipment materials can be used for the benefit of larger numbers of pupils.

"8. The television screen gives the teacher an effective means of directing and controlling the attention of pupils."

The writer then pointed out the following, which are a few of the limitations of ETV:

"1. It is a one-way channel of communication which informs but cannot answer questions except as they are anticipated. Since the teacher does not actually see the pupils, he must rely on his past teaching experiences to help him with the pacing of the lesson.

"2. Unless plans are made to prevent it, the televised lesson can easily turn into a passive 'being told about' experience in which the class does nothing but sit and watch the telecasts.

"3. The ability to communicate facts with great speed brings about a danger of covering a great amount too quickly.

"4. The possibility exists of using television to influence large numbers of pupils with one person's biases or produce undesirable uniformity in the acceptance of ideas or fashions."[101]

With regard to the opposition of conservative educators to the introduction of ETV, the writer points out that: "It is interesting to note that the book was frowned on at first as a mechanical product which would debase academic learning, ruin the memory, lower the status of learning, disseminate trivia on a colossal scale, come between the teacher and pupil, produce undesirable conformity and do far more harm than good to the educational process."[102]

While no claim has been made that ETV will save a school system money, administrators in Hagerstown have pointed out that the present instructional staff of 700 would have to be increased by 63 teachers during the present period of teacher shortages in order to maintain the present program without television.[103]

Role of ETV. From these reports, it can be inferred that ETV techniques should not be employed to eliminate or reduce the need for personal instruction. ETV should remain a teaching tool whose primary purpose is to supplement, illustrate, and enrich oral instruction, not to replace it. It should make it possible for a teacher to do better, not less, teaching.

In the critical area of science instruction, effective utilization of ETV techniques could do much to attract more students into science courses by making these courses more interesting,

more complete, and of greater value. This point has been well made in an article by Arnold Perry, Dean of the School of Education of the University of North Carolina, in which he states: "In all of the experiments the emphasis seems to be on better instruction and quality programs rather than on saving money. With education now a more critical factor in national survival than at any other time in history, educators and the public alike are inclined to want Harvey White to teach our youth physics even if it has to be done by TV at greater expense than to have someone do the job less well at less cost in a conventional manner. Undoubtedly hundreds of thousands of children and youth today can get better teaching of some subjects by TV than they are currently getting from their classroom teachers."[104]

Like any other type of tool, ETV can be misused. It cannot be denied that there have been instances where over-zealous administrators have misused ETV in an attempt to reduce the number of faculty and staff members. There are unfortunate instances where professors have been replaced by filmed lectures, projectors, and CCTV systems. At one college, nearly a thousand students in first-year psychology never see a lecturer, and over a thousand freshmen algebra and English students are film-fed most of the time. There are very few supporters of ETV who would agree with a policy as drastic as the one just cited.[105]

One of the best analyses of findings dealing with the role of television in education has been provided by H. K. Newburn, who makes the following statements:

1. Television provides the educator with a new and exciting means to education.

2. People can learn through television.

3. Effective use of television for teaching requires the close coordination of a variety of skills.

4. The television presentation must be supported by additional educational experiences if optimum results are to be achieved.

5. Effective use of television for education requires substantial financial support.[106]

The validity of the second statement made in the preceding study was further confirmed by a detailed study made by an evaluation committee headed by Arthur E. Traxler of the Educational Records Bureau. This committee compared the achievements of 14,326 students in large experimental classes with those of a carefully-equated group of 12,666 students taking the same courses in the same cities in conventional control classes. At the conclusion of the first year of the experimental television program, the evaluation committee reported the following:

"The test results clearly showed that students who received part of their instruction over television in large classes did as well as—and in many cases significantly better than—students who were taught by conventional methods in small classes."[107]

Another writer has offered the following summary of what has been discovered about ETV as a result of a quarter-century of experiments and studies:

1. Television, both live and recorded, shares with motion-pictures the ability to:

a. Bring high grade instruction to school.

b. Bring distant places and events to the classroom.

c. Speed up or slow down operations for better observation.

d. show objects in detail.

e. Bring into classroom experiences, materials, and demonstrations not readily available to the classroom instructor.

2. Television also shares with motion pictures the lack of personal contact, rapport and intercommunication that are available with conventional instructional methods.

3. Television, both live and recorded, is superior to motion-picture films in being easier and cheaper to keep up-to-date.

4. Live television is superior to recorded television and motion-picture films in its ability to:

a. Transmit special events as they occur.

b. Retain a spontaneity that stimulates and holds the viewer's interest.

5. Recorded television is superior to live television in that it:

a. Requires less capital investment, equipment maintenance, and operating expenditures.

b. Can be used over and over again.

c. Can be stored and distributed like motion-picture films.

6. Recorded television is superior to conventional instructional motion-picture films in that it can be produced at less cost in less time.[108]

The argument is sometimes brought up that ETV is just another one of the series of educational innovations such as educational radio and sound motion-pictures, and that like them it will also fail to live up to the expectations of its advocates. In reply to this argument, Arnold Perry states:

"All of these innovations have helped education tremendously and will continue to do so, but TV has certain advantages which will overcome many of the difficulties which have confronted teachers who have used the other media. First, there is the all-powerful visual element which is lacking in radio; second, there is the 'up-to-minute' content that few films provide; third, there is the dependable sound which modern TV speakers tuned with FM provide; fourth, there is simplicity of mechanical operation; and fifth, there is feasible utilization in a well-lighted room."[109]

Finally, John L. Burns, president of RCA, lists the following advantages of ETV:

1. It can bring about a higher level of instruction by extending the influence of the best teachers far beyond the confines of their own classrooms.

2. It can help raise the level of instruction, relieving the instructor of repetitive teaching and giving him the chance to do the things for which he is best suited. Through its more effective use of teaching talent, it can make higher salaries in the teaching profession a reality.

3. By freeing the instructor from many of the chores he now performs, ETV can make it possible for him to give greater attention to the individual student.[110]

ETV and school construction. In many large cities, such as New York City, it is now required that all school buildings planned or under construction be equipped with television installations consisting of conduits running vertically from the roof to stations throughout the building and branching off on each floor to various rooms. ETV is also affecting school architecture by making decentralized building arrangements more practical and by making large auditoriums less essential.

Many other boards of education have displayed their confidence in the future of educational television. For example, in January 1959, when a Yonkers, New York, taxpayer questioned the expenditure of over 9,000 dollars to install a complete closed-circuit television system in a junior high school under construction, the Board of Education replied that this installation was functional and was not a frill. Referring to educational television, the president of the board stated: "It may take time to prove its value, but we are building a school for 50 years and it will be cheaper to make this installation now than later after the building is completed."

27.29 Applications of ETV

Broadcast ETV over commercial channels. There have been many examples of cooperation between commercial television stations and local boards of education in presenting ETV programs. In December 1956, NBC made available its network facilities to the country's non-commercial educational-television stations at no charge, providing five half-hour programs each week.

Another notable example of cooperation is "The Living Blackboard," a cooperative undertaking by station WPIX and the New York City Board of Education to provide instruction for homebound children. In 1958, the New York State Board of Regents made arrangements to utilize the facilities of station WPIX for a 35-hour-per-week series of educational-television programs for the benefit of schools in the metropolitan New York area.

Although all concerned seemed pleased with the results of this type of cooperation, the conclusion has been reached that few commercial television stations can be expected to give large segments of in-school viewing time to an educational agency, and that the full utilization of television as an aid to teaching is possible only through separate ETV stations.[111] This point of view was ably expressed in a report made by

A. J. Stoddard, former superintendent of the Los Angeles School System, to the Fund for the Advancement of Education, in which he stated: "The schools and colleges must have their own stations . . . . all the time that can or will be given by commercial stations for educational programs is but a drop in the bucket of what will soon be needed."[112] [113] [114]

Broadcast ETV over non-commercial channels. This need for broadcast ETV facilities was recognized by the FCC in 1952 when it reserved 258 channels for non-commercial ETV. Unfortunately, two-thirds of these channels are in the UHF band.

A second retarding factor is human inertia. It takes a long time for new ideas to gain acceptance, and many boards of education are reluctant to spend money on new unproven devices and techniques. Furthermore, many school systems and educational institutions have lacked either the foresight or the financial resources needed to take advantage of this opportunity, notwithstanding the fact that several philanthropic foundations have made money available on a matching basis. As a matter of fact, between 1952 and 1959, well over 60 million dollars was spent in promoting and developing ETV facilities.[115] Despite this enormous expenditure of money, as of 1960, there were only 44 non-commercial ETV stations on the air, many of them broadcasting for only two to four hours a day.[116] [117]

The first of these non-commercial ETV stations opened in 1953 in Houston, Tex. Thus far, Alabama alone has been the only state to have developed an effective state-wide ETV network, and Pittsburgh, Pa., has been the only city to establish two ETV stations.[118] [119]

There is a strong likelihood that many of these educational channels will be taken over by default by commercial-television interests. By the time educators and the public become aware of the desirability and importance of ETV, these educational channels will have been assigned permanently to commercial stations, thus affecting adversely the course of American education and the welfare of all citizens for generations to come.

ETV in higher education. Colleges and universities have also become interested in employing ETV. For the past few years institutions such as Pennsylvania State University, the University of Michigan, the University of California, and Western Reserve University have been offering courses via television. In most instances, these institutions have granted full credit toward regular degrees to viewers who register for these telecourses, pay the tuition fees, complete the assignments, and take the examinations.

Other institutions of higher learning, such as Stephens College and New York University have received grants from the Ford Foundation to conduct experiments on the use of closed-circuit television systems to aid instruction on the college and university level. In October 1958, a survey conducted by the Joint Council on Educational Television revealed that CCTV had been incorporated within the curricula of 119 schools and colleges.

In the fall of 1957, New York University inaugurated Sunrise Semester, a regular undergraduate-credit course in comparative literature. It employed the facilities of the CBS television station between 6:30 and 7 a.m., Mondays through Fridays. Some indication of listener response even at this early hour of the morning is shown by the fact that the first week's discussion of Stendhal's works produced a run on copies of "The Red and the Black" that kept booksellers and librarians in a frenzy of activity trying to locate additional copies to satisfy the unexpected demand for this work. By noon of the day the book had been assigned for study, the century-old novel had become as rare as a collector's item. Random House closed out 4,000 copies within three days. According to an official of a famous New York book store: "It was fantastic. We sold hundreds of copies of a book we usually only sell a few copies of a year." One-hundred and seventy persons met the requirements of the university, paid a 75-dollar tuition fee, watched the program each morning, read the prescribed 16 novels in 16 weeks, wrote a term paper, and submitted to two examinations at home and a final on-campus examination. However, this number is dwarfed by the estimated daily audience of non-registered onlookers, which ranged between 65,000 and 125,000—certainly one of the largest single "classes" in academic history.

In 1960, the Chicago Board of Education published a report covering the first three years of its successful experiment in offering ETV courses for credit in Chicago City Junior College. According to this report, the experiment began in 1956, and an average of 1,261 students enrolled for credit each semester, taking approximately two courses each. Some 3,550 students enrolled on a non-credit basis, while it is estimated that up to 35,000 persons watched the programs without enrolling. By 1960, the college was offering 51 periods of ETV instruction per week and a large number of students had already earned degrees via ETV.

A research program attempted to compare these ETV students with conventional classroom ones who covered the same material and took the same examinations. According to 29 comparisons made, ETV students did better in 10, conventional classroom students did better in 1, and in the remainder, there were no significant differences.

ETV and military instruction. The various departments of the armed forces have also been employing ETV to facilitate military and technical instruction. As far back as 1948, the Navy Special Devices Center on Long Island carried out a joint experiment with Fordham University to determine whether Army and Navy reservists could be effectively trained by television programs sent over commercial channels.[120] The successful results obtained gave great impetus to the use of television for military instruction.

The large military service schools are using this technique for teaching basic military subjects as well as technical subjects. Thus, the 21-in. television screen has become standard equipment in classrooms at the U.S. Army Southeastern Signal School, Ft. Gordon, Ga., where 17 of the school's 20 courses now use television as a medium of instruction. During a typical month, November 1957, 142 regular class periods of instruction were televised, and it was anticipated that this number would increase each month as additional kinescopes were produced.

The world's largest military ETV system has been placed in operation at the U.S. Army Signal School at Ft. Monmouth, N.J. This installation employs seven channels and 466 television receivers that bring instruction to 6,000 students and are capable of being viewed by as many as 15,000 people. It is interesting to note that studies conducted concerning the effects of ETV at these service schools revealed that the average grade achieved by a television-trained student is significantly higher than that of the non-television student and that while all types of students profit from the use of television, learning effectiveness is increased most for those student's in the lower I.Q. brackets.[121][122]

One interesting innovation in military education is the telecasting of a two-hour course on guided missiles over a 280-mile CCTV system constructed between the U.S. Army Guided Missile School at Huntsville, Ala., and the U.S. Army Armor School at Ft. Knox, Ky.[123] Another is a CCTV system by means of which the operations of maintenance specialists working on jet aircraft at Lowry Air Force Base in Denver can be viewed by students in the classrooms of the Training Center.[124] As of 1960, there were 21 ETV systems in operation in military training institutions.

Special applications of ETV. Passing mention has been made in some of the preceding sections of certain special applications of ETV. One is the use of closed-circuit color-television systems by medical schools to provide an unlimited field of vision in the operating room and give the student a bird's-eye view of surgical operations and procedures.[125] Thus, in 1959, P. Moore and H. von Leden of the Medical School of Northwestern University announced the solution of the problem of how a professor of medicine could simultaneously show a group of students the inside of an ear or nose of a patient. The solution involved the use of a portable CCTV camera mounted on a helmet, which in turn, was mounted on the professor's head. A periscopic lens and mirror system made it possible for the television camera to obtain pictures of the body cavities. This system, which was connected to the eyepiece, was so constructed that the image was reflected upward to the camera lens while it allowed the same image to pass through to the eye of the examiner.[126]

A second educational application, developed by RCA, employs both a microscope and a CCTV camera. The microscope is mounted beneath the camera, and a televised microscope scene can then be transmitted by cable to a standard television screen (Fig. 27-106). The advantage of this system is that the great degree of contrast obtainable makes it unnecessary to stain and thus kill the specimens being examined.

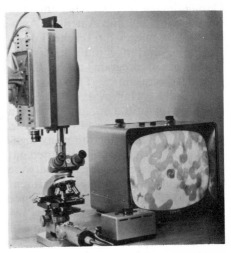

Courtesy, Elgeet Optical Co. Inc.

FIG. 27-106. ELGEET   CLOSED-CIRCUIT   TV MICROSCOPE

A third interesting ETV application has been developed by the Board of Examiners of the New York City School System. In New York City, candidates for the position of school principal or assistant principal must observe a class and write a supervisory report on the strengths and weaknesses of the teacher and the students. In the past, this procedure produced difficulties because the presence of these observers made the students self-conscious and also because the various candidates wrote reports on different teaching situations. The latter weakness complicated the grading of the candidate's observations. The procedure has now been revised so that all of the applicants sit in a large auditorium and observe the same class on the large screen of a closed-circuit television system. This innovation has helped make the examination fairer and more uniform, resulting in fewer protests and complaints by the applicants.[127][128]

A fourth application of ETV is its use in upgrading science instructors. During the fall of 1958, NBC, the Ford Foundation, and the American Association of Colleges for Teacher Education inaugurated a daily half-hour, college-credit program called Continental Classroom.[129] This program, produced by Harvey E. White, was broadcast at 6:30 a.m., and covered a year's work in college physics. It was designed primarily for the many high-school science teachers who started out as teachers of other subjects and were drafted into the science department because of the shortage of science teachers. The course was carried by 144 stations and reached an audience of over 400,000 persons, including 15,000 physics teachers, which is approximately 20 per cent of the number of physics teachers in this country. About 3,000 of these teachers took the course for credit at 243 colleges, and 27,000 of the 400,000 viewers wrote in for a copy of the syllabus.[130] Of the teachers interviewed, more than 80 per cent reported that as a result of their television studies, they planned to introduce new and better demonstration techniques to their classes during the following year. More than 50 per cent indicated that they intended to introduce new concepts in physics to their classes, and 97.4 per cent regarded the televised physics lessons of inestimable value. Obviously, the main objective had been achieved, namely the im-

provement of teaching methods in high-school science courses.

In 1959, an evaluation and appraisal conducted under the leadership of the Visual Aids Committee of the American Association of Physics Teachers found minor points to criticize in the handling of Continental Classroom, but in general, paid tribute to the careful and effective handling of the subject matter of physics by Dr. White, and concluded that the venture was well worth the effort.[131]

As a result of the success of the Continental Classroom, it was expanded to an hour during the 1959-1960 season. During the first half-hour, between 6 and 6:30 a.m., the atomic-age physics course was repeated to an audience of 66,000 persons. During the following half-hour, NBC, the American Association of Colleges for Teacher Education, and seven contributors from the world of business and industry inaugurated a similar course of 160 lessons in modern chemistry that reached an estimated 414,000 viewers.[132][133][134]

Perhaps the best way of concluding this section dealing with special ETV applications, is by quoting the final paragraph of Stoddard's report to the Fund for the Advancement of Education on the possibilities of ETV: "The use of television in the educational program, not only to supplement and enrich, but also to perform certain functions heretofore performed by teachers, and to cover areas of the regular curriculum as an integral part, offers great hope for meeting teacher and building shortages, but more important, for raising the level of teaching. There is already no doubt about the great effectiveness of television as a teaching medium. It is being used widely at the college level. Its use in the schools is not very extensive as yet because of problems of adapting teaching techniques, rearrangement of instructional groupings, practical difficulties involving schedule making, and the challenge of presenting dynamic television programs. But these road blocks can and will be surmounted as more experimentation takes place in these areas—they are not insurmountable."[135]

27.30 *Future developments in television*

During the past ten years, tremendous progress has been achieved by scientists, engineers, and manufacturers in improving television equipment and in designing equipment suitable for specialized tasks. The paragraphs which follow will describe some of the developments and innovations currently being produced by the pioneers who have been laboring near the frontiers of television research.

27.31 *Forward scatter*

A recently discovered high-frequency phenomenon known as forward scatter offers the possibility of obtaining reliable television and microwave signal transmission over long distances without intervening relay stations. The topic of forward scatter will be discussed in greater detail in Chapter 31.

27.32 *Transoceanic radio relay*

A somewhat prosaic solution to the problem of transoceanic television has been suggested by Boyd of Bell Telephone Laboratories. This system calls for hourly trans-Atlantic flights of large planes at altitudes of 11,000 ft. Each plane would carry the necessary microwave-relay equipment, plus a five-ton payload. The planes would fly at intervals of 200 miles between New York and London, relaying television and telephone signals on a carrier frequency of approximately 6,000 mc. Each plane would receive signals on one carrier frequency and would transmit them on another. In the event of trouble to one plane, the four nearest planes could fill in the gap by adjusting their speeds to maintain a distance of 267 miles between each plane.[136]

This plan bears some resemblance to the Stratovision airplane-television relay system proposed by C. E. Nobles, a Westinghouse engineer, during the 1940's. In tests conducted by Westinghouse at that time, a Stratovision B-29 achieved a coverage of 225 miles compared with the 50-mile range of that time.[137]

In July 1958, an airborne relay system was successfully used for television transmission between two continents, Europe and Africa. Programs originating in Algiers were relayed by Radio Television Francaise across the Mediterranean to France and telecast over the entire French television system. The demonstration was repeated in reverse two months later when a program originating in France was relayed to North African television transmitters. The relaying was accomplished by using a single relay plane flying at an altitude of 20,000 ft near the Balearic Islands. Although the airborne transmitter interfered with the navigation of the plane, both of these experimental demonstrations of airborne television relay succeeded in delivering a satisfactory television picture and seemed to indicate that the day of transoceanic television was not very far off.[138]

27.33 *Stratovision ETV*

In the fall of 1959, the FCC authorized Purdue University to employ eight UHF channels to test the effectiveness of the Stratovision system for ETV broadcasting. Arrangements were provided for an experimental system of airborne multichannel ETV for schools and colleges in a six-state region of the Midwest. This system is operated by the Midwest Council on Airborne Television. Cooperating with this Council are many schools and colleges within this area, the Westinghouse Electric Company, the CBS Laboratories Division of CBS, and General Dynamics Corporation. Beginning February 1961, classroom courses on video tape are now being relayed from a DC-7 airplane flying in a 10-mile circle above Purdue University at an altitude of 20,000 ft. The programs are transmitted to the airplanes from four transmitters on Purdue's campus via Channels 41, 47, 53, and 59. The plane relays these programs to the classrooms via Channels 72, 75, 76, and 78 (Fig. 27-107). It is estimated that these programs are being received by 13,000 schools and colleges with an enrollment of 5 million students that are located within a radius of 200 miles from the source of the telecasts.[139]

Courtesy, Westinghouse Electric Corp. and the Midwest Program on Airborne Television Instruction

FIG. 27-107. FLYING TV STATION

Packed with six tons of telecasting equipment, the interior of this plane represents a "flying" television station. Facilities include a master control panel, two video tape recorders, two high-powered transmitters, and a vidicon camera to transmit announcements and station identification.

27.34 *Satellite reflectors*

In 1946, scientists succeeded in bouncing a radar signal off the moon. They succeeded in doing the same thing with a voice-modulated signal in 1954. In 1959, they managed to use a moon-relay system for reflecting a one-way message across the Atlantic, and in 1960, succeeded in maintaining a two-way trans-Atlantic conversation via moon relay.

Early in 1960, scientists at MIT credited amateur radio operators Perry Klein of Bethesda, Md., and Rafael Soifer of New York City with having conducted what was probably the world's first successful two-way radio communication by means of artificial satellites. The two operators transmitted and received coded signals that were reflected by the ionized trails left by satellites.

Early developments in this area led many scientists and writers to suggest the use of artificial satellites as reflectors or repeaters for television and telephone signals.[140] In fact, it is claimed that Arthur C. Clarke proposed the first use of artificial satellites for providing global television in an article entitled "Extra-terrestrial Relays" in the October 1945 issue of *Wireless World.* Clarke suggested the use of three satellites in a 22,000-mile orbit above the equator.[141]

In 1958, John R. Pierce, director of research of Bell Telephone Laboratories suggested the use of between 24 and 50 100-lb satellites, each 100 ft in diameter, with reflective metallized coatings, revolving in a transpolar orbit 3,000 miles above the earth. These satellites would be passive reflectors and would require no electronic equipment (Fig. 27-108).[142][143][144] Pierce also pointed out that while in the forseeable future these satellites would not be able

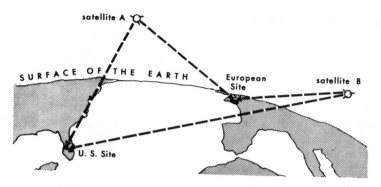

FIG. 27-108. PASSIVE REFLECTOR SATELLITES OF METALLIZED MYLAR
Satellites would be tracked at U.S. and European sites in a proposed trans-Atlantic communications system operating at microwave frequencies.

to compete with present cable land circuits and microwave-relay systems, they could compete over ocean areas.

Miller of Ramo Wooldridge has proposed a chain of solar-powered satellite repeaters orbiting at altitudes of 22,000 miles in the equatorial plane. He claims that this arrangement could provide line-of-sight relaying facilities for thousands of radio and television channels and that transmission of signals over ranges of 10,000 miles would be little more difficult than present transmission of such signals over distances of less than 75 miles.[145] [146]

Henri Busignies, president of International Telephone and Telegraph Laboratories, has advanced a proposal called the "Earth Net Dialing System" which he claims would make possible the achievement of global communication via satellites within the very near future. This system would utilize a network of three unmanned solar-powered satellites at an altitude of 22,300 miles. They would be launched in an equatorial 24-hr orbit and would be spaced 120 deg apart from each other (Fig. 27-109). Under these conditions, the satellites would appear to be motionless relative to the earth, since their orbital speeds would coincide with the

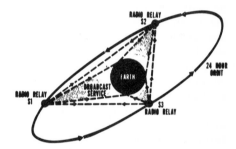

FIG. 27-109. ORBITAL RADIO AND TV RELAY SATELLITES
Satellites located at S1, S2, and S3 and placed 22,000 miles above the earth's surface can cover practically the entire globe with a communications service.

earth's rotational speed. Signals relayed from each satellite would blanket almost half the earth, each overlapping the other. Stations in the overlap regions would be used as inter-hemisphere relay points. Busignies claims that this system would be capable of handling 30,000 one-way voice circuits or 15,000 two-way voice circuits, plus three television networks. It would also be capable of transmitting facsimile, high-speed radio-telegraph, and teletype messages.[147] It might also be noted that similar proposals for establishing global television have been advanced by Soviet engineers.[148]

In the summer of 1959, RCA Astro-Electronic Products released information concerning its projected plans for an "Orbital Post Office" (Fig. 27-110). This system would employ three or four equally spaced manned satellites rotating in synchronous orbits 22,000 miles above the equator. Each satellite would remain in a fixed position with respect to the earth and would contain narrow-beam microwave antennas aimed at specific cities. Mail could be converted into radio signals that would be transmitted to any part of the world via the satellite repeater stations and would be converted back into letter form at the receiving end. It is claimed that this system could handle all of the world's communications and would also make possible simultaneous around-the-world television transmission and reception.[149] Under these conditions, letters would never require more than a day's time between any two points on earth.

In 1959, the National Aeronautics and Space Administration announced plans to launch a group of 24 communication satellites. The first satellite was to be a 100-ft aluminized polyester-film balloon in a 1,000-mile orbit. It would act as a passive reflector to beam signals from the West Coast to a Bell Telephone Laboratory station on the East Coast. This was to be followed by reflectors orbiting at a height of 22,000 miles. According to the estimates of their engineers, 30 passive reflectors of this type would permit world-wide radio and television broadcasting, improve navigation and weather forecasting, and provide many other types of increased communications facilities.[150][151]

In August 1960, the first step of this program was achieved when NASA launched Echo I, a sphere 100 ft in diameter, into a 1,000-mile orbit. It made history when it relayed a recorded message by President Eisenhower from the Jet Propulsion Laboratory in Goldstone, Calif. to the Bell Telephone Laboratory in Holmdel, N.J. According to measurements, the sphere provided a radio reflectivity of 98 per cent up to frequencies of 20,000 mc. This marked a successful beginning of a long-range program which is expected to culminate in world-wide television, radio, and telephone communications.

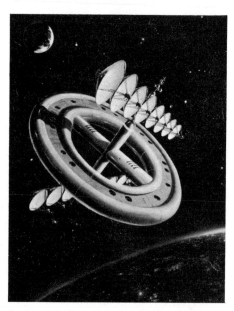

Courtesy, Astro-Electronic Products Div., Radio Corporation of America

FIG. 27-110. ORBITAL POST OFFICE
Communications space stations of this type may become future "orbital post offices" and relay messages around the world by microwave radio. The satellite would remain in fixed orbit at 22,000 miles altitude, with antenna beamed at receiving and transmitting stations on the earth.

Early in 1959, details were also revealed of a plan to link Hawaii with Washington, D.C., via the moon by means of a UHF broad-band scatter-communication system. With this system, the Navy will be capable of transmitting between 100 and 200 simultaneous radioteletype signals back and forth to Hawaii, during a period of five to seven hours each day. The developers also envisage trans-Atlantic telephone transmissions via lunar reflection within the next five years.

In this system, 100 kilowatts of power, at a frequency of approximately 445 mc, are delivered from the transmitter to an 84-ft dish-shaped, steerable antenna. The directional characteristics of this antenna concentrate this energy into a beam with an effective power of 400 megawatts. It requires 2.5 seconds for the signal to reach its destination. Since this system does not make use of the reflecting characteristics of the ionosphere, it can be used when ionospheric disturbances prevent normal long-distance radio transmission.

However, in order to establish communication, both the transmitting and receiving points must be able to view the moon simultaneously. Consequently, depending upon the moon's orbital position, the moon-relay system can be used for only three to 12 hours a day. On the other hand, this may be an advantage in military applications, since anyone desiring to jam this transmission would also have to be able to see the moon at the same time.[152]

In July 1962, NASA boosted the Bell system's Telstar satellite from Cape Kennedy, Fla., into a nearly perfect elliptical orbit. The principal purpose of Project Telstar was to test the actual use and reliability of active satellites for the transmission of broadband microwave radio signals. Bell scientists successfully transmitted a telephone call from Andover, Me., to Washington, D.C., via the satellite shortly after its launching. This achievement was followed by the first television transmission by means of a satellite and then by the telephotoing of a still picture up to Telstar and back again. The next night this country's three major networks

aired the first East-West telecasts from the French and English earth stations. The greatest portion of the work in the Telstar experiments has been done on the ground. A powerful continuous signal (2,000 watts and 25 megacycle bandwidth) is "shot" up to the satellite in space and the extremely sensitive ground receiver—a 177-ft-long by 94-ft-high horn antenna—picks up the comparatively weak signals coming back to earth.

27.35 Long-distance waveguides

In addition to employing the facilities of microwave-relay stations, television programs may be carried from one city to another either by coaxial cable or by hollow metallic waveguides (Fig. 27-111). The characteristics and capabilities of both coaxial cable (Fig. 27-112) and of waveguides (Fig. 27-113) will be discussed in later chapters dealing with radar and microwaves. However, it may be mentioned that both coaxial cables and waveguides possess the disadvantage of producing increased attenuation or loss of signal strength as the frequency of the signal is increased. Coaxial cable is expensive, while a waveguide loses much of its effectiveness if it is necessary to make a sharp bend in it.

In 1955, Bell Telephone Laboratories announced the development of a new flexible type of long-distance waveguide that is capable of carrying signals around curves (Fig. 27-114). Unlike conventional waveguides, it produces less attenuation for high-frequency signals and operates very well at frequencies between 50,000 and 100,000 mc. The attenuation produced when a signal travels along 40 miles of this waveguide is less than that produced by 12 miles of coaxial cable.[153] The

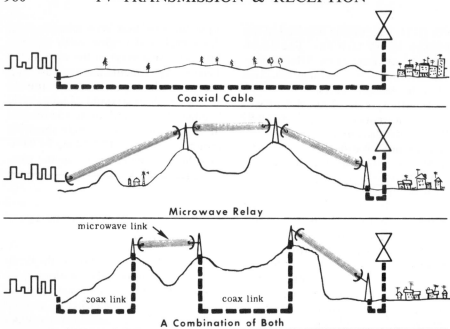

Coaxial Cable

Microwave Relay

microwave link

coax link   coax link

A Combination of Both

FIG. 27-111. LONG-DISTANCE TRANSMISSION OF TELEVISION SIGNALS

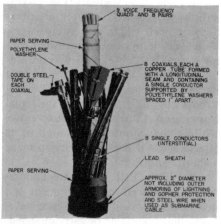

Courtesy, American Telephone and Telegraph Co.

FIG. 27-112. FANNED-OUT SECTION OF AN EIGHT-TUBE COAXIAL CABLE

Courtesy, American Telephone and Telegraph Co.

FIG. 27-113. INSTALLING A HOLLOW-TUBE WAVE-GUIDE

frequency band transmitted within this waveguide is nearly four times as wide as the entire band that is now used for radio communications.

This new waveguide is a hollow tube, 2 in. in diameter. It consists of a

tightly coiled helix of thin copper wire wrapped inside a flexible outer coating designed to hold the coiled wire in place. It is believed that when these waveguides are eventually applied to carrying super-high-frequency signals,

Courtesy, Bell Telephone Laboratories

FIG. 27-114. BELL LABORATORIES FLEXIBLE WAVEGUIDE

The flexible copper tube channels radio waves any way it is bent. Here, scientists examine wood forms used in testing transmission around curves.

their diameters will be no greater than that of a fountain pen. Transmission via this type of waveguide system would not be vulnerable to atmospheric effects, interference, and fading, and would not require any governmental allocations of frequencies. A waveguide system of this type would make possible an all-purpose underground circuit between the East and West Coasts, capable of carrying hundreds of broadcasts and closed-circuit television programs, thousands of simultaneous telephone calls, telegraph circuits, facsimile, and business machine services. It is estimated that it could provide a handling capacity for 200,000 voice circuits or 200 television-picture circuits.[154] It may also make possible the eventual construction of a transoceanic circuit for international television and other communications.

Another interesting new triple-service waveguide has been developed by Barlow of University College, London. This waveguide consists of a hollow copper tube. The outside of the

tube can be used to transmit UHF waves, while the inside of the tube carries another group of microwaves. The body of the metal tube can be used to carry ordinary 50- or 60-cps current for power purposes.

27.36 *Telephone television*

Picture-Phone. A system of transmitting pictures along with sound over telephone wires is now ready to leave the laboratory and go into commercial production. The development of this system, called Picture-Phone, was announced by Bell Telephone Laboratories in November 1956 (Fig. 27-115). It has been used to send pictures as well as sound between New York City and Los Angeles, using only one additional pair of ordinary telephone wires. Previously, it was necessary to use expensive coaxial cable for transmission of television pictures. The picture is smaller and less detailed than a conventional television picture, and one picture is sent every two seconds. However, the picture has good contrast, and facial expressions are readily apparent.

The picture is taken by means of a miniature television camera containing both a vidicon tube and the necessary horizontal and vertical sweep circuits

Courtesy, *Radio-Electronics* and Bell Telephone Laboratories

FIG. 27-115. EXPERIMENTAL MODEL OF THE BELL PICTURE-PHONE SYSTEM

for producing a raster. The raster consists of 60 lines, each with 40 dots. A complete picture is transmitted every two seconds; hence a bandwidth of 600 cps is required. Since scanning occurs at the rate of 20 pictures per second in the camera tube, 40 pictures are provided in 2 seconds. One of these scans is selected and the other 39 are rejected. The information from this scan is recorded on a magnetic drum. The stored information is then picked off the drum at one-fortieth of the rate at which it was recorded. The drum is then erased and made ready for the next picture.

Since the low-frequency components of the 600-cps picture signal are likely to be attenuated by the telephone wires, the picture signal is used to amplitude-modulate a 1,200-cps carrier. The resulting amplitude-modulated signal contains sideband frequencies ranging between 600 and 1,800 cps. These frequencies lie within the range of optimum transmission of telephone lines.

At the receiving end, conventional techniques are used to demodulate the signal. The picture information is applied to a pair of electrostatic-storage direct-view, two-gun picture tubes called Iatrons (Fig. 27-116). The Iatron tube is based upon a principle first suggested by Farnsworth in 1927. Each Iatron has an insulated inner mesh screen just behind the fluorescent coating, upon which a picture may be stored by the electron gun. During this storing process, the face of the tube remains dark. When the complete picture has been stored, it may be made visible by means of a beam of electrons provided by a second electron gun. The picture lasts several minutes and may be erased by applying the correct potential to one of the electrodes.

The equipment employs two Iatrons placed at right angles to each

other and with a half-silvered mirror placed at an angle between them. The observer looking at the mirror can see the image of one of the tubes when the other is dark. Information is written on one tube while the other is being used. A switching arrangement then permits the viewer to see the picture on the former tube while a new picture is being placed on the latter. This picture switching occurs once every two seconds. Improvements are constantly being made on this system. Work is in progress in the direction of reducing the size of the receiving equipment by combining the two Iatron tubes in one envelope and by using transistors in the electronic portions of the circuit.[155]

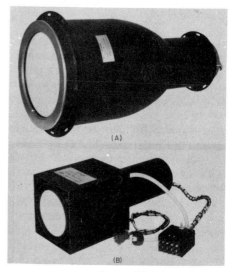

Courtesy, ITT Federal Laboratories
FIG. 27-116. TWO MODELS OF THE IATRON STORAGE CATHODE-RAY TUBE
(A) Type 248; (B) Type FW 234.

According to Pierce of Bell Telephone Laboratories, the pictures produced are too fuzzy to be of any real use. He has suggested that a picture of higher quality can be obtained by converting the picture signal into a pulse-code-modulated signal, which can be amplified simply and cheaply without any degradation of the picture.[156]

Other systems. A wide variety of different types of telephone-television systems have been developed by other organizations for special applications. Kin Tel has developed one such system designed for identifying bank and department-store customers and for interviewing visitors seeking admittance at plant gates (Fig. 27-117). General Electric has also developed a slow-scan television system in which one picture is produced every four seconds. It is intended for use in transmitting pictures without much action, such as a picture of a check for signature comparison.

Courtesy, *Radio-Electronics*
FIG. 27-117. KIN TEL TELEPHONE SYSTEM

In March 1957, Kraus of Bell Telephone Laboratories demonstrated two narrow-band television systems which produced signals that could be carried over ordinary telephone cable pairs. In the ordinary television system, there are 60 fields per second and 525 lines. The resulting signal has a bandwidth of 4 mc. One of the newly developed television systems has 60 fields per second and 125 lines, whereas the other has 30 fields per second and 184 lines. Both of these systems have a frequency bandwidth of only 250 kc. The signals produced can be transmitted successfully up to distances of 15 miles over ordinary conductors. This decrease in bandwidth produces pictures of somewhat less resolution than regular broadcast transmissions. However, the pictures are acceptable for use in industrial applications where high picture quality is not a primary consideration.[157]

During the spring of 1959, another similar system of telephone television was patented by Floyd F. Becker and assigned to Bell Telephone Laboratories. This system also permits both parties to see and hear each other during a telephone conversation transmitted via standard 4,000-cps telephone channels.[158]

In June 1959, the British Broadcasting Corporation demonstrated the successful operation of a system of transmitting a limited amount of television-newsreel film over the trans-Atlantic telephone cable. Less than two hours after Queen Elizabeth had left London for a Canadian tour, pictures of her departure were telecast by stations of the Canadian Broadcasting Company and the National Broadcasting Company. At the transmitting end of this system, there was a slowdown of the rate at which the separate pictures or frames were converted into electrical impulses capable of being carried over the cable. At the other end, these impulses were used to make a duplicate film that could be run off at normal speed. Approximately 50 minutes were required for the transmission of 30 seconds worth of film.[159] [160]

In March 1960, the International Telephone and Telegraph Corporation demonstrated a slow-scan television system that it had developed for the U.S. Air-Force. A telephone circuit between Rome, New York, and Buffalo,

N.Y., was used to relay "scrambled" signals containing information, which when decoded, appeared at the receiving end as graphs providing simulated battle information. The rate of scan is very slow, the average time-per-frame being 40 seconds. The wide-band television signal is reduced in width 1,000 times by means of scan-conversion storage tubes. At the receiving end, the signal is reconverted into its original bandwidth.

The system can be employed at Air Force bases where data required for command decisions must be assembled rapidly. By means of this system, pictures, charts, and maps can be sent over telephone lines to any part of the United States and via trans-Atlantic cable to and from European locations.[161]

27.37 Flying-spot scanning

Vitascope. The DuMont Vitascope is a new type of economical television-camera tube designed for studio use in reproducing transparent slides and motion-picture films. Its operating principle, involving flying-spot scanning, is the reverse of that of a conventional television-pickup tube. Instead of receiving light through a lens, the scanner emits a moving or flying spot of light from a cathode-ray tube. The flying spot scans the object to be televised and the reflected or transmitted light is picked up by a cluster of four photomultiplier tubes in the studio (Figs. 27-118, 27-119, and 27-120).

In each cluster of four tubes, one has a blue filter, one has a green filter, and two have red filters. The reason for using two red-filtered phototubes is that the phototubes are less sensitive to red than to other colors. These phototubes convert the three colors into electrical signals, amplify them, and

deliver the signals to conventional color-transmitting equipment.

One of the requirements of this system is that there must be no other light source present during the scanning periods. Since the illumination provided by the flying-spot scanner is insufficient for the actors, use is made of the vertical-retrace blanking period when the flying-spot scanner is blanked out. Stroboscopic studio lights are synchronized in such a manner that they go on during the blanking periods and go off during the scanning periods. To the human eye, the studio appears continuously and sufficiently lighted. The actors thus obtain the needed illumination, while the scanner obtains the darkness it requires. The necessity for strong lighting is removed, the actors perform in greater comfort, and there is a tremendous reduction in the studio air-conditioning load.[162] [163]

THE FLYING-SPOT SCANNER

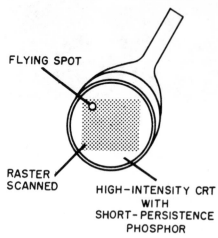

FLYING SPOT

RASTER SCANNED

HIGH-INTENSITY CRT WITH SHORT-PERSISTENCE PHOSPHOR

FIG. 27-118. THE FLYING-SPOT SCANNER
The scanner produces a beam of light that is focused on the scene to be reproduced.

Flying-spot microscopes. The flying-spot microscope, as is implied by its name, is a combination of a microscope

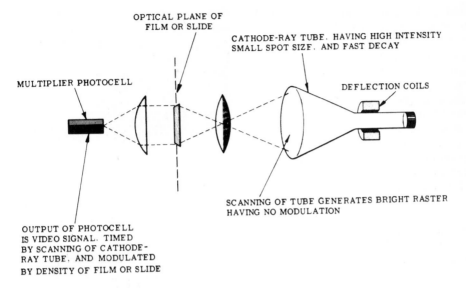

FIG. 27-119. DIAGRAM OF FLYING-SPOT SCANNER PRINCIPLE

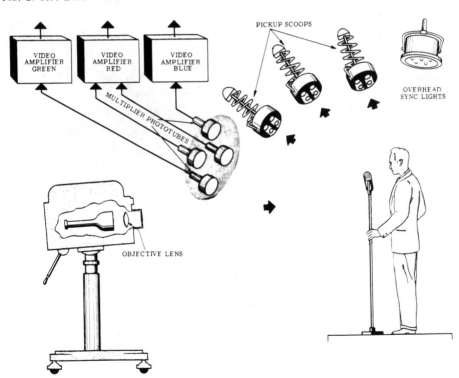

Courtesy, Allen B. DuMont Laboratories

FIG. 27-120. SIMPLIFIED SKETCH OF FLYING-SPOT COLOR-TV SYSTEM

and a flying-spot video generator. It employs conventional microscope optics, but the light source is a rapidly moving spot of light which scans a regular pattern of sequential lines. The light that is transmitted through the slide or object is modulated in accordance with the density and configuration of the object. These light changes are converted into an electrical signal by a photomultiplier tube. The signal is then fed to a video amplifier. The output of this amplifier is displayed visually on a monitor picture tube as a magnified image of the microscope specimen. Magnifications of 8,000 diameters and resolutions of 0.0001 cm are easily obtained. Because of the low average value of intensity of the scanning light spot, live specimens suffer no damage even when viewed for prolonged periods of time.

A modified version of this device, employing ultraviolet light for scanning purposes, is known as the ultraviolet flying-spot microscope. Because the wavelengths of ultraviolet light are much shorter than those of visible light, this instrument is capable of producing a degree of resolution that is twice as good as that of the conventional flying-spot microscope.[164]

With the aid of certain auxiliary units, a flying-spot instrument can perform several additional functions (Fig. 27-121). It is capable of automatically counting the number of particles contained within the field of the objective. It is also able to size these particles automatically. These characteristics make this type of microscope very useful in cancer research, fuel spray-size analysis, dust analysis, and studies of filters. One such device, used in scanning slides for the presence of uterine cancer, is called the Cytoanalyzer.[165] Another flying-spot counter developed by DuMont Laboratories for rapidly

Courtesy, Instrument Corporation of America

FIG. 27-121. RANK CINTEL FLYING SPOT PARTICLE RESOLVER

counting large numbers of bacterial colonies or particles on Petri-dish culture plates, is called the Iconumerator (Fig. 27-122).[166]

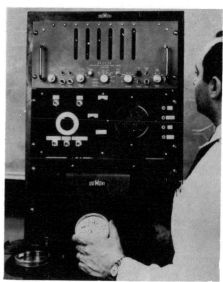

Courtesy, Allen B. DuMont Laboratories

FIG. 27-122. DUMONT ICONUMERATOR

Flying-spot office duplicator. A recent development at Stanford Research Institute has brought television a step closer to being standard equipment in many business offices. This development is a high-speed duplicating device which employs a closed-circuit television network for multiple reproduction of communications. It can also be used to transmit documents from a central location to printer units—a television counterpart of teletype. The reproduction rate exceeds that of standard facsimile transmission. It is capable at present of duplicating 17,000 characters or about three standard sheets of paper each second.

The document is scanned by a flying beam of light at the transmission point at the rate of 1,700 horizontal sweeps each third of a second. Phototubes, positioned to receive light reflected from the document, emit electrons in numbers proportional to the amount of light striking them. The video signal that is produced is amplified and may be transmitted to receivers by a coaxial cable or may be broadcast as a television signal.

At the receiver, the signal is amplified and applied to the grid of a cathode-ray tube. Signal variations in grid potential cause the deposition of a corresponding electrical charge on copy paper adjacent to the tube faceplate. After one-third of a second or 1,700 successive scannings, the copy paper is pulled past the faceplate and mechanically dusted with black powder, which clings to the charges on the surface of the paper. The powder is then heated and pressed into the paper to make a permanent record.[167]

27.38 *Duoscopic television receivers*

A new type of receiver known as the DuMont Duoscopic has recently been developed. It performs as two separate receivers in one and permits two audiences to view two different television programs at the same time from the same screen. The cabinet contains two receivers and two picture tubes mounted at right angles to each other (Fig. 27-123). A semi-transparent mirror placed between the two tubes

and at an angle to both superimposes the two pictures. The viewer looks at the screen through a pair of Polaroid glasses which filter out one or the other of the pictures. Earphones are used to transmit the sound to each individual listener.

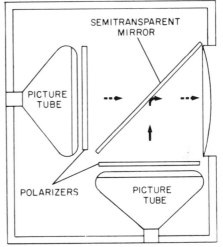

Courtesy, Popular Science Publishing Co. Inc.

FIG. 27-123. OPERATING PRINCIPLES OF THE DUOSCOPIC TV RECEIVER

27.39 *Three-dimensional television*

Several groups of scientists and engineers have been working on the problem of producing life-like stereoscopic television pictures. One proposed system resembles the 3-D system used by the motion-picture industry. Two properly spaced cameras are used to produce the required electrical signals. At the receiver, a picture is produced corresponding to each camera signal. However, the picture corresponding to the left camera and left eye is polarized horizontally and the other picture is polarized vertically. Observing the picture on the screen through a pair of Polaroid spectacles, in which one lens is vertically and the other horizontally polarized.

produces a stereoscopic image. One limitation of this system is the fact that the transmitter requires a channel whose bandwidth is twice that of a normal television channel. A second limitation is the reluctance of many people to wear Polaroid spectacles.

Sanabria system. Another attempted solution to the stereoscopic-television problem has been demonstrated in Chicago by U. A. Sanabria. It also employs two cameras, and an electronic switch alternately permits each camera to transmit what it sees. A viewer at home watches the screen of his receiver through a viewing tube containing eye slots. A shutter, synchronized with the transmitter, alternately uncovers each eye slot, permitting each eye to see only the picture intended for it. The present system produces an annoying flicker, but it produces an image that seems to step right out of the screen.[168]

General Electric system. Three-dimensional CCTV systems are capable of being extremely useful for the remote observation and supervision of processes involving handling and control operations. Both General Electric and RCA have developed systems designed for applications such as these. The General Electric system, which is the first 3-D color CCTV system, was developed for the remote servicing of reactors used in nuclear-aircraft-propulsion systems. It permits use of color-coded parts in reactor components and provides the degree of precise depth perception required for the correct remote positioning of these parts. The equipment was designed for use by the General Electric Aircraft Nuclear Propulsion Department at the AEC installation at Idaho Falls, Idaho.

The conventional color-television camera employed for this purpose has an optical system whose perspective resembles that of the two eyes of the human observer. By use of a rotating shutter, the two images are impressed on the single sensitive surface of the camera tube on a time-sharing basis. There are 90 pictures produced each second, 45 pictures for each eye.

In the viewing console, rotating polarizing filters cause alternate picture frames to be polarized alternately vertically and horizontally. Consequently, all left-eye pictures are polarized vertically and all right-eye pictures are polarized horizontally. When an observer views the screen and wears a pair of polarized spectacles in which the lens over one eye is polarized vertically and the other horizontally, he will see a color stereo-vision picture with no objectionable flicker.[169][170]

RCA system. The RCA system, developed by Pritchard and Gibson of RCA Laboratories, makes the claim that it is capable of producing either a yellow or a black-and-white stereo picture that does not have to depend upon rotating mechanical devices or polarized light. It is all-electronic and uses standard camera equipment and a standard color-television receiver. Its two black-and-white cameras have approximately the same separation and convergence as the human eye. In the color receiver, the amplified output of the left camera is applied to the green gun of the color picture tube and the amplified output of the other camera to the red gun. The blue gun is biased at cutoff. When the simultaneous red and green images are viewed through a pair of glasses containing one green and one red filter, a yellow stereoscopic image is seen. If a black-and-white image is desired, the blue gun of the color-picture tube can be driven in parallel with either the red or the green gun.[171]

Kin Tel system. The Kin Tel Division of Cohu Electronics, Inc., has also developed a black-and-white, 3-D,

CCTV system which makes possible three-dimensional remote observation at distances of up to 1,000 ft. The overlapping images from each of two cameras are presented on a single viewing plane. One image is vertically polarized and the other is horizontally polarized. When the two images are viewed through special glasses or through a viewing head containing vertically and horizontally polarized lenses, a three-dimensional picture is obtained.[172]

Electroflor system. Before concluding this section, mention should be made of another system that may, in the future, produce colored 3-D pictures without the use of special glasses. This system employs electroflors, which have been discussed in an earlier chapter. The electroflors can store energy and emit visible light when stimulated by relatively low voltages.

Experimental 3-D color displays using these materials have been demonstrated. These displays employ three thin plates sandwiched together, each plate glowing with one of the primary colors. These plates are made of glass or plastic and contain tiny holes. A gridwork of fine wires or thin evaporated-metal coatings crisscrosses each hole. These holes are filled with a given electroflor and are sealed. When stimulated by special scanning signals, the various electroflors glow and produce a colored picture with true depth.[173]

27.40 *Picture-on-the-wall television*

Current developmental work on miniature electronic components, switching circuits, and electroluminescent phosphors have led scientists and experts, such as Lee de Forest, R. D. Siragusa, president of the Admiral Corporation, and DeVore of the General

Electric Electronic Laboratory, to predict that within the next few years television sets capable of receiving color signals will be produced with a picture tube so thin that the entire unit can be hung like a painting on a living-room wall (Fig. 27-124).[174] In place of the conventional cathode-ray tube, there will be an electroluminescent screen containing millions of tiny spots capable of glowing in three colors when excited electronically in sequence. The circuitry of such a device would be built into the picture frame and would employ printed wiring and miniaturized components. The controls would be placed in a small box conveniently located on a table beside one's easy chair.

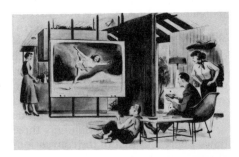

Courtesy, General Electric Co.

FIG. 27-124. PICTURE-ON-THE-WALL TV RECEIVER

Toulon kinescope. An indication of progress in this direction is the granting to Toulon of a patent on a flat kinescope. This device eliminates the electron gun. It contains phosphor dots coated in rows on a screen. The tube contains a gas which is maintained in a partially ionized condition. When a phosphor dot is energized, the gas in the neighborhood of the dot glows. The dots may be energized by applying the correct voltages to the proper electrodes through a high-speed distribution system.[175]

Sylvatron. Sylvania Electric Products has developed a picture-screen system called Sylvatron. The Sylvatron employs the principles of electroluminescence and photoconductivity and is only $\frac{1}{4}$ in. thick. At present, the company plans to utilize this device for radar displays, air-traffic-control boards, tracking devices, and computer memories and readouts.[176][177] With the aid of appropriate circuit modifications, Sylvatron could function as the heart of a commercial picture-on-the-wall television system (Fig. 27-125).[178]

Elf screen. Scientists at the Westinghouse Research Laboratories have developed a new flat television display screen that is said to be brighter than any previously reported (Fig. 27-126). Its name, the Elf screen, is derived from the words electroluminescent and ferroelectric. It contains an electroluminescent panel and a ferroelectric storage and control unit that distributes excitation to the screen in accordance with an applied electrical charge. The excited screen then produces a complete frame or picture that has a brightness three times as great as that of the conventional television picture tube. Images can be stored for several minutes or can be changed many times each second. In addition, there are no inherent limitations to the size of the screen. In fact, it is easier to construct a very large display panel than a small one.[179][180]

Other flat television tubes. Flat television tubes of a somewhat less unconventional design, and employing electron guns, have been developed by Gabor of the Imperial College of Science and Technology of London and by William R. Aiken of Willys Motors. The two tubes are very similar, and the patents for both have been pooled by agreement. An ingenious system of electron lenses curves the beam so that it runs parallel to the face of the tube

until it is finally deflected toward the screen by a series of parallel conductors. The tube has a total depth of 4.5 in. for a 21-in. screen and is capable of being used in color-television systems. It is claimed that the main problems of development have been solved and that commercial production will begin soon (Figs. 27-127 and 27-128).[181]

27.41 *Subliminal television*

The possibility of the development of a new type of commercial television-advertising technique employing the principle of subliminal perception has aroused concern on the part of a large number of people. The term *subliminal perception* or *subception* is derived from the words sub (below) and limen (threshold). It refers to the effect of a stimulus that is too weak or that occurs for too short a period of time to be perceived above the threshold of the conscious mind. Thus, brief visual images, flashed at frequent intervals for periods of time less than 0.02 seconds, are not noted by the conscious mind, but they do register on the nervous system, do affect the subconscious mind, and can affect a person's actions.

History. The basic principles of subliminal perception have been investigated by psychologists during the past hundred years. Thus, in 1917, Otto Poetzl, an Austrian neurologist, flashed landscape slides on a tachistoscope for periods of 0.01 seconds. The next day, many of his subjects told him of dreams that included details of the landscape slides that they had not consciously seen the day before.

In 1956, an experiment on subliminal perception was tried on the audience watching a BBC television program of ballet dancers. The message which was flashed subliminally at one twenty-fifth of a second was "Pirie Breaks World

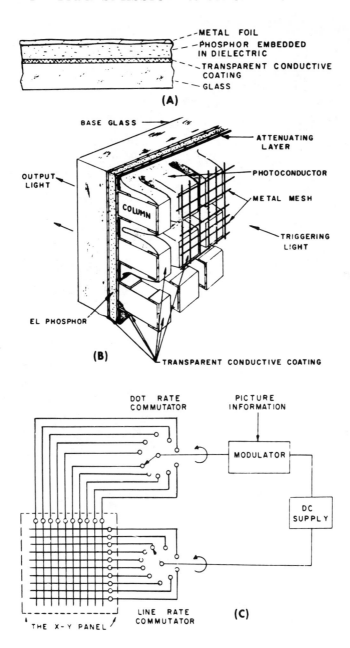

FIG. 27-125. SYLVATRON PICTURE-ON-THE-WALL TELEVISION SYSTEM
(A) Cross section of the image converter; (B) cross section of the mosaic EL panel; (C) commutator system for TV using EL display panel.

Courtesy, Westinghouse Electric Corp.

FIG. 27-126. THE ELF (ELECTROLUMINESCENT-
FERROELECTRIC) DISPLAY SCREEN
*This small "checkerboard," an important step in
the development of television-on-the-wall, combines an electroluminescent panel with a "solid
state" device to control it. The screen shows
contrast ratios between light and dark areas as
high as 200 to one and is less than $\frac{1}{4}$ in. thick.
It may be broken up into squares of light only
a few thousandths of an inch across instead of the
half-inch squares shown here.*

Courtesy, Office of Naval Research, Department of the Navy

FIG. 27-127. FLAT-PLATE TELEVISION TUBE

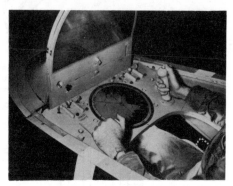

Courtesy, Office of Naval Research, Department of the Navy

FIG. 27-128. FLAT-PLATE TELEVISION TUBES IN
AIRCRAFT COCKPIT
*One plate is mounted vertically and a second
lies horizontally between the pilot's hands.*

Record". Viewers were asked to write in if they had seen anything. Of the 430 replies received, 20 had the message word perfect, 130 more were nearly correct.

In another experiment reported at approximately the same time, several New York University psychologists stated that they had fooled 20 subjects into thinking that an expressionless projected drawing of a man's face was changing from happy to angry merely by intermittently flashing the word happy on the screen for a few thousandths of a second and then replacing it by the word angry.[182]

Recent developments. However, these experiments did not attract much attention from the general public until September 1957, when James M. Vicary, a marketing researcher and psychologist, described a subliminal-perception experiment conducted upon a motion-picture audience in Ft. Lee, N.J. During the showing of the film, announcements urging the audience to purchase popcorn and a certain brand of soft drink were flashed every 5 seconds. The announcement appeared on the screen for one three-thousandth of a second. During the six weeks of the experiment, popcorn sales increased by 57.7 per cent and the sales of the soft drink increased by 18.1 per cent.[183]

Vicary also announced the formation of a company that would employ this technique for television commercials. In January 1958, Vicary staged a closed-circuit television demonstration in Washington, D.C. The audience was requested subliminally to buy popcorn and to fight polio. The results obtained were rather inconclusive.

Public reaction. The reaction from the public to this new technique was generally unfavorable. When television station KTLA in Los Angeles declared that it would transmit subliminal public-service messages advising the public to drive safely and to refrain from littering the streets, the torrent of adverse mail received caused the station to cancel its plans. The National Association of Radio and Television Broadcasters, which includes the three major television networks and 300 other television stations, announced that they would not employ subliminal advertising.

In March 1958, the New York State Senate unanimously passed a bill banning subliminal advertising. There has also been talk in Congress of enacting national legislation against the use of subliminal advertising. In response to Congressional protests, the FCC has stated that it saw no reason for taking any action, since subliminal perception was not being used anywhere at the moment. However, the agency has undertaken a study of this technique and has promised that upon the completion of this study it would take such action as would be warranted by the circumstances.

Effectiveness. There is a considerable difference of opinion concerning the question of whether or not the effects claimed for subliminal perception are only a myth. Thus, J. C. Naylor and C. H. Lawshe of Purdue University have published a 40-page analysis of the experiments on subception since 1863, in which they conclude: "There does not appear to be substantial evidence for subception as a distinct phenomenon . . . . Until someone can demonstrate in an experiment which has complete and adequate controls that subception exists, the concern of many seems slightly premature."[184]

On the other hand, many other psychologists believe that the evidence seems to indicate that subception does exist and can affect human behavior. However, they also believe that one's response to a subliminal message depends upon one's original interest in the topic of the message and that while subception can affect behavior, it cannot direct it. Thus, a message urging a non-beer drinker to purchase a certain brand of beer would have no effect. It could be used to reinforce existing habits but not to create new ones. Consequently, subliminal advertising can appeal only to those who already possess an interest in the practice or some desire to respond. The advertiser cannot present complex thoughts and can never be sure that even a simple thought will be received and interpreted in the way he wants.[185]

However, the current expressed opinion concerning the use of subliminal perception is that it is immaterial whether it is as effective as Vicary claims, or whether it is no more effective than visible advertising, as is claimed by its detractors. It is fundamentally unfair to the viewer and is an invasion of his privacy and free will.[186] [187] [188] [189] [190]

REFERENCES

1. Herbert E. Ives and others, "Image Transmission System for Two-way Television." *Bell System Technical Journal*, 9:448, July 1930.
2. "TV's 30th Birthday," *Popular Electronics*, 6:48, June 1957.
3. "Record Number of Sets in Use During '58," *Radio and TV News*, 61:136, Mar. 1959.
4. R. D. Kell and others, "Scanning Sequence and Repetition Rate of Television Images," *Proc. IRE*, 24:559, Apr. 1936.
5. "Split-Grid TV," *Electronic Design*, 5:1, June 1, 1957.
6. "Wobbled Scanning with a New CRT," *Radio and TV News*, 58:52, Aug. 1957.
7. "Wobbled Image Prolongs TV Camera Life," *Electronic Design*, 5:11, Oct. 1, 1957.
8. "Dipoles and Yagis," *Radio-Electronics*, 29:103, Nov. 1958.
9. *Electronics Reference Data*, Howard W. Sams and Co., Indianapolis, Ind., 1957, p. 1.
10. Edward M. Noll, "Trends in Television I.F.'s," *Radio-Electronics*, 22:49, Jan. 1951.
11. "Intercarrier Method of Sound Reception," *Sylvania News*, 16:T3-T4, Jan. 1949.
12. E. M. Noll, *Op. cit.*, p. 48.
13. R. F. Bergdahl, "Understanding Flyback Circuits," *Sylvania News*, 23:7, Oct. 1956.
14. O. H. Schade, "Characteristic of High-Efficiency Deflection and High-Voltage Supply Systems for Kinescopes," *RCA Review*, 11:5, Mar. 1950.
15. R. S. Mautner and O. H. Schade, "Television High-Voltage RF Supplies," *RCA Review*, 8:43, Mar. 1947.
16. *Electronics Reference Data, Op. cit.*, pp. 10-11.
17. Sidney C. Silver, "Sunspots Mar TV Reception," *Radio and TV News*, 58:98-9, Aug. 1957.
18. M. E. West, "TV and Sunspots," *Radio-Electronics*, 28:33-34, Aug. 1957.
19. *UHF—What it Means to Television*, Radio Corporation of America, New York, 1952, pp. 15-16.
20. "50-TV-Channel Allocation Plan Projected," *Electronics World*, 62:30, July 1959.
21. Robert Felber, "Coaxial Cables for Community-TV Systems," *Amphenol Engineering News*, 10:44, Apr. 1957.
22. "Report on Community TV," *Electronics Illustrated*, 2:91, Jan. 1959.
23. "Commercial Antenna Installations for Fringe Areas," *Radio-Electronics*, 30:34, June 1959.
24. *Electronics Reference Data. Op. cit.*, p. 13.
25. David Lachenbruch, "Who Owns the Signal?," *Radio-Electronics*, 30:94, Feb. 1959.
26. "Nearly 1,000 Illegal TV Boosters Found Operating in West," *Electronics World*, 62:28, Dec. 1959.
27. "FCC's Booster Stand Reversal," *Radio-Electronics*, 30:6, June 1959.
28. Robert B. Cooper, Jr., "Translators . . . . Television's Last Frontier," *Radio-Electronics*, 29:40-41, July 1958.
29. Dave Scher, "TV—Over the Hill and into the Dale," *Popular Electronics*, 6:39, Jan. 1957.
30. D. Lachenbruch, *Op. cit.*, p. 95.
31. Furman Hebb, "Color TV Today," *Popular Electronics*, 11:46, Sept. 1959.
32. G. L. Quint and P. M. Reinhardt, "Tri-Color Television Picture Tubes," *Sylvania News*, 21:5-8, July 1954.
33. Edward L. Michaels, *New Developments in Cathode-Ray Tubes*, Hughes Aircraft Co., Los Angeles, Calif., 1959, p. 3.
34. Ken Kleidon, "Practical Color TV for the Technician—Part IV," *Radio and TV News*, 58:48, Nov. 1957.
35. Robert B. Tomer and William R. Sullivan, "The CBS Colortron," *Radio and Television News*, 50:63, 182, Dec. 1953.
36. Darrell Huff, "Scientist Invents Simple Color-TV Tube," *Popular Science*, 160:145-147, 252, Jan. 1952.
37. Lloyd W. Allen, "Color Selection with the Chromotron Tube," *Radio-Electronics*, 29:115, Apr. 1958.
38. Leonard Lieberman, "The Color CRT," *Radio-Electronics*, 25:31-32, July 1954.
39. Walter H. Buchsbaum, "The Chromatic Color Picture Tube," *Radio and Television News*, 51:52, March 1954.
40. "Lawrence Color Tube," *Radio-Electronics*, 30:14, May 1959.
41. "Aperture Mask and Post Acceleration Type Picture Tubes," *General Electric Techni-Talk*, 8:3, Apr. 1956.
42. H. R. Colgate, "How the Apple Tube Works," *Radio-Electronics*, 28:40-42, Jan. 1957.
43. "New Color TV System," *Radio-Electronics*, 30:6, June 1959.
44. "New Color TV Design Makes Its Debut," *Electronics World*, 62:106, July 1959.
45. "Color Made Easy," *Scientific American*, 200:62, 65, Mar. 1959.
46. "New Color Theory," *Radio-Electronics*, 30:6, July 1959.
47. Ray Whitman, "Startling New Theory Promises a Revolution in Color," *Science and Mechanics*, 36:85-88, Oct. 1959.
48. Eric Leslie, "IRE Stresses Human Side," *Radio-Electronics*, 30:47, June 1959.
49. Furman Hebb, "New Color-TV Projection System," *Popular Electronics*, 10:45-48, May 1959.
50. "Color TV Gains," *Radio-Electronics*, 30:6, 10, Aug. 1959.
51. Furman Hebb, "Color TV Today," *Popular Electronics*, 11:41-46, 120-121, Sept. 1959.
52. "The Case Against Pay-TV," *Radio Age*, 14:30, July 1955.
53. Mike Bienstock, "Will You Pay for TV?," *Popular Electronics*, 7:60, Oct. 1957.
54. Mike Bienstock, "How Pay-TV Will Work," *Science Digest*, 42:61, Dec. 1957.
55. A. W. Bernsohn, "Pay-TV Today," *Electronics World*, 62:145, Sept. 1959.
56. Rudolf F. Graf, "Skiatron's Subscriber-Vision," *Radio and Television News*, 50:58, Oct. 1953.

57. "2 TV Programs to a Channel," *Radio-Electronics*, 28:6, Nov. 1957.
58. "Two TV Programs on One Channel," *Radio and TV News*, 58:105, Dec. 1957.
59. Ira Kamen, "Pay ... As You Go," *Radio-Electronics*, 25:47-48, Feb. 1954.
60. "Toll TV and the Service Technician," *Radio and Television News*, 54:8, Nov. 1955.
61. "First Customers to Pay Television," *Life*, 43:63-73, Oct. 14, 1957.
62. "The Case Against Pay-TV," *Op cit.*, p. 12.
63. "Three-Year Toll-TV Program Set Up," *Electronics World*, 61:26, June 1959.
64. "Two Anti-Pay TV Bills Presented in Senate and House," *Radio and TV News*, 61:31, Apr. 1959.
65. "Bill Introduced for FCC Control Over Wired Pay-TV," *Electronics World*, 62:30, July 1960.
66. Tom Shea, "Closed-Circuit TV," *Radio and TV News*, 59:145, May 1958.
67. *Ibid*, p. 146.
68. *Ibid*, p. 144.
69. *Ibid*, p. 35.
70. Walter H. Buchsbaum, "Industrial TV," *Radio and Television News*, 54:37, Oct. 1955.
71. "Radio-TV Service Industry News," *Radio and Television News*, 50:120, Aug. 1953.
72. "Atypical Television," *Radio-Electronics*, 29:35, Oct. 1958.
73. G. H. Wilson, "Television in Industry," *Electrical Engineering*, Feb. 1953, p. 1.
74. *Ibid*, p. 1.
75. *GPL TV-for-Brokers System*, General Precision, Inc., Pleasantville, N.Y. 1960, pp. 2-3.
76. *Kin Tel Closed Circuit TV Systems*, Kin Tel Division of Cohu Electronics, Inc., San Diego, Calif., p. 1.
77. *What Every Businessman Should Know About Closed Circuit TV*, General Precision, Inc., Pleasantville, New York, pp. 5-6.
78. "Medical TV—Just What the Doctor Ordered," *Radio Age*, 16:13, Jan. 1957.
79. "Cells Stained Electronically by New Instrument," *Aminco Lab. News*, 4:3, July 1957.
80. "Nurse's Electronic Eye," *Think*, 22:25, June 1956.
81. *Safety in Air Navigation*, Radio Corporation of America, New York, 1957, p. 22.
82. Jerome Goldhammer and Robert Rubenstein, "High-Speed Aerial Reconnaissance System," *Amphenol Engineering News*, 13:566-567, Mar. 1960.
83. "TV Eye Keeps Munich on the Move," *The Lamp*, 42:6-9, Summer 1960.
84. "Bandit-Proof Bank," *Electronic Age*, 19:22-24, Winter 1959.
85. William E. Miles, "Industry's Private Eye," *Think*, 23:13, May 1957.
86. Harry Wexler and Sigmund Fritz, "Tiros Reveals Cloud Formations," *Science*, 131:1708-1709, June 10, 1960.
87. Aaron Nadell, "Electronics Works on the Railroad," *Radio-Electronics*, 30:46-47, Nov. 1959.
88. "World's Largest TV Network Installed in Pennsylvania Station," *Amphenol Engineering News*, 10:426, May 1957.
89. W. R. Stamp, "Underwater Television," *Scientific American*, 188:32, June 1953.
90. W. E. Miles, *Op. cit.*, p. 15.
91. Herbert O. Johansen, "TV Robot Roams Ocean Bottom," *Popular Science*, 170:141, Jan. 1957.
92. R. S. Yeandle, "Television in Education," *General Electric Educational Service News*, 8:3, Oct. 1955.
93. *The Modern School Looks at Television*, RCA-Victor Division, Camden, N.J., pp. 12-14.
94. Robert B. Kimble, "ETV—Boon or Boondoggle?," *Educational Forum*, 23:433-435, May 1959.
95. *Design for ETV—Planning for Schools with Television*, Educational Facilities Laboratories, New York, 1960, p. 3.
96. "Teaching by Television," *Science*, 129:1601, June 12, 1959.
97. *Design for ETV, Op. cit.*, p. 22.
98. T. Shea, *Op. cit.*, p. 38.
99. Arnold Perry, "Teaching by Television in Today's Schools," *Educational Forum*, 24:394, May 1960.
100. "Teaching by Television," *Op. cit.*, pp. 1601-1602.
101. William M. Brish, "Television as a Resource for Instruction," *Educational Forum*, 24:144-145, Jan. 1960.
102. *Ibid.*, p. 141.
103. A. Perry, *Op. cit.*, p. 395.
104. *Ibid.*, p. 395.
105. "Battle Over TV in California," *Phi Delta Kappan*, 40:152, Jan. 1959.
106. H. K. Newburn, "Television and the Future of Education," *Educational Forum*, 22:389-396, May 1958.
107. A. Perry, *Op. cit.*, p. 394.
108. R. B. Kimble, *Op. cit.*, pp. 439-440.
109. A. Perry, *Op. cit.*, p. 393.
110. John L. Burns, "The Challenge of Quality in Education," *Electronic Age*, 19:12-13, Winter 1959.
111. *Report of the Superintendent of Schools, The City of New York, 1953—Our Public Schools, Part IV*, p. 39.
112. Worthington A. Gregory, "Why Don't We Have More Educational TV?," *Electronics Illustrated*, 2:28, Jan. 1959.
113. "TV in Schools," *Radio-Electronics*, 28:6, Apr. 1957.
114. Alexander J. Stoddard, *Schools for Tomorrow, An Educator's Blueprint*, Fund for the Advancement of Education, New York, 1957, pp. 32-33.
115. R. B. Kimble, *Op. cit.*, p. 433.
116. "Educational TV," *Radio-Electronics*, 30:18, Aug. 1959.
117. *Design for ETV, Op. cit.*, p. 22.
118. W. A. Gregory, *Op. cit.*, p. 29.
119. Kenneth R. Hobbs, "A New Dimension in Teaching," *Phi Delta Kappan*, 40:161, Jan. 1959.
120. C. V. Newsom, "Radio and Television," *Scientific Monthly*, 79:250, Oct. 1954.
121. "News," *Electronics Illustrated*, 2:14, May 1959.
122. "Expanded Military Closed-Circuit TV," *Electronics World*, 61:63, May 1959.

123. "Closed-Circuit TV Provides Instruction on Guided Missiles," *Radio and TV News*, 61:33, Jan. 1959.
124. "On-the-Spot TV Instruction," *Electronics World*, 62:62, Sept. 1959.
125. "An Eye for an Eye," *Radio and TV News*, 59: 37, May 1958.
126. "Camera on Head," *Radio Electronics*, 30:56, July 1959.
127. "Teachers Grade Teachers on TV," *Life*, 38: 112, May 9, 1955.
128. "Testing of Candidates for Supervisory Licenses," *Curriculum and Materials*, New York City Board of Education, 13:15, Nov. 1958.
129. *Teaching by Television*, The Ford Foundation, New York, 1959, pp. 32-33.
130. "TV Physics Course," *Think*, 24:27, Nov. 1958.
131. Robert H. Randall and others, "A Look at the Continental Classroom," *American Journal of Physics*, 28:263-269, Mar. 1960.
132. "Looking Ahead to NBC-TV Educational Programming," *NBC Program Information*, Summer 1959, p. 1.
133. *Design for ETV, Op. Cit.*, p. 22.
134. "Continental Classroom," *Radio-Electronics*, 30:8, 10, Nov. 1959.
135. A. J. Stoddard, *Op. cit.*, p. 60.
136. "Trans-Atlantic Radio Relay," *Radio Electronics*, 27:141, Nov. 1946.
137. "Stratovision," *Radio-Electronics*, 30:6, Dec. 1959.
138. A. V. J. Martin, "Airborne Relay for Intercontinental TV," *Radio and TV News*, 61:46-47, Jan. 1959.
139. "New Council Announces Airborne Instructional TV Experiment," *Phi Delta Kappan*, 41: 85, Nov. 1959.
140. Jordan McQuay, "Space Relay Station," *Radio-Electronics*, 30:42-45, June 1959.
141. Arthur C. Clarke, *Faces from the Sky*, PRL-174, Curtis Publishing Co., Philadelphia, Pa., 1959, p. 1.
142. Martin Mann, "Talking Satellites to Speed Mail," *Popular Science*, 174:83-86, 242, Apr. 1959.
143. John R. Pierce, "Communication Satellites," *Bell Telephone Magazine*, 38:25-31, Winter 1959.
144. "Passive Satellites," *Radio-Electronics*, 30:10, Dec. 1959.
145. "Solar-Powered World-Wide Satellite Repeaters Urged," *Radio and TV News*, 60:30, Oct. 1958.
146. Matt Johnson, "TV to Circle Globe," *Electronics Illustrated*, 1:68-70, July 1958.
147. Henri G. Busignies, "World-Wide Television," *Industrial Research*, 1:21, Spring 1959.
148. "Russia Proposes Global TV," *Popular Electronics*, 8:51, 53, June 1958.
149. "Defense in the Space Age," *Electronic Age*, 18:17, Summer 1959.
150. "Balloon-Communications-Satellite Launching," *Electronics World*, 62:30, Sept. 1959.
151. James F. Phillips, "Space Projects Offer Great Civil Benefits," *Planes-Aerospace*, 15:1, 7, Nov. 1959.
152. "Messages Sent Via Moon," *Science News Letter*, 77:103, Feb. 13, 1960.

153. "A New Approach to Long-Distance Transmission," *Radio and Television News*, 53:45, Apr. 1955.
154. Estill I. Green, "Progress and Problems in World Communications," *Bell Telephone Magazine*, 39:29, Spring 1960.
155. "Picture-Phone Uses Telephone Lines," *Radio and Television News*, 56:43, Nov. 1956.
156. J. R. Pierce, "Telephones of Tomorrow," *Science Digest*, 43:10-11, Feb. 1958.
157. "Phone Cable Carries TV," *Industrial Laboratories*, 9:56, May 1957.
158. "Television Telephone," *Science Digest*, 45:87, June 1959.
159. "First Step to Intercontinental TV," *Radio-Electronics*, 30:18, July 1959.
160. "Transatlantic TV Via Phone Cable," *Electronics World*, 62:99, Sept. 1959.
161. "Ft. Wayne Slow-Scan TV," *ITT Laboratories in the News*, 2:8, Apr. 1960.
162. "Vitascan for Color TV," *Radio and Television News*, 54:98-99, Aug. 1955.
163. R. E. Graham, "Continuous Scanner for Televising Film," *Bell Laboratories Record*, 32:25, July 1954.
164. P. O. Montgomery and W. A. Bonner, "A Flying-Spot Microscope," *Scientific American*, 198: 39, May 1958.
165. "New Electric Machine Helps Detect Uterine Cancer," *Science Digest*, 42:48, November 1957.
166. DuMont Type 3003 Iconumerator, East Paterson, N.J., Allan B. DuMont Laboratories, p. 2.
167. "High-Speed TV Office Duplicator," *Stanford Research Institute News Bulletin*, 9:1-2, Jan. 1957.
168. "3-D TV?," *Popular Science*, 162:107, June 1953.
169. "3-D Color TV," *Electronic Design*, 5:12-13, Oct. 1, 1957.
170. Louis E. Garner, Jr., "3-D Color-TV Is Here!," *Popular Electronics*, 9:31-33, July 1958.
171. L. I. Mengle, "Three Dimensional TV System," *Radio and TV News*, 60:45, Oct. 1958.
172. "3-D Closed-Circuit Television," *Design News*, 15:129, June 20, 1960.
173. Milton S. Snitzer, "3-D Color TV for the Future?," *Radio and TV News*, 59:39, May 1958.
174. "Picture-on-the-Wall TV Forecast." *Design News*, 9:13, Sept. 15, 1954.
175. "Flat Kinescope," *Radio-Electronics*, 28:169-170, Jan. 1957.
176. "Pictures on a Flat Panel," *Radio and TV News*, 58:55, 103, Sept. 1957.
177. R. M. Bowie, "Picture on the Wall Television—Part 1," *Sylvania News*, 26:5, Mar. 1959.
178. R. M. Bowie, "Picture on the Wall Television—Part 2," *Sylvania News*, 26:5-7, Apr. 1959.
179. "New Progress Reported for On-the-Wall TV," *Design News*, 13:4-5, Apr. 28, 1958.
180. "Television-on-the-Wall is Step Closer," *Science Digest*, 44:47, July 1958.
181. Eric Leslie, "Flat TV Tube," *Radio-Electronics*, 28:43-45, Mar. 1957.
182. G. Talese, "Most Hidden Hidden Persuasion," *New York Times Magazine*, Jan. 12, 1958, p. 22.
183. D. H. Radler, "Subception, or Deception," *Industrial Research*, 1:60, Spring 1959.

184. *Ibid.,* pp. 61-62.
185. Richard P. Barthol, "Subliminal Ads Won't Sell," *Science Digest,* 45:69, Feb. 1959.
186. "Subliminal Ads Tried on TV," *Radio and TV News,* 59:143, Feb. 1958.
187. Roy A. Gallant, "The Case of the Invisible Salesman," *Science World,* 3:20, Feb. 20, 1958.

188. Herbert Brean, "Hidden Sell Technique is Almost Here," *Life,* 44:102-114, Mar. 31, 1958.
189. "TV's Invisible Ads Called Ineffective," *Science Digest,* 43:22-23, May 1958.
190. Wesley S. Griswold, "TV's New Trick: Hidden Commercials," *Popular Science,* 172:95-97, Apr. 1958.

28 - FACSIMILE AND RELATED SYSTEMS

28.1 *Nature and history of facsimile transmission*

Facsimile is a system of transmitting drawings, photographs, and pages of graphic material by wire or radio and receiving them in permanently recorded form on paper. The basic principles of transmitting pictures by means of electricity were first conceived in 1842 by an English scientist named Alexander Bain. As a consequence of his original design of an electrochemical recording telegraph, he is called the father of facsimile.

In 1862, Abbé Caselli successfully transmitted drawings between Amiens and Paris. Edison also became interested and invented a facsimile system in 1873 that was moderately successful. In 1904, Arthur Korn a German physicist, developed a facsimile system employing a selenium cell. He succeeded in transmitting wire-photos over telephone lines from Munich to Nuremberg, a distance of 600 miles. In 1907, he sent a picture of the president of France by wire from Berlin to Paris in 12 minutes, and he transmitted the first wire-photo from the Continent to England. During the same year, Richard H. Ranger, an American engineer, developed a facsimile system that was used for transmitting pictures between London and Paris.

Korn's next important contribution was the development of a radio-facsimile system. In 1922, Korn succeeded in sending a picture by wire from Rome to Berlin. From Berlin this picture was sent by means of radio to Maine, and the first trans-Atlantic radio-photo appeared shortly afterwards in a New York newspaper.

In 1924, RCA transmitted a radio-photo from New York to London. Two years later, as a result of the radio-photo system developed by Ranger, commercial trans-Atlantic and point-to-point radio-facsimile service was inaugurated by RCA. In this Ranger radio-photo system, the film was wrapped around a glass cylinder. Inside the cylinder was a powerful light. The picture was scanned by moving a photocell down the length of the cylinder. When the cell reached the end of the cylinder, the cylinder was advanced slightly and the scanning process was repeated (Fig. 28-1). In this manner, the picture was converted into a series of strong and weak electrical impulses corresponding to the light and dark elemental areas of the picture. These impulses were then used to modulate a radio-frequency carrier wave. At the receiving end, the wave was demodulated and a pen was actuated to produce corresponding white, gray, or black elemental areas on a piece of paper wrapped around a cylinder, thus reproducing the original picture.

Courtesy, Radio Corporation of America
FIG. 28-1. PHOTOGRAPH FLASHED BY RADIO FACSIMILE

Black box-like installation between the operator's hands is the scanner.

In some receiving systems, the picture was reproduced by using chemically prepared paper designed to turn dark when current passed through it. A platinum-tipped needle was pressed against this paper, and the darkness of the line produced became a function of the strength of the current.

28.2 *Facsimile operation*

The post-war radio facsimile that was standardized by the FCC during the late 1940's utilizes FM radio transmission to deliver four magazine-size pages during a regular 15-minute broadcast period. A page of text and pictures is wrapped around the drum of a scanner. As the drum revolves at constant speed, a photocell scans the page, line by line, 105 lines to the inch, changing the graphic material into a fluctuating current. The amount of photocurrent produced at any given instant is proportional to the whiteness of the point being

scanned. This current is amplified and then used to modulate an FM carrier or is transmitted directly over wire circuits (Fig. 28-2).

When this FM signal is picked up by the FM receiver, it is converted back into a current of varying amplitude, and is fed into the facsimile recorder. The recorder contains a roll of paper which has been treated so that it will conduct current. As the motor-driven reel pulls the paper between two thin metal blades, the facsimile current is fed into one of the blades and passes from it, through the paper, to the other blade. In the process it carries metal from the printer blade and deposits it on the paper, making it black where the current is strongest, shades of gray where it is weaker, and white where no current passes through. The result is a continuous strip of paper, emerging from the recorder at the rate of about 3.5 in. per min and delivering pages 8.2 in. wide and 11.5 in. long.[1] Another interesting development is Colorfax, a system of color-facsimile transmission that may be received on any ordinary type of paper.[2]

28.3 *Electro-Rex*

A recently developed type of facsimile known as Electro-Rex also starts with an optical scanning system that picks up images placed on a drum (Fig. 28-3). The images are converted into electric currents and amplified and the impulses are then transferred to a cutting stylus located on the reproduction drum. A copy sheet, stencil, or offset plate is mounted on this drum. The reproduction stylus, which is 0.004 in. in diameter, produces several thousand holes per second, transferring an exact duplicate of the original to the sheet, plate, or stencil. If a stencil or plate is used, it can be employed to duplicate thousands of additional copies.

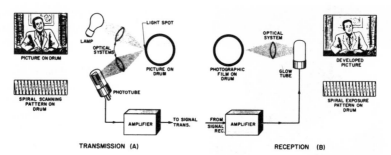

FIG. 28-2. PRINCIPLES OF ONE TYPE OF FACSIMILE OPERATION

28.4 *Military facsimile*

In 1957, the U.S. Department of the Army announced the development of the fastest conventional facsimile set in the world. It was designed by Erhart of the Signal Corps Engineering Laboratories with the assistance of the Times Facsimile Corporation. A reproduced picture can be obtained within 5 minutes after the photographer clicks his shutter.

The photographer employs a Polaroid Land camera which produces a completely developed picture within 1 minute. This picture is then put into a facsimile transmitter that is installed in the back of a jeep (Fig. 28-4). This equipment contains a revolving polygonal mirror scanner which permits scanning the photo without wrapping it around the drum. Transmission can be over either wire or radio facilities.

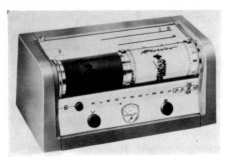

Courtesy, Rex-Rotary Distributing Corp.
FIG. 28-3. ELECTRO-REX

The set can also be mounted in an airplane or helicopter, allowing an aerial photographer to send surveillance pictures continually to battle headquarters. This equipment may eventually have important commercial applications. For example, by installing this equipment in radio cars now operated by large newspapers, it could change present methods of photo-reporting.[3][4]

28.5 *Ultrafax*

Mention has been made in an earlier chapter of the development in 1947 by RCA and Eastman Kodak of Ultrafax, a system capable of transmitting written material at the rate of 1 million words per second. This system is a hybrid type of facsimile combining features of both photography and television.

The material to be transmitted is photographed on motion-picture film. The film is then placed between a flying-spot cathode-ray tube and a phototube (Fig. 28-5). The beam from the flying-spot tube scans the film, and the resulting light variations are converted into electrical variations by the phototube. These variations are then transmitted in a manner similar to the transmission of conventional television signals over a microwave-relay system (Fig. 28-6).

Courtesy, U.S. Army Signal Corps.

FIG. 28-4. GXC-5 PORTABLE SIGNAL CORPS RADIO FACSIMILE EQUIPMENT

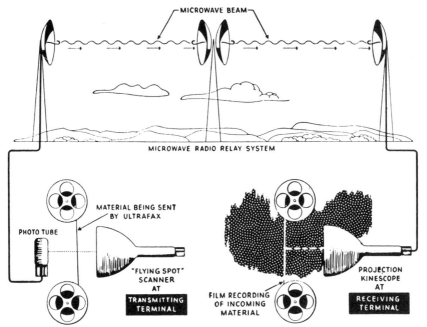

Courtesy, Radio Coporation of America

FIG. 28-5. ULTRAFAX SYSTEM

Courtesy, Radio Corporation of America
FIG. 28-6. ULTRAFAX SENDING TERMINAL

At the receiving end, the signal are reproduced on the kinescope tube. A continuously moving film records the patterns on the kinescope. The film is passed through heated chemicals which develop and fix the film within 15 seconds (Fig. 28-7).

The capabilities of Ultrafax were illustrated in a previously described demonstration conducted in Washington in 1948, in which the entire text of the 1047-page book, *Gone With the Wind,* was transmitted by Ultrafax in 2 minutes and 21 seconds.

28-6 *Facsimile applications in telegraphy*

The Western Union Company has also been experimenting with improved facsimile facilities. In 1951, it announced the development of High-Speed Fax, a system capable of transmitting over any distance at a rate of 3,000 words per minute. The copy requires no advance preparation, and the received material is instantly reproduced

Courtesy, Radio Corporation of America
FIG. 28-7. ULTRAFAX RECEIVING TERMINAL

on an electro-sensitive dry recording paper called Teledeltos.

This paper is also employed in Desk-Fax, a device designed for facsimile transmission of telegrams in either direction between a businessman's desk and a main telegraph office (Fig. 28-8). As of 1959, there were 36,000 Desk-Fax units in operation, and Western Union announced the development of a facsimile network linking the major cities of the United States. This network was designed to make the same type of service available to the general public, at charges ranging between 2 and 4 dollars a page.

Another innovation, announced during 1951, is the Telecar, designed to speed delivery of telegrams to outlying areas of a large city. When these messages are received by the central telegraph office, they are sent by wire to a transmitting station. They are then

Courtesy, Western Union Telegraph Co.
FIG. 28-8. DESK-FAX EQUIPMENT

sent by radio-facsimile to the roving Telecar vehicle closest to the address of the recipient of the message. The Telecar contains a radio-facsimile receiver which reproduces the message. The driver, notified of the address by radio, often arrives at the house before the entire message comes out of the facsimile machine.[5]

28.7 Meteor-trail radio facsimile

In a discussion of forward-scatter propagation, which will be found in the chapter on microwaves, mention will be made of the fact that meteors produce some of the inhomogeneities in the ionosphere that are responsible for this type of propagation. When a meteor enters the atmosphere, its high velocity causes the air molecules to ionize. This trail of ionized air, which may be present for periods of one-tenth of a second up to several minutes, scatters the radio signals which would otherwise radiate out into space. Across a typical long-distance transmission path, such ionized meteor trails usually appear several times a minute.

The history of meteor-burst radio communication began in the early 1940's when FCC engineers, who were monitoring FM transmissions on the old band of 42 to 50 mc, noted that short signal bursts were occasionally received over distances of almost 1,400 miles. This far exceeded the customary line-of-sight transmission range of 100 miles. In 1948, Allen suggested that these bursts were caused by the ionization of the atmosphere produced by individual meteors.[6]

About 1950, the idea occurred simultaneously to several engineers that the ionization produced by meteor bursts might provide useful paths for point-to-point communications. Amateur-radio hobbyists began to experiment with these techniques, and several large organizations, including the National Bureau of Standards, Stanford Research Institute, and RCA Laboratories began work to develop reliable transhorizon communications employing these principles.

It was found that a system employing meteor-burst transmission possessed several advantages which compensated for the complex message-handling system necessitated by the erratic and random nature of its operation. In comparison with conventional iono-spheric forward-scatter transmission, meteor-burst transmission can employ higher frequencies and requires less power and simpler antennas.[7]

Early in 1958, Bliss, Wagner, and Wickizer of RCA, working in conjunction with the Air Research and Development Command, announced that they had succeeded in using this technique to transmit images of printed materials a distance of 910 miles without relays. This transmission was accomplished between the 20-kilowatt, 40-mc transmitter of the National Bureau of Standards at Havana, Ill., and the RCA Laboratories installation at Riverhead, Long Island.

At the transmitter, the material was scanned at the rate of two scans per second, and the signal was transmitted continuously. The receiver was also operated continuously with a recording unit that was maintained in a standby condition. When a meteor completed the transmission path, the signal tripped the recorder. The image that appeared on the phosphor screen was recorded automatically, and the circuit was then automatically reset for the next signal burst.

According to the RCA experts, the optimum distance for facsimile transmission by this means is 600 to 1,200 miles. This new technique promises to increase the versatility of radio communications by providing a means of sending information at times and over distances for which other means may not be available.[8][9][10]

28.8 *Post-office facsimile*

The Post Office has announced plans for developing a microwave facsimile service, and in October 1960, it placed one such system in operation between two major cities. It has been predicted that ultimately this service, called Speed Mail, will comprise a network of 178 cities and serve two-thirds of the population of the United States. It will employ conventional facsimile techniques and use the facilities of American Telephone and Telegraph and Western Union. A machine has been developed for use at the receiving end that will fold the letter, place it in an envelope, and seal and address it, thus preserving the privacy of the message.

A development contract for facsimile mail was also awarded by the Post Office in 1959 to the International

Telephone and Telegraph Co. The company has installed equipment in Washington, D.C., and Los Angeles and has conducted experimental transmissions of mail via wire lines. It is claimed that the cost of this "instant-mail" service could be below 2 cents per letter, which is considerably lower than the 8 cents required today for air-mail service.[11]

Some experts predict that if this service is successfully established, it could produce serious impacts upon Western Union's telegram business and upon the airlines, railroads, and trucking lines that now carry the mail.

28.9 *Other applications of facsimile*

The most obvious application of facsimile and radio-photo systems is for the transmission of newspaper photographs. However, a recent analysis has revealed that 35 per cent of all radio-photographs are sent by business concerns transmitting diagrams, charts, maps, legal documents, and financial statements. The President of the RCA Radiophoto Service has recently stated that the time is rapidly approaching when the business use of radio-photo and facsimile reproduction will exceed newspaper use.

In Washington, D.C., a Joint Weather Analysis Central containing expert Air Force, Navy, and Weather Bureau meteorologists, prepares daily more than 50 weather maps and charts, using information received by teletype and facsimile from more than 700 weather stations. These maps are then transmitted over a facsimile network to airfields, weather offices, and ships at sea (Fig. 28-9). This frees the local meteorologists from much of their tedious routine work and permits them to spend more time in analyzing and

FIG. 28-9. FACSIMILE EQUIPMENT FOR TRANS-
MITTING WEATHER MAPS
*Receiving unit is in foreground; transmitter unit,
in background.*

forecasting conditions which affect the
weather in their immediate localities. In
addition, simple duplicating methods
make it convenient to furnish pilots
with facsimile copies of weather maps.

A rather spectacular demonstration
of radio-facsimile was provided late
in 1959 when the Soviet satellite Lunik
transmitted back to earth a photograph
of the previously unseen back side of
the moon. At approximately the same
time, CBS Laboratories announced the
development of a Photoscan system for
transmitting high-quality photographs
from aircraft or satellites to ground. It
is claimed that this system produces a
picture on the ground that is fully as
sharp in detail as the original because
the use of the newly developed Line
Scan tube enables the Photoscan picture to contain about 120 million elements compared with the approximately
250,000 elements of the conventional
television picture.

It has been proposed to use facsimile to make the contents of centrally
located archives accessible to research

workers located all over the country.
This system is described as an "integrated high-density direct-access photo
storage and retrieval system for library
materials." The Council on Library
Resources has issued a 200,000-dollar
contract to the Crosley Division of
AVCO Manufacturing Co. for the
development of an experimental system.
When it is developed, a scientist who
presses a series of buttons in accordance
with a certain code will be able to
indicate to a distantly located archive
his desire to use a certain issue of an
obscure periodical previously recorded
on microfilm (10,000 microfilmed
pages are contained on a single card).
The signal would cause the desired card
to be pulled out and positioned for
electronic transmission. At the receiving end, the desired page or pages
would appear on a device that resembles a television picture tube. By
operating the correct controls, the
researcher could turn the pages of the
periodical, and he could also obtain
a permanent facsimile print.

An RCA facsimile system is now
being used at the Oak Ridge Atomic
Laboratory to make data from a central
library available to scientists in widely
scattered plants. When a scientist
requests a particular article by speaking
into an intercommunication system,
the librarian places the copy to be
transmitted on a flat stand and presses
a button. A flying-spot scanner converts the copy into varying electrical
impulses, which are amplified and sent
over telephone lines to the receiver.
At the receiver, the signal is fed to a
spiral wire, which produces a scanning
action by moving across a rotating
cylindrical drum. Around this cylinder
is a piece of paper that has been treated
with diazonium dyes. When a varying
signal current passes from the wire to
the paper, a reaction occurs in the dye,

which produces the printing action. The paper is then passed over ultraviolet light, which bleaches the unprinted dye and fixes the facsimile print permanently. This system not only saves time and trouble but also eliminates the danger of possible radioactive contamination of irreplaceable library material.[12]

The Pennsylvania Railroad is experimenting with facsimile in its Philadelphia station. A facsimile machine is used to reproduce Pullman or reserved-seat tickets. A facsimile system is also being used to transmit reserved-space tickets into offices of subscribers in the Philadelphia area.

An interesting medical application is the transmission of X-ray pictures by facsimile. This system is similar to that used for transmitting news photographs, except for the fact that it is modified to accommodate the much-wider range of light intensities found in an X-ray negative. In 1956, an experimental circuit was set up over telephone lines between Mt. Sinai Hospital in New York City and the Albert Einstein Medical Center in Philadelphia. It is expected that the eventual perfection of this system will enable small hospitals to consult radiologists in large medical centers. It will also permit radiologists in different cities to hold consultations on the same case. The Defense Department has shown interest in the potentialities of this system and has established experimental facsimile circuits between several Air Force hospitals.

A dynamic demonstration of facsimile was offered to the public during the 1956 Republican National Convention in San Francisco when a New York City daily newspaper used facsimile to produce a California edition. An entire issue took about a half hour to transmit. The facsimile film produced at the other end was developed and

sent to engravers, and the complete edition was off the press within 4 hours.

28.10 *Facsimile systems in business offices*

Many different types of facsimile systems have been designed to lighten the burden of paper-work in large business offices. One such system, developed by the Addressograph-Multigraph Corporation photoelectrically scans the information appearing on card records (Fig. 28-10). The resulting electrical impulses are amplified and used to energize printing elements that produce facsimile images of the scanned letters and numerals upon various types of paper forms. The writing speed is 200 four-line message units per minute. It can be used to imprint mailing tape and various types of preprinted continuous forms such as bills, checks, notices, and sales-promotion literature.

A second system, developed by Standard Products, Inc., is used to transmit records of printed matter such as office memoranda, invoices, vouchers, and bills of lading, to any one of several destinations (Fig. 28-11). If desired, the received copy can be used as a master to make duplicate copies in photocopying machines such as Ozalid and Copyflex. These units may be employed for either short-haul and intercommunications circuits or for long-distance transmission via telephone or microwave-radio circuits.

A third system, known as Stenafax, has been developed by the Westrex Co. It is fundamentally an electronic method of low-cost, mimeograph-stencil preparation by means of which any graphic material, such as office forms, news clippings, and engineering drawings, may be accurately reproduced (Fig. 28-12).

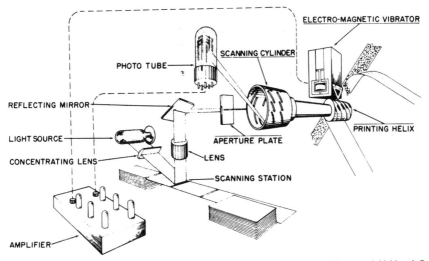

Courtesy, Addressograph-Multigraph Corp.

FIG. 28-10. PRINCIPLE OF THE ADDRESSOGRAPH-MULTIGRAPH SYSTEM

Courtesy, Standard Products, Inc.

FIG. 28-11. ELECTRONIC MESSENGER UNIT

Courtesy, Westrex Co.

FIG. 28-12. STENAFAX UNIT

The equipment contains two drums which rotate at the same speed (Fig. 28-13). The copy to be duplicated is mounted on one drum, which is scanned by a photocell. A special plastic stencil blank is placed on the second drum. When the photocell scans a black area, it sends an electrical impulse to a recording stylus that is moving in synchronization across the second drum. This electrical impulse causes arcing between the stylus and the metal drum, producing a small black dot on the plastic sheet. Where dots are closely packed, the sheet will appear black;

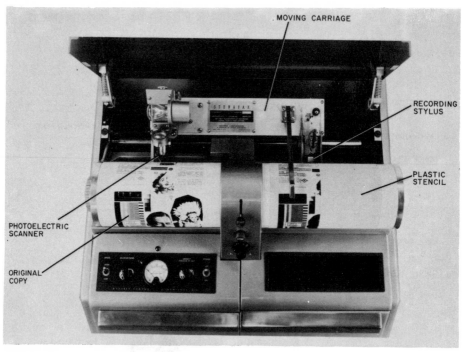

Courtesy, Westrex Co.

FIG. 28-13. PRINCIPLES OF STENAFAX OPERATION

where they are loosely spaced, the sheet will appear gray; and where no dots are produced, the sheet will appear white. A stencil can be produced in 6 minutes, and 10,000 mimeograph copies can be made from just one of them.[13]

28.11 *Xerography*

A process closely related to office facsimile is xerography, invented by C.F. Carlson in 1938. It was improved by technicians and scientists working for the Batelle Memorial Institute and the Haloid Company. Xerography is a dry, electrical copying process used to produce direct positive copies of letters, engineering drawings, office forms, and similar materials within 3 minutes. It can also be used to produce offset paper masters for offset duplicators; translucent intermediates for diazo-type machines; and masters for spirit duplicators.

The device (Fig. 28-14) employs a special selenium-coated plate of aluminum, which is passed under fine wires charged to a potential of several thousand volts (step 1) in order to give the plate a positive charge (step 2). The copy to be duplicated is projected through a camera lens upon the charged plate (step 3). The areas exposed to light lose their positive charge (white space), while the areas corresponding to the darker portions of the copy retain their charge. Thus, an electrical image or latent image is produced. The plate is then dusted with a negatively charged powder, which clings to the positively charged shaded portions of

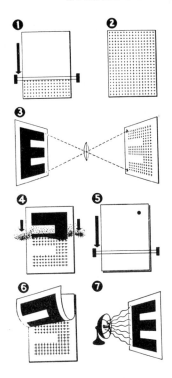

FIG. 28-14. HOW XEROGRAPHY WORKS

plate to a positively charged intermediate tissue. The image is then transferred electrostatically from the intermediate tissue to the copper-clad laminate. Heat is then applied to fuse the black-powder image to the copper surface of the laminate. In the conventional etching process that follows, the etching solutions eat away all areas of the copper unprotected by the black-powder Xerographic resist, and the copper is left in the desired circuit patterns. The resist is then removed by a solvent.

FIG. 28-15. PRINTED CIRCUIT PREPARED BY XEROGRAPHY

the electrical image on the plate (step 4). A positively charged sheet of paper is then placed over the plate (step 5). The paper attracts the powder from the plate, forming a direct positive image (step 6). The print is then heated for a few seconds to fuse the powder and form a permanent print (step 7).

A very recent and interesting application of xerography is its use in making printed circuits (Fig. 28-15). From an original opaque drawing, it is possible within 15 minutes to prepare for etching a copper-clad laminate designed to serve as a printed-circuit wiring board. Conventional methods usually require about 2 hours. This process resembles the one previously described, except that the image of the desired circuit is transferred from the light-sensitive

28.12 Xero-radiography

The General Electric Company has developed a rapid and low-cost process called xero-radiography. This modified xerographic technique makes it possible to obtain an X-ray picture in only 40 seconds without the use of a darkroom. A conventional X-ray source is used to produce an image on a selenium-coated aluminum plate (Fig. 28-16). The plate is given a positive charge before exposure (step 1). The X-rays pass through the object being examined and partially discharge the plate (step 2). The extent of this discharge is in inverse proportion to the density of the object. A latent electrostatic image is produced on the plate.

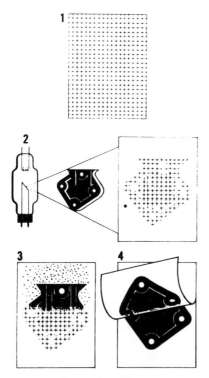

Courtesy, General Electric Co. X-Ray Dept.
FIG. 28-16. HOW THE XERO-RADIOGRAPHY PROCESS WORKS

This image can be made visible by spraying with a negatively charged powder (step 3). The powder collects on the various charged portions of the plate in proportion to the amount of charge remaining. The picture then can either be wiped off the plate or can be converted into a permanent record (step 4).[14] Because of the speed of this process, it is believed that it may make possible continuous, 100-per cent, X-ray inspection of products in certain types of manufacturing processes involving castings, welds, and small assemblies.[15]

28.13 *RCA Electrofax*

In addition to xerography, several other major systems of electrostatic printing have been described in the literature. One such system is called the RCA Electrofax process. Like xerography, this process also makes use of photoconductivity, but the paper itself is coated with a zinc oxide photoconductor, and the image-transfer step is eliminated. The written or photographic information is projected upon a paper covered with the photosensitive coating, which has been given a negative charge. When the paper is brushed with a pigmented powder, a positive electronic image is made visible. The image may be fixed permanently by brief exposure to heat.[16] It is planned to use this process for the production of printing plates, making master copies for office duplicators, enlarging microfilm records, addressing packages, and producing printed circuits.

28.14 *Burroughs Electrographic process*

A second process is called the Burroughs Electrographic printing technique. In this system, charges are deposited directly on the paper from the ends of a linear array of wires. A separate electronic switch controls the voltage on each wire. Paper is pulled past the wires at right angles to the array, and charge patterns are formed by pulsing the voltage on the wires in the proper sequence. The paper is then dusted with powder and fixed. The Burroughs Corp. has also developed an electrostatic printer that can accept teletype signals at a speed of 3,000 words per minute. By use of a combination of electron guns and special coated paper, it can print four lines per second. According to this company, the theoretical top speed of an all-electronic page-printing system could reach 500,000 words per minute.[17]

28.15 *General Dynamics/ Electronics CHARAC-TRON-xerography*

Another electronic-electrostatic printing system is the S-C 5000 system developed by General Dynamics/Electronics (Fig. 28-17). It employs a CHARACTRON Shaped Beam tube (Fig. 28-18), in which a beam of electrons that is shot from an electron gun through a character aperture is shaped into the form of a character (Fig. 28-19). This shaped beam is then displayed on the screen of the tube. It is then projected to the sensitized surface of the revolving, selenium-coated drum of a xerography printer. As the drum rotates, the shaped light beam illuminates the selenium surface, discharging correspondingly shaped areas. An electrically charged powder is then poured over the drum. This powder adheres only to the discharged areas. Printing is accomplished by placing a roll of paper in contact with the drum. The powder, which functions as the ink of this process, is transferred to the paper electrostatically and fixed to it by heat exposure. When this printing cycle has been completed, the drum surface is cleaned and recharged; it is then ready to repeat the printing process. This system enables 10,000 characters per second to be dry-printed upon any grade of untreated paper.[18]

28.16 *A.B. Dick Videograph*

In 1959, announcement was made of the development of a high-speed electronic transmitting and printing process employing an electrostatic printing tube. The system, called the Videograph, is the product of a joint effort by the A.B. Dick Co. and the Stanford Research Institute. It is

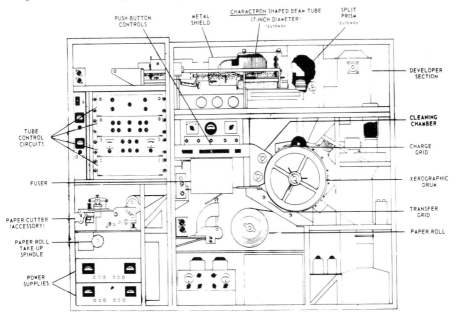

PUSH-BUTTON CONTROLS — METAL SHIELD — CHARACTRON SHAPED BEAM TUBE (7-INCH DIAMETER) (CUTAWAY) — SPLIT PRISM (CUTAWAY) — DEVELOPER SECTION — CLEANING CHAMBER — CHARGE GRID — XEROGRAPHIC DRUM — TRANSFER GRID — PAPER ROLL

TUBE CONTROL CIRCUITS — FUSER — PAPER CUTTER (ACCESSORY) — PAPER ROLL TAKE-UP SPINDLE — POWER SUPPLIES

FIG. 28-17. S-C 5000 HIGH-SPEED ELECTRONIC PRINTER

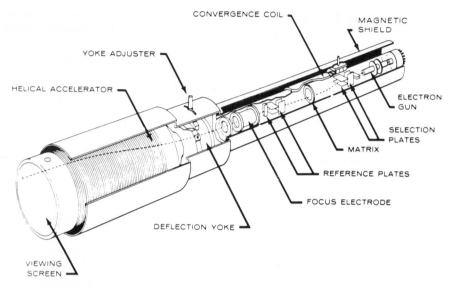

Courtesy, General Dynamics/Electronics

FIG. 28-18. CHARACTRON SHAPED BEAM TUBE

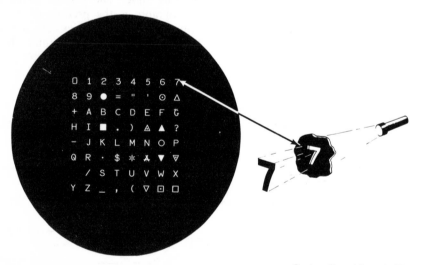

Courtesy, General Dynamics/Electronics

FIG. 28-19. FORMATION OF A CHARACTER BY SHAPED BEAM TUBE

claimed that this system, which combines electronic scanning and printing, is capable of duplicating and transmitting any printed materials, pictures, symbols, and codes via microwave or wire at the rate of 20,000 letters, numbers, or symbols per second. It is also claimed that the process can print pictures of moving objects that pass in front of a specially adapted television camera. Its operating principles resemble those of the previously described General Dynamics/Electronics system, except for the replacement of the

Charactron tube by a cathode-ray tube that shapes the beam of electrons by means of a matrix of negatively charged wires (Figs. 28-20 and 28-21).

The Denver and Rio Grande Railroad has announced plans to employ this system for high-speed facsimile transmission of waybills and other documents over a microwave-communication system connecting its main freight stations. This system can also be employed in conjunction with a television camera to record the movements of railroad cars in and out of the yards (Fig. 28-22).[19] [20] [21] [22]

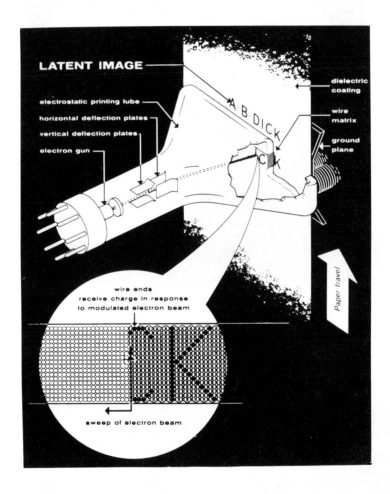

LATENT IMAGE

dielectric coating

electrostatic printing tube

horizontal deflection plates

vertical deflection plates

electron gun

A.B. DICK

wire matrix

ground plane

Paper travel

wire ends receive charge in response to modulated electron beam

sweep of electron beam

Courtesy, A.B. Dick. Co.

FIG. 28-20. BASIC PRINCIPLE OF VIDEOGRAPH PRINTING WITH MATRIX TYPE CATHODE RAY TUBE

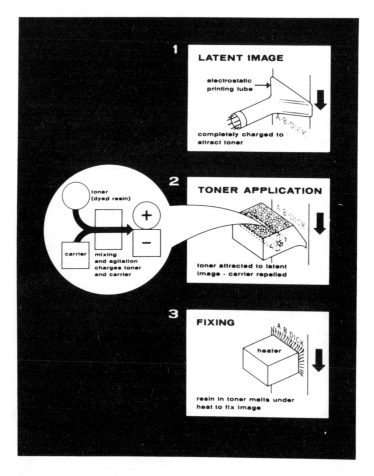

Courtesy, A.B. Dick Co.

FIG. 28-21. IMAGE DEVELOPMENT IN ELECTROSTATIC PRINTING

Courtesy, A.B. Dick Co.

FIG. 28-22. APPLICATION OF VIDEOGRAPH IN RAILROADING

REFERENCES

1. "New Facsimile Is Fast," *Radio-Craft,* 17:680, July 1946.
2. "Tune in a Painting," *Popular Science,* 151:113, Nov. 1947.
3. "Speeded-up Facsimile," *Radio-Electronics,* 28:14, Aug. 1957.
4. "New Facsimile System Speeds Battle Picture," *Science Digest,* 42:92, Sept. 1957.
5. Fred Shunaman, "Telecar Speeds Telegrams," *Radio-Electronics,* 22:22, July 1951.
6. E. W. Allen, Jr., "Reflections of Very-High Frequency Radio Waves from Meteoric Ionization," *Proc. IRE,* 36:346, Mar. 1948.
7. G. Franklin Montgomery, "Communication Via Meteor Bursts," *Radio-Electronics,* 29:88, July 1958.
8. "Radio Via Meteor Trails," *Electronic Age,* 17:18, Jan. 1958.
9. "Use Meteor Trails to Send Radio Pictures," *Science Digest,* 43:68, Feb. 1958.
10. "Facsimile Signals Bounced from Meteor Trails," *Radio and TV News,* 59:116, Mar. 1958.
11. "Instant Mail by Facsimile," *Radio-Electronics,* 31:18, Jan. 1960.
12. Martin Mann, "How Atomic Scientists Read Books 8 Miles Away," *Popular Science,* 158:124, Apr. 1951.
13. "Fax Machine Cuts Mimeograph Stencil," *Popular Science,* 158:168, Jan. 1951.
14. "Blackboard X-Ray," *Think,* 22:27, Apr. 1956.
15. "Dry Process Extends Use of X-Ray," *Design News,* 11:12, Nov. 15, 1956.
16. Norman R. Reamer, *The Graphic Arts--Present and Future,* Stanford Research Institute, Menlo Park, Calif., 1960, pp. 16-17.
17. "Fastest Teletypewriter Forms 3,000 Words Per Minute," *Design News,* 13:10, Nov. 24, 1958.
18. *S-C 5000 High Speed Electronic Printers,* San Diego, Calif., Stromberg-Carlson Co., p. 3.
19. "Print-Display Development Promises Communication Speed-Up," *Industrial Laboratories,* 10:10-12, Sept. 1959.
20. *Videograph Process,* Chicago, Ill., A. B. Dick Co., pp. 1-10.
21. "Railroads Get the Picture," *Stanford Research Institute Research For Industry,* 11:8-10, July 1959.
22. "Videograph Process," *Instruments and Control Systems,* 33:439, Mar. 1960.

29 - RADAR SYSTEMS AND APPLICATIONS

29.1 *The Nature of Radar*

Radar is an application of electronic principles by means of which it is possible to detect the presence, direction, range, and character of distant objects.[1] Its name is derived from some of its functions—radio detection and ranging. According to authorities, the word radar was first coined by Capt. S. M. Tucker of the U.S. Navy. The process of detection is accomplished by directing a stream of ultra-high-frequency radio energy over the area to be searched. When the beam strikes a reflecting object, energy is re-radiated. A small portion of this energy is returned through the radio receiver of this system (Fig. 29-1).

The main reason for using UHF waves, otherwise known as microwaves, is based upon the fact that in order to obtain echoes from reflectors as small as airplanes and guided missiles, the wavelength of the radiated energy

must be short in comparison with the dimensions of the targets. Consequently, a high-definition radar system uses wavelengths of the order of centimeters.

A second reason for using microwaves is based upon the natural desire to develop equipment capable of detecting targets at relatively long ranges. Since the strength of the reflected signal received from the target is inversely proportional to the fourth power of the range, doubling the range of a system requires that the power of the system be increased 16 times. This excessive demand for power can be reduced by using very highly directional antennas capable of providing high antenna gain (Fig. 29-2). When microwaves are employed, it is possible to obtain easily high antenna gains in structures of reasonable size. Thus, great range may be obtained without the use of excessively high transmitter power.

The frequencies employed in various radar systems range from 225 to 33,000 mc. This portion of the radio-frequency spectrum is divided into several bands on the basis of wavelength. The 1-meter band is the P band, the band between 80 and 20 cm is the L band; the band from 20 to 5.5 cm is the S band; the X band ranges from 5.5 to 2.5 cm; the K band covers 2.5 cm to a fraction of a centimeter. In addition, there is a C band composed of portions of the S and X

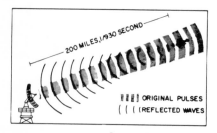

FIG. 29-1. HOW RADAR IS USED TO DETERMINE DISTANCE

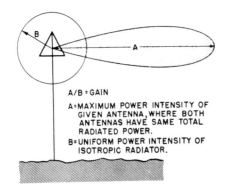

A/B = GAIN

A = MAXIMUM POWER INTENSITY OF GIVEN ANTENNA, WHERE BOTH ANTENNAS HAVE SAME TOTAL RADIATED POWER.

B = UNIFORM POWER INTENSITY OF ISOTROPIC RADIATOR.

FIG. 29-2. MEANING OF ANTENNA GAIN

bands, ranging from 7.7 to 4.8 cm.

It may be noted as a matter of historical interest that the earliest airborne radars, which were used to detect German submarines, operated on the VHF band. The German countermeasure was to equip their submarines with receivers that operated on the same frequencies. In this manner, a submarine could use a directional antenna to determine the direction of an Allied anti-submarine aircraft and could make an approximate estimate of the range by measuring the strength of the radar signal. This was partially circumvented by training Allied radar operators to attenuate their radar signals as they neared the submarine, thereby giving the submarine operators the impression that the plane was going away, rather than approaching for the attack.

However, the device that proved most helpful in increasing the effectiveness of anti-submarine operations was the development of microwave radar operating at a wavelength of approximately 10 cm. The Germans concluded that our VHF radar had been replaced by a new type of equipment operating on infrared radiation emitted by the submarine and made no attempt to develop microwave receivers.

The directional nature and constant-velocity characteristics of UHF radio waves make it possible to determine the azimuth, elevation, and distance of the object producing the reflection (Fig. 29-3). Since attenuation seems to increase with increase in frequency, long-range radar systems are compelled to use lower-frequency signals, which produce displays with low definition.

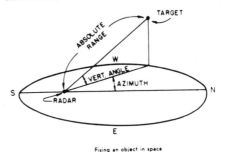

Fixing an object in space

Courtesy, Allen B. DuMont Laboratories

FIG. 29-3. FIXING AN OBJECT IN SPACE

29.2 History of radar

While radar itself is a relatively new development, a type of natural radar has been in existence for millions of years. Evidence produced by the study of fossils reveals that as far back as the Eocene period, the ancestors of the present-day bats employed a radar-like system of detecting and ranging which utilized ultrasonic vibrations. This system closely resembled the sonar system which will be described in a later chapter.

In 1886, Hertz demonstrated that radio waves obeyed the same laws as light waves. He showed that they could be refracted by certain prisms made of insulating materials and that they could be reflected by metal surfaces.

In 1900, Tesla predicted that radio waves might be used to determine the relative position, course, and speed of a moving object. Writing in *Century Magazine*, he described the principles of radar as: " . . . a wave reflected from afar. . . . We may determine the relative position or course of a moving object, such as a vessel at sea, the distance traversed by the same, or its speed."[2] Again in 1917, Tesla described plans for detecting distant objects, such as ships, by concentrating a beam of short-wave impulses upon these objects and viewing the reflected beam on a fluorescent screen—an extremely accurate prediction of modern radar techniques.[3]

Marconi was another prophet of radar. In 1922, speaking before the Institute of Radio Engineers he stated: "It seems to me that it should be possible to design apparatus by means of which a ship could radiate or project a divergent beam of the (Hertzian) rays in any desired direction, which rays, if coming across a metallic object, such as another steamer or ship, would be reflected back to a receiver screened from the local transmitter on the sending ship, and thereby immediately reveal the presence and bearing of the other ship in fog or thick weather."[4]

During the same year, 1922, it was announced that Albert H. Taylor and Leo C. Young of the U. S. Naval Research Laboratory had discovered that large objects, such as boats and trucks, passing between a radio transmitter and a receiver produced a noticeable interference with radio reception.

In 1925, it was found that the surface of a large object or target could be used as a reflector of high-frequency radio waves. This enabled the radio transmitter and receiver to be placed at the same location instead of opposite sides of the target. During that same year, Louis A. Gebhard of the U. S. Naval Research Laboratory developed a radio transmitter which employed

the principle of the generation of short pulses that is used in modern radar equipment. Also during that same year 1925, Merle A. Tuve and Gregory Breit of the Carnegie Institute measured the height of the ionosphere by utilizing radio pulses and a cathode-ray tube.

A patent was issued to H. Lowry of Vienna in 1926, which disclosed the basic idea of using radio to determine the distance of an object. This apparatus, of course, was very crude when judged by modern standards.

In 1930, scientists working at the U.S. Naval Research Laboratory on the problem of developing a high-frequency radio aircraft-blind-landing system noted interference produced by nearby planes. During the following year, it was announced that reflected radio waves could be used to reveal the presence of airplanes.

In 1932, RCA held a demonstration for the U.S. Army Signal Corps at Sandy Hook, N.J. A transmitter was used to generate radio waves. The reflections produced by a passing ship were detected by a radio receiver. By 1934, engineers had developed the cathode-ray tube into an effective means of measuring the distance between the transmitter and the target.

In 1957, it was revealed that the real father of the radar idea in the United States was Colonel William R. Blair of the U.S. Army Signal Corps, a former director of the Signal Corps Laboratories. His contributions were recognized by the awarding of a fundamental radar patent, Patent No. 2803819, which gave the government a royalty-free license. In 1930, Blair had conceived of the pulse-echo method of direction finding and ranging. In 1937, a complete, workable radar set based upon his principles was demonstrated for the Secretary of War and members of Congress.[5] Because of the secrecy surrounding the development of radar, Blair postponed filing a patent until 1945. Although the government is permitted to make use of the patent on a royalty-free license arrangement, the patent grant will enable Blair to collect royalties from organizations that are now manufacturing or using radar for commercial applications.[6]

The year 1938 marked the first installations by RCA of airplane radar anti-collision and altimeter systems. During the same year, RCA constructed the U.S. Navy's first seagoing radar system for the battleship New York. Shortly afterwards, the U.S. Naval Research Laboratory announced that radar equipment had succeeded in detecting airplanes at a distance of 50 miles. By early 1940, several of these primitive radar units had been installed in ships of the U.S. Navy.

In 1940, a British technical mission came to the United States with a new high-powered microwave generator called a cavity magnetron. This device had been developed by scientists at the University of Birmingham. The development of a microwave radar system employing this magnetron was turned over to the Radiation Laboratory of MIT. This system soon moved out of the class of a laboratory curiosity into a leading wartime role. It is estimated that more man-hours were spent on the development of radar during World War II than had previously been spent upon the entire development of radio communications. During World War II, over 3 billion dollars was invested in radar research, in contrast with the investment of 2 billion dollars for atomic-energy research. Within five years after they had begun, the scientists of the MIT Radiation Laboratory had made as much progress in radar development as might have been produced in 25 years under normal peacetime conditions.

Mention should also be made of the contributions of a British physicist, Sir Robert Watson-Watt, who has sometimes been called the "father of radar." In 1935, he began to study methods of using the pulse-measuring techniques previously developed by Breit and Tuve for the purpose of detecting airplanes. Under his direction, many new types of radio transmitters, antennas, amplifiers, and cathode-ray-tube display systems were designed and developed. As a result, in 1935, a chain of five radar stations was secretly established on the east coast of England. Fifteen more stations were added in 1937. By 1939, England was protected by a radar blanket hundreds of miles in extent, of which the general public was unaware. Watson-Watt was knighted in 1942, and shortly afterwards it was announced that the VHF radar system that he had helped to develop and establish had played a major part during 1940 in enabling the relatively weak RAF fighter forces to be always in the best possible position to defend Great Britain against the onslaught of the German Luftwaffe.

Because of radar, the average losses of the Luftwaffe during raids over England mounted to 15 per cent (Figs. 29-4 and 29-5). The night of September 15, 1940, proved to be the turning point of the Battle of Britain. The RAF downed 185 out of 500 German aircraft, and the back of the German air assault was broken. In 1946, President Truman awarded Sir Watson-Watt one of the few Medals for Merit which have ever been presented to a British subject.

Space limitations do not permit a complete discussion of the role played during World War II by radar, blind-bombing, and GCA (Ground-Controlled Approach) systems in enabling the Allied forces to defend themselves against German airpower in the

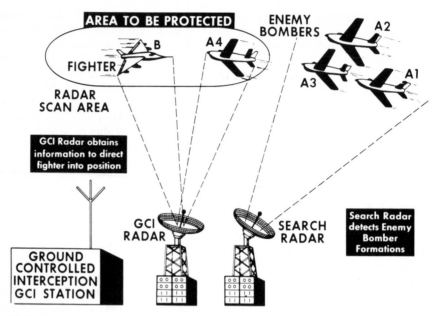

FIG. 29-4. GROUND CONTROLLED INTERCEPTION RADAR

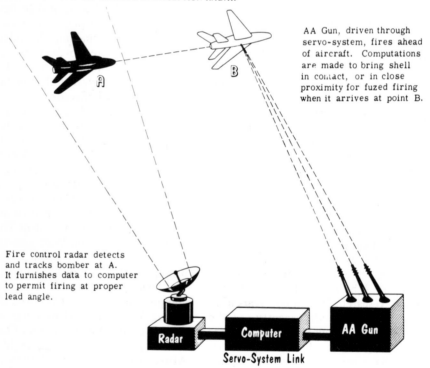

AA Gun, driven through servo-system, fires ahead of aircraft. Computations are made to bring shell in contact, or in close proximity for fuzed firing when it arrives at point B.

Fire control radar detects and tracks bomber at A. It furnishes data to computer to permit firing at proper lead angle.

FIG. 29-5. FIRE CONTROL BY RADAR DETECTION

European Theatre, against Japanese seapower in the Pacific Theatre, and in helping to neutralize the effectiveness of German submarines in the North Atlantic. It might be pointed out as a matter of historical interest that because the early development of radar was shrouded in secrecy, its value was not generally recognized during the early days of World War II. Commanding officers often opposed the installation of radar equipment on battleships and airplanes and refused to trust the equipment after it had been installed. For example, in the disastrous naval engagement between the British battleship Hood and the German ship Bismarck, the British commanding officer chose to use the range given him by an optical range finder in preference to the information provided by his radar system. As a result, he failed to hit his opponent. The commanding officer of the Bismarck employed radar range-finding equipment and hit the Hood with his first salvo.

The end of World War II saw radar being applied in proximity fuses designed to explode anti-aircraft shells as they approached the desired target (Fig. 29-6). It also saw the beginning of the application of radar for the control of guided missiles (Fig. 29-7).

During the year 1946, the U.S. Army Signal Corps announced that it had picked up a radar signal that had been reflected by the moon (Figs. 29-8 and 29-9). It is possible to obtain some idea of the sensitivity requirements of the receiver employed when it is indicated that the electrical power of the received echo signal was only one-billionth of a microwatt.

In 1952, these techniques were applied to the long-distance transmission of a 418-mc UHF radiotelegraph signal. The message "What hath God wrought?" was sent by a transmitter located at the plant of the

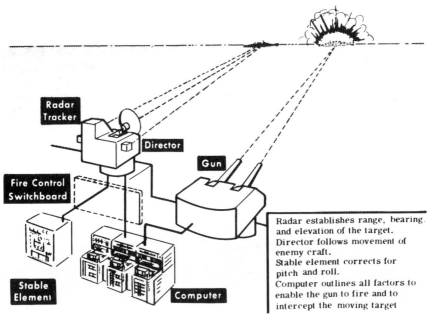

Radar establishes range, bearing and elevation of the target.
Director follows movement of enemy craft.
Stable element corrects for pitch and roll.
Computer outlines all factors to enable the gun to fire and to intercept the moving target

FIG. 29-6. RADAR FIRE CONTROL

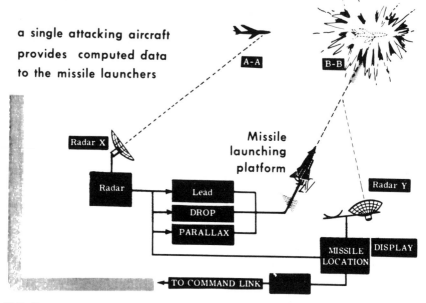

a single attacking aircraft
provides computed data
to the missile launchers

FIG. 29-7. RADAR ANTI-AIRCRAFT APPLICATIONS

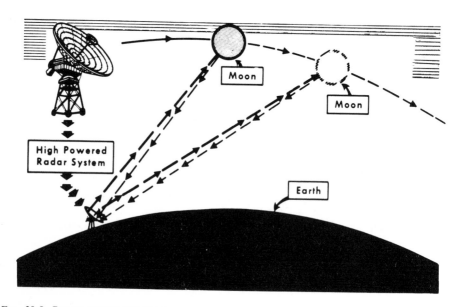

FIG. 29-8. RADAR REFLECTION FROM THE MOON

FIG. 29-9. ANTENNA USED IN ESTABLISHING RADAR CONTACT WITH THE MOON

Collins Radio Company. Cedar Rapids, Iowa. It was bounced off the moon and received at the station of the National Bureau of Standards at Sterling, Va., 775 miles away, covering a total distance of 460,000 miles. This successful demonstration opened the door to three possibilities for the future:

1. Use of the moon as a dependable reflecting medium for the long-distance transmission of radiotelegraph, facsimile, and television signals on the UHF bands.

2. Accurate radio control of satellite space-ships.

3. Unjammable radio guidance of long-range, remotely controlled missiles.

29.3 *Components of a radar system*

While there are many types of radar systems designed for such different purposes as aircraft surveillance,

blind-landing, ground-controlled approach, and weather observation, practically every radar system contains the following major components: a timer, a modulator, an oscillator, an antenna, a duplexer or transmit-receive switch, a receiver, and an indicator (Figs. 29-10 and 29-11).

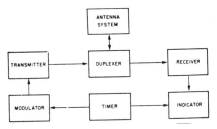

FIG. 29-10. SIMPLE BLOCK DIAGRAM OF A RADAR SET

29.4 *The timer*

The timer, also known as the synchronizer or keyer, is used to generate electrical pulses of short duration several hundred or several thousand times per second. One pulse is sent to the modulator and used first to turn on the transmitter for a microsecond and then to turn it off for a millisecond. The timer also sends a simultaneous synchronizing or timing pulse to the indicator of the receiver to start operation of the time-base circuits used for measuring the range. The timer thus insures that the interval between pulses is of the proper duration and that all circuits of the radar system operate in a definite time relationship with respect to each other.

29.5 *The modulator*

The modulator, which is closely related to the timer, is a device for taking pulses from the timer and forming suitable voltage pulses to drive the

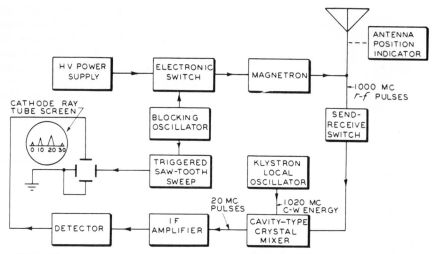

Fig. 29-11. More detailed block diagram of a radar set

r-f oscillator of the radar transmitter. It is the modulator which turns the oscillator on for a microsecond, turns it off sharply, and keeps it in repose until time for the next burst.

29.6 *The oscillator*

The r-f oscillator is an electronic circuit that is designed to oscillate at the desired radio frequency when it is connected to the modulator. Since the oscillator is turned on only during a small fraction of the time, the average power is hundreds of times less than the peak power, but even this average power may run up to the order of one kilowatt. Some long-range aircraft radar transmitters generate over a million watts of pulse power. The following types of oscillator tubes are generally used in radar systems:

1. The magnetron or similar tubes in which a magnetic field serves in lieu of a grid.

2. The klystron or other similar forms of velocity-modulated tubes.

3. The lighthouse or other forms of disc-seal tubes.[7]

4. Conventional tubes in special circuits such as Barkhausen-Kurz circuits.

29.7 *The antenna*

The function of the radar antenna is to project into space the narrow beam of microwave energy produced by the transmitter. It must then collect the weak signals reflected by the objects that have been struck by the radio beam. The shape and the size of the antenna depend upon the type of beam desired and the wavelength of the microwaves used by the system.

Some types of radar systems contain billboard antennas consisting of a flat reflecting screen in front of which are placed many metal rods (Fig. 29-9). A more common type of radar antenna consists of a bowl-shaped parabolic reflector antenna (Figs. 29-12 and 29-13). Another type of directional radar antenna that is sometimes encountered is the horn antenna. This consists of an open-ended waveguide that is flared out at a gradual angle. The subject of waveguides will be discussed

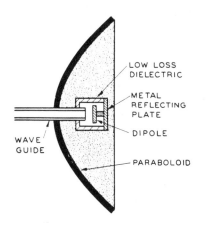

FIG. 29-12. PARABOLIC ANTENNA WITH WAVE-GUIDE FEED

Courtesy, Stanford Research Institute
FIG. 29-13. 60-FOOT PARABOLIC RADAR ANTENNA

more thoroughly in Chapter 31 which deals with microwave principles, techniques, and applications.

The nature and design of the antenna will also depend upon the purpose of the radar equipment. Thus, the antenna of a fire-control radar must produce a narrow beam for the accurate measurement of the altitude, azimuth, and range of a target; the antenna of an aircraft-control radar must produce a beam that covers the region above a ship and that enables the height of a plane to be determined; whereas the antenna of a search radar should be capable of rotating in azimuth through 360 deg and of producing a rather broad beam so that scanning may be accomplished within a fairly short period of time (Fig. 29-14).

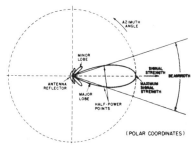

FIG. 29-14. BEAMWIDTH OF PARABOLIC ANTENNA

A suitable radar antenna should possess the following characteristics:

1. It must be directional. A high-gain antenna or antenna array will illuminate the target with a maximum amount of radiation so that a maximum amount of reflected signal will be obtained. This reduces the amount of power output required of the transmitter.

2. It must be highly efficient. All of the generated power must go into the beam and none must leak off into "side lobes" in other directions.

3. It must be capable of being directed or scanned from one point in space to another. With regard to this third characteristic, the mechanical

beaming of the antenna requires heavy electromechanical equipment and places a limitation on the scanning speed of the radiated beam. This necessity also makes it virtually impossible to obtain continuous three-dimensional coverage from a single antenna structure.

Hughes Aircraft has offered one solution to this problem by developing an electronic-scan antenna system. In this radar system, called Frescanar (Frequency Scan Radar), the narrow radiated beam from a single antenna can be made to scan very rapidly in space by changing the operating frequency of the radar. This vertical electronic scan, coupled with mechanical horizontal rotation of the antenna, provides complete three-dimensional coverage using only one radar system compared with the two or more radars that are required by other systems designed to measure range, bearing, and height. It also increases the speed with which targets can be detected, improves the degree of resolution obtained between targets closely spaced in altitude, and increases the number of targets that can be handled.[8] A radar system

employing this type of antenna will be described in a later section.

In ordinary transmitters, wires and coaxial cables are used to carry the r-f energy from the transmitter to the antenna. For the efficient transmission of the microwaves used in radar, it has been found more efficient to employ waveguides. These waveguides are essentially hollow pipes.[9]

29.8 *The radar receiver*

The purpose of the receiver is to amplify the weak signals returned by the target and to convert them into video pulses which are applied to the indicator. The typical radar receiver is a UHF superheterodyne receiver possessing a low noise figure and capable of handling the bandwidths required to reproduce the radar pulse (Fig. 29-15).

The local oscillator employed to produce the frequency conversion is usually a special type of resonant-cavity tube called a reflex klystron. The most commonly used intermediate frequencies are 30 mc and 60 mc. An automatic-frequency-control (AFC) system

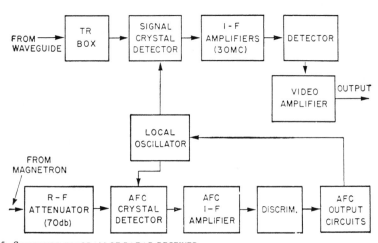

FIG. 29-15. SIMPLIFIED DIAGRAM OF RADAR RECEIVER

is usually provided to maintain a constant difference in frequency between the klystron local oscillator and the magnetron oscillator of the transmitter (Fig. 29-16).

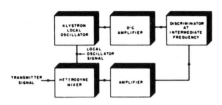

FIG. 29-16. AFC CIRCUIT BLOCK DIAGRAM

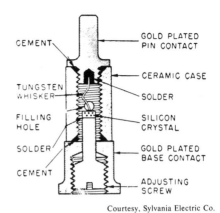

Courtesy, Sylvania Electric Co.

FIG. 29-17. SILICON CRYSTAL DIODE

Since the power of the returning echo pulse may be as small as several millionths of a microwatt, the receiver must be extremely sensitive. It does not have to be capable of tuning over a wide frequency range, since it is only required to respond to the same frequency as that of the signal produced by the transmitter of the same radar system.

It is worth noting that the crystal, once considered almost obsolete for use as a detector and mixer, has again come into its own in radar receivers for the purpose of mixing and detecting UHF microsecond pulses (Figs. 29-17, 29-18, and 29-19). The output of the mixer is amplified by intermediate-frequency amplifier stages, detected, and

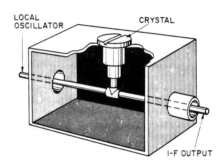

FIG. 29-18. MICROWAVE CRYSTAL MIXER

the resultant pulses are amplified by video-amplifier stages. The output of the video amplifier is then used to drive the indicator. Because the problems

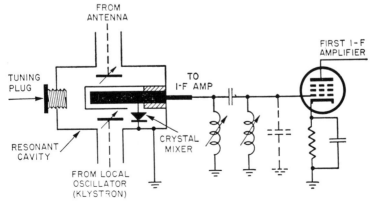

FIG. 29-19. MIXER CIRCUIT OF RADAR RECEIVER

encountered in designing the inter-mediate-frequency and video amplifier stages of a radar receiver are very similar to those encountered in designing the corresponding stages of a television receiver, the intermediate-frequency and video amplifiers of both systems bear a close resemblance to each other.

29.9 *The transmit-receive switch*

An interesting and particularly difficult piece of engineering design is concerned with a part that is closely connected with the receiver. This is the duplexer or transmit-receive electronic switch for disconnecting the receiver from the antenna while the transmitter is operating, so that the sensitive crystals and vacuum tubes of the receiver will not be burned out by the radio-frequency energy generated by the transmitter (Fig. 29-20). It also prevents the energy of the received signal from being absorbed by the transmitter circuit. Within a millionth of a second after the transmitter has completed its pulse, the receiver circuit must be opened to receive the weak echo signals.

The transmit-receive switch that accomplishes this task is often called a

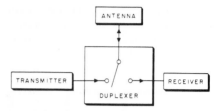

FIG. 29-20. DUPLEXER BLOCK DIAGRAM

T-R box; it is designed to connect the antenna first to the oscillator or transmitter and then to the receiver. Part of the transmission-line structure, it normally connects the antenna with the receiver. When the transmitter produces a pulse, the T-R switch automatically connects the antenna to the transmitter and disconnects the receiver, thus protecting the receiver from being damaged by the tremendous amount of energy released by the transmitter during that microsecond. As soon as the pulse ends, the switch automatically connects the receiver to the antenna so that the equipment is ready to pick up any reflected radio waves.

The switch itself consists of a length of waveguide and two gas-filled tubes (Fig. 29-21). When the transmitter is operating, a strong electrical pulse from the oscillator ionizes the gas molecules and the tubes conduct, establishing a connection between the transmitter

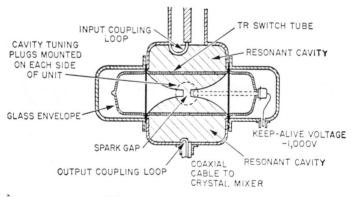

FIG. 29-21. CROSS SECTION OF T-R SWITCH

and the antenna and blocking the path between the antenna and the receiver. When the pulse ends, the tubes de-ionize, blocking the path between the transmitter and the antenna and establishing a connection between the antenna and the receiver. The reflected echo pulses are too weak to ionize the gas-discharge tubes, and as a result, most of the received power goes through the cold T-R box to the receiver circuit. The development of this T-R switch permitted the transmitter and the receiver to share the same antenna. This is an important advantage in radar equipment that makes use of rotating antennas.[10]

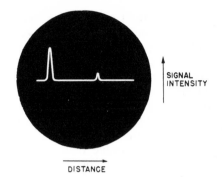

FIG. 29-22. A-SCAN RADAR DISPLAY

29.10 *The indicator*

The indicator of a radar device usually consists of a cathode-ray tube that presents the information that has been collected in the form of a visual pattern. In the simplest type of presentation, called the A-scan, the electron beam is given a deflection in the horizontal direction that is proportional to the time and a deflection in the vertical direction that is proportional to the strength of the echo pulse (Fig. 29-22). The horizontal sweep is started at the same time as the transmitter pulse, while the reflected-signal output of the receiver is applied to the vertical deflecting plates. Consequently, the return signal appears as a vertical spike or pip. The position of the pip along this horizontal time-base line is an indication of the distance of the reflecting object or target.

Other types of radar systems employ the PPI (Plan Position Indicator) tube (Fig. 29-23). The original patent on PPI radar was granted to Gloess, a French scientist, who developed the PPI principle in 1937 while he was working in the Paris laboratories of the International Telegraph and Telephone

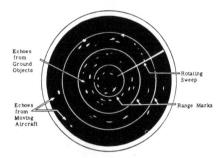

Courtesy, Civil Aeronautics Admin.

FIG. 29-23. PPI PRESENTATION

Corp. Other important contributions in this area were made by Robert M. Page and by Lee De Forest who, in 1941, patented a device employing the principle of radial scanning.

In the PPI tube, the time base starts from the center of the tube and moves radially outward in a direction corresponding to that in which the antenna is pointing. This time base rotates in synchronism with the rotating antenna.

This effect can be achieved by using a cathode-ray tube that employs external magnetic-deflection coils which carry the varying current that is used to produce the time-base deflection of the electron beam. By means of a servo-mechanism system employing selsyn or synchro motors and generators, the coil is made to rotate around the neck of the cathode-ray tube in step with the rotation of the antenna. This rotation of the coil causes the time base to rotate with it in synchronism with the antenna. The PPI cathode-ray indicator tube has a screen that possesses a high degree of persistence and afterglow in order to enable the pattern that is produced by the rotating time base to persist until it is repainted by the next rotation of the antenna and the time base.

It is also possible to use an electrical method to cause the PPI sweep to travel in sychronism with the antenna. This method employs a rectangular deflection yoke on each leg of which is wound a coil. Each coil is fed with voltages obtained from a potentiometer that is mounted on the antenna shaft. Each of these voltages varies sinusoidally at a rate that corresponds to the rate

of rotation of the antenna. If the deflection currents supplied to each coil are made to vary in amplitude according to this voltage, a varying magnetic field will be produced. This varying magnetic-deflection field will rotate in synchronism with the antenna and will cause the sweep to rotate at the same rate.

In any type of PPI presentation, the returning signal, instead of causing a break in the time base, simply intensifies its brilliance for an instant. A map-like presentation of all reflecting objects is thus produced upon the face of the cathode-ray tube (Fig. 29-24).

The cathode-ray tube type of indicator is sometimes eliminated in order to make the equipment lighter and

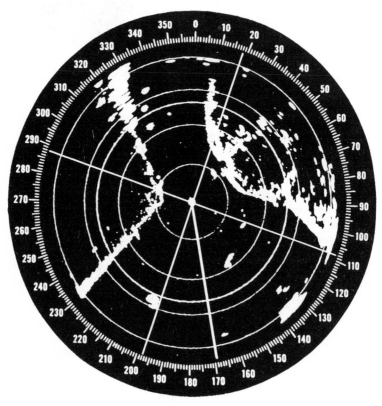

FIG. 29-24. PPI RADAR PATTERN OF THE NARROWS OF NEW YORK HARBOR

more rugged. For example, in 1957 the U.S. Army announced the development of a 35-lb, portable radar system for battle-area surveillance (Fig. 29-25). This unit, built by the Sperry Gyroscope Company, is capable of spotting in the dark a single enemy moving at a distance of a half mile. The motion of vehicles and larger groups can be detected at distances as great as 3 miles. Since this device contains no cathode-ray tube, the presence of objects is indicated by audible signals of distinctive character that are produced by a pair of headphones as a consequence of the Doppler effect.[11]

During the same year, 1957, a somewhat similar device appeared on the commercial market. Called Radar-Eye, this instrument employs radar principles for sensing any movement within a radius of 25 ft. When this sophisticated portable anti-burglar device is triggered, it turns on floodlights and sets off sirens or other alarm signals.

29.11 *Special types of indicator tubes*

During the past few years, new types of cathode-ray tubes have been developed for radar, computer, and microwave-television display applications. Among these are the Hoffman Color Tube, the General Dynamics CHARACTRON, the Sylvania Wamoscope, and the Lawrence Chromatron.

The Hoffman color tube. The Hoffman Color Tube is a twin-gun color cathode-ray tube that can be used to add a third dimension to standard PPI presentations. By means of this tube, information from a horizontal radar is shown in one color and information from a vertical radar in another. This tube contains no deflection-grid wires or shadow masks. Instead, it uses a face plate with fine vertical grooves. Two different phosphors are applied to alternate faces of the grooves. Each electron

Courtesy, Sperry Rand Corp.

FIG. 29-25. TYPE AN/PPS-4 PORTABLE RADAR

gun is located and aimed in such a manner that it can excite only one type of phosphor.

The CHARACTRON. The aforementioned General Dynamics CHARACTRON is a cathode-ray tube that is designed to be used in radar aircraft-surveillance systems in which targets are identified in the form of symbols. These symbols or characters are produced by shaping the beam by passing it through a stencil-like matrix containing an array of 64 characters. A computer that is associated with this system causes each of the formats of identifying data produced on the screen to move in accordance with changes in the position of the corresponding targets.

The Wamoscope. The Sylvania Wamoscope or wave-modulated oscilloscope combines the essential functions of an entire radar receiver within a single tube envelope, thus eliminating many of the components and tubes required by conventional radar receivers (Fig. 29-26). The radar echo signals go directly from the antenna to the appropriate electrode of this tube. The neck

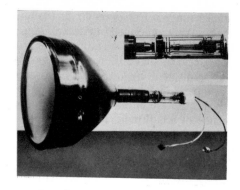

Courtesy, General Telephone & Electronics Laboratories
FIG. 29-26. WAMOSCOPE

of the tube contains a helix, making the Wamoscope a combination traveling-wave amplifier and cathode-ray tube (Fig. 29-27).

An r-f signal input causes a d-c beam that is passed down the helix to become velocity-modulated by the r-f input signal in accordance with the amplitude of this r-f signal. At the end of the helix, the emerging electrons are sorted according to velocity. Those electrons whose velocities exceed the d-c velocity of the original beam are allowed to strike the screen of the

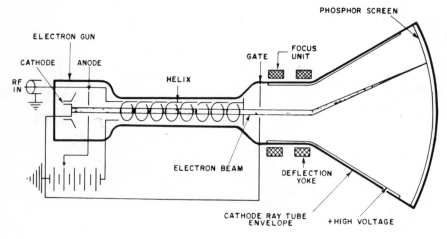

FIG. 29-27. DIAGRAM OF WAMOSCOPE

Courtesy, General Telephone & Electronics Laboratories

cathode-ray tube whereas the slower moving electrons are reflected.

As a result, this tube is capable of both amplifying and detecting the signal and then displaying it on a fluorescent screen. This enables the designer to eliminate the mixer, local oscillator, i-f amplifier, detector, and video-amplifier stages of conventional receivers.[12]

It is claimed that the two basic advantages of the Wamoscope are the following:

1. Reduction in the number of tubes and components required.

2. Wide-bandwidth (300 mc) capabilities, which make possible the amplification, reproduction, and display of extremely short pulses and the display of information contained in wide-band systems.[13]

Radio engineers are now working on possible applications of the Wamoscope in miniaturized commercial and industrial closed-circuit television systems.[14] In 1959, an improved version of the Wamoscope was announced. Among the claimed advantages of this new tube were the following:

1. Elimination of the solenoid previously located around the neck of the tube.

2. Incorporation of the signal coupler within the tube envelope.

3. Reduction of the length, so that the tube is only 2 in. longer than a standard cathode-ray tube of equivalent display area.

The Lawrence Chromatron. The operation of this tube has been described in the section of Chapter 27 dealing with color-television tubes. Litton Industries is now incorporating the Chromatron in radar receivers. One application is its use in showing friendly planes in one color and enemy planes in another. Color differences may also be employed to distinguish between bombers and fighters. The color tube can also be applied in radar to show land masses in one color and planes in another or to indicate moving objects in one color and stationary objects in another color.

The tube can also be employed in connection with equipment used for air-traffic control. Planes coming in for a landing are indicated in one color, ascending planes in a second color, and other aircraft within a given distance in a third color. This simplifies and facilitates quick and accurate decisions by those who are responsible for traffic control. It also reduces fatigue, an essential safety factor in both military and commercial airport operations.[15]

29.12 *IFF Systems*

One special radar development is known as IFF (Identification, Friend or Foe). In this system, a short pulse of coded radio-frequency energy is radiated by a ground unit called the interrogator-responder or I-R unit. This signal trips an apparatus called a transponder, which is carried by friendly planes. Upon being tripped, this apparatus sends back a coded signal. The return signal is picked up by the receiver section of the responder and is presented on the scope of the IFF system, where it shows up as a series of long and short pips. It is possible to change the code of these signals at desired intervals.[16]

29.13 *Radar speed-measuring devices*

The Doppler effect, which will be described in greater detail in Chapter 30, can be used to measure the relative speed of a target. If there is relative motion between the target and the radar system, there will be a change in the apparent frequency of the reflected signal. Some radar systems contain circuits that are capable of measuring the difference in frequency between the transmitted and the received waves and of using this information to compute the relative speed of the target. Radar speed-measuring devices now in use by highway and traffic patrols employ circuits of this type.

These devices operate on a frequency of 2,455 mc. The reflected signal from the moving car is mixed with the continuous-wave signal radiated by the transmitter. The resulting audio-frequency signal produced by this heterodyning action is converted into units of speed, which may be read directly on a meter or recorded on tape. Thus, an audio-frequency signal of 731 cps is produced by a Doppler shift corresponding to a relative speed of 100 miles per hour.[17] Joseph Barker is generally credited as being the inventor of the first practical anti-speeding radar of this type.

There have been instances in which Doppler-radar evidence has not been upheld by courts of law. One such case was the reversal in 1958 in Westchester County, New York, of the radar conviction of an alleged speeding offender. After hearing the testimony of an engineer that the rustling of leaves or the jangling of the policeman's keys could cause inaccuracies in the radar equipment, the judge concluded that while the equipment was capable of detecting the existence of a moving object, its use for measuring the speed of a vehicle was subject to grave probability of error

A similar decision was made by a magistrate in a New York City Court early in 1960. However, when the instrument has been properly calibrated and tested, radar-speedometer readings have usually been accepted as evidence in court proceedings.[18]

According to published reports, motorists have attempted many schemes—including placing foil strips on the radio antenna, spraying aluminum paint on the engine fan blades, placing ball bearings in the hub caps, and operating whistles and two-way radio transmitters—in an attempt to deceive or foil the radar speed-measuring equipment. However, none of these methods which have just been described will affect the radar equipment. Techniques that would really work—such as jamming the system with signals produced by another radar transmitter or covering the car with jiggling chains and blinking fluorescent lights—would involve the motorists in many additional complications with the law.[19] The best that has thus far been developed is an instrument that warns the motorist when he is under radar surveillance (Fig. 29-28).

FIG. 29-28. RADAR-GARD CAR RADAR DETECTOR

An interesting device employing the Doppler-radar principle has been developed by A. J. White of Motor Vehicle Research, Inc., and is now in use at the Portsmouth Air Force Base. When a car approaches a radar-equipped billboard, the radar system computes the car's speed. If it exceeds the speed limit, a relay switch is tripped which lights the sign, warning the driver that he is speeding. A second warning is given a short distance away, if the driver does not slow down. Finally, if a speeder ignores both warnings, a motion-picture camera is set into operation. This records the license number and speed of the vehicle. The device, nicknamed Big Brother, has practically eliminated all speeding.

Doppler-radar sensing devices have also been employed by the New Jersey Turnpike Authority in order to obtain interesting information about the driving habits of motorists. Each sensing unit, which is mounted on an overpass, directly above a lane of traffic, detects and measures the speed of each vehicle in its lane. The information is transmitted over telephone wires to analyzing equipment. From these data, interesting conclusions may be drawn about the reactions of motorists to bad weather and traffic congestion, and the relationship between the degree of traffic congestion and the extent to which each lane is used. It is claimed that this type of information is extremely valuable in planning for future traffic-control devices and for future expansion in highway capacity.[20]

A radar speed-measuring device developed by Raytheon is now being used aboard aircraft carriers to gauge the approach speeds of planes coming down for a landing and to inform the landing signal officer and the pilot whether the speed of a plane should be increased or decreased.

In the field of guided-missile research, most of the precision tracking and positioning of missiles is accomplished by continuous-wave radar systems (Fig. 29-29). One of the most important of these systems is called Dovap (Doppler Velocity and Position). As indicated by its name, it is a continuous-wave system utilizing the basic Doppler principle of determining the speed of an object's movement by means of the apparent change in signal frequency.[21]

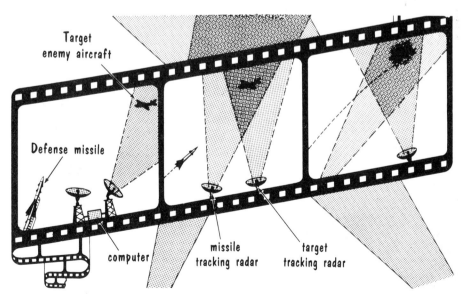

FIG. 29-29. MISSILE-TRACKING RADAR GUIDES MISSILE TO TARGET

Joseph Barker, the previously mentioned inventor of anti-speeding radar, has also developed a radar traffic-control unit designed to give warning of impending traffic jams. This is being employed experimentally in New York City. It employs the Doppler effect to distinguish between stationary and moving objects. It then counts and records the speed of all moving objects.[22]

Another interesting application of radar speed-measuring devices, developed by the Union Switch and Signal Co. is used in railroad classification yards such as the Southern Pacific's Englewood Radar Gravity Switching Yard and Pennyslvania Railroad's Conway Yard near Pittsburgh, Pa. As cars that are to be classified roll freely down the hill of the yard, the speed of each car is automatically measured by a series of radar units located between the rails. The speed measurement is relayed to a computer, which then correlates this with other information, such as the load and weight of the car, its rolling characteristics or tendency to roll, and the length and curvature of the track. This information is usually supplied by means of punched cards or perforated tape. The computer then produces a signal which causes an electric retarder to squeeze the car wheels and to slow the car down to just the right speed to roll to its destination and to couple smoothly with the other cars of a newly-formed train.[23] [24]

The Doppler effect has also been employed in radar equipment contained in special types of GCA (Ground Controlled Approach) units in order to distinguish between moving aircraft and stationary buildings and other reflectors. The receiver has two signal inputs. One is from the transmitter, and the other is the echo that is picked up by the antenna of the receiver. If the target is moving, there will be a difference between the frequencies of these two signals, and the receiver is designed so that it will operate only when such a difference in frequency exists. It therefore ignores all signals of the same frequency as that of the transmitter, and consequently signals reflected from stationary targets will not appear on the screen of the indicator.

29.14 *Electronic automobile control*

Several companies have been working on the development of radar systems that would make automobile driving easier and safer. Thus, Westinghouse engineers have developed a system that would make it possible to drive an automobile along the turnpikes from coast to coast without touching the steering wheel (Fig. 27-30). In this system, radar equipment would cause the car to follow a guide line of foil or conductive paint running down the center of the road. Slowing, stopping, speed control, and branching to other roads could be made automatic by a system of code symbols on the main guidance strips and smaller areas parallel to these guidance strips. The radar

Courtesy, Westinghouse Electric Corp.
FIG. 29-30. AUTOMOBILE RADAR SYSTEM

system could also be used for anti-collision purposes and to provide a panoramic view of the road for a mile ahead when driving at night or through fog.

The Delco Radio Division of General Motors has also developed an anti-collision car-radar system (Fig. 29-31). It employs Doppler-radar principles to produce an audible warning if a car is closing in too rapidly upon an object that is located up to 100 ft ahead of it. A reflex klystron generates a signal at a frequency of 16,140 mc. This signal is beamed out of a transmitting reflector. When it strikes an object ahead, the signal is reflected back to a similar receiving reflector. A crystal detector is used to mix and compare the frequencies of the transmitted and received signals. A warning signal is then generated whose intensity increases with any increase in the rate of approach to the object ahead.[25][26]

Mention may also be made of the fact that other electronic systems of car control that do not involve radar are also in the process of development. One of the leading systems of this type employs induction loops that are buried in the roadbed and fed by high-frequency currents (Fig. 29-32). When the car passes over a loop, currents induced in the car's body produce a signal that can be used to control traffic lights, warning signs, and the speed controls of following cars.[27][28] It is estimated that the cost of installing such a system on a new highway would range between 5 and 10 per cent of the overall cost of the construction of the highway.

Courtesy, Delco Radio Div., General Motors Corp.

FIG. 29-31. BREADBOARD STAGE OF DELCO RADAR PROXIMITY WARNING DEVICE

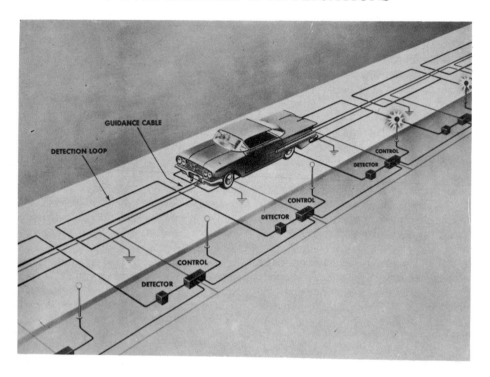

FIG. 29-32. RCA ELECTRIC HIGHWAY

Courtesy, Radio Corporation of America

29.15 *The tellurometer*

At this point, it might be appropriate to mention another application of radar in transportation, although this is not an example of the application of the principles of Doppler radar. Highway engineers have recently developed tellurometry (earth measurement), a new radar technique for surveying that is both quick and accurate. In this technique, a transmitter sends a radio pulse which is picked up by a receiver located at the other end (Fig. 29-33). The signal is then retransmitted by the remote unit, and a comparison of the phase differences between the two signals reveals the transit time of the radio signal between the two stations. The number of milliseconds required for the pulse to reach the receiver is converted into miles, feet, and inches, and is indicated either on the face of a cathode-ray tube or by means of a direct-reading counter. By means of this equipment, the distance between two points located 40 miles apart may be measured within 40 minutes with a maximum error of 11 in. The operators at each end do not have to see each other but can communicate by means of two-way radio. This technique can be employed in fog, rain, snow, or darkness. It is anticipated that the use of this system will reduce the time required for surveying and laying out the National Interstate Highway system by many months and will save millions of dollars in costs.[29][30][31]

FIG. 29-33. CUBIC ELECTROTAPE ELECTRONIC SURVEYING EQUIPMENT

29.16 Marine radar

The sinking of the Andrea Doria in 1956 served to drive home the fact that the use of conventional radar equipment has not served to make sea disasters a thing of the past. During that year, there were 182 collisions involving ships of over 180 tons, and 90 of these involved ships which carried radar equipment.

Undoubtedly, factors such as the lack of adequate radar training for deck officers, and the lack of bridge-to-bridge communications facilities are responsible for some of these accidents. However, many of these accidents are due to the inadequacy of conventional radar equipment. This equipment shows only the relative and apparent motion of objects in relation to each other.

Thus, stationary landmarks may appear to be moving, whereas ships that are moving in one direction may appear to be moving in another direction. In order to determine an object's actual motion, it is necessary to plot its successive positions on a chart.

In 1957, the Sperry Gyroscope Co. and Decca Radar, Inc., announced the development of a radar system that shows all objects that are actually moving as being in motion (Fig. 29-34). In a similar manner, stationary objects remain motionless. This helps the navigator to determine which ships are following a probable collision course. At the same time, Raytheon announced the development of a radar system with a memory tube that is capable of storing all of the received information and plotting automatically the track of other ships, thus eliminating the necessity of plotting by the navigator. It is hoped that these devices will eventually make navigation much safer than it is at present.[32]

FIG. 29-34. RAYTHEON MODEL RAY-240 RADAR TRUE MOTION INDICATOR

In 1959, Sperry officials announced that they were developing a voice-radar system capable of linking microwave voice communication to a radar scope display. With this device, officers on ships in a probable collision situation would be able to communicate with each other via the radar microwave link.

At about the same time, officials of the research and development program of the Maritime Administration announced that this organization was accepting bids from electronic manufacturers for a prototype radar computer. This device would be designed to eliminate the time-consuming plotting that is now required in maritime radar operations. It would be sensitive to signals produced on the radar scope and would activate warning lights and bells whenever a radar target entered a danger zone and became a potential hazard.

A rather novel application of marine radar was the installation by the Raytheon Co. of a radar system on the aerial lift bridge over the canal leading to the Lake Superior ports of Duluth, Minn., and Superior, Wisc. This system enables the bridge tender to spot incoming vessels 32 miles away in the foggiest weather and to detect outgoing ships as soon as they have left their piers. Consequently, these radar images enable the bridge tender to time his bridge openings more efficiently and with a greater margin of safety.

29.17 *The proximity fuze*

Still another outcome of military radar research is the radar proximity fuze (or fuse). This device, which was responsible for a tremendous increase in the efficiency of artillery and anti-aircraft fire, was developed by the Applied Physics Laboratory of Johns Hopkins University (Fig. 29-35). It contains a tiny, self-powered transmitter and receiver, whose construction utilizes printed-circuit and miniaturization techniques.

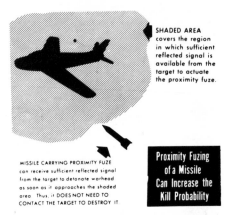

SHADED AREA covers the region in which sufficient reflected signal is available from the target to actuate the proximity fuze.

MISSILE CARRYING PROXIMITY FUZE can receive sufficient reflected signal from the target to detonate warhead as soon as it approaches the shaded area. Thus, it DOES NOT NEED TO CONTACT THE TARGET TO DESTROY IT.

Proximity Fuzing of a Missile Can Increase the Kill Probability

FIG. 29-35. PROXIMITY FUZING

A proximity fuze mounted in the nose of a shell emits a continuous-wave signal. When these waves are reflected by a nearby target, such as an enemy airplane, the echo signal is used to trigger a thyratron tube, which then detonates the explosive charge at exactly the right moment to accomplish the maximum amount of damage to the enemy target. Proximity fuzes of this type were first used in combat in 1943 and later proved to be very effective against the buzz-bomb variety of guided missile that was launched by the Germans.

29.18 *Radar guided missiles*

The development of the radar proximity fuze led logically to the development of a new offensive weapon, the radar guided missile. For the sake of maintaining the completeness of the historical record, it should be pointed out that in 1940, Lee de Forest submitted working blueprints for a simple guided missile, a photoelectrically controlled, self-directing night bomb. The idea was examined and tested in a perfunctory manner by the Army and Navy and dismissed as highly impractical.[33] Today, the guided missile seems destined to become the most important single military weapon.

In December 1945, the U.S. Navy announced the development of the Bat, the first fully automatic guided missile to be used in combat by any nation (Fig. 29-36). This device was usually launched by a bomber plane against an enemy vessel. Once launched, the device moved toward its target at high speed, guided by the reflections of radar signals emitted by its own transmitter. The radar echoes enabled it to make appropriate corrections to compensate for any evasive maneuvers by the target ship (Fig. 29-37).

A more modern type of missile system is the Western Electric Nike Zeus. This has a ground guidance system containing computers and three radars (Fig. 29-38). One radar, known as the acquisition radar, first detects the approach of distant aircraft. The second, or target-tracking radar, picks up the oncoming target and follows it, meanwhile feeding information into a computer concerning the course of the approaching plane. The third, or missile-tracking radar, is trained on the Nike missile, which is launched at supersonic speed while the target is miles away.

The computer receives a steady stream of information from both the target-tracking and the missile-tracking radar. Any evasive action by the target causes the computer to produce new flight instructions which are transmitted

Courtesy, Bureau of Ordnance, U.S. Navy

FIG. 29-36. NAVY BAT—RADAR GUIDED GLIDER BOMB

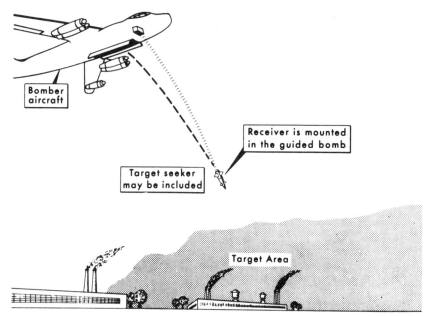

FIG. 29-37. PRINCIPLE OF THE BAT MISSILE

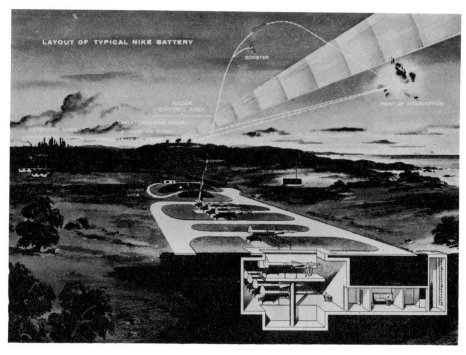

Courtesy, Western Electric Co.

FIG. 29-38. LAYOUT OF TYPICAL NIKE BATTERY

to the missile. Thus the course of the missile is modified until it keeps its destructive rendezvous with its target.[34]

The command guidance system of the Air Force's Titan ICBM (Intercontinental Ballistic Missile) is very similar in principle. While the missile is in powered flight, a ground-based radar continuously provides information concerning the position of the missile (Fig. 29-39). This information is fed to a ground-based digital computer that issues the appropriate orders required to keep the missile on its assigned path. These orders are transmitted via radio to the missile where they actuate the missile's automatic pilot and control system.[35]

29.19 *Other recent military radar developments*

Since 1946, national security requirements have prevented the dissemination of much information concerning many advances in military radar. Consequently, most of the publicized advances have been in peacetime, commercial applications, such as radar blind-landing, navigational, and weather-detecting equipment. Several of these devices will be described shortly. However, the security veil has been lifted from several military-radar applications.

Counter-mortar system. One application, first used in Korea, is a counter-

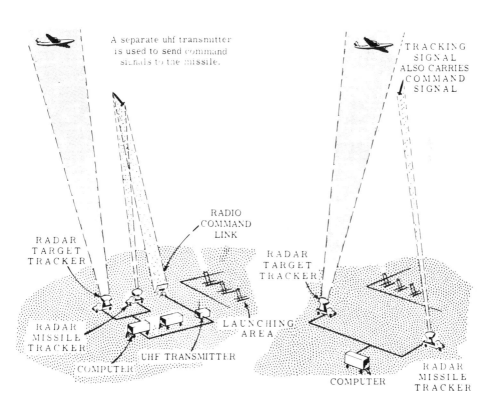

FIG. 29-39. TWO RADAR COMMAND GUIDANCE SYSTEMS

mortar system. An automatic radar tracker is used to track enemy mortar shells (Fig. 29-40). As soon as a shell is detected, the device "locks on" to the missile and traces its trajectory back to the enemy position where it started. The map coordinates of this position are then relayed to an artillery fire-direction center, which directs a return barrage against the enemy mortar in a matter of minutes.

Surveillance-radar set. The Armed Forces has also announced the development of a small surveillance-radar set that is powered by a tiny magnetron tube the size of a golf ball. This device, the AN/TPS-25, uses pulse-Doppler techniques and is designed to warn a soldier aurally of the approach of vehicles or infiltrating enemy troops (Fig. 29-41). This model is so sensitive that it can detect a soldier crawling on the ground 2 miles away, spot a jeep at 10 miles, and distinguish between moving trains and moving vehicles at distances of 20,000 yards. Under ideal conditions in the desert, it can spot a soldier walking 15 miles away. It is also claimed

Courtesy, Sperry Rand Corp.
Fig. 29-40. MPQ-10 RADAR MORTAR LOCATER

that it can tell the difference between a man and a woman walking at a distance of 600 yards at night or in fog (Fig. 29-42).[36][37]

Development of guided missiles. A third publicized military application of radar is in connection with developmental work on long-range guided missiles that is being conducted at the Patrick Air Force Base in Florida. Before a missile is launched, radar is used to scan the sea for ships that might be in dangerous areas. After the missile has been electronically launched, its subsequent behavior is recorded in three ways: by radar, by motion-picture camera, and by magnetic-tape recording of telemetered UHF signals transmitted by the missiles. Some of these missiles also employ radar in their guidance systems.

SAGE. A fourth military application of radar is its use in a continental air-defense system called SAGE (Semi-Automatic Ground Environment). This system, developed by scientists at the Lincoln Laboratory of MIT, is the electronic medium for the control of modern air-defense interceptors and missiles. It consists of a network of computer-equipped direction centers which process radar-obtained data and produce orders for defense against hostile forces. In operation, information from ground-based radars (Fig. 29-43), Texas towers, picket ships, aircraft-warning planes, ground observers, weather stations, flight plans, and other sources is transmitted via telephone lines or microwave radio to the computer (Fig. 29-44).

The high-speed digital computer translates this information into a picture of the entire situation, and displays this upon a scope screen (Fig. 29-45). It thus provides human operators with the necessary facts with which they can make sound and immediate judgments.

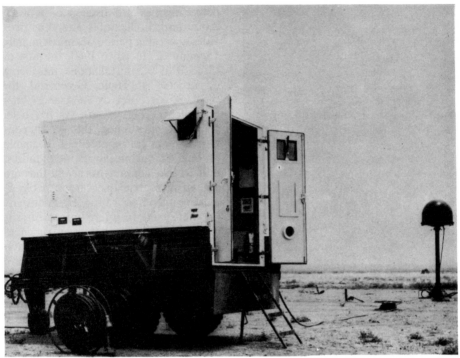

Courtesy, Hazeltine Corp.

FIG. 29-41. AN/TPS-25 COMBAT SURVEILLANCE RADAR

This system also computes the most effective means of applying defense weapons—such as anti-aircraft, interceptor planes, and guided missiles—and transmits by means of radio links vectoring instructions that guide these weapons to their targets.[38]

After the battle has moved away from the region served by a given air-defense center, its computer automatically enters all of the pertinent information that it contains into the computer that serves the appropriate adjoining area. This type of equipment may one day be used to help solve ever-increasing civil air-traffic-control problems of our country.[39][40][41]

Anti-missile missile systems. In 1957, the U.S. Air Force announced that it had perfected a new radar system that was capable of picking up an ICBM 3,000 miles away. It is planned to use this system in connection with an anti-missile missile designed to intercept and destroy enemy missiles. The need for greatly increased radar range is due primarily to the development of very-high-speed aircraft and missiles. To allow time for defensive action, such targets must be detected at much greater distances than those that were considered sufficient for detecting and tracking propeller-driven airplanes.

Early Warning System. This has been the primary reason for the development of the Air Force's BMEWS (Ballistic Missile Early Warning System) in the far north. This system employs long-range radar that emits megawatt signals that enable the system to

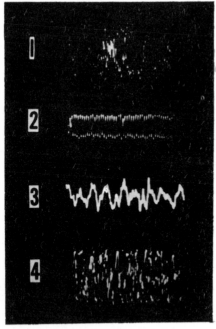

FIG. 29-42. SCOPE TRACES PRODUCED BY AN/TPS-25 COMBAT SURVEILLANCE RADAR

detect missiles at a distance of between 2,000 and 3,000 miles and thus provides a warning period of approximately 15 minutes. In early 1960, the first of three BMEWS installations was being constructed at Thule, Greenland, for the U.S. Air Force by RCA and General Electric (Fig. 29-46). As has been previously mentioned, this system contains a radar transmitter that is capable of sending out megawatt radar pulses, and it also contains receivers that are so sensitive that they are capable of picking up echoes whose strengths must be measured in micro-micro-micro-watts. When this system commences operation, gigantic antennas, each larger than a football field, will send out twin fan-shaped beams of radio-frequency energy (Fig. 29-47). When a missile passes through the two beams, the signals from the reflected echoes will indicate the missile's trajectory and speed (Fig. 29-48). When this information is fed into an associated

FIG. 29-43. A MODERN SURVEILLANCE RADAR INSTALLATION

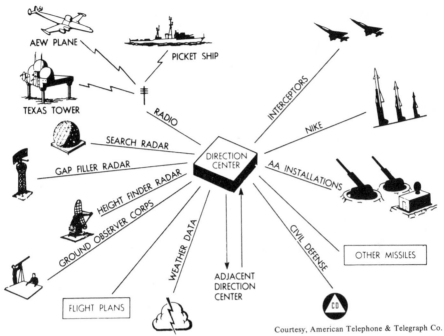

Courtesy, American Telephone & Telegraph Co.

FIG. 29-44. COMPONENTS OF A TYPICAL SAGE AIR DEFENSE SECTOR

FIG. 29-45. SAGE CONTROL ROOM

Courtesy, General Electric Co.

FIG. 29-46. BMEWS ANTENNA UNDER CONSTRUCTION

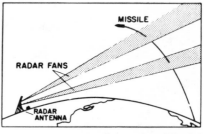

Courtesy, General Electric Co.

FIG. 29-48. HOW   BMEWS   WILL   DETECT
MISSILES

computer, it will calculate the missile's destination and impact time.

Extending range of radar systems. One method of enabling radar devices to scan greater distances with clarity is to use more power in the transmitter, thus producing a stronger signal. One tube that can be employed for this purpose is the Amplitron, which was developed in 1957 under the sponsorship of

Courtesy, General Electric Co.

FIG. 29-47. BMEWS SITE I, THULE, GREEN-
LAND

the U.S. Army Signal Corps Engineering Laboratories. The peak power of this tube is equal to that required to light a city of 200,000 people. It boosts the energy output of the signal as much as 14 times. When it is added to FAA air-traffic-control systems, it increases the effective range of these units from a distance of 200 miles to one of 350 miles.[42] The Amplitron will be discussed further in Chapter 31.

However, there are limitations to this method of extending the range of radar systems. Since the strength of a radar echo decreases as the fourth power of the distance to the target, it is necessary to increase the power by 16 times in order to double the range. Similarly, a 10,000-fold increase in power is required in order to increase the range by 10 times.

Signal enhancement. During 1957, the U.S. Air Force and Columbia University announced the development by Bernstein, Fisher, Bose, and O'Neill of a new technique called signal enhancement. This system makes optimum use of the reflected signal energy and greatly increases the effective range of radar equipment. Details of this technique are highly classified. The information that has been released states that it employs frequency-modulated, continuous-wave propagation. A special receiver is used which enhances or raises the level of the reflected radar signal relative to the strength of the background noise. It also lengthens the appearance of the returned radar signal from a period of 1 microsecond to a period of 100 microseconds, making possible more careful analysis and differentiation from background interference.[43 44]

MADRE. Several other systems have been developed to provide radar with the capability of detecting targets far beyond the horizon. One of them,

called MADRE (Magnetic Drum Receiving Equipment), was developed by Robert M. Page of the Naval Research Laboratory and employs ionospheric-scatter techniques.

Project Teepee. Another promising technique is the previously mentioned High-Frequency Ionospheric Back-Scatter Radar, developed by William J. Thaler, a Navy physicist. Also known as the Project Teepee detection method, it is designed to detect nuclear explosions as well as the ionized exhausts of a rocket missile. In this system, transmitters whose powers range between 15 and 50 kilowatts generate high-frequency radio waves that are reflected from the ionosphere to the earth and back to the ionosphere (Fig. 29-49). In this manner, the waves travel a great distance around the earth. At each reflection, a slight back-scatter is produced which returns a signal to the starting point. The hot gases from a rocket exhaust or from a nuclear explosion also produce an ionized reflecting surface, and some of the signal is backscattered and returned to the source. The returned signals produce a blip on the screen of the cathode-ray tube of the receiver, and the abnormal blip produced by this additional backscatter provides information concerning the disturbance that produced it.

This system does not provide the degree of target delineation that conventional radar does; but it does double the present warning time, increasing it to 30 minutes. Consequently, at present, it is intended that this system will complement, rather than supplant the BMEWS or DEW Line systems.[45]

Satellite observation systems. Both the Army and the Navy have developed radar systems designed to detect the presence of observation satellites orbiting at altitudes of thousands of miles. The Army system, known as Doploc,

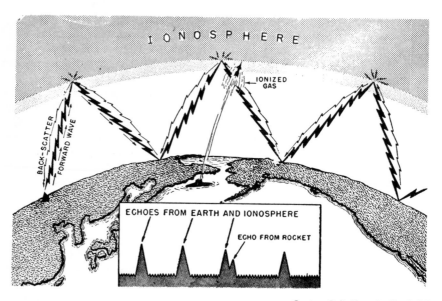

FIG. 29-49. HOW PROJECT TEEPEE WORKS

was designed by the Ballistics Research Laboratory, Aberdeen Proving Ground. It was originally designed for tracking our own satellites. Employing the Doppler principle, it is a modified version of the radar devices used by police to detect speeding cars. The equipment detects the satellite and gauges its speed by measuring the Doppler shift in frequency of the waves that are reflected by the satellite.

The Navy system is a modification of the Minitrack system, which was also developed by the Naval Research Laboratory for following our own satellites. It employs the same principle as the optical interferometer. Radar signals are reflected by the satellite, and the device counts the difference in the number of wave crests arriving at antennas located a known distance apart from each other. From this information, it is then possible to obtain the position of the satellite that reflected these radar signals.[46]

29.20 *Frequency-scanning radar*

In 1958, Hughes Aircraft Co. announced the development of the previously mentioned three-dimensional, frequency-scanning radar system called Frescanar (Figs. 29-50, 29-51, and 29-52). It was designed to be used in the Missile Monitor, a tactical air-defense guided-missile fire-distribution system, intended for mobile use with a field army. This Missile Monitor is fundamentally an electronic co-ordination and control system designed to be used by the Nike and Hawk missile batteries of that field army.

In this radar system, the scanning radar beam is moved without causing the antenna to move. This is accomplished by changing the frequency of the radar signal that is applied to a special antenna. The directivity of this antenna is related to the frequency of the signal applied to it. This causes the

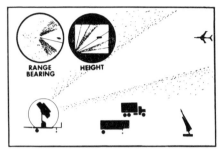

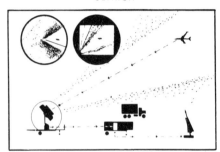

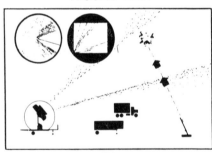

SEARCH

PROCESS DATA

KILL

FIG. 29-50. USE OF FRESCANAR BY FIELD ARMY *At top, pencil-beam antenna scans skies. In center, antenna flashes range, bearing, altitude of enemy bomber. At bottom, electronically relayed information launches missiles to score "kill."*

FIG. 29-51. FRESCANAR MASTER CONTROL SCOPES (RANGE AND BEARING AT LEFT. ALTITUDE AT RIGHT).

FIG. 29-52. FRESCANAR CONSOLE SECTION

radar beam to move more rapidly than would be possible by moving the antenna physically. Thus, the beam can monitor very-high-speed aircraft or missiles at various bearings and altitudes.

Among the advantages claimed for this system are the following:

1. It can compute bearing, altitude, and range at the same time.

2. It can concentrate all of the available energy in a very sharp beam. Consequently, it can pinpoint targets at great distances with extreme accuracy.

3. It requires but a single operator and antenna and reduces weight, bulk, and personnel requirements.

4. It transmits bearing, altitude,

and range to missile batteries with greater speed than other systems can achieve.

5. It increases the number of targets that can be tracked at the same time and provides better separation of closely spaced targets.[47] [48] [49]

29.21 *Radar photography*

In 1960, scientists at the Willow Run Laboratories of the University of Michigan announced that they had developed an airborne-radar system for the U.S. Army that was capable of producing sharp and detailed pictures of distant terrain in any kind of weather, both day and night. In this system, radar pulses are transmitted from an antenna that is located on the underside of the airplane. The returning echo is recorded on film in such a manner that it can be processed into a picture that is similar to one that has been taken directly by a camera that is located over the distant territory.[50]

29.22 *Electronic counter-measures*

Electronic countermeasures, or ECM, is a term that has been applied to a variety of devices and techniques developed by the military to confuse and misdirect enemy radar equipment. The first and simplest type of ECM was employed by the British against the Germans in 1943. It consisted of the dropping of thousands of strips of aluminum from an airplane. This was known as window, rope, or chaff and successfully confused the German anti-aircraft radar equipment.

During the Normandy invasion, the Allies placed an arrangement of three, large, mutually perpendicular metal sheets known as a corner reflector on several motor launches. The strong echoes reflected by these de-

vices made them appear as a fleet of battleships on the German radar scopes.

Modern bombers carry a variety of ECM equipment designed to fool radar-guided anti-aircraft missiles. One piece of equipment consists of a transmitter that sends out series of pulses each time that it receives one pulse from the enemy radar. The enemy radar equipment then receives this series of pulses, making it difficult to distinguish the true target in the midst of the false echoes.[51]

Another ingenious countermeasure used during World War II was known as Tuba. It consisted of a powerful tunable jammer located in England that sent out a powerful radar signal. This signal blinded the radar equipment of German fighter planes and disrupted their tactics of homing in on the radar signals emitted by British night bombers.[52]

Mention may also be made of the fact that late in 1959, Otto Halpern was awarded 340,000 dollars by the United States government for his development of a method of absorbing high-frequency radar signals. This technique was used by the U.S. Navy during World War II and was adopted later by the U.S. Air Force for use in Korea to frustrate enemy radar.[53]

Anti-radar paint. Another relatively new development is that of a coating designed by Air Force scientists to permit bombers to sneak past radar defense systems, such as the DEW Line, with only a slight chance of detection. The new paint consists of heavy coatings of radar-absorbent materials, such as rubber bonded to ceramics or horsehair impregnated with carbon. When these materials are mixed with a paint base, they absorb radar waves instead of reflecting them back to the radar transmitter. They do not hide an object completely from radar but reduce greatly the chance of detection.

At present, these paints suffer from the disadvantages of great weight, tendency to crack and flake off under strain, and lack of resistance to weathering. However, it is anticipated that the development of these paints will make necessary a sweeping revision of our radar warning systems and of our anti-missile-missile development program.[54][55]

29.23 *Radar failure predictor*

In 1957, the American Machine and Foundry Co. announced the development of an automatic failure predictor that is capable of improving the reliability of a radar receiver by as much as 240 per cent. The device monitors functions within a radar receiver and predicts impending failure. This permits replacement of a unit before it fails during the operation of the receiver. The sequence and type of monitoring are automatically programmed and can be started from a remote station. Both a visible and audible warning of impending failure can be delivered to the remote station.[56]

29.24 *Radar astronomy*

In recent years, radar astronomy, and its sister science, radio astronomy, have provided scientists with a new window into the universe. Unlike radio astronomy, which, as will be described in the chapter on microwaves, makes use of the radio signals reaching us from space, radar astronomy makes use of the echoes of radar signals that are transmitted from the earth and employs these echoes to obtain information about the planets, the moon, the sun, and interplanetary space.

In 1946, the entire scientific world was stirred by the news that the U.S. Army Signal Corps had established radar contact with the moon. This remarkable feat was exceeded over a hundredfold in 1958 when a team of eight physicists and engineers from the Lincoln Laboratory of MIT, headed by Robert Price and Paul E. Green, Jr., reported establishing radar contact with the planet Venus, over 28 million miles away. It required about 5 minutes for the signals to reach Venus and to return. This radar system was 10 million times more sensitive than the one employed in 1946.

The transmitter used a high-power klystron oscillator at a frequency of 440 mc. The power of the transmitted signal was 265 kilowatts. The signal intercepted by Venus had a power level of about 0.5 watts, and the return echo had a power level that was of the order of 0.01 micro-micro-microwatts.

The front end of the receiver contained a low-noise amplifier consisting of a three-level solid-state maser in liquid helium. The operation of the maser will be described in the chapter on microwaves. One significant conclusion derived from the data obtained was that the value of an Astronomical Unit, which is equal to the mean radius of the earth's orbit around the sun, is about 0.0013 per cent smaller than the value generally assumed. This means that interplanetary distances may be somewhat shorter than had been previously believed.[57][58] A second useful by-product of this accomplishment was the determination of the distance of Venus to within 100 miles. Heretofore, astronomical methods of measurement had yielded an uncertainty of approximately 50,000 miles.[59]

Another series of radar experiments conducted by K.M. Siegel, head of the Radiation Laboratory of the University of Michigan, have led to the conclusion that the surface of the moon may be 100 times smoother than the Sahara Desert. According to these experiments, the moon has the properties of a smooth surface at radar frequencies and is probably covered with a layer of sand or pumice.

Early in 1960, a group of Stanford University scientists led by Von R. Eshleman announced that they had succeeded in establishing radar contact with the corona of the sun. This was accomplished by using a 40-kilowatt transmitter and an array of rhombic antennas to beam a signal of 25.6 mc at the sun. The echoes that returned 1,000 seconds later were analyzed with the aid of an electronic computer (Fig. 29-53). The scientific information gained about the sun as a consequence of this first radar experiment is rather limited, but it is quite apparent that this method of probing the solar system with the aid of man-made radar waves provides another new scientific technique that will complement and extend the knowledge the scientists have acquired by means of ordinary visual astronomy, radio astronomy, and rocket-probing techniques and may help scientists to forecast radio "blackouts" produced by sunspots, solar flares, and magnetic storms.[60][61][62]

The Stanford Research Institute and the Radio Propagation Laboratory of Stanford University are in process of constructing a parabolic radar telescope 142 ft in diameter. When it is completed, it will be America's largest and the world's second-largest radar telescope. Associated with it will be a one-million dollar, 300-kilowatt radar transmitter operating at frequencies between 20 and 60 mc, and the combined installation will cost over 1.5 million dollars. Financial support is being provided by the Air Force Cambridge Research Center. It is expected that the device will be used for making measurements of cosmic distances, for making radar surface explorations of the moon and the planets, for measuring the rotational speed of Venus, and for making observations concerning the corona of the sun.[63]

Plans are also being made to employ radar astronomy for probing and mapping the large-scale surface features of Venus and Mars, for probing and determining the surface characteristics of Jupiter and the other major planets, for studying our own ionosphere, and for determining the density of the interplanetary dust.[64]

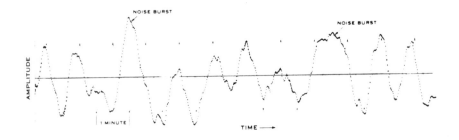

Courtesy, Ampex Data Products Co.

Fig. 29-53. The history-making solar radio echo

REFERENCES

1. *Radar Systems Fundamentals,* Bureau of Ships, Department of the Navy, Washington, D.C., 1944, p. 1.
2. O. E. Dunlap, Jr., *Radio and Television Almanac,* Harper and Bros., New York, 1944.
3. Kenneth M. Swezey, "Nikola Tesla," *Science,* 127:1156, May 16, 1958.
4. O. E. Dunlap, Jr., *Radio's 100 Men of Science, Op. cit.*
5. John C. Monahan, "Radio Detection and Ranging," *Sperryscope,* 15:6-7, Second Quarter, 1960.
6. "Radar Patent No. 2,803,819," *Radio-Electronics,* 29:137, Apr. 1958.
7. *The Lighthouse Tube,* General Electric Co., Schenectady, N.Y., 1949, p. 1.
8. "Radar Now Sees in 3-D," *Vectors,* 1:6-7, Fourth Quarter, 1959.
9. Virginia Walters, "Micro-Waveguides," *Radio-Electronics,* 20:24, Dec. 1948.
10. A. L. Samuel and others, "The Gas-Discharge Transmit-Receive Tube," *Bell System Technical Journal,* 25:48, Jan. 1946.
11. "Sonar Radar," *Military Automation,* 1:93, Mar. 1957.
12. "The Wamoscope," *Radio and Television News,* 56:105, Nov. 1956.
13. "Picture Tube Receiver Functions in a Single Package," *Electrical Engineering,* 75:1056, Nov. 1956.
14. "Simplified Radar to Use Wamoscope," *Popular Electronics,* 5:40, Nov. 1956.
15. "Multicolor Radar," *Popular Electronics,* 2:24, June 1955.
16. "I.F.F.—Identification, Friend or Foe," *Radio-Craft,* 17:332, Feb. 1946.
17. "Radar on the Highway," *Popular Electronics,* 4:36, May 1956.
18. "You Can't Beat the Mechanical Cops," *Science Digest,* 42:40-43, Aug. 1957.
19. Ralph W. Sanders and Martin Mann, "Why You Can't Fool the Radar Cops," *Popular Science,* 174:67-70, 232-234, May 1959.
20. "Record of Traffic Conditions Reveal Motorists' Habits," *Sanborn Right Angle,* 7:8, Feb. 1960.
21. Robert L. Moora, "RCA's Role in Tracking Missiles," *Electronic Age,* 17:8, July 1958.
22. "Radar Traffic Control," *Radio-Electronics,* 30:14, Nov. 1959.
23. "Radar and Electronic Brain Speed Freight Movements," *Exide Topics,* 30:6, Mar. 1956.
24. "Frielinghaus on Railroad-Yard Automation," *Instruments and Control Systems,* 32:1701-1702, Nov. 1959.
25. "Automobile Radar," *Radio-Electronics,* 30:10, May 1959.
26. "Auto Radar Spots Highway Dangers," *Popular Electronics,* 10:93, June 1959.
27. "How Soon Before Electronics Drives Your Car?," *Electronics Illustrated,* 2:30, Feb. 1959.
28. Vladimir K. Zworykin and Leslie E. Flory, "Electronics Guide Your Car," *Radio-Electronics,* 30:99-101, Apr. 1959.
29. "New Survey Techniques Speed Highway Construction," *Science Digest,* 44:91, July 1958.
30. "Electronics Blazes the Trail," *Electronics Illustrated,* 1:53, Sept. 1958.
31. George D. Whitmore and others, "Modern Instruments For Surveying and Mapping," *Science,* 130:1064-1065, Oct. 23, 1959.
32. Mike Bienstock, "Will There Be Another Andrea Doria?," *Popular Electronics,* 7:47-50, Oct. 1957.
33. *Lee de Forest, Father of Radio,* Wilcox and Follet Co., Chicago, 1950. pp. 428-432.
34. *Nike,* Western Electric Co., New York, pp. 8-9.
35. E. P. Felch, *Missile Guidance,* Bell Telephone Laboratories, New York, 1959, p. 5.
36. "Woman-Spotting Radar," *Radio-Electronics,* 30:6, 8, Oct. 1959.
37. "Ultra-Sensitive Combat Radar," *Electronics World,* 62:48, Nov. 1959.
38. "Sage Electronics Integrate Air Defenses," *Industrial Laboratories,* 7:10-11, Mar. 1959.
39. E. D. Morgan, "SAGE," *Popular Electronics,* 5:43, Aug. 1956.
40. *MIT Lincoln Laboratory,* MIT Lincoln Laboratory, Lexington, Mass., pp. 2-3.
41. Ernest W. Baker, "SAGE in Air Defense," *Bell Telephone Magazine,* 37:5-9, Summer 1958.
42. "Amplitron Boosts Basic Radar Signals," *Industrial Laboratories,* 8:103, Apr. 1957.
43. "Develop Radar That Sees Farther," *Science Digest,* 42:92, Nov. 1957.
44. "Revolution in Radar," *Scientific American,* 197:56-57, Oct. 1957.
45. "Missile Firings," *Radio-Electronics,* 30:6. Oct. 1959.
46. Martin Mann, "U.S. Space Fence on Alert for Russian Spy-Satellites," *Popular Science,* 175:62-65, 198, July 1958.
47. "New Frequency Scanning Radar," *Radio and TV News,* 61:69, Jan. 1959.
48. "Three-Dimensional Radar Spots Targets," *Science Digest,* 45:52, Jan. 1959.
49. Nicholas A. Begovich, "3-D Radar-AN/MS-23 Frequency Scanning Radar," *Industrial Science and Engineering,* 6:44, Feb. 1959.
50. "New Radar Takes Detailed Pictures," *Science News Letter,* 77:280, Apr. 30, 1960.
51. Philip Julian, "Electronic Countermeasures," *Electronics Illustrated,* 1:55-58, July 1958.
52. *Electronics Warfare—A Report on Radar Countermeasures,* U.S. Office of Scientific Research and Development, U.S. Government Printing Office, Washington, D.C., 1951, p. 34.
53. "Anti-Radar Inventor," *Radio-Electronics,* 30:12, . Sept. 1959.
54. "Anti-Radar Paint," *Science Digest,* 44:92, July 1958.
55. "Is Military Radar Doomed?," *Radio-Electronics,* 29:31, Sept. 1958.
56. "Failure Predictor Improves Radar Reliability," *Military Automation,* 1:268, Sept. 1957.
57. R. Price and others, "Radar Echoes From Venus," *Science,* 129:751-753, Mar. 20, 1959.

58. "Calling Venus," *Scientific American*, 200:74, 76, May 1959.
59. "Road to Universe Opened," *Radio-Electronics*, 30:47, May 1959.
60. V. R. Eshleman and others, "Radar Echoes from the Sun," *Science*, 131:329-332, Feb. 5, 1960.
61. "Radar to the Sun and Back," *Science News Letter*, 77:103, Feb. 13, 1960.
62. "Echoes from the Sun," *Science World*, 7:33-34, Feb. 17, 1960.
63. "Our Largest Radar Telescope," *Electronics World*, 62:96, Oct. 1959.
64. Von R. Eshleman and Allen M. Peterson, "Radar Astronomy," *Scientific American*, 203: 50-59, Aug. 1960.

30 - AVIONICS AND ELECTRONIC NAVIGATION

30.1 *Radio direction finders*

The development of electronic aids to navigation began with the introduction by Marconi in the early 1900's of the wireless direction finder. This consisted of (1) a single rotatable loop antenna; (2) a sensitive tunable receiver; (3) a pair of earphones; and (4) an azimuth or position indicator (Figs. 30-1 and 30-2). The operation of this device depends upon the principle that the signals received from a station whose position is known are at maximum strength when the loop is pointing toward the station and at minimum strength when the loop is at right angles to the station (Fig. 30-3). The loop is usually adjusted to produce a null point or minimum signal, which indicates that the station is located on a line at right angles to the loop. By obtaining bearings from at least two such stations and determining their point of intersection, it is possible to determine the position of a ship or airplane. Before the advent of radar and Loran, radio-direction-finding equipment of this type provided almost the only means by which aircraft and ships could determine their positions during bad weather.[1] [2]

30.2 *Radio ranges*

The low-frequency radio range was introduced by the CAA (now the FAA) in order to aid aerial navigation. In

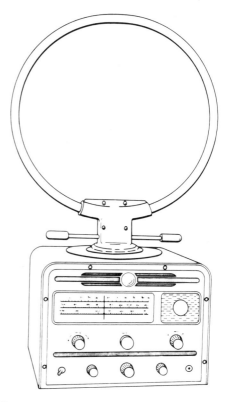

FIG. 30-1. A RADIO DIRECTION FINDER

this system, one pair of antennas transmits dot-dash or "A" signals at a frequency that is between 200 and 400 kc. A second pair of antennas transmits dash-dot or "N" signals (Fig. 30-4). When the pilot is "on the beam" and heading correctly toward the station, he hears a steady tone and cannot distinguish either the "A" or the "N".[3]

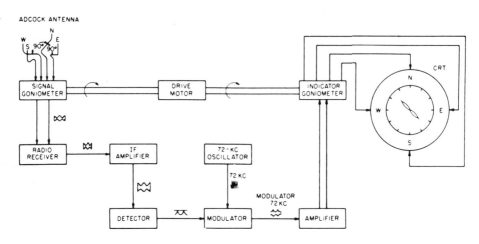

FIG. 30-2. BLOCK DIAGRAM OF A RADIO DIRECTION FINDER

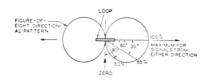

FIG. 30-3. DIRECTIONAL PATTERN OF A LOOP ANTENNA

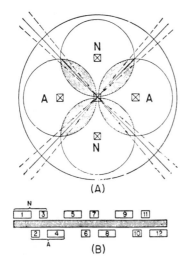

Courtesy, Civil Aeronautics Administration

FIG. 30-4. RADIATION PATTERN (A) AND SEQUENCE OF DOTS AND DASHES (B) IN LOW-FREQUENCY RADIO RANGE

Associated with these range stations are marker beacon stations located on the range course about 20 miles from the station. Each marker radiates a characteristic directional signal that provides the pilot with information concerning his position along the range course. Each range station generally provides four courses. These low-frequency aural radio ranges are being replaced by a VHF omnidirectional system called VOR, which will be described in detail in a later section of this chapter.

The big impetus to avionic aids came with the advent of radar during World War II. Airborne radar permits a pilot to navigate over land or within a hundred miles of land by employing radar check points, such as cities, islands, and characteristic expanses of shoreline. These radar check points replace the visual check points employed in conventional aerial navigation. Since radar navigational techniques are ineffective when planes are flying over large bodies of water, a different type of navigational system known as Loran must be employed

under these conditions. The Loran system will also be discussed in a later section of this chapter.

30.3 *Radar beacons*

Radar beacons or "racons" send out a characteristic coded signal when they are triggered by an interrogating radar impulse that is directed toward the radar beacon by a plane's antenna. The presentation that is produced on the scope of the plane's radar set by this coded signal provides information which enables the pilot to identify the beacon and to determine its range and bearing. The effective range of racon operation is limited only by the horizon or line-of-sight distance.

The radar beacon has also made in-flight refueling of Air Force planes a routine operation. A beacon is installed in a rendezvous airplane. Other planes can then home on the beacon by sending out interrogating radar pulses that trigger the beacon. The beacon then sends out a coded reply which enables the inquiring plane to identify the beacon plane and to determine its range and bearing. Thus, a squadron of planes can locate tanker planes hundreds of miles away and rendezvous with these tankers in any kind of weather

Radar beacons also possess many potential applications in air-traffic-control systems. Most radar traffic-control systems depend upon the reflection of ground-transmitted signals from the surface of an aircraft. The beacon system makes use of actual radar-pulse replies from aircraft. These pulses are produced by a triggering signal from the airport that actuates a transponder, which then sends back a pulse in reply. This system not only makes it possible for the controller to detect the aircraft but also, through use of an electronic

decoding device, enables the controller to identify the plane immediately. It can operate at greater distances and higher altitudes than other radar systems can.[4][5]

In 1959, radar-beacon networks of this type were installed at Kennedy, La Guardia, and Newark airports to enable traffic controllers to identify all aircraft and to extend their radar vision by one-third to a distance of 120 miles. As soon as possible, this system will be extended to 250 traffic-control towers in the United States and eventually to most international airports.

Another type of radar-beacon application makes use of radar marker beacons or "ramarks." When interrogated by radar, these transponders send out continuous-wave radar signals in all directions. When these signals are picked up by the directional antenna of the radar receiver, a sharp line appears on the PPI indicator. This line indicates the bearing of the ramark, and two such lines are required to give the pilot or navigator his position with respect to the ramarks.

30.4 *Radar altimeters*

Radar altimeters are designed to measure accurately the distance between a plane and the ground (Fig. 30-5). The first successful demonstrations of altimeter equipment were performed in 1937 and 1938 by two groups of scientists, one working for Bell Telephone Laboratories, and the second, under the supervision of Irving Wolff, working for RCA.

Altimeters may be divided into two classes: the pulse-type altimeter and the FM altimeter. The pulse type, which resembles the conventional radar set, sends a very short pulse of radio energy of about 0.1 microseconds duration

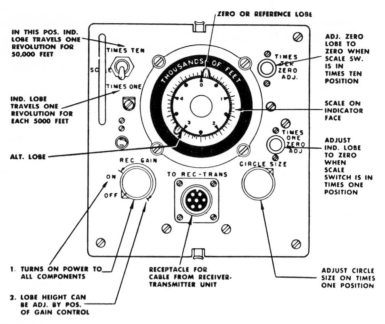

FIG. 30-5. RCA RADIO ALTIMETER

toward the ground approximately 2,000 times per second. The time is measured between the departure of a pulse and its return after being reflected by the ground. From this time measurement, the distance to the ground may be calculated easily and rapidly. This type of altimeter is satisfactory for the measurement of relatively high altitudes. It is capable of measuring elevations to within plus or minus 10 ft at altitudes between 1,000 and 30,000 ft.[6]

In 1957, the Air Research and Development Command of the U.S. Air Force announced the development of a pulse-type radar altimeter that is accurate to within 40 ft at an altitude of 60,000 ft. Instead of using a cathode-ray tube for data presentation, the device feeds the information into servomechanisms which display the altitude on standard altimeter dials and which also feed the information to potentiometers and recording mechanisms.[7]

However, unless this type of altimeter is designed to produce very short pulses of considerably less than a microsecond in duration, it is ineffective at altitudes of less than 500 ft, since the echo returns before the end of the original transmitted pulse.

The FM altimeter was designed to solve this problem of measuring low altitudes. The radar transmitter sends out a continuous signal rather than short pulses. However, this output is an FM signal whose frequency varies from instant to instant. Consequently, the echo signal possesses a frequency different from that of the signal being transmitted at that instant. The circuits of the altimeter measure the difference in frequency and convert this difference into an electric current which moves the pointer of an altimeter dial.

This type of altimeter produces an error that is related to the altitude indication, being plus or minus 2 ft at altitudes between zero and 40 ft and plus or minus 5 per cent of the correct reading at altitudes between 40 and 20,000 ft.

30.5 *Anti-collision radar*

Since the early 1950's, it has become increasingly obvious that aviation has reached the point where a human pilot can no longer rely solely upon his powers of vision to avoid mid-air collisions. It is apparent that the pilot requires the assistance of some electronic aids that will provide him with adequate warning and with an indication of the safest course of action in time to enable him to react to avoid a mid-air collision.[8]

In 1956, the Collins Radio Co. announced the development of a radar airplane-proximity-warning device. Operating on the same principle as an FM radar altimeter, it contained six antennas and provided complete coverage of a section of space 2 miles long and 7.5 deg above and below the plane. It also covered those sections of space 800 ft directly above and below the plane. While the early models merely warned the pilot of the approach of another plane, later models contained an electronic computer which told the pilot how to maneuver so as to prevent a collision.[9] Unfortunately, the company ran into manufacturing difficulties that created grave doubts that the original design would produce practical and usable equipment within the time scale specified in its contracts for this research and delivery program. As a result, it was compelled to cancel more than 10 million dollars of orders covering some 900 anti-collision radar sets. However, it is continuing its research and development program and is attempting to find a workable solution of the collision-avoidance problem.

In 1958, the Federal Telecommunications Laboratories of the International Telephone and Telegraph Corp. announced that it had developed an electronic collision-avoidance system capable of providing sufficient warning for planes approaching each other at almost twice the speed of sound. The system requires four miniature antennas which radiate signals produced by the plane's weather radar. It provides positive aural and visual collision-avoidance indications for a 90-deg sector extending 8 miles from the nose of the plane and provides proximity warning for a 225-degree sector. When reflected radar pulses are picked up by the antennas, they are fed to an electronic computer which determines the degree of hazard and the possibility of collision. If there is a possibility of collision, the computer determines the course to safety and designates this by a red arrow or indicator. A warning horn alerts the pilot, who then veers his plane in the direction indicated.[10] [11]

However, despite the progress that has been made, the problem appears to be far from solved. In 1959, James T. Pyle, Deputy Administrator of the FAA, stated that the FAA had studied more than 150 proposals for anti-collision devices, but that none of the systems appeared to be completely adequate. Even less optimistic is Major General Joseph D. Caldara, Deputy Inspector General for Safety of the United States Air Force. With regard to current achievements in airborne anti-collision radar, he stated:

"Considerable progress has been made .... toward development of such a device, but a satisfactory piece of hardware is not yet available."[12]

30.6 *Weather radar*

During World War II, radar operators aboard American bombers reported that their scopes could indicate the presence of storm clouds far ahead. In 1942, Kerr of MIT observed some fluffy images on the screen of a radar set, which he interpreted as rain-filled thunderclouds. Another pioneer in applying radar to meteorology was Bent of MIT, who studied the appearance of "weather clutter" on radar scopes and found that radar could be used to detect raindrops. As a result of the work of Kerr and Bent, the Weather Service of the U.S. Air Force and the U.S. Weather Bureau began to investigate the applications of radar to weather studies and weather forecasting.

It was found that radar could be used to detect showers, thunderstorms, warm and cold fronts, hurricanes, tornadoes, and typhoons. The radar system does not detect thunderstorms or hurricanes directly but depicts instead only that portion of the disturbance which contains sufficiently large and numerous droplets of water or crystals of ice to produce echoes on the screen of the scope. Strong echoes are produced by many large raindrops; weaker echoes by a few fine raindrops or snowflakes; whereas cloud particles produce either very weak echoes or none at all.[13] It was also discovered that storms could be studied from the ground at distances as great as 175 miles and at even greater ranges when airborne radar was employed.

Further investigations revealed that the severity of the storm was indicated by the strength of the echo, since the echo strength was dependent upon both the quantity of water and the size of the drops. It was also discovered that regions of the atmosphere where there was a sharp change in dielectric constant would also reflect radar waves. This enabled meteorologists to determine air-mass boundaries and similar atmospheric discontinuities.

Thus, while it is not yet possible to detect tornadoes themselves at a distance by means of radar, it is possible to identify the type of storm that may generate tornadoes by means of its radar picture. An approaching squall shows up on the scope as a line of intense echoes, whereas a concentrated storm produces a bright image that can be traced by vertical scanning high into the atmosphere.[14]

After the war ended, the U.S. Army Signal Corps and the Navy began to apply the radar-tracking techniques previously used in conjunction with anti-aircraft and guided-missile equipment to the location of storms. By 1955, there were 37 Weather Bureau offices equipped with storm-detection radar.

Today, the U.S. Weather Bureau, the Air Force Weather Service, and the Navy Hurricane Weather Control cooperate in keeping track of hurricanes in the Gulf and Caribbean areas. Suspicious developments are scouted by radar-equipped reconnaissance planes. When a hurricane approaches within 300 miles of the mainland, its position is pinpointed by radar, and warnings are sent to the threatened areas (Fig. 30-6).

The utilization of these radar weather-spotting devices in saving lives is illustrated by the following incident which occurred in April 1956. A tornado struck Bryan, Tex., a city of 20,000 residents. It cut a path 6 miles long and 0.75 miles wide, producing an estimated damage of 1 million dollars. Yet the residents escaped without a scratch. Credit for this saving of life and limb was given to the warning provided by the Texas A and M College tornado spotter. Information provided by this radar spotter and broadcast by radio gave residents a chance to take necessary safety measures, such as opening windows and holding children in school after the normal time for dismissing afternoon classes. For the same reason, the

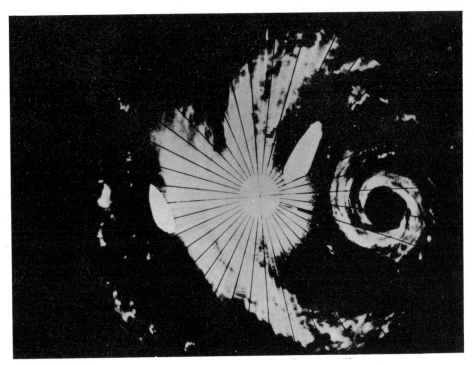

Fig. 30-6. "Eye" of typhoon Marge shown to the right of the radar scope

death toll of Hurricane Carla in 1961 was only 23, although it was stronger than a hurricane in the same region that in 1900 killed 6,000 persons in Galveston, Tex.

Weather radar also helps the Weather Bureau in gauging the amount of precipitation. Since this device is capable of showing where and how much rain or snow is falling, while it is still falling, it provides information needed to forecast flash floods.[15]

RCA, Bendix, and Collins Radio have developed lightweight radar weather-detection systems. These systems, with a range of 150 miles, have now been installed in most of the airplanes of United Airlines, American, Trans-World, Pan-American Airways, and other major airlines. By September 1957, it was estimated that 40 per cent of the nation's commercial airliners were equipped with weather radar.

Smaller systems have also been developed by the Trident Corp. and other manufacturers for use in lighter business and private aircraft.

The most serious flying conditions are found in the centers or cores of thunderstorms. Consequently, storm-warning systems employ a new type of PPI scope-presentation circuit called the Iso-Echo Contour. On the resulting screen presentation, a storm core is represented by a black area surrounded by a bright return. By by-passing these areas, the pilot can avoid regions of high turbulence.

The radar beam may be tilted if desired, to examine other altitudes, or for general terrain-mapping purposes. The system is capable of identifying river beds, lakes, mountain roads, peaks, and other surface features.[16]

An indication of the effectiveness

of airborne weather-radar systems is provided by the fact that in the fall of 1959, the Federal Aviation Agency announced that because of the excellent safety record of airlines using weather radar, it was considering a proposal to require all passenger-carrying transport-type airplanes to carry radar.[17] At an estimated cost of 25,000 dollars per plane, this requirement would cost the airlines over 20 million dollars.

In 1959, it was announced that Radiation, Inc., had delivered an experimental Doppler-radar tornado-detecting device to the U.S. Department of Commerce Weather Bureau at Wichita Falls, Tex. The device is being used to study the feasibility of using Doppler radar for tornado detection. It is based on findings that a tornado possesses a unique Doppler-spectrum distribution which will serve as a warning. It is claimed that this device is capable of recording the Doppler spectrum of thunderstorms 95 miles away and has identified tornadoes 23 miles away.

30.7 *Radiosonde*

Before leaving the subject of the meteorological applications of radar, mention should be made of its use in following the course of radiosonde balloons. The radiosonde-balloon technique was developed under the direction of John H. Dellinger of the National Bureau of Standards. It employs balloons that carry a sonde unit containing instruments capable of measuring barometric pressure, humidity, and temperature. These balloons can reach altitudes as high as 100,000 ft.[18]

When a pulse transmitter, called an interrogator, sends a series of pulses to the balloon, a unit called the transponder transmits or telemeters radio pulses which indicate the readings of the various measuring instruments. Simultaneously, as the balloon rises

and travels with the air currents, radar tracking techniques are used to record automatically and continuously the direction and speed of the wind at various altitudes. In this manner, a complete record of atmospheric conditions is quickly and easily obtained.

The U.S. Army Signal Engineering Laboratories has developed a radiosonde electronic weatherman that is capable of spotting high-altitude indications of hurricanes, tornadoes, and other bad weather far faster and far more accurately than any device previously developed. It can also chart high-velocity winds, such as the jet stream. Balloons can be tracked to an altitude exceeding 24 miles and distances exceeding 200 miles. The coded signals transmitted by the balloon are received and fed into an electronic computer. There they are processed and recorded on paper as wind velocity, humidity, temperature, and pressure readings.

In 1956, the U.S. Navy announced the development of the Transosonde System. This term, a contraction of transocean sounding, is used to designate a telemetered, high-altitude, drifting weather station. Whereas ordinary radiosonde employs small balloons which provide local reports based on short flights, Transosonde can provide weather information at an altitude of 30,000 ft for distances as far as 3,000 miles.[19]

30.8 *Instrument landing system*

The Instrument Landing System, commonly called ILS, is one of the oldest avionic systems. As far back as 1929, the U.S. Department of Commerce had begun developmental work on an electronic landing system designed to achieve all-weather flight reliability. The present system (Fig. 30-7) consists of the following three basic elements:

1. A localizer radio beam to furnish directional guidance to the airport runway. This beam is produced by a localizer transmitter located on a line extending from the center of the airport runway and placed far enough from the end to prevent it from being a collision hazard. This transmitter provides an on-course signal at a minimum distance of 25 miles and a minimum altitude of 2,000 ft.

2. A glide-path radio beam to furnish vertical guidance down the correct descent angle to the runway. This beam is projected from a transmitter located 1,000 ft from the approach end and 400 ft to one side of the center line of the runway. The path of this beam is generally adjusted to an angle of 2.5 deg above the horizon.

3. Fan markers to provide accurate radio fixes along the approach course. These are low-powered transmitters that radiate a vertical, fan-shaped field pattern. The outer marker is located 4.5 miles from the runway, whereas the middle marker is located 3,500 ft from the approach end of the

runway. The outer marker transmits in Morse code the first two letters of the transmitter identification code, such as ID, and energizes a purple indicator light on the airplane. The middle marker sends the last two letters, such as DL, and energizes an amber light.

The ILS gauge located on the instrument panel transmits directions to the pilot once he has placed his plane in the guide path. In the center of the gauge is a circle, which represents the plane. Crossing the circle are a horizontal needle and a vertical needle. When the plane veers to the left of the correct course, the vertical needle moves to the right. The plane then appears to be to the left of the needle. Thus, the pilot knows he must turn right to correct his glide. Similar information is provided by the horizontal needle.[20] It has been estimated that today, every 30 seconds somewhere in the world, an aircraft completes an instrument low-approach landing using the ILS equipment.

Approach coupler. By 1957, half of the airlines in the United States were also equipped with a device called an approach coupler. This coupler connects the automatic pilot with the ILS equipment. It relieves the pilot of making

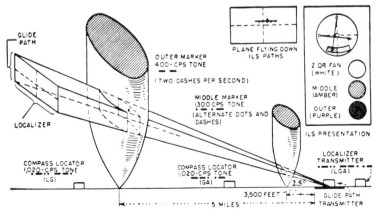

Courtesy, *Electronics*

FIG. 30-7. INSTRUMENT LANDING SYSTEM

manual corrections as he glides toward the runway by transferring the work to the automatic pilot. At an altitude of about 200 ft, the human pilot takes over once again.

Automatic landing systems. The Army and FAA have been working in coordination with Bendix and several other large companies in developing an automatic-landing system. This system also combines the ILS equipment with the automatic pilot and feeds ILS signals into the automatic-pilot system so that the latter device performs the operations needed to land the plane. Linkage of ILS and the automatic-pilot systems is accomplished by an electronic computer, which interprets the received radio signals and sends corresponding impulses to the various servomotors of the automatic-pilot system. These servomotors operate throttles, elevators, ailerons, and rudders so as to guide the plane down a landing path with an even greater degree of precision than is possible with manual control. This system is also capable of instantaneous disconnection, to permit the pilot to take over control in the event of malfunctioning or any other emergency.

In 1957, the U.S. Air Force and the Navy announced that Bell Aircraft had developed for their use a device capable of automatically landing a plane on the deck of a rolling aircraft carrier during the worst weather and in zero-visibility conditions. This is accomplished with no help from either the pilot or the deck crew. The device, called ALS for Automatic Landing System, consists of a SHF precision-radar system that operates at a frequency of 35,000 mc, a computer, and an automatic pilot. The radar set, which is located on the ground or on the deck of the carrier, follows the plane as it glides towards the runway. The information is fed to a nearby computer. The computer calculates the plane's motion and the roll, pitch, and yaw of the ship. It then compares the plane's path with an ideal path stored in a memory drum. It figures out where the ship's deck will be at the moment the plane is due to land and transmits corrective signals, at the rate of 10 per second, to the plane's automatic pilot. If a sudden, unexpected wave should throw off the ship at the last minute, the computer sends a "wave off" signal to the plane. A warning light flashes in the pilot's cockpit, and the human pilot then takes over the controls and circles about for another landing attempt.[21][22]

It is estimated that if an airport installs two of these systems to guide and control alternate aircraft, over 120 airplanes an hour can be brought in under conditions of poor visibility.[23] This figure may be compared with the 12 planes an hour brought in at the average airport when ceiling and visibility are minimum. This device should help make it possible for airlines to operate with the regularity of railroad systems in almost any kind of weather.[24]

In 1960, it was announced that the Sperry Phoenix Co. had developed for the U.S. Air Force a system capable of the remote-control guiding of the descent and the landing of manned and unmanned spacecraft. In this system, the spacecraft follows a radar beam which is locked onto the descending vehicle. An electronic computer calculates the best approach heading and transmits signals that operate the flight controls of the vehicle. This system also issues corrective commands as needed.[25]

30.9 Ground-controlled approach

The term Ground-Controlled Approach, or GCA, is applied to a radar system by means of which airplanes can be guided down safely to a runway in fog, rain, or snow (Fig. 30-8). In order to direct a plane down to a runway, an operator on the ground must have continuous information concerning the height of the plane, its distance, and its direction from the airport. In GCA, radar provides the operator with the data required to land the aircraft. Part of the GCA is the Airport Surveillance Radar Unit or ASR. This is essentially a PPI radar system that produces a map of planes and obstructions in the air around the airport for a radius of 50 miles.

In the GCA system, the operator, who is usually the airport-traffic controller, can follow the movements of all aircraft in the area by observing the corresponding movements of the luminescent spots on the face of a cathode-ray tube. He can then use voice radio to

guide each plane to the beginning of the approach path to the runway.

The second part of this system is the Precision Approach Radar Unit, or PAR, which indicates whether or not a plane is descending at the correct angle and speed and shows immediately how much correction is necessary.[26] Thus, by means of precision radar, the approaching plane is tracked, and its range, azimuth, and elevation are determined. An electronic device compares this approach with the ideal glide path and displays on an indicator the amount of deviation from the ideal path. An approach controller, who watches these indicators, informs the pilot by radio of his precise position relative to the ideal glide path.

GCA demonstrated its usefulness during the Berlin airlift operations of the winter of 1948. When it was installed at three Berlin airports, it doubled the

Courtesy, Radio Div. The Bendix Corp.

FIG. 30-8. BENDIX GCA AIRPORT RADAR EQUIPMENT

daily incoming tonnage and enabled transport planes to land at the average rate of one per minute.

The name most closely associated with the development of GCA is that of Alvarez of the Radiation Laboratory of MIT. Alvarez conceived the idea of using radar to track an incoming landing plane while he was watching a demonstration of a radar-operated, automatic-gun-laying system. He suggested that it would be possible to use radar to obtain data concerning the plane's range, azimuth, and elevation. The information could then be compared with a glide path that had been previously established, and the errors and deviations from the ideal approach could be determined. The information thus obtained by means of radar could then be used by a ground operator to "talk down" the pilot.

In 1942, he constructed the first successful experimental GCA system. By 1944, production models were being delivered by Gilfillan Brothers and Bendix Radio to the Air Force. In 1946, Alvarez was presented with the Collier award by the President of the United States for these contributions to American aviation.

The major advantages of GCA are the mobility of the ground station and the fact that the aircraft requires no special equipment other than an ordinary radio receiver. Its disadvantages lie in the possibility of errors produced by the human links in the chain and the fact that the landing responsibility is taken out of the hands of the pilot.

30.10 *Teleran*

Teleran (Television-Radar-Air Navigation) is another radar system used to help airplanes make safe landings. It was developed between 1941 and 1945 by Loren F. Jones of RCA in an attempt to combine the advantages of television with those of radar by providing the pilot with a televised picture of the presentations produced by GCA equipment.

A television camera located at the airport scans a radar map of the area (Fig. 30-9). This is then reproduced in a small kinescope tube located on the instrument panel of the airplane. Thus, the pilot is provided with a picture showing the position of his own plane relative to the ground and to other nearby planes. The televised picture can also be used to provide the pilot with printed instructions and with information concerning wind direction and the condition of runways.

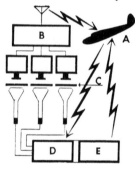

Courtesy, Radio Corporation of America
FIG. 30-9. FUNCTIONAL DIAGRAM OF BASIC TELERAN SYSTEM
(A) Airplane; (B) television transmitter; (C) transparent charts showing maps and other geographical data; (D) radar receiver; (E) radar transmitter.

30.11 *Omnirange— VOR/DME*

Omnirange is a type of navigational system designed to replace the old-fashioned radio beam. It is sometimes called the VOR system, meaning Very-High-Frequency Omnidirectional Range. The Omnirange transmitter radiates in all directions a signal whose frequency is between 112 and 118 mc. The VHF-band transmission provides all-weather, static-free radio communications. The pilot of a plane can employ an instrument called an azimuth selector, which indicates his bearing by means of the signal received from the transmitter (Fig. 30-10). By tuning in on a DME (Distance-Measuring Equipment) device, he can then determine his distance from the transmitter. Finally, by turning on a device called a R-Theta Computer or a Courseline Computer, which will soon be described in greater detail, he can employ the omnirange signals to guide him on any course that he desires.

The ground equipment for DME is similar to that used for the racon radar-beacon system. However, the airborne equipment differs in that distance information is shown on a dial indicator instead of appearing on a PPI scope. The DME equipment consists of an interrogator on the airplane and a responder or transponder located at the ground station. The transmitter of the interrogator emits a specific number of microsecond pulses. When these pulses reach the transponder, a circuit

is triggered which causes its own transmitter to radiate a reply pulse to the plane. One such station is capable of handling simultaneous interrogation signals from as many as 50 aircraft. When the reply pulses reach the airborne receiver, the time interval between the transmitted and the received pulses is converted into a voltage by means of distance-measuring circuits (Fig. 30-11). This voltage, which is proportional to the distance, is applied to an indicator meter that is calibrated in miles. This DME equipment may also be used in conjunction with the previously described ILS equipment.[27]

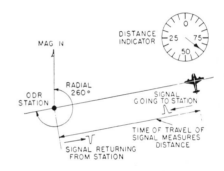

Courtesy, Radio Div., The Bendix Corp.
FIG. 30-11. PRINCIPLE OF DME

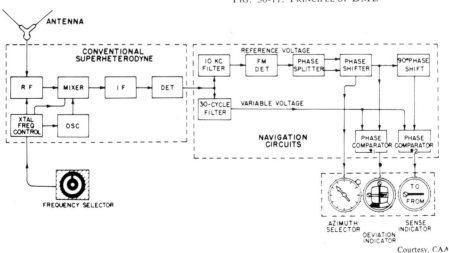

Courtesy, CAA

FIG. 30-10. BLOCK DIAGRAM OF VHF OMNI-RANGE RECEIVER

The principle of determining an airplane's bearing by means of VOR omnirange is based upon comparison of the phase difference between two radiated signals. These signals are transmitted from VOR stations which are located along airlanes and are spaced approximately 100 miles apart from each other.[28] The phase difference between the two received signals varies with a change in azimuth. One of these signals, called the reference phase, is non-directional and has a constant phase throughout its 360 deg of azimuth. The other signal, called the variable phase, rotates at 30 rps and varies in phase with azimuth (Fig. 30-12). This signal is produced by connecting two pairs of stationary antennas to a motor-driven goniometer. The rotating goniometer causes the radio-frequency voltages that are fed to each pair of antennas to vary sinusoidally at the rate of 30 cps (Fig. 30-13). This produces the desired rotating field.

The rotating signal is initially set so that the reference and the variable signals are in phase with each other at magnetic north. For any other direction, the positive maximum of the variable signal will lag the positive maximum of the reference signal. The measurement of this phase angle or the number of degrees of lag observed at a given point enables the equipment to translate these signals into readily usable instrument-panel readings that indicate the azimuth angle at that point.

Determination of the actual position of an aircraft usually requires obtaining bearings from two stations. The position of the aircraft can then be plotted on a map by triangulation (Fig. 30-14).[29]

As has been mentioned previously, VOR operates within a frequency range where natural static is usually absent. It is called omnidirectional, because in contrast with the aural-range system, which establishes only four lanes, this

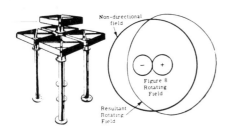

FIG. 30-12. ROTATING FIELD PATTERN

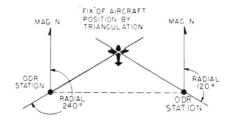

Courtesy, Bendix Radio Div., The Bendix Corp.
FIG. 30-14. OBTAINING AIRPLANE POSITION BY TRIANGULATION

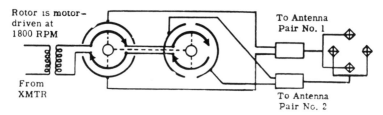

FIG. 30-13. GONIOMETER CONNECTED TO ANTENNAS

system provides bearing information to planes in all directions. However, since it operates in the VHF range, it can be received only under line-of-sight conditions and cannot usually be employed by low-flying planes that are located at a considerable distance from the transmitter.

The ever increasing acceptance of VOR is revealed by a Federal Aviation Agency survey which shows that the percentage of general aviation aircraft employing VOR more than doubled between 1954 and 1958, increasing from 20.8 per cent in 1954 to 42.5 per cent in 1958. It may also be noted that in April 1960, the International Civil Aviation Organization voted to adopt VOR/DME as the standard short-range air-navigation system.

The R-Theta Computer. The R-Theta Computer is a device that is designed to be used with VOR/DME equipment (Fig. 30-15). It accepts the bearing and range information provided by the latter and then automatically computes the course that should be followed by the pilot in order to reach his desired destination.

30.12 *Tacan*

In 1954, the International Telephone and Telegraph Corp. announced that it had developed, in cooperation with the Armed Forces, a new navigational system called Tacan (Tactical Air Navigation), which may eventually supersede the VOR/DME omnirange system. Whereas the omnirange system requires the determination of bearings from two stations in order to obtain a fix on the position of an aircraft, Tacan supplies the distance and bearing information required for such a fix by means of one composite signal emitted by one transmitter (Fig. 30-16). This reduces the bandwidth requirement, as well as the weight and volume of airborne equipment required.

Tacan provides bearing information with five times the accuracy of Omnirange or any other system and can measure distances to an accuracy of one-fifth of a mile. The range of Tacan is over 200 miles, and it can provide simultaneous distance-measuring information to 100 planes on each one of its 126 channels—or to a total of 12,600 aircraft—while providing bearing-measuring service to an unlimited number of aircraft. Tacan is also applicable for use on sea-going vessels and is currently regarded as the most refined system for furnishing both bearing and range.

In order to measure distance, a transmitter on the airplane or other craft sends out pairs of interrogation pulses at a specific repetition rate (Fig.

RMI
DIRECTION
TO DESTINATION

DEVIATION
FROM COURSE

DISTANCE TO
DESTINATION

FIG. 30-15. R-THETA COMPUTER INDICATIONS

Courtesy, ITT Federal Laboratories

FIG. 30-16. COCKPIT INSTRUMENT FOR AIRBORNE TACAN

30-17). This repetition rate is an individual transmitter characteristic, and no two transmitters possess the same repetition rate. The signals are transmitted on the 1,000-mc portion of the UHF band to the Tacan ground transmitter. These pulses trigger the ground transmitter into replying, and these reply pulses have the same spacing as the interrogating pulses, enabling the equipment on the aircraft to recognize the reply to its own signal.

The pulses require about 12 microseconds round-trip travel time per nautical mile of distance from the ground transmitter. An electronic computer then measures the time interval between query and reply signals and converts this round-trip travel time into distance in nautical miles.

Bearing is measured in a manner very similar to that employed in the Omnirange system. Audio signals are used to amplitude-modulate the pulse-modulated carrier. The strength of the transmitter output remains constant; the amplitude modulation is produced by means of a rotating parasitic-antenna system (Fig. 30-18). This generates a cardioid or heart-shaped radiation pattern which rotates at 15 rps. A reference signal, consisting of a closely spaced group of pulses, is sent out when the maximum radiation of the signal is due north. The phase difference between this reference signal and the point of maximum signal amplitude is converted by means of a computer into the aircraft's bearing to within 1 deg.[30]

Tacan has been officially adopted

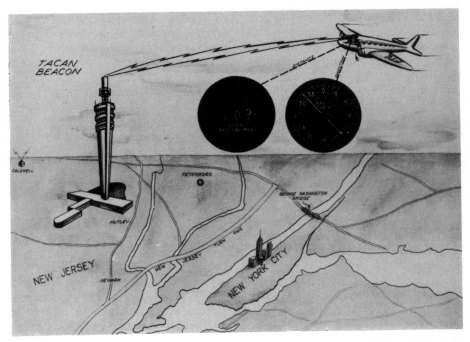

FIG. 30-17. CHARTING AIRCRAFT POSITION BY USE OF TACAN

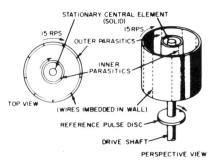

FIG. 30-18. TACAN ROTATING PARASITIC ANTENNA SYSTEM

as a common-system navigational aid to be used by both military and civil aircraft. It is now standard with the U. S. Armed Forces and with several NATO countries. It is operational on many U.S. Navy aircraft carriers, including the Forrestal and the Saratoga,
and at Air Force bases throughout the world.

30.13 *Vortac*

The VOR omnirange stations now blanketing the country are being equipped to provide Tacan service as well, and the composite system is known as Vortac or VOR/DMET (VOR plus the Distance Measuring Equipment of Tacan).[31] As indicated by its name, this new system combines the direction or bearing-giving features of VOR omnirange with the distance-measuring features of Tacan. The FAA has inaugurated a six-year program for the installation of this new system. It began in 1959 and called for a total expenditure of 314 million dollars by 1965. At the completion of this program, there will be 1,230 VHF ground stations to provide complete enroute coverage for all commercial and private aircraft. As of 1960, 600 of these stations were in operation.

Early in 1960, it was announced that the National Aeronautical Co. had won a Federal Aviation Agency design competition for a lightweight distance-measuring Vortac unit for use in general and business aircraft. It was expected that this set would be commercially available by 1961, and that by 1965 the potential market for this equipment would be approximately 40 million dollars, with a continuing market of between 5 and 10 million dollars each year thereafter.

In 1960, ACF Electronics announced the development of an inexpensive, lightweight, pictorial navigational system. When the pilot tunes to the VOR/DME, a small red dot appears on a transparent map and indicates the pilot's location with reference to known ground-based radio transmitters.

In 1957, another device was developed to supplement the Vortac system. Known as the Automatic Reporting Data Link, it provides information which rides piggy-back on the Vortac transmission. These transmissions can provide complete data concerning altitude, position, speed, course, and identification every six seconds. The ground station can issue instructions covering speed, height, direction, and rate of descent by pressing buttons. Orders then appear, in the language of the pilot, on the face of the corresponding meters located on the instrument panel of the aircraft.[32]

Push buttons may also be used by the pilot to acknowledge receipt of ground-station commands and to initiate anyone of 31 prepared air-to-ground messages. It is expected that this system will help reduce the number of accidents caused by the inability of foreign pilots to comprehend fully instructions given by the tower.

30.14 Volscan

The Volscan Air Traffic Control System was developed under Benjamin F. Greene, Jr., of the Cambridge Air Force Research Center and is now being manufactured by the Crosley Corp. Volscan is a large analog computer that forms a link between airport-traffic-control radar and GCA systems. It is capable of bringing aircraft to the final-approach entry point at the rate of 120 planes per hour, thus tripling the capacity of an airport (Figs. 30-19 and 30-20). This is particularly important at airports where jet planes are used, since the fuel consumption of jet aircraft increases enormously when these planes are compelled to fly at low altitudes. Thus, a typical jet uses almost three

Courtesy, Avco Corp.
FIG. 30-19. AN/GSN-11 VOLSCAN AIR TRAFFIC CONTROL CENTER

Courtesy, Avco Corp.

FIG. 30-20. AIR TRAFFIC CONTROLLERS IN VOLSCAN CONTROL ROOM

times as much fuel at an approach altitude as it does at a cruising altitude. If the landing operation is unduly delayed by the stacking up of traffic, a jet plane may run out of fuel and crash.

When a plane comes within 40 to 60 miles of the airport, a corresponding blip appears on a PPI scope. Its location is spotted by pointing a device called a light gun at the blip (Figs. 30-21 and 30-22). This assigns a device called an Antrac to the radar target. The Antrac continuously reports to a channel of a computer called a Datac the exact position of the target.

Each Volscan system contains 14 Antracs and 14 Datacs. The Datac calculates the plane's direct flight time, selects a scheduled arrival time which will not conflict with other inbound traffic, and calculates heading and altitude orders which will make this schedule operate. When the plane reaches the entry gate, which is located 1,000 ft above and 2 miles from the runway touchdown point, either the ILS or the GCA system takes over for the final approach.[33] In this manner, Volscan can handle one landing every 30 seconds, thus reducing the dangerous

practice of stacking airplanes that are waiting around an airport for an opportunity to land.[34]

30.15 *Loran*

Loran (Long-Range-Navigation) is a navigational system which is an outgrowth of a pulse-navigation system designed during World War II to enable the Royal Air Force to guide its bombers to and from targets over Germany. The modern version of this system was developed in 1941 by the Radiation Laboratories of MIT and by A. Alford of the Federal Telephone and Radio Co., a subsidiary of the International Telephone and Telegraph Corp. In 1960, the U. S. Patent Office disclosed that the International Telephone and Telegraph Corp. had been awarded a patent covering the basic principles of hyperbolic navigational systems such as Loran.[35]

Loran is also based upon ideas suggested by A. L. Loomis and upon a hyperbolic radio-navigational system developed in 1941 by F. G. Bac of Le Materiel Telephonique of France. The present system employs waves of greater

Courtesy, Avco Corp.

FIG. 30-21. VOLSCAN MONITOR CONSOLE
Operator supervises entire operation of up to 18 aircraft under GSN-11 control, assigns landing times, and alters sequence in event of an emergency.

length than those of the British system and operates at a frequency that is between 1,700 and 2,000 kc. These waves, being of the same length as those used for long-range radio transmissions, follow the curvature of the earth, and can be used by ships and airplanes located 1,500 miles away from the Loran stations. During the daytime, this distance is reduced to 700 miles.

It is claimed that a recently developed modification of this device, known as Loran-C, which employs pulses in the 90- to 110-kc band, can produce fixes that are accurate to within less than 800 ft at distances of 1,000 nautical miles at night and 1,400 miles during the day. The Navy also reports that by using ionospheric reflection of

the signals, which reduces their accuracy somewhat, fixes can be obtained at distances of 1,800 miles during the day and 2,300 miles at night.[36] [37]

The fixes are obtained by measuring the differences between the arrival times of two pairs of synchronized radio pulses (Fig. 30-23). Each pulse of a given pair is sent from a separate special transmitting station whose position is known. These Loran transmitting stations operate in pairs and are separated by distances of 100 to 600 miles. One station is termed the master and the other the slave. When a pulse from the master is received by the slave station, a similar signal is produced by this slave station. Thus, both stations transmit pulses at the same rate, but the master

Courtesy, Avco Corp.

FIG. 30-22. SPOTTING THE BLIP
Operator of each arrival console is responsible for control of up to six aircraft.

pulse always leads the slave pulse. Master and slave pairs can be identified by means of their radio frequencies and their pulse-repetition rates.

The Loran receiver contains a cathode-ray-tube indicator, on the screen of which the pulses may be observed. A particular pair of stations may be tuned in by selecting their frequency and switching the receiver to their specific pulse-repetition rate. By adjusting a receiver control so as to superimpose the slave pulse on the marker pulse, the time difference in microseconds between the two received pulses can be measured.

This Loran reading that is obtained from one pair of transmitting stations determines the navigator's position as being somewhere along a hyperbolic curve called a Loran line of position. This is a line on a Loran chart, which is simply a standard Mercator chart upon which Loran hyperbolic curves have been superimposed (Fig. 30-24). A second measurement, obtained from a second pair of transmitting stations, places the navigator on a second hyperbolic line of position. The navigator's true position is obviously located at the intersection of these two curves.

Fixes obtained in this manner produce an error of less than 1 per cent of the distance between the ship and the transmitting station and are as accurate as those obtained by celestial observation.[38] Loran measurements do not require favorable weather conditions,

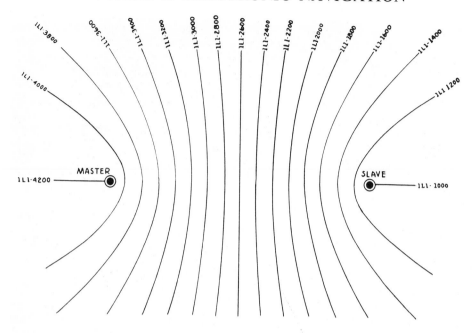

Courtesy, Radio Div., The Bendix Corp.

FIG. 30-23. LORAN LINES OF POSITION OBTAINED FROM A SINGLE TRANSMITTING PAIR
Actual Loran charts show line at 20-microsecond intervals instead of 200-microsecond intervals as shown here.

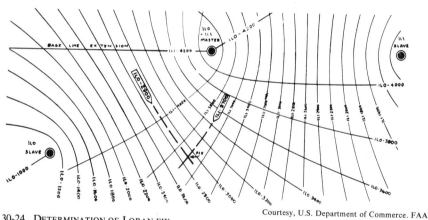

FIG. 30-24. DETERMINATION OF LORAN FIX

Courtesy, U.S. Department of Commerce. FAA

and a fix may be obtained within two to three minutes. Consequently, Loran has become the basic navigational system for practically all long-range ships and airplanes, and Loran signals are on the air and are available to navigators throughout a large part of the major shipping lanes of the world for 24 hours out of every day.

It should be noted that Loran differs from radar in that it does not require a transmitter aboard the ship or plane, nor does it employ the principle of using a reflected signal. However, the system does resemble radar in that pulses are transmitted, and when these pulses are received, they are displayed on the screen of a cathode-ray tube.

The power requirements for Loran are more modest than those of radar, being as low as 135 watts, but the cost of the equipment for use aboard small craft is approximately the same.[39] For example, the Sperry Rand Corp. markets a compact 38-lb Loran set developed for the small-craft market that is priced at 1,495 dollars, which is approximately the same price as that of comparable radar equipment.

Another development in this field is the previously mentioned low-frequency Loran known as Loran-C. This system operates at a frequency of approximately 100 kc and provides much more accurate fix information. By employing time-sharing techniques, Loran-C stations are operated on the same basic frequency in all areas and at the same pulse-repetition rate in any one area, in contrast with the older Loran-A system that requires three basic frequencies in all areas and at least two pulse-repetition rates in any one area. This produces a considerable reduction in the frequency spectrum required for obtaining navigational fixes. It is claimed that the Loran-C system is capable of providing unambiguous quarter-mile fixes accurately at distances greater than 1,000 miles from the transmitters.[40]

30.16 *Cytac*

Cytac is a precise, long-range navigation system developed by the Air Force and the Sperry Gyroscope Corp. Its operating principle is essentially an extension of Loran, employing similar types of master and slave stations. However, Cytac achieves longer range by using a lower-frequency

transmission of approximately 100 kc. In addition, it is capable of achieving greater precision. This precision is acquired by utilizing the ground wave only and not allowing the received signal to be contaminated by the skywave that arrives later. This is accomplished by confining all measurements to the first 30 microseconds of the leading edge of the ground-wave pulse. This portion of the pulse is uncontaminated by the skywave. Finally, Cytac instrumentation is automatic in operation, eliminating inaccuracies due to personnel error.[41]

30.17 *Navarho*

Navarho is a long-range, global-navigational aid operating at low frequencies (90 to 118 kc), which may eventually supplant Loran. It was developed in 1955 by the Air Research and Development Command Headquarters. It consists of three 15-kilowatt transmitters which beam signals via three 625-ft towers in all directions, supplying position information to all aircraft within a radius of 3,000 miles from the station.

The station incorporates a timing unit with an accuracy of 1 part in 1 billion. The transmitted signal provides the navigator with information concerning his bearing and distance from the station. It is capable of directing planes to within 100 miles of their destination, at which point, more precise local navigational aids can take over. If the results obtained at the first station located in Camden, N.J., prove successful, the Air Force plans to build a world-wide chain of these installations.

30.18 *The Decca system*

The Decca radio-navigational system of the Decca Navigation Co., Ltd., although invented by two Americans, was developed in England and has never been used in the United States. In fact, it does not even appear in the current U.S. Navy listing of radio-navigational aids, despite the fact that it was used as far back as D-Day, June 6, 1944, to guide the Allied invasion armada.

A Decca system consists of a master and three slave stations, designated purple, red, and green respectively. A navigational fix can be obtained by measuring the phase differences between the master and any two slave stations. The position can then be indicated automatically upon a gridded map or chart that unrolls in front of the pilot.

One of the claimed advantages of Decca over VOR/DMET is that the latter uses VHF signals that cannot be received at low altitudes beyond the horizon, whereas Decca uses lower frequency waves that are more subject to static but possess a longer range.

The British, who have been advocating Decca as an international navigational aid for a long time, also claim that Decca, in the form of its long-range extension known as Dectra, is superior to Loran for long-range navigation, possessing an accuracy that is measured in yards. Its operation and equipment are simpler and more economical than Loran, and it uses a smaller portion of the radio-frequency spectrum.[42]

On the other hand, the FAA has reported that tests of Decca have convinced it that this system does not meet requirements either for a primary instrument-flight-rules navigational aid or for an air-navigation steering device. When the matter was brought to a vote before the International Civil Aviation Organization in March 1959, the result was a defeat for Decca, and a recommendation for a continuation of VOR

and adoption of DME as international standards. This decision was reaffirmed in April 1960 when the ICAO, by a bare two-thirds vote, accepted VOR/DME as the standard international short-range air-navigation system over the opposition of the representatives of the United Kingdom.

30.19 *Radan and other Doppler navigation systems*

Doppler navigational systems, which were declassified by the Defense Department in 1957, were developed in 1948 by the General Precision Laboratory, the Laboratory for Electronics, and engineers of the Navigation Branch of the Wright Air Development Center. By 1954, this type of system was in quantity production for the U.S. Air Force.

A Doppler system is based upon a principle first suggested by Tull and Hibbert of MIT. As its name indicates, it employs the famous effect discovered in 1842 by the Austrian physicist, Christian Doppler. Doppler discovered that there was a relationship between the relative speed of a moving object and the shift in frequency of the sound wave that it generates as it moved towards or away from an observer (Fig. 30-25). It was later discovered that this principle could also be applied to other kinds of waves. Consequently, the Doppler principle has today been extended and generalized so that it now states that if a wave-propagating source moves toward an object, the frequency of the waves observed by the object is higher than the propagation frequency. The increase in frequency, or the decrease if the source is moving away, is called the Doppler shift. The shift is a result of, and is proportional to, the relative velocity of the source. In 1938,

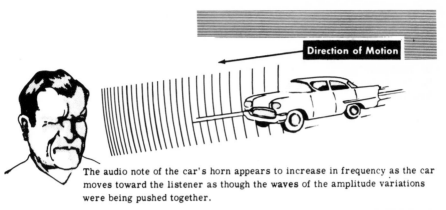

The audio note of the car's horn appears to increase in frequency as the car moves toward the listener as though the waves of the amplitude variations were being pushed together.

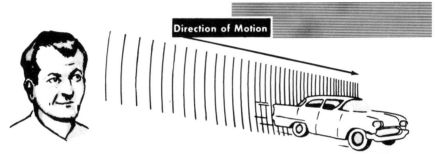

The audio note of the car's horn appears to decrease in frequency as the car moves away from the listener as though the waves of the amplitude variations were being pulled apart.

FIG. 30-25. DOPPLER EFFECT

scientists at the Naval Research Laboratory demonstrated that the Doppler principle could be applied to radio waves (Fig. 30-26).

In a typical airborne Doppler velocity-measuring system, several beams of microwave energy, generally four in number, are transmitted at various angles from the airplane to the surface of the earth (Fig. 30-27). As the signals bounce back from the ground to the plane, they undergo a Doppler frequency shift that is proportional to the speed of the plane relative to the ground.[43][44][45][46][47] These changes in frequency are fed into a computer, which translates this information into ground speed and drift. When these are known, position, course to destination, and distance to destination can be calculated by automatic computers.

If desired, the Doppler measurements can be fed through a computer to an automatic pilot in order to keep the plane on course without manual help. One manufacturer claims that the margin of error is only plus or minus 1 per cent longitudinally along the route from the last check point and plus or minus 3.5 per cent laterally. This system is completely independent of ground installations, making it considerably less expensive than other systems built around ground transmitters.[48]

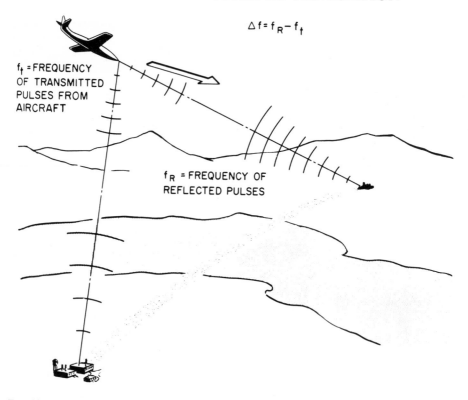

FIG. 30-26. DOPPLER RADAR

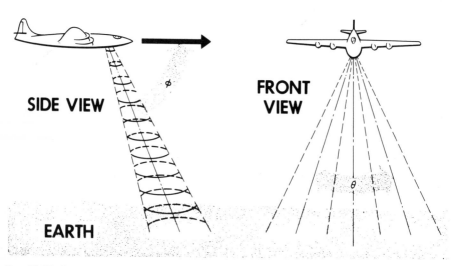

FIG. 30-27. DOPPLER APPLICATION TO NAVIGATION

This independence of ground stations is also enjoyed by inertial-guidance systems containing accelerometers and gyroscopes, which are being used to guide missiles (Figs. 30-28 through 30-33). The accelerometers employ Newton's Second Law of Motion to sense the rate change of velocity, and the gyroscopes are used to sense angular motions of the missile.[49] However, these inertial-guidance systems are currently much more expensive than Doppler systems and are not nearly so far along in development. Doppler navigational equipment has been in operational use since 1954 in military aircraft and has been available for use by commercial aircraft since 1959.

In 1959, it was also announced

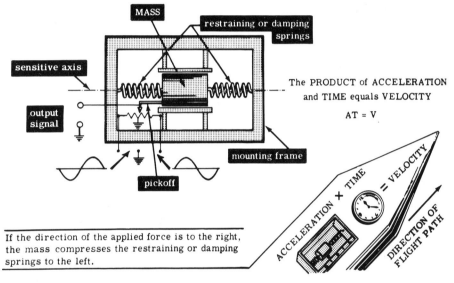

FIG. 30-28. LINEAR ACCELEROMETER

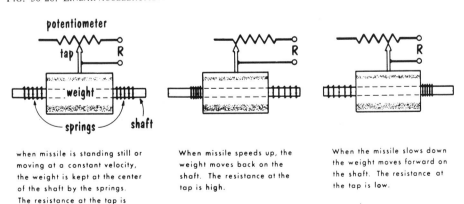

FIG. 30-29. HOW AN ACCELEROMETER WORKS

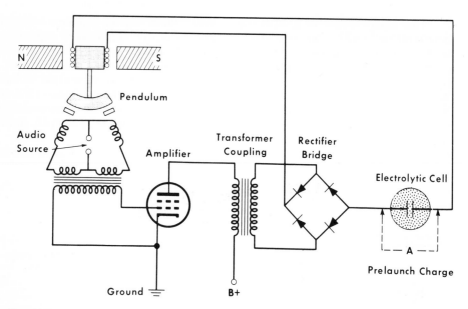

FIG. 30-30. PENDULUM-TYPE ACCELEROMETER

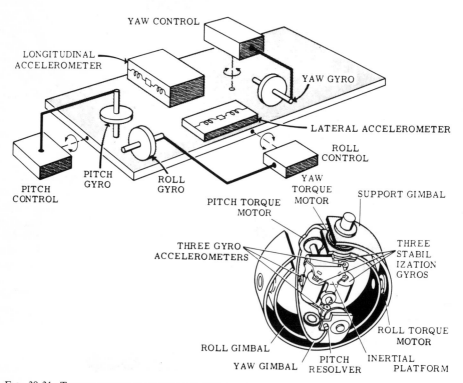

FIG. 30-31. TYPICAL STABLE PLATFORM FOR INERTIAL GUIDANCE

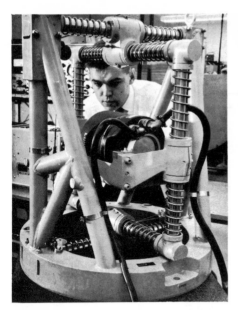

Courtesy, United Aircraft Corp.
FIG. 30-32. INERTIAL PLATFORM

that the Radan Doppler Navigational System had been successfully employed by the Aero Service Co. to make an aerial survey of 40,000 square miles of the central Sahara Desert in Libya and that it was planned to make a similar survey of part of the Spanish Sahara in southwestern Morocco. In each instance, the objective of the exploration was the discovery of oil. It is claimed that this system makes it possible to map wastelands at a fraction of the time and cost formerly required and makes it unnecessary to set up landmarks or expensive manned stations in the desert.[50]

30.20 *Transit satellite navigational system*

The Transit satellite navigational system also makes use of the Doppler principle. It requires the establishment of our Transit satellites in evenly spaced orbits around the earth. Each satellite will emit distinctive signals which can be picked up by planes or ships. By measuring the changes in frequency of the signal, it will be possible to determine when each satellite is at the closest point and what the distance is. From this information, it will be possible for the navigator to determine his own position to within one-quarter to one-tenth of a mile.

30.21 *Contact analog system*

The Contact Analog is an instrument that was developed in 1957 for the U.S. Navy for the purpose of simplifying the cockpit instrument panel. It employs a flat, transparent cathode-ray tube called the Horizontal Situation Display, which gives the pilot an all-weather view or visual roadway in the sky that is equivalent to what he might see if he could look out of the cockpit (Fig. 30-34).

Signals for this display are provided by an airborne computer which processes input data from nearly 20 different sensors. The output of the computer is projected in analog form as a moving and changing two-dimensional picture which presents the plane's position with respect to earth and sky in the same way as the pilot sees it under actual sight contact (Figs. 30-35 and 30-36). It also shows the pilot where he should be going, how fast, and at what altitude. Litton Industries and General Electric are developing newer types of computers of advanced design that will not only be capable of performing the air-data and navigational computations that the present model can perform but will also be able to handle Doppler and inertial-navigational computations.[51] [52]

30.22 *Shoran*

Shoran (Short-Range Navigation) is a high-precision, position-finding

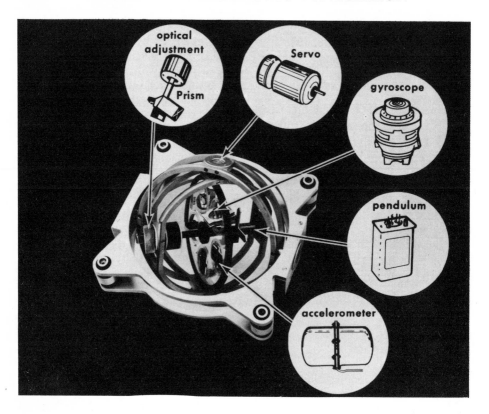

FIG. 30-33. COMPONENTS OF AN INERTIAL GUIDANCE SYSTEM

radar navigational aid conceived in 1938 by Seeley of RCA and developed during World War II. It was designed to function as an accurate bombing and reconnaissance-mapping system. It was first used to provide bombers with an extremely precise indication of their position from two Shoran ground stations. These stations were really radar beacons.

When an airplane employs this system, the airplane transmits signals to the two ground stations. Each signal triggers a radar-beacon transmitter that sends a signal back to the plane. From the length of time required for the round trip, it is possible to compute a plane's distance from that station and thus to establish that the plane is somewhere on a given circular line of position from that station. The information provided by the signal from a second beacon provides a second circular line of position. The intersection of these two lines provides the required fix.

Although its name indicates that it was designed for use as a short-range navigational system, it has operated satisfactorily for distances exceeding 250 miles. During the war, it was demonstrated that the results obtained by blind bombing of invisible targets with the aid of Shoran equalled, and often exceeded, those obtained by bombing visible targets. The peacetime applications of Shoran include its use in

FIG. 30-34. CONTACT ANALOG DISPLAY SYSTEM

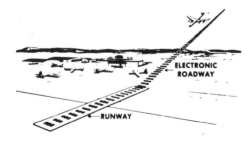

FIG. 30-35. HOW THE DISPLAY SYSTEM GUIDES THE PILOT

surveying and mapping vast areas of land and sea. It has been extensively employed to obtain the positions of vessels in hydrographic surveying and in off-shore geophysical explorations. In conjunction with the airborne magneto-meter, it is widely used for the aerial exploration of large areas for oil and mineral deposits.[53]

30.23 *Digitair interceptor radar*

The Hughes Aircraft Co. has developed a radar system which is combined with an airborne digital computer and a fire-control system. This Digitair system is capable of controlling the routine functions of navigation, search, attack, and flight, leaving the pilot free to make the all-important tactical decisions necessary for completion of interceptor missions (Fig. 30-37).

Before the interceptor takes off, the device automatically tests vital operations of the airborne system and indicates whether the system is ready to carry out its mission. After takeoff, the computer determines the course which will take the interceptor to its target in the shortest time, with a minimum

FIG. 30-36. NORDEN CONTACT ANALOG EQUIPMENT FOR GUIDANCE OF HELICOPTER

of fuel consumption, and sends instructions and steering signals directly to the aircraft's automatic-flight-control system.

As the interceptor closes on its target, the system establishes a "lead-collision" attack course. The radar is located on the target, and guided missiles are "shown" the target, armed, and lowered into position. At the correct time, the computer automatically fires the weapons and signals the pilot to break off the attack and pull out. The computer then takes over once more and flies the interceptor back to its base or to an alternate base. A similar system, developed for supersonic bombers, automatically navigates the plane, controls the target approach and bomb release, directs defensive armament, and controls evasive escape maneuvers.[54]

30.24 Other computer-controlled navigational devices

Librascope, Inc., has developed a small digital computer employing printed circuits and silicon transistors that is capable of solving most navigational problems of aircraft and missiles. The computer handles the data from Tacan, celestial, inertial, and Doppler guidance systems, as well as information that can be fed manually during flight, and provides information concerning position, distance, and bearing to a desired location.[55]

FIG. 30-37. DIGITAIR INTERCEPTOR RADAR SYSTEM

Another device, developed by General Mills, consists of a computer and an optical star-gazing instrument called a pendulum astrolabe. By observing the positions of a number of stars, the computer is able to determine the location of the observation site to within 0.1 seconds of arc, which is approximately 10 ft (Fig. 30-38).

The development of another navigational system was announced by the U.S. Navy in 1959. This system, which employs both optical and electronic techniques, is called SCAR (Submarine Celestial Altitude Recorder). When it is fitted into the periscope of a submarine, it enables a navigational fix to be taken while the ship is submerged, without causing the ship to be exposed to enemy observation.

During a sighting, the desired star or the moon or sun are observed through the periscope. When a switch is pressed, the altitude of that body is computed automatically, the angle of sighting

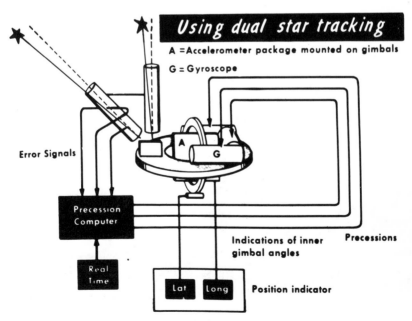

FIG. 30-38. STELLAR SUPERVISED INERTIAL AUTONAVIGATOR

is given in degrees and minutes, as well as the time in hours, minutes, and seconds. From the printed information provided by two or more such sightings, the navigator can easily determine the location of the submarine.[56]

30.25 *The radio sextant*

In 1959, the Collins Radio Co. announced the development of a precision radio sextant capable of tracking both the moon and the sun under all weather conditions between moonrise and moonset and sunrise and sunset (Fig. 30-39). This device, the AN/SRN-4 uses a 5-ft steerable parabolic antenna to determine the positions of the moon and sun automatically and continuously through the reception of microwave energy emitted

by these bodies at a frequency of 16,500 mc.

The radio-sextant information is fed into an ultrasensitive radio receiver, whose output is then coupled with the vessel's precision time standard and presented to a navigational computer, which combines celestial and inertial data to determine the ship's location and true north with an accuracy ten times greater than that attainable by the use of conventional marine compasses. Since the device emits no signals, it cannot be detected. This makes it possible for ships to rendezvous at any desired point without breaking radio silence. This sextant has already been installed on one naval vessel, the U.S.S. Compass Island, where it is being used for navigational research.[57 58 59]

Sun's Radiation of
Radio Signals at 8.7 mm

CONTROL UNIT FOR
SHIPBOARD RADIO SEXTANT

SHIPBOARD RADIO SEXTANT

Fig. 30-39. The Radio sextant—a Sun Tracking Device

REFERENCES

1. Fred M. Link, "Direction Finders for the Boatsman," *Electronics World*, 61:29-32, 90-93, June 1959.
2. Ralph Rosenfeld, "The Radio Direction Finder," *Popular Electronics*, 11:81-83, July 1959.
3. Brooks Curray, Jr., "Finding Your Way in Space," *Popular Electronics*, 8:33-35, May 1958.
4. "Lighthouses of the Sky," *Monsanto Magazine*, 38:9, Nov. 1958.
5. "Air Traffic Safety," *Radio-Electronics*, 30:6, November 1959.
6. "Airborne Profile Recorder MK 5," *Amphenol Engineering News*, 11:498-499, June 1958.
7. "An Electronic Altimeter," *Radio and TV News*, 58:14, Oct. 1957.
8. Joseph D. Caldara, " 'Instrumenting' Air Safety," *Industrial Research*, 2:76, June 1960.
9. Joseph Dorlaque, "Radar Bumpers to Prevent Plane Collisions," *Popular Science*, 170:129-132, 238, Jan. 1957.
10. *Airborne Collision Avoidance Equipment*, Federal Telecommunications Laboratory, Nutley, N.J., pp. 1-4.
11. Paul Beame, "What Are They Doing About Mid-Air Collisions?," *Electronics Illustrated*, 1:100, Dec. 1958.
12. J. D. Caldara, *Op. cit.*, p. 78.
13. *Storm Detection Radar*, Aviation Series No. 6, U. S. Department of Commerce Weather Bureau, Washington, D.C., 1955, pp. 2-3.
14. Morris Tepper, "Tornadoes," *Scientific American*, 198:36-37, May 1958.
15. Hal Foster, "Radar and the Weather," *Scientific American*, 189:34, July 1953.
16. "Weather Radar—Seeing Eye for Aircraft," *Stanford Research Institute News Bulletin*, 8:6-8. Nov. 1955.
17. "All Planes May Soon Be Required to Carry Weather Radar," *Electronics World*, 62:28, Dec. 1959.
18. M. Ira Dubins, "Pressure Variation and the Radiosonde," *Science Teacher*, 23:420, Dec. 1956.
19. "Transosonde Intercontinental Weather Balloon," *Popular Electronics*, 4:42, Apr. 1956.
20. Sidney Pickles, "Army Air Forces Portable Instrument Landing System," *Elec. Communication*, 22:262, No. 4, 1945.
21. "Robot Device Lands Planes," *Science Digest*, 42:92-93, July 1957.
22. "Down on a Dime," *CEC Recordings*, 12:3, Jan. 1958.
23. "Recording Systems Help Bring Planes Safely Home," *Brush Recorder*, 3:9, No. 1.
24. Devon Francis and Philip Gustafson, "No-Hands System to Land Airliners in any Weather," *Popular Science*, 173:112-113, Oct. 1958.
25. "Automatic Radar System," *Design News*, 15:63, Aug. 1, 1960.
26. *What is GCA?*, Bendix Corp., Baltimore, Md., 1947, p. 3.
27. Samuel Freedman, "Non-Communications Applications of Microwaves," Radio and Television News (Engineering Edition). 47:11A-12A, May 1952.
28. James A. Niland, "Air Traffic Control by Electronics," *Electronics World*, 63:39, Jan. 1960.

29. H. C. Hurley and others, "The Civil Aeronautics Administration VHF Omnirange," *Proc. IRE*, 39:1506, Dec. 1951.
30. J. Whalen, "Tacan," *Radio-Electronics*, 27:88-92, Nov. 1956.
31. "Tacan," *Collins Signal*, 6:9, Fall 1957.
32. "Tacan Data Link," *Radio-Electronics*, 28:8, May 1957.
33. Angie Pascale, "Volscan Speeds Up Air Traffic," *Radio-Electronics*, 25:75, July 1954.
34. Shane Smith, "Radar Tames the Wild Blue Yonder," *Popular Electronics*, 5:75, Nov. 1956.
35. "Award ITT Basic Loran Patent," *ITT Laboratories in the News*, 2:3, Mar. 1960
36. "Loran-C Receiver Pinpoints Fixes at 1000 Mile Ranges," *ITT Laboratories in the News*, 2:3 Mar. 1960.
37. James P. Van Etten, "Loran-C," *ITT Laboratories in the News*, 2:12, Mar. 1960.
38. Arthur P. Miller, Jr., "Loran Comes of Age," *Sperryscope*, 14:13, Second Quarter, 1956.
39. Clark E. Jackson, "Radar and Loran," *Popular Electronics*, 11:89, July 1959.
40. E. M. Lipsey, "Loran-C—A Prospectus " *Sperryscope*, 15:12-15, Third Quarter, 1959.
41. Wilbert P. Frantz and others, "Precision Multi-Purpose Radio Navigation," *Military Automation*, 1:150, May 1957.
42. C. M. Stansbury, "Decca 160's Last Chance," *Radio-TV Experimenter*, 7:55-56, 1959.
43. F. B. Berger, "The Nature of Doppler Velocity Measurement," *IRE Trans. on Aeronautical and Navigational Electronics*, ANE-4:103-104, Sept. 1957.
44. Art Zuckerman, "Doppler Radio Charts the Airlanes," *Popular Electronics*, 10:44, May 1959.
45. Paul G. Wulfsberg, "Doppler Theory and the Sensor," *Collins Signal*, 8:9-13, No. 2, 1960.
46. E. H. Fritze, "Computing Position and Navigation Situation," *Collins Signal*, 8:14-15, 18, No. 2, 1960.
47. "How Doppler Sensor, Computer Are Used on a Typical Flight," *Collins Signal*, 8:16-17, No. 2, 1960.
48. *Radan Navigation Systems*, General Precision Laboratory, Pleasantville, N.Y., pp. 3-7.
49. Gerald B. Speen, "Inertial Guidance," *ITT Laboratories in the News*, 2:12, Apr. 1960.
50. "Mapping the Wastelands," *Radio-Electronics*, 30:6, Apr. 1959.
51. "Airborne Closed-Circuit Television," *Radio and TV News*, 59:95, May 1958.
52. "Tomorrow's Instrument Panel," *Control Engineering*, 4:29, Dec. 1957.
53. "Shoran Helps the Mapmakers," *Radio Age* 15:26, Nov. 1955.
54. *Digital Airborne Digital Computers*, Hughes Systems Development Laboratories, Culver City, Calif., 1957, pp. 2-3.
55. "Small Computer Aids Aircraft Navigation," *Industrial Science and Engineering*, 6:1, Mar. 1959.
56. "Underwater Fix," *Think*, 25:35, Nov. 1959.
57. "Radio Sextant," *Scientific American*, 200:70, Apr. 1959.
58. "Radio Sextant Tracks Moon," *Electronics World*, 61:104, May 1959.
59. "Radio Guidance from the Sky," *Collins Signal*, 7:22-23, No. 4, 1959.